RSGB

Amateur Radio Operating Manual

EIGHTH EDITION

by Mike Dennison, G3XDV
and
Steve Telenius-Lowe, PJ4DX

Radio Society of Great Britain

RSGB Amateur Radio Operating Manual
8th edition

Published by the Radio Society of Great Britain, 3 Abbey Court, Fraser Road, Priory Business Park, Bedford MK44 3WH. Tel 01234 832700. Web www.rsgb.org

First published 2015.

ISBN 9781-9101-9313-6

Cover design: Kevin Williams, M6CYB

Design and layout: MIke Dennison, G3XDV, Emdee Publishing

Production: Mark Allgar, M1MPA

Printed in Great Britain by CPI Anthony Rowe Ltd. of Chippenham, Wilts

Contents

Preface

Every radio amateur will have operated on the air at some time. Even those whose primary interest is in construction need to operate in order to test their latest project. This book is aimed at helping everyone, no matter how active they are, get the best out of operating on the bands with the minimum of embarrassment due to inexperience.

One of the joys of amateur radio is the wide range of activities available, from ragchewing on an FM repeater to bouncing signals off the Moon. Our bands cover almost all of the radio spectrum from LF to microwaves, and each performs differently due to differences in propagation. And then there's the variety of transmission modes available, from CW through phone to the increasing number of specialist digital activities.

The RSGB's *Amateur Radio Operating Manual*, first published in 1979, has been a valuable source of advice for all radio amateurs, both experienced and newly licensed. There is help here for the beginner struggling to make his first contact and also for someone who is an expert in HF DXing but wants to try moonbounce or unravel the mysteries of using the local digital repeater.

In addition to the continuous updating process, this new edition has the most up to date information on the recently revised UK amateur radio licence, RSGB awards and contests, the newly released band at 472kHz, the eleven 5MHz channels now available to all Full licensees, a code of ethics and the boom in digital repeaters. It also acknowledges that almost all shacks will have a computer of some kind, running digital modes, controlling the station, logging or simply accessing relevant Internet pages; this now includes apps that will run on smart phones and tablets.

Each chapter includes numerous references, so if you feel you need to know more about a particular topic there are signposts to information in the form of books, magazine articles or web sites. Although web pages tend to be less permanent than printed matter, each reference was checked shortly before this book went to press so most will still be useful, or at the very least provide a clue for a web search.

Other publications that complement this book include the annual *RSGB Yearbook* which includes much date-sensitive information such as beacon lists, repeater lists and contest dates, the *RSGB Prefix Guide* and, for those wanting theoretical and constructional information, the *Radio Communication Handbook*.

Finally, thanks are due to all who contributed to this revision, without whose efforts this edition would have been impossible. With apologies to anyone accidentally omitted, these include Robin Page-Jones, G3JWI; Alan Melia, G3NYK; Graham Shirville, G3VZV; John Gould, G3WKL; John Quarmby, G3XDY; John Regnault, G4SWX; Stan Lee, G4XXI; Murray Niman, G6JYB; Dave Mann, G8ADM; Ciaran Morgan, M0XTD; those responsible for the RSGB and ARRL web pages and all who helped to produce previous editions that provided the foundations for this update.

Mike Dennison, G3XDV
Steve Telenius-Lowe, PJ4DX
September 2015

1

An Introduction to Amateur Radio Operating

THE AMATEUR SERVICE and Amateur Satellite Service, as they are referred to in official documents, have always been about self-training in the art of communications by radio. As radio amateurs we are privileged to have the use of a wide range of frequencies throughout the electromagnetic spectrum, many of which are regarded with interest by commercial users who would like to get their hands on those frequencies. In return for that privilege, we are expected to use those frequencies to enhance our knowledge and skills in radio communication. Of course, it's only reasonable that, in the process, we should have fun too!

There are two areas in which we develop our skills. One is through the technical aspects of the hobby, setting up our station and ensuring it works effectively without causing annoyance or interference to other users of the radio spectrum. To this end, the RSGB publishes a companion volume to this book, the *Radio Communication Handbook* [1], which covers the whole gamut of the technical and constructional side of amateur radio.

Even if your station consists entirely of commercial equipment, you will need to exercise at least some skills in connecting everything up, with attention to various factors such as effective earthing. Beyond this, many amateurs take

pleasure in designing or, at least, building their own equipment, often to extremely high standards.

The other area of self-training is in learning to operate effectively, and this book is aimed at that area. There are many aspects to consider if you are to be able to establish communications with another station or stations, pass information in an accurate and timely way and, in the process, to do so with the least inconvenience to fellow amateurs and others with whom we share our bands.

Historically, there was a line drawn at 30MHz between the HF spectrum and VHF / UHF. This is largely because HF propagation is characterised by ionospheric refraction, allowing radio waves to travel long distances, whereas VHF / UHF is assumed to be essentially line-of-sight (though anyone who has operated on the VHF or even UHF bands when there is any sort of enhanced propagation, knows that this is far from the truth). In the UK, this HF - VHF split was previously also part of our rules and regulations, with operators being required to pass a Morse code test before an HF licence was granted to them. As a result of decisions made at the 2003 ITU World Radio Conference this is no longer the case in most countries (although certain restrictions may apply to introductory or intermediate forms of licence in many countries, even

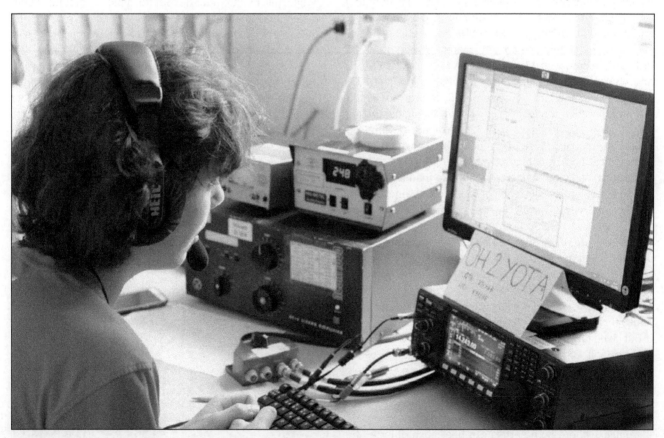

Ricky, MW6GWR, operating the OH2YOTA special event station at the international Youngsters on the Air event held in Finland in 2014. Organised by the IARU, the YOTA gathering involved youngsters from fifteen countries.

if a Morse code test is not required.) A Morse code test is still a requirement before an HF licence is granted (even in 2015) in a few countries, Malaysia being just one example.

Although operating practices vary to some extent according to waveband, they vary too according to the mode of operation. This book sets out to cover all aspects. The chapter headings should be self-explanatory. The breakdown is largely by type of operating, but don't assume the book only addresses 'competitive' operating such as DXing and contesting. This is by no means the case. It also covers all levels of experience from beginner to expert, so there is sure to be valuable information for both the newly-licensed Foundation or Intermediate licensee right up to the Full licensee with decades of operating behind him (or her - the masculine form is used in this book for convenience, but there are of course many female radio amateurs).

Many of the general principles are covered in this chapter and in Chapter 7, and will get you started if your interest is in 'casual' day-to-day operating, whatever the band. But there are plenty of tips in other chapters which you will find helpful, even if you don't expect to be chasing DXpeditions or entering contests.

WHY AN OPERATING MANUAL?

One of the great joys of amateur radio is the enormously wide range of subject matters it covers. Home-construction of transmitters, receivers and other equipment, experimenting with antennas, working with satellites, moonbounce, direction-finding, radio orienteering (so-called 'fox-hunting'), writing computer software for amateur radio applications and day-to-day operating on HF or VHF only touches the surface. Even within that one area of 'operating' we have LF, HF, VHF, UHF, microwaves, Morse code (CW), voice (SSB, FM, AM and - these days - digital voice), data modes (not just RTTY but also PSK, JT65 and the numerous 'new' data modes that have appeared in the last decade or so), DXing, contesting, 'rag-chewing' (chatting away at length about a variety of subjects), mobile operating, repeaters, nets, emergency communications and so much more.

Not many radio amateurs can tick more than a few of the above boxes: most will tend to specialise in one area or another. But if you have only ever operated FM on 2m or 70cm then give HF SSB a go! Or if you enjoy taking part in 'natter nets' on 40 or 80m how about chasing some VHF DX as well? If you are a 100% CW man (or lady), try RTTY. That is one very good reason for *The Amateur Radio Operating Manual* - it will help you to get the most out of your amateur radio operating by encouraging you to try areas of this great hobby that you might not have otherwise considered.

But if you have spent time listening on the amateur bands, you may still wonder why an operating manual is necessary at all. Surely anyone who can hold a conversation, use a telephone or conduct a business meeting, ought to be able to sit in front of a radio and start operating? To some extent this is true. But bear in mind that almost all radio contacts are not full duplex (where both parties can hear each other all the time, just as with a telephone). Rather they are half-duplex: in other words they operate in only one direction at a time.

The HF / 6m station of PJ4DX. Left to right: Notebook computer for logging etc, 13.8V 20A power supply, Yaesu FT-2000 HF / 6m transceiver with Bencher CW paddle and Heil mic / headset in front, Acom 1500 linear amplifier with Yaesu G-800 antenna rotator control box on top, two-way antenna switch. The table fan is not an essential part of the station equipment unless you live in PJ4!

This requires an understanding of operating procedures in order to avoid losing contact or, on the other hand, both ends transmitting at once, neither hearing the other.

Then there are net operations, which are a form of round-table discussion. There needs to be some understanding of the order in which the participants make their transmissions, how and when others can join the net and similar matters. This is complicated by the fact that, radio propagation being what it is, it is quite possible that not all net participants can necessarily hear each other.

While full duplex may appear to make operating much simpler, it is technically more difficult to accomplish, as it is necessary to be able to transmit and receive simultaneously, which means using two discrete frequencies sufficiently far apart for one's own transmitter not to interfere with your receiver, as well as other technical issues to be overcome. There are other factors to be borne in mind too, such as the possibilities of interfering with users of other services, the necessity of identifying yourselves at regular intervals, and so on.

All this goes to demonstrate that, whether consciously or not, we need a set of procedures to establish, maintain and finally end our various communications. Commercial and

Age, gender and religion are no barriers in amateur radio.

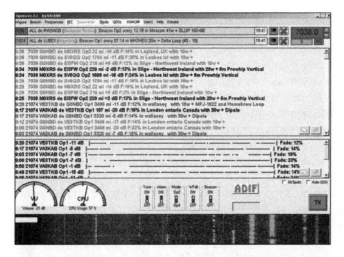

Some digital modes such as Opera (illustrated above) and WSPR involve one-way beacons with reports received via an internet connection

military users of radio communications have always recognised the need for this. If a commander, in the field of battle, issues an order, it needs to be absolutely clear to whom that order is addressed and the commander needs to know not only that the message has been sent but that it has been received accurately at the far end and will be acted upon. Fortunately the demands on amateur radio communications are usually less onerous, though those amateurs who offer their services in emergency situations (such as after 9/11, and after the devastating earthquakes and tsunamis in the Indian Ocean on Boxing Day 2004 or off Fukushima in 2011) have to be extremely conscious of the need for accuracy and accountability at all times.

TYPES OF OPERATING

Of course, operating interests vary widely. Some use amateur radio to keep in touch with friends at the local radio club, perhaps through a well-sited repeater. Others maintain regular scheduled contacts ('skeds') with a friend overseas. For the technically-minded, operating may simply be a way of checking out that newly-built piece of kit. For others, their operating may focus on a net of like-minded enthusiasts, maybe sharing a common interest in fishing or motor cars.

It has been noticeable in recent years, though, that the amount of 'rag-chewing' (chatting) on the bands has decreased dramatically. Unless there is DX (long-distance) propagation, bands such as 6m can appear dead for long periods. In contrast, competitive operating, in the sense of DXing and contesting, is growing in popularity. Perhaps this is a sign of the times, with radio amateurs finding less time in their busy diaries for casual operating, but able to mark out specific slots for contests, or to get on the air briefly to make a short DX contact. It is likely that VoIP services such as *Skype* and others have to some extent replaced radio communications for rag-chewing, providing, as they do, more consistent communications without the vagaries of propagation.

On the other hand, there are signs that digital technology is, in its turn, helping to revive amateur radio. The digital modes (RTTY, PSK, WSJT and the like) are on the ascendant

across the frequency spectrum, and *Echolink* is providing a way of interconnecting radio and the Internet to achieve the best of both worlds, allowing communications while on the move, but benefiting from the ubiquity of the fixed Internet network.

Whatever your operating preferences, there will be something in these pages of interest, but do also use these pages as a resource when trying out new operating experiences.

WHAT IS A CONTACT?

An amateur radio contact, often referred to as a QSO (see Chapter 7 for an explanation of Q codes, and a list of the commonly-used ones), consists of establishing two-way communications, maintaining them long enough to pass whatever information is appropriate (which may be a pleasant chat or, for example in the case of a contest, a set of data defined by the sponsors which will enable them to validate that a contact has taken place), and an end to communications. If the contact is to count for the various operating awards or, as mentioned, as a valid contest QSO, then this complete cycle must take place, even if it's all over in a matter of seconds. If communications are lost part-way through, no contact is deemed to have taken place (how can you be sure, for example, if you haven't heard the other party confirm the exchange, that he has received your greetings, contest exchange, or whatever?)

Having said this, amateur radio is a hobby and there are no hard and fast rules as to what that contact must include. For the most popular operating awards, such as the RSGB's IOTA awards and the ARRL's DXCC (see Chapter 10), there is no requirement even to exchange signal reports, though this is usually considered appropriate. All that is necessary is to copy each other's callsign accurately. Even for awards such as Worked All Britain (based on NGR grid squares) or the various VHF awards based on QTH Locator squares, it's not actually necessary to pass the locator information during the contact. It can be written or printed on the QSL card which you send to confirm the contact. In practice, you'll almost certainly wish to exchange location information, but that's for personal interest only.

One exception to the 'two-way' definition of a contact described above can be made for so-called 'beacon modes', such as WSPR (Weak Signal Propagation Reporter, pronounced "whisper"). Standard WSPR data transmissions can be decoded at levels down to -28dB (in a 2500Hz bandwidth) and reception reports are uploaded to the Internet, where maps of the received signals can be viewed. Thus WSPR transmissions can be thought of as one-way contacts.

ESTABLISHING CONTACT

There are three ways of establishing a contact. The first is to put out a call, inviting others to call you. The second is to answer such a call. Finally, you can call in as another contact is just finishing, often referred to as 'tail-ending'. Let's deal with these in turn.

In the first instance, you might put out a general call (usually referred to as a CQ - "seek you" call), having first checked that the frequency you intend to use is free. You do this by first listening for a brief period of time then, if nothing is heard, asking "Is this frequency in use?" at least twice, waiting several seconds for a reply each time. On CW, send "QRL?" and again wait a few seconds before repeating. Only if there is no response should you put out a CQ call. Calling procedures for repeaters are different and are detailed in Chapter 13.

You may also wish to make a directed CQ call. You might, for example, call "CQ VK / ZL" if you are looking specifically for contacts with Australia (VK) and New Zealand (ZL). Or in the extreme, you might call only for a specific station: "PJ4DX, this is G3XDV calling".

On the VHF and UHF bands, NBFM (narrowband frequency modulation, usually abbreviated to just 'FM') activity is usually channelised. In other words, rather than tune your radio to anywhere in the band, communications take place on discrete channels, widely recognised and listed in the various band plans. These are published annually, usually in February, in the RSGB members' magazine *RadCom*, or can be found in the *RSGB Yearbook* [2] or the RSGB website [3] for the complete band plans.

If, perhaps, you have a 'sked' (a pre-arranged scheduled contact) with a friend, you may have chosen a suitable channel beforehand, in which case you will call on that channel. Ideally, though, you will have made some sort of pre-arrangement that, if the channel is in use by others you will, for example, use the first clear channel above that one. Remember, this is amateur radio, and none of us, whether an individual, a club or even a national radio society, has any greater call on a specific frequency than any other (though there are a few exceptions, for instance specially licensed stations such as beacons and repeaters). If you have no pre-arrangement, the usual practice where channelised operation is the norm is to make your call on the designated calling channel and, once communications have been established, vacate that channel and move to a free channel elsewhere in the band.

Outside the channelised parts of the VHF / UHF bands and almost universally on the HF bands (there are some exceptions), no defined channels exist. You can, quite simply, transmit on any frequency that your licence allows. The band plans designate certain sectors of the bands for particular modes, depending on the bandwidth required, and these plans should be followed for several good reasons. Firstly, if you transmit in the 'wrong' part of the band you are likely to cause interference to amateurs using different modes of transmission, even without realising it. Secondly, if you were to call CQ (for example) on SSB in the CW part of any of the HF bands, or on FM in the SSB part of the VHF bands, (a) you would be very unlikely to get any contacts, and (b) you would certainly annoy your fellow amateurs who were trying to operate in the correct part of the bands!

Follow the band plan and find a slot wide enough for your transmission, which is not already in use, and make your CQ call. This may be easier said than done, and even when you have conscientiously done this and established your contact, propagation may change such that others who were using the frequency but inaudible to you may suddenly be interfering

with you and you with them, as propagation changes. In such a case, it's not a matter of arguing right and wrong, as no 'wrong' has taken place. It's a matter of courtesy to sort matters out, with one pair of operators agreeing to move to an alternative frequency.

Already you may be realising that there is more to even the simple matter of establishing a contact than you might previously have thought. Let's turn, now, to answering someone else's call (which you will probably have heard by tuning around the band, or using the scanning facility on your transceiver). Firstly, if he is making a directional call, do not answer if you are not included. If you are within the scope of his call, or if he is making a general CQ call, feel free to answer.

Your call will normally be of the form "PJ4DX, this is G3XDV calling" or perhaps "PJ4DX from G3XDV". Unless the station being called already knows you, the phonetic alphabet should be used for your own callsign, because even under good conditions "A" can sound like "J" or "K", "B" can sound like "D" or "G" or "V", and so on.

On Morse (CW) you would send "PJ4DX de G3XDV KN".

Most importantly, avoid launching into "PJ4DX, this is G3XDV near London, you are 59 and my equipment is . . ." as is sometimes heard. After all, you may not be the only one calling, and you could simply be causing unnecessary interference. Instead, make a short call, and hand the transmission back to determine whether you have been heard and acknowledged.

If there is interference or signals are weak, you may need to send your callsign a couple of times and once again, do so phonetically. There is usually no need to send the other station's callsign repeatedly: he already knows what it is! In a DX or contest situation, it is normal not to send his callsign at all, only your own. This is covered in more detail in the relevant chapters.

Finally, calling at the end of an existing contact. If you have been listening to what has gone before, it should be obvious which of the stations is likely to stay on frequency and who will move off (by convention, the station who originally found

Amateur radio should be fun! These five ladies from the Wythall Radio Club operated as GB100RSGB during the Society's centenary year in 2013.

the frequency clear and called CQ will continue to use it until he's ready to close down). Call as you would when answering a CQ call, but do be absolutely sure that the previous contact really has ended and that you are not causing interference.

THE MEAT OF THE CONTACT

Once contact has been established, pretty well anything goes. A so-called 'rubber stamp' contact usually consists of an exchange of signal reports and perhaps name and location (QTH). You might also exchange details about equipment or maybe the weather. But there is absolutely no need to limit your exchange to that. Apart from certain licence restrictions regarding conducting business over the air, conducting a political campaign etc, pretty much anything goes, and one of the joys of the hobby is making new friends and sharing experiences well outside amateur radio. Just because we use the technology of radio to make communications possible, doesn't mean that is all we should talk about, any more than using a mobile phone means that you can only talk about mobile phones.

Of course, if the other operator doesn't have English as his native language, there may be limitations on how deeply you can discuss existentialism (for example!), but there again amateur radio is an excellent medium with which to practice your language skills.

ENDING THE CONTACT

Ending the contact is straightforward, but it is always helpful to make it clear to anyone listening as to whose frequency it is (following the convention described above, that the frequency remains with whoever was there first - no one 'owns' the frequency of course), in case anyone wants to call either you or the station you have been in contact with. Actually, it's surprising how often DX stations seem to leave some ambiguity as to whether or not the contact is complete (remember, those listening may not be able to hear both sides of the contact), and then get upset when others start calling when the station with whom they are in contact is still transmitting. So try to make it clear when you are signing. For example, "Thanks for the contact. Listening for any final comments from you before checking the frequency, G3XDV from PJ4DX", thus making it clear that you are not yet ready for other callers. When the contact has finished, you might then say, "73, this is PJ4DX listening for any further calls", or more commonly "This is PJ4DX, QRZ?".

On CW, it should be clear from the way you end your transmission. ". . . G3XDV DE PJ4DX KN" clearly indicates that you are going back specifically to G3XDV. ". . . G3XDV DE PJ4DX SK" is somewhat more ambiguous. It indicates this is your last transmission but, of course, it may not be your frequency and your QSO partner may still be expecting to make a final transmission. A DX or contest station often ends a QSO with "TU" ("thank you"), indicating that he is now ready for other callers as in ". . . G3XDV DE PJ4DX TU".

". . . G3XDV DE PJ4DX CL" indicates that your have finished and are closing down. More on these abbreviations and

procedure signals can be found in the section on Morse operating in Chapter 7.

NET OPERATIONS

'Net' operations are an excellent way of bringing together operators with a common interest and using spectrum in an efficient way. An example might be a club net, where club members can meet on the air and exchange news and views. In the DX context, much has been said about net and 'list' operations over the years, because making a DX contact with any sort of perceived assistance from an MC (Master of Ceremonies) or Net Controller is, in the view of many DX chasers, a form of assistance too far. For any sort of net to work, though, there needs to be a level of discipline over and above that which would be necessary for the sort of two-way contacts already described.

Military operators have very strict guidelines for net operations so that in the heat of battle, for example, everyone is absolutely clear what is going on, which messages are intended for which stations, when it is permissible to transmit, and so on. As radio amateurs, we certainly don't need to be so formal, but without some structure a net can quickly deteriorate, especially if not every station can hear every other station.

The simplest solution for net operations is to have a designated 'Net Controller', ideally one who every participant can hear and who, in turn, can hear every participant. He can then make clear to everyone the order in which they should transmit, ask them to stand by from time to time to allow others to join the net, and whatever else is required. Of course, this also needs him to be there when the net starts and still there when it closes. Alternatively, the role of Net Controller can be passed from individual to individual as time goes on, if this is convenient.

For small nets of just a handful of stations it's possible to dispense with a Net Controller altogether, with the participants imposing their own discipline. Usually they will follow some obvious sort of system, such as passing the transmission progressively to the next one who joined the net, and allowing a short break between transmissions for others to join. As long as every participant knows who to hand over to at the end of his own transmission, this is usually sufficient to avoid confusion. As participants leave the net, they simply need to ensure that the station preceding them in order of transmission is aware of who the next station is down the line.

FM AND REPEATER OPERATIONS

Many new operators start with some sort of VHF or UHF hand-held transceiver, and their first experience of operating is via the channelised approach found in the FM bands. Such a transceiver will also give access to the repeater network, allowing contacts to be made over greater distances.

The earlier discussion has focused in general terms on how to establish, conduct and conclude an amateur radio contact. But it hasn't dealt with actually finding people to speak to, or the protocols associated with using frequencies which are shared with thousands of other users, unlike most

A new dual-band (2m / 70cm) FM and digital transceiver, the Icom ID-5100.

commercial operations where each group of users is allocated its own frequency.

By convention, parts of the VHF and UHF bands, as well as part of the 10m band, are allocated to channelised operation (see NOTE 1 below) in which rather than treating the radio spectrum as a continuous entity, operations take place on discrete frequencies that are far enough apart to avoid mutual interference.

Given that VHF / UHF propagation is limited in distance, and there may be relatively few users within your coverage area, picking a channel at random to call CQ could be very unproductive, unless someone else just happened to be tuning from channel to channel and ran across you. Instead, the usual approach is to use recommended calling channels. This is where you are much more likely to make a contact, as those who are looking for contacts will have their transceivers tuned to this channel. For this very reason, though, once contact is established it is normal procedure to move to a nearby channel (one not already in use) to continue the contact, rather than hog the use of the calling channel. Of course, if you have a pre-arranged contact, for example a club net, this can start on any pre-arranged channel though, again, courtesy demands that if that channel is already in use you should move elsewhere, probably to the first clear channel above or below. After all, as radio amateurs we all have equal rights to the frequencies covered by our licences, so no one has precedence and the rule is that the first users to arrive on a channel have use of it for as long as they need it.

Repeater operation is slightly different. In any given part of the country, there may only be one or two repeaters accessible. Each has a single channel (they actually use two frequencies, one for input and a second for output, but your transceiver should take care of this automatically, along with generating any access tone required at the beginning of each transmission). A single channel means that all repeater

NOTE 1: The 60m / 5MHz 'band' - in the UK available to Full licensees only - falls into a separate category, as it is made up of 11 separate narrow bands of frequencies. Some of these are only 3 or 4kHz wide and therefore are only wide enough for a single SSB 'channel'.

users need to make suitable allowances for each other. If the station you make contact with through the repeater turns out to be within range of a direct contact, you should move to a clear simplex (non-repeater) frequency. If not, by all means continue to use the repeater as long as no one else wishes to. But allow pauses between your transmissions in case someone else is trying to access it, maybe a mobile station trying to get hold of a friend. Repeaters were first set up essentially for the purpose of enabling mobile operators to make longer-distance contacts, and mobile stations should be accorded priority. Within reason, several stations can use a repeater simultaneously, always keeping transmissions short and allowing everyone to have their turn. This doesn't have to be a formal net operation as described in previous sections, provided common sense prevails.

NON-CHANNELISED OPERATION

Those parts of the VHF / UHF bands used for DX working, and almost all of the HF amateur bands, are treated as continuous spectrum rather than channels. For anyone who has become used to channelised operation, this can be daunting at first. Except in specific instances, for example particular interest groups like Islands on the Air (IOTA) or modes such as Slow Scan Television (SSTV), there are no recognised calling channels. Standard procedure is to find someone who is calling CQ and to answer him, or to find a frequency that isn't in use and call CQ yourself as described earlier in this chapter. While there are no frequencies recognised as calling channels, the various different modes of transmission each have their own particular place in the band plans, typically with Morse code (CW) at the lower-frequency end of the band, SSB at the higher-frequency end, and data modes in between. To maximise your chances of making a wanted contact, and to avoid causing unnecessary interference to other band users, you should always follow the published band plans.

The constantly changing nature of HF (and occasionally VHF/UHF) propagation also means that a frequency that is clear when you start a contact may not be clear a few minutes later, so you must be prepared to make allowances for this, maybe even to move frequency if there is too much mutual interference. It is this very unpredictability of HF propagation which makes it interesting to so many amateurs as, even with the best propagation-prediction programs, you can never be sure just where you may be speaking to next. It is also that unpredictability which means that you have to be prepared to be flexible as propagation changes. Of course, it is that same unpredictability which has driven commercial and broadcast users increasingly to other means such as satellite, as they need to be able to plan their schedules well ahead of time and with a high degree of confidence.

TO QSL OR NOT TO QSL

In this introductory discussion, a word about QSLing seems worthwhile. From the earliest days of the hobby it has been common to exchange QSL cards, some sort of written confirmation of the contact that has taken place. Indeed, a typical 1930s QSL card would be perfectly recognisable today,

Montage of QSL cards from DX stations active in 2014 and 2015.

though improvements in printing technology mean that many contemporary QSL cards are quite elaborate compared with their predecessors.

A QSL card serves several purposes. Firstly, it is an ongoing memento of a contact. This may seem rather unnecessary nowadays, as contacts are easy to come by and, if desired, it's quite easy to record your contacts for posterity (some logging programs offer an option for a digital recording of the QSO to be permanently associated with the corresponding log entry). In the early years of amateur radio, though, every contact was an achievement and so the QSL card was very much valued.

The other purpose of exchanging QSL cards is to have some sort of proof of contact for claiming operating awards. This is also becoming less relevant with the advent of the ARRL's *Logbook of The World* (*LoTW*) [4], an electronic database of

QSO information accessed over the Internet which allows you to gain credits for the DXCC awards programme and some other awards. In due course *LoTW* may become available to other organisations such as RSGB for their awards programmes. However, at the time of writing, and almost certainly for the foreseeable future, QSL cards will remain a popular way of providing a permanent memento of contacts - not necessarily all contacts, but certainly those which are worthy of commemoration, such as a special event station or a rare DX station.

Which begs the question, what should you do about QSLing? The subject is covered in more detail in Chapter 10. But it is one which often comes up in the course of a contact. Your QSO partner may ask you for a QSL to confirm the contact, perhaps because he needs your card for an award. This is the time to give a clear reply, indicating perhaps that you will send him one with your own next batch to the QSL bureau, that you will reply on receipt of his, or whatever is appropriate.

TECHNICAL CONSIDERATIONS

There will be more to say later in this manual with regard to the station and antennas. However, it's worth mentioning a few areas that relate directly to what has been said so far.

Firstly, do remember that the nature of radio transmissions is that they can be heard by anyone within range, and they are therefore insecure. The good operator is aware of this and not only avoids bad operating practices, but actually goes out of his way to operate well at all times. Not only does this avoid the censure of others, but serves as an example to them of how they themselves should operate.

Secondly, amateurs are encouraged at all times to use the minimum power appropriate for effective communications. This helps to reduce the potential for interference to other band users and, possibly, breakthrough on other electronic

DXCC Entity	160M	80M	40M	30M	20M	17M	15M	12M	10M
1A0KM - SOV MILITARY ORDER OF MALTA			1A0KM			1A0KM	1A0KM	1A0KM	1A0KM
3C0 - ANNOBON						3C0BYP	3C0BYP		3C0BYP
3V - TUNISIA					3V8SS				3V8SS
4J - AZERBAIJAN							4K6FO		
4L - GEORGIA		4L8A	4L8A		4L8A		4L8A		4L8A
4O - MONTENEGRO			4O3A		4O7TC		4O3A	4O7CC	4O3A
4S - SRI LANKA					4S7DFG				
4U1ITU - ITU HQ						4U1ITU	4U1ITU	4U1ITU	
4W - TIMOR - LESTE					4W/K7CO			4W/K7CO	4W/K7CO
4X - ISRAEL		4X6KA	4X4DK		4X1ZQ	4X6TT	4X1UN	4X4DK	4X6KA
5B - CYPRUS		5B4AGN	5B4AHK		5B4AIF	5B4AHJ	C44C	5B4AHJ	5B4AHJ
5H - TANZANIA					5I0DX		5I0DX		5I0DX
5R - MADAGASCAR			5R8M		5R8M	5R8M	5R8M	5R8M	5R8M
5V7 - TOGO					5V7TH				
5W - SAMOA			5W0AF		5W0AF	5W0AF	5W0AG	5W0AF	5W0AF
5Z - KENYA					5Z4/DJ4EL	5Z4/DJ4EL	5Z4/DJ4EL	5Z4/DJ4EL	

Logbook of The World screen, showing DXCC entities confirmed, and the stations' callsigns, on each band.

devices in the vicinity. Of course, it's almost impossible to determine what that level of power should be, especially on HF where signal strengths can vary enormously in the course of a single contact. But, equally, if you are engaged in a contact across town on 70cm, with huge signals at both ends, then it is quite clear that a reduction in power would be entirely appropriate. As always, experience and good sense help to decide the best power level to use at any given time.

Thirdly, be aware of the capabilities and limitations of your own equipment. Many modern transceivers allow sophisticated tailoring of the transmitted waveform, which you can vary according to whether you want maximum 'punch' for DX working or best quality for local rag-chewing. And, of course, even the best equipment can be abused, for example by excessive use of speech processing or by using break-in on CW with equipment that hasn't been specifically designed for the task.

The moral is to get know your equipment and how it sounds on the air, perhaps by running tests with another local amateur. By not doing so, you run the risk of causing interference to other band users, of transmitting signals that are almost unintelligible and of causing problems for your neighbours. If problems do arise during your communications, always be prepared to reduce power or close down until they can be resolved.

STRUCTURE OF THIS BOOK

This chapter has given a brief overview of amateur radio operations and the need for a structured approach to operating. The remainder of the book goes on to flesh out these considerations, starting with a more formal look at the Amateur Service. There follows some basic advice on setting up a station, including a chapter devoted to the use of computers in the shack. This is followed by a comprehensive look at operating procedures, as they apply to the majority of amateur radio operations. However, each mode of operation has its special requirements, so these are covered in more detail in a separate chapter. There is a chapter describing each of the amateur bands, from LF through to the microwave region. This is followed by a general discussion of propagation modes, though it must be emphasised that a full treatment of propagation is well beyond the scope of this book. The purpose is to discuss how propagation affects operating techniques, rather than to instil a detailed technical understanding. The book ends with chapters covering several relevant topics that don't sit conveniently elsewhere, such as QSLing and operating awards, and DXpedition and special event station operation.

There is certainly no need to read this book in sequential order; it is intended more as a reference and refresher. There is a certain amount of overlap between sections. For example, the descriptions of the bands will make reference to modes commonly used and the chapter dealing with modes will refer to specific bands. This is both inevitable and, at the

Front page of the RSGB website (April 2015).

same time, helpful as you can cross-refer to the relevant chapter as appropriate.

Wherever possible in the following chapters, suggestions are given for further reading and useful websites (see the references at the end of each chapter). Bear in mind though, that websites may come and go. If there is a specific topic that you want to follow up, it is always worth putting a query into Google or one of the other popular search engines and see what you come up with. There is a vast amount of helpful information available.

A very useful - perhaps essential - book for operators is the *RSGB Yearbook* [2] and is much more than a list of callsigns and addresses. It includes a huge amount of data such as an international prefix list, UK repeaters, currently available satellites, IARU band plans, beacon lists, etc. This data is, of course, updated annually. An editorial decision has been made, therefore, to omit much of that data from this manual, where it would be more likely to become out of date. If you don't wish to purchase the *Yearbook* every year, many of those tables and data sources are also available on the RSGB website [3].

The *ARRL Operating Manual* [5] is also an invaluable resource, though some sections are less relevant in the UK, being specific to amateur radio in North America.

You should also ensure that you read and understand the operating instructions for your station equipment (transceiver, amplifier, etc) and software (logging program, data mode or whatever). Each one is different, and it is impossible to give anything but generic advice in a manual of this kind.

REFERENCES

[1] *Radio Communication Handbook*, RSGB. Available from www.rsgbshop.org
[2] *RSGB Yearbook*, RSGB (published annually). Available from www.rsgbshop.org
[3] RSGB website: www.rsgb.org
[4] https://lotw.arrl.org
[5] *The ARRL Operating Manual*, ARRL. Available from www.rsgbshop.org

2

The Amateur Service and Your Licence

MATEUR RADIO IS unusual as a hobby in that it is two officially recognised services, the Amateur Service and the Amateur Satellite Service, bound and protected by both national and international legislation. While it is possible to engage in two-way radio communications without a licence, through Citizens' Band (CB) radio or PMR446 (known as the Family Radio Service in the USA), radio amateurs are required to demonstrate a minimum level of proficiency before they can apply for a licence. In return, they gain privileges which are unavailable to those other types of radio communications, in terms of the range of frequencies available for their use, the power levels they may use, the modes of operation allowed and the unique opportunity to use home designed and/or home built equipment.

The necessity of achieving a level of proficiency is two-fold. Firstly, many amateur bands are shared with other services, and it is important that radio amateurs appreciate how to co-exist with those other services without causing problems to their users. Secondly, due to the power levels and wide range of frequencies available to radio amateurs, there is always a risk of electromagnetic incompatibility with other electronic devices in the neighbourhood, such as telephones or broadcast receivers, both radio and TV, computer systems etc. Whilst the radio amateur may not legally be required to respond to a complaint by a neighbour, good relations with neighbours works two ways, so there is an inherent need to understand how to handle any such electromagnetic compatibility (EMC) issues which may arise.

The need for radio licensing to be covered not only by national but also by international legislation is self-evident, in that radio waves do not recognise national boundaries, and it is therefore crucial to harmonise the rules between countries. There are, of course, instances where certain bands, such as 4m (70MHz), are only available in selected countries. In some cases Effective Radiated Power (ERP) - that takes into account antenna gain as well as transmit power to the antenna - and frequency limits will have been set by the national administration to avoid interference to the users in nearby foreign countries.

In terms of the international arena, amateur radio is governed, as are all radio services, by a specialised agency of the United Nations, the International Telecommunication Union (ITU) [1]. Nationally, radio services are regulated by a national telecommunications administration, which in the UK is the Office of Communications (Ofcom) [2]. Within the hobby, there are bodies which match those official organisations. Nationally, all major countries have one or more national amateur radio societies. Internationally, the largest of the societies in each country work together through the International Amateur Radio Union (IARU) [3].

The official bodies lay down regulations which must be followed by radio amateurs. These regulations govern both the issuing of an amateur licence and the rules which apply to that licence once in force. The amateur radio societies lobby the official bodies as appropriate, to influence the rules and regulations which govern the hobby. They also agree voluntary codes of practice, band plans and other operating guidelines which, while not mandatory, help radio amateurs to co-exist amicably.

This chapter expands on the foregoing, giving more background to each of those bodies which is involved in governing and running amateur radio, and then goes on to look at the mandatory rules and regulations as set out in the licence.

THE INTERNATIONAL TELECOMMUNICATION UNION

The ITU is the intergovernmental agency responsible for the coordination, standardisation and planning of worldwide information and communication technologies. Founded in 1865 and incorporated as a specialised agency of the United Nations in 1947, the ITU unites the telecommunication administrations of over 190 member states. Its headquarters are located in Switzerland.

ITU regulations cover the activities of all telecommunication services, including amateur radio, and are published by the general secretariat of the ITU. The ITU Radio Regulations define international telecommunication law, and are therefore the cornerstone of amateur licence conditions in all countries.

Every three or four years, the ITU organises a World Radiocommunication Conference (WRC) attended by delegates from national administrations where aspects of the ITU Radio Regulations and Rules of Procedure are reviewed to take into account developments in information and communications technologies. These conferences have significant agendas, and thus take place over a four week period. Preparation for the next conference starts immediately after the end of the preceding conference.

Before the 1990s these conferences used to be held every 20 years or so, but it was realised that such conferences were going to have to take place more frequently because technology was changing so rapidly and more countries were requiring access to sections of the radio spectrum. It was also realised that they would have to be more specialised, either in subject or range of frequencies under consideration.

It is important that amateurs understand the basis of the service that they use.

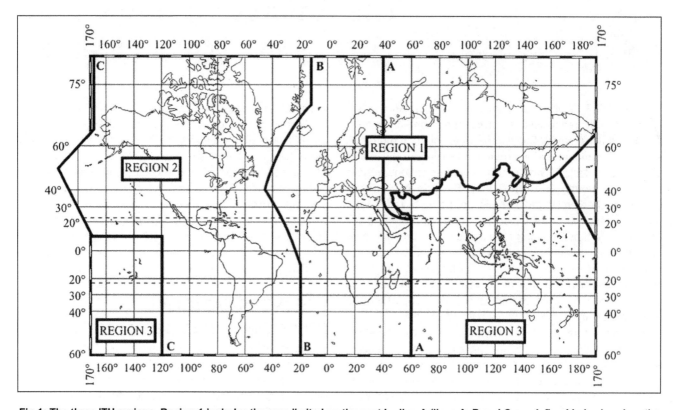

Fig 1: The three ITU regions. Region 1 includes the area limited on the east by line A (lines A, B and C are defined below) and on the west by line B, excluding any of the territory of the Islamic Republic of Iran which lies between these limits. It also includes the whole of the territory of Armenia, Azerbaijan, the Russian Federation, Georgia, Kazakhstan, Mongolia, Uzbekistan, Kyrgyzstan, Tajikistan, Turkmenistan, Turkey and Ukraine and the area to the north of the Russian Federation which lies between lines A and C. Region 2 includes the area limited on the east by line B and on the west by line C. Region 3 includes the area limited on the east by line C and on the west by line A, except any of the territory of Armenia, Azerbaijan, the Russian Federation, Georgia, Kazakhstan, Mongolia, Uzbekistan, Kyrgyzstan, Tajikistan, Turkmenistan, Turkey and Ukraine and the area to the north of the Russian Federation. It also includes that part of the territory of Iran lying outside of those limits. The lines A, B and C are defined as follows: Line A extends from the North Pole along meridian 40° East of Greenwich to parallel 40° North; thence by great circle arc to the intersection of meridian 60° East and the Tropic of Cancer; thence along the meridian 60° East to the South Pole. Line B extends from the North Pole along meridian 10° West of Greenwich to its intersection with parallel 72° North; thence by great circle arc to the intersection of meridian 50° West and parallel 40° North; thence by great circle arc to the intersection of meridian 20° West and parallel 10° South; thence along meridian 20° West to the South Pole. Line C extends from the North Pole by great circle arc to the intersection of parallel 65° 30' North with the international boundary in Bering Strait; thence by great circle arc to the intersection of meridian 165° East of Greenwich and parallel 50° North; thence by great circle arc to the intersection of meridian 170° West and parallel 10° North; thence along parallel 10° North to its intersection with meridian 120° West; thence along meridian 120° West to the South Pole.

DEFINITIONS

Within the ITU Radio Regulations the **Amateur Service** is defined as:

> A radiocommunication service for the purpose of self-training, intercommunication and technical investigations carried out by amateurs, that is, by duly authorised persons interested in radio technique solely with a personal aim and without pecuniary interest.

It should be noted that the ITU considers amateur satellite activities as a separate **Amateur Satellite Service** defined as:

> A radiocommunication service using space stations on earth satellites for the same purposes as those of the Amateur Service.

The section of the Radio Regulations dealing specifically with amateur radio is Article 25, and this is available at [4].

CALLSIGNS

It is a requirement of the regulations that all radio amateurs identify themselves by transmitting an identification code, known as the callsign, at short intervals during their transmissions. The current (April 2015) licence issued by Ofcom is less specific on the requirement than the previous wording of the licence, but the intent is the same, and requires that "the station is clearly identifiable at all times". Licence holders should refer to Clause 13(1) of their licence for more detailed information.

The initial characters of the callsign denote the country to which the amateur station belongs and is operating from. The ITU allocates the administration of each country blocks of letters and numbers in order to form callsigns, not just for amateur stations but for all radio stations in that country. The ITU allocation blocks are of three types:

FIRST SYMBOL:
Type of modulation of main carrier
1. Emission of unmodulated carrier: N.
2. Emission in which the main carrier is amplitude modulated including cases where sub carriers are angle modulated. Double sideband: A. Single sideband, full carrier: H. Single sideband, reduced or variable carrier: R. Single sideband, suppressed carrier: J. Independent sideband: B. Vestigial sideband: C.
3. Emission in which the main carrier is angle modulated. Frequency modulation: F. Phase modulation: G.
4. Emission in which the main carrier is amplitude or angle modulated either simultaneously or in a pre-arranged sequence: D.
5. Emission of pulses. Unmodulated sequence of pulses: P. A sequence of pulses (a) modulated in amplitude: K, (b) modulated in width/duration: L, (c) modulated in position/phase: M, (d) in which the carrier is angle modulated during the period of the pulse: Q, (e) which is a combination of the foregoing or is produced by other means: V.
6. Cases not covered above, in which an emission consists of the main carrier modulated, either simultaneously or in a pre-established sequence, in a combination of two or more of the following modes amplitude, angle, pulse: W.
7. Cases not otherwise covered: X.
Note: Emissions where the main carrier is directly modulated by a signal which has been coded into quantised form (eg pulse code modulation) should be designated by A, H, R, J, B, C, F, or G as appropriate.

SECOND SYMBOL:
Nature of signal(s) modulating main carrier
1. No modulating signal: O.
2. A single channel containing quantised or digital information without the use of a modulating subcarrier (excluding time division multiplex): 1.
3. A single channel containing quantised or digital information with the use of a modulating subcarrier (excluding time division multiplex): 2.
4. A single channel containing analogue information: 3.
5. Two or more channels containing quantised or digital information: 7.
6. Two or more channels containing analogue information: 8.

7. Composite system with one or more channels containing quantised or digital information, together with one or more channels containing analogue information: 9.
8. Cases not otherwise covered: X.

THIRD SYMBOL:
Type of information to be transmitted
1. No information transmitted: N.
2. Telegraphy for aural reception: A
3. Telegraphy for automatic reception: B.
4. Facsimile: C.
5. Data transmission, telemetry, telecommand: D.
6. Telephony (including sound broadcasting): E.
7. Television (video): F.
8. Combination of the above: W.
9. Cases not otherwise covered: X.
Note: In this context the word 'information' does not include information of a constant, unvarying nature such as provided by standard frequency emissions, continuous wave and pulse radars etc.

EXAMPLES OF EMISSION CODES
Telephony (speech)
Single sideband, suppressed carrier (SSB)	J3E
Frequency modulation (FM)	F3E
Phase modulation (PM)	G3E
Amplitude modulation	A3E
Morse code	
Hand sent, on / off keying of carrier	A1A
Hand sent, on / off keying of the audio tone (FM transmitter)	F2A
RTTY / AmTOR / PSK	
Direct frequency shift keying of carrier	F1B
Frequency shift keyed audio tone (FM transmitter)	F2B
Frequency shift keyed audio tone (SSB transmitter)	J2B
Packet / Data	
Direct frequency shift keying of carrier	F1D
Frequency shift keyed audio tone (FM transmitter)	F2D
Frequency shift keyed audio tone (SSB transmitter)	J2D
Television	
Vestigial sideband (AM transmitter)	C3F
Slow scan TV (SSB transmitter)	J2F
Facsimile	
Frequency shift keyed audio tone (SSB transmitter)	J2C

Table 1. Classification of emissions and practical examples of how they are used in amateur radio.

(a) letter letter letter, e.g. LAA - LNZ;
(b) digit letter letter, e.g. 2AA - 2ZZ; and
(c) letter digit letter, e.g. H4A - H4Z.

Amateur callsigns are normally made up of the first two characters from the allocation, followed by a single digit and then a group of not more than three (occasionally four) letters. However, if a country has the whole of a 'letter letter letter' block, eg WAA - WZZ, it is also entitled to form callsigns consisting of the first letter in front of the digit (in this case W).

For example, the UK has been allocated GAA - GZZ, MAA - MZZ and 2AA - 2ZZ. This means that UK amateur callsigns can have GA, GB, GC etc as the first two characters, but, as

the UK has the whole GAA - GZZ block, and it is also entitled to use the single letter G. Similarly, it can form callsigns starting with MA, MB, MC etc and 2A, 2B, 2C etc. Within the ITU Radio Regulations the UK cannot use 2 as a single character callsign to designate the nationality of the station. For this reason a second nationality prefix character is required, hence 2E (denoting England), 2M (denoting Scotland), etc are formed.

The first two characters of the allocation are usually unique to a country but the ITU occasionally allocates 'half series': eg 3DA - 3DM to Swaziland and 3DN - 3DZ to Fiji. In practice, Swaziland amateur radio callsigns commence with 3DA and Fiji amateur radio callsigns with 3D2.

Certain limitations are imposed in the ITU Radio Regulations to ensure that callsigns issued cannot be confused with internationally-agreed distress signals such as SOS (e.g. G4SOS was not issued) or the international Q code (QAA - QZZ was not allocated by the ITU and also, for example, G4QAA was not issued).

Further information on the allocation of callsigns is given in the later section dealing with the work of the national telecommunications administration.

DESIGNATION OF EMISSIONS

There are very many ways in which a radio signal can be modulated so as to convey information. In order to define the types of emission a special code has been internationally agreed and implemented by the ITU. The code is in two parts, the first specifying the Necessary Bandwidth and the second the classification of emission.

Necessary Bandwidth is defined for a given class of emission as the width of the frequency band which is just sufficient to ensure the transmission of information at the rate and with the quality required under specified conditions. It is specified as follows: between 0.001 and 999Hz in hertz (H); between 10 and 999kHz in kilohertz (K); between 1.00 and 999MHz in megahertz (M); between 100 and 999GHz in gigahertz (G). For example, 400Hz would be '400H', 2.4kHz as '2K40' and 12.5kHz as '12K5'.

The classification is specified by three symbols. The first denotes the type of modulation of the main carrier, the second the nature of the modulating signal(s) and the third the type of information to be transmitted. **Table 1** gives the symbols and their meanings. Some examples relevant to amateur radio are also shown.

FREQUENCY ALLOCATIONS

One of the most important tasks of the ITU is to allocate parts of the radio spectrum to various radio services in such a way that the spectrum is utilised as efficiently as possible without mutual interference. The claims on the available frequency space are many and are continually changing.

The range of radio frequencies covered by the present ITU regulations is 8.3kHz to 275GHz. For the allocation of these frequencies, and for various administrative reasons, the world has been divided into three regions (see **Fig 1**). Region 1 comprises Europe, Africa, the Middle East (west of the Persian Gulf including Iraq), and Northern Asia (the Commonwealth of Independent States and Mongolia). Region 2 comprises North and South America, Greenland and some eastern Pacific islands. Region 3 comprises the rest of Asia (including Iran), Australasia and most of Oceania.

The more formal ITU definitions of these areas are given in Fig 1. Note that these three ITU regions should not be confused with the ITU broadcasting zones, which are used for scoring purposes in some amateur radio contests.

Sometimes the ITU finds it necessary to allocate part of the radio spectrum to two or more radio services. Where this is done it is always specified which if any of the services has priority over the others, by designating the service as Primary or Secondary.

Services allocated a band on a Secondary basis must not cause *harmful interference* to Primary users, and cannot claim protection from harmful interference caused by the latter. They can, however, claim protection from interference generated by stations in the same service or other Secondary services. The term *harmful interference* has a specific meaning within the ITU Radio Regulations: "Interference which endangers the functioning of a *radionavigation service* or of other *safety services* or seriously degrades, obstructs, or repeatedly interrupts a *radiocommunication service* operating in accordance with Radio Regulations (CS)"

What this means is that Primary services have the 'right of way' over Secondary services. When operating in a shared allocation in which the Amateur Service is a Secondary service, the amateur operator must take care not to cause interference to Primary users. If these start transmitting on the same frequency, even while an amateur contact is already in progress, the amateurs must change frequency and leave the channel clear. Special attention should be made to operating on the 472kHz band as the Amateur Service has a specific obligation not to cause harmful interference to the co-Secondary Aeronautical Radionavigation service.

The *RSGB Yearbook* [5] shows all amateur allocations between 9kHz and 275GHz in the three ITU regions, the status of these allocations and the nature of services (if any) sharing the allocations. The information is shown in generalised form, and may not apply to particular countries within each ITU region. Major variations from these allocations are given in Chapter 5 on a band-by-band basis.

NATIONAL ADMINISTRATION

This is the government department in each country which has the responsibility of controlling all its information and communication services and the issue of licences. This same body usually represents that government at the ITU conferences. In the UK this function is undertaken by Ofcom, the Office of Communications.

Although based on the ITU regulations, the amateur licence conditions for each country can be quite different: some countries do not allow amateur radio at all, while in others its operation is restricted.

The national administration assigns callsigns to individual amateur stations using its ITU-allocated character blocks as previously noted. It may choose to use these to denote the geographical area or licence category of the station. Similarly the single digit following the ITU characters is sometimes used to denote licence category or geographical area, while in other cases it has no particular significance and may be regarded as part of the serial letter group.

The serial letters following the single digit, or the second digit if there is more than one (often called, though inaccurately, the 'suffix'), is the part of the callsign which identifies individual stations. In a few countries the first or last letter of this group indicates geographical area or licence category. The serial letters are often assigned in alphabetical order, but in some countries it is possible to request specific letter combinations, for example to correspond with the licensee's

Callsign suffixes of up to four letters have been permitted by the ITU since 2003.

initials. A decision taken at the 2003 World Radiocommunication Conference (WRC-03) makes provision for callsign suffixes of up to four letters. This has been implemented in Australia for their Foundation (beginners') licences, with callsigns such as VK1FAAA being issued. Similarly in the UK we have seen special event callsigns such as G100RSGB, GW100RSGB etc being used to celebrate the centenary of the national society.

The part of the callsign which precedes the serial letters is known as the 'prefix'. If the single digit is simply part of the serial allocation it is not included in the prefix, though it is customary in amateur usage not to split two consecutive figures, e.g. P29 (not P2, which is more correct) is often given as the prefix for Papua New Guinea.

Sometimes the administration will temporarily allocate special callsign prefixes outside its normal series to stations commemorating some national event or celebration, and this results in some strange callsigns being heard on the air from time to time which may be difficult to identify. The important thing to note is that any prefix so used must conform to the ITU block allocation(s) for the country concerned, and the list of these in the *RSGB Yearbook* or the *RSGB Prefix Guide* [6] should be consulted in cases of doubt.

It is also possible for a callsign to have a suffix, which is separated from the rest of the callsign by a solidus (oblique stroke: "/"). A suffix usually indicates temporary operation away from the registered address of the station. In the UK, for example, '/M' denotes a mobile station and '/P' a temporary location. Occasionally some countries use country prefix characters as a suffix to denote that a licence has been issued to a foreign amateur.

OPERATION ABROAD

Most countries allow foreign amateurs to operate within their boundaries, but the conditions are set by the national administration and vary widely. In some cases, the administration acts unilaterally and permits amateurs from certain countries to apply for licences, while in others there must exist a formal reciprocal agreement with the amateur's home country.

A welcome development is the increasing number of countries world-wide which permit temporary operation (generally taken to be three months at the most) according to

Recommendation T/R 61-01 of the European Conference of Postal and Telecommunication Administrations (CEPT), which is a group of national telecommunications administrations from over 48 European countries. Once an administration has confirmed that its amateur radio licence conforms to the CEPT minimum standard, defined by T/R 61-02, its amateurs may operate when physically present in the other participating countries with the minimum of formality. However, it should be noted that T/R 61-01 applies only to Full UK licence holders, not to Foundation and Intermediate licensees. Not all member administrations have implemented this Recommendation but the list is growing all the time. The text of the Recommendation, and a list of those who have implemented it, is available on the Internet at [7]. In addition, some non CEPT countries - Australia, Canada, Israel, the Netherlands Antilles (in the Caribbean), New Zealand, Peru, South Africa and the USA - authorise operation on similar lines. The CEPT Radio Amateur Licence has been incorporated into the UK licence, and is not a separate document.

The foreign country prefix is added to the amateur's own callsign before the call and separated by a solidus (/, usually pronounced "stroke"). For example, MW0xxx may become OE/MW0xxx in Austria. In some smaller countries, or in other cases for extended operating periods, a separate callsign may be issued.

Before visiting a country where you plan to operate:

- check that your licence class qualifies for a CEPT Licence. The UK Full Licence states this explicitly - note that the Intermediate and Foundation licence is not covered by T/R 61-01. Then look up T/R 61-01 at the European Radiocommunications Office (ERO) [8] on the Internet to check:
  - what national licence class in the country to be visited is equivalent to the CEPT Licence;
  - the operating privileges and regulations covering the use of that national licence class in the country to be visited; and
  - what the appropriate prefix is for use with your callsign.

The key point is that the operating privileges for the visitor operating under the CEPT Licence are defined *by the country being visited*, and *not* the privileges in his or her own country.

The following should be noted:
1) T/R 61-01 does not cover remote access to stations from outside the boundaries of that country - one has to be physically visiting the country for T/R 61-01 to apply;
2) Conditions of use vary from country to country, so it is important to refer to the latest version of T/R 61-01;
3) Special conditions often apply to overseas territories such as those of France. Local permission will often be required in such locations;
4) T/R 61-01 bears no relation to the import and export of amateur radio equipment, which is subject only to relevant customs regulations.

For the radio amateur who is moving permanently to another country use can sometimes be made of another CEPT Recommendation, namely T/R 61-02. This covers the

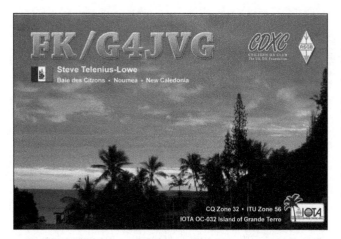

Operation from New Caledonia (prefix FK) by a UK licensee under the terms of the CEPT Licence.

Harmonised Amateur Radio Examination Certificate or HAREC for short. The HAREC is recognised by countries who are signatories to T/R 61-02 and provides automatic exemption from national amateur radio examinations relevant to some of the licence classes in the country to which you are moving. The ECO website is the place to look for more information but in the UK Ofcom issues the HAREC. For some countries you still may also need to show you have passed a Morse test. For other countries the possession of a UK licence is enough for a local licence to be granted. It is also worth noting that in some countries you may need to show that you have made a *bona fide* move to that country in order to be issued with a local callsign.

The RSGB has published a book, the *World Licensing and Operating Directory* [9], which provides detailed information about licensing in nearly all the countries and territories of the world, while the most useful website for licensing information is that of OH2MCN [10]. Further information on operating abroad is given in Chapter 12.

INTERNATIONAL AMATEUR RADIO UNION

The Amateur Service and Amateur Satellite Service have their own international organisation, the International Amateur Radio Union (IARU) [3] which has the specific objective of promoting, protecting and advancing these services within the framework of regulations established by the International Telecommunication Union. It also provides support to member societies in the pursuit of these objectives at the national level, with special reference to the following:

(a) representation of the interests of amateur radio at and between conferences and meetings of international telecommunications organisations;

(b) encouragement of agreements between national amateur radio societies on matters of common interest;

(c) enhancement of amateur radio as a means of technical self-training for young people;

(d) promotion of technical and scientific investigations in the field of radio communications;

(e) promotion of amateur radio as a means of providing relief in the event of natural disasters;

(f) encouragement of international goodwill and friendship;

(g) support of member societies in developing amateur radio as a valuable national resource, particularly in developing countries; and

(h) development of amateur radio in those countries not represented by member societies.

The International Amateur Radio Union was founded in 1925 and its International Secretariat is located at ARRL HQ in Newington, Connecticut, USA; it has separate organisations in each of the ITU regions.

Membership is restricted to national societies just as the members of the ITU are national administrations, not radio services or individuals. There are over 160 national societies which are members of the IARU. The largest region is Region 1 which contains nearly 100 societies located in Europe, Africa, the Middle East and Northern Asia.

In a similar way to that in which the ITU regulates and coordinates frequency allocations as a whole, the IARU regulates and coordinates amateur activities within individual amateur bands. This is on a voluntary basis within the UK but mandatory in some other countries. IARU is also the

The IARU Region 1 Executive Committee at the 2014 General Conference held at Varna-Albena, Bulgaria.

coordination body for frequency assignments to the Amateur Satellite Service.

Whether mandatory or voluntary, the recommendations and guidelines issued by IARU should be followed because they have resulted from long debate and discussion within the world's national amateur radio societies. Band Plans are discussed in Chapter 5, and the UK Band Plans are detailed in the *RSGB Yearbook* [5].

The IARU Region 1, which is relevant to RSGB interests, operates its day-to-day business through several specialist Standing Committees. External matters are managed through the External Relations Committee, the Political Relations Committee and the EMC Committee. These deal with a range of interrelationships with the ITU, CEPT, the European Commission and several EMC Standards bodies. Within the amateur community there are two spectrum committees, one that covers all frequencies below 30MHz and the other that covers frequencies above 30MHz. In addition there are several specialist working groups to cover international events such as Amateur Direction Finding (ARDF) and High Speed Telegraphy (HST). STARS is an important working group that works to assist amateur radio in developing countries.

In addition there are working groups to support Emergency Communications, the IARU Monitoring System (IARUMS), that monitors unauthorised transmissions by other services within amateur allocations, and a group that monitors the behaviour of amateur operators, specifically addressing deliberate interference. Both of these groups are supported by RSGB volunteers through the RSGB Intruder Watch and AROS, see the *RSGB Yearbook* [5] for more information.

IARU MEMBER SOCIETY

The fourth arbiter of operating standards and practice is the IARU Member Society of the country concerned. In the UK this is the Radio Society of Great Britain (RSGB) [11].

Recommendations may come from the specialist committees within each society whose recommendations are considered and debated at IARU Regional General Conferences. Within the UK these areas are represented by the RSGB Spectrum Forum, which replaced the previous Microwave Committee, VHF Committee and HF Committee.

The Amateur Radio Observation Service (AROS) is an advisory and reporting service of the RSGB which is intended to assist radio amateurs and others who may be affected by problems which occur within the amateur bands or which develop on other frequencies as a result of amateur transmissions. The Service investigates reports of licence infringements, or instances of poor operating practice which might

bring the Amateur Service into disrepute. After investigation and where there is evidence of deliberate malpractice or malicious abuse of amateur radio facilities, a formal report may be made to the appropriate authorities. This report will contain sufficient detail and information to enable further investigations to be made and the authorities may take such action as is appropriate. However, AROS prefers to settle problems - great or small - within the Amateur Service. Problems arising are referred to the authorities only as a last resort. For more details, see the *RSGB Yearbook* [5].

THE AMATEUR RADIO LICENCE

In 2015, following consultation, Ofcom made some changes to the UK Amateur Radio licence. In part this was a tidying exercise to bring recent changes that had been notified by the Notification of Variation process into the body of the licence. Other changes that were made in 2015 introduced more generic licence conditions, allowing Ofcom to provide guidance, as well as advice on specific aspects of amateur radio, on their website. The Licence therefore needs to be interpreted along with this additional guidance information.

In this manual we will seek to bring out some of the main points of our licensing conditions in the UK. This is intended to help not only licensed amateurs resident in and operating from the UK but also licensed amateurs from overseas who are able to operate when visiting the UK under the agreement termed CEPT ECC Recommendation T/R 61-01 [7].

The Wireless Telegraphy Act of 2006 brought in the new 'lifetime' Amateur Radio Licence in the UK. Although valid for life, it is the responsibility of the licensee to re-validate his or her licence at least every five years. This can be performed on the Ofcom website [12]. Following a major exercise in 2014/15 to encourage licence re-validation it is understood that Ofcom plan to revoke licences that are no longer valid.

The UK amateur licence is quite a lengthy document so it is not reproduced here, but for those who do not hold a UK amateur licence and are interested in understanding the how to be compliant with the licensing conditions when operating in the UK a sample copy is available on the Ofcom website [13].

The following commentary on the licence and its provisions highlights areas of general interest, and specifically helps UK amateurs and overseas visitors understand better amateur operation in the UK.

Section 1:
Licence details
The UK Amateur Radio Licence starts with the class of the licence, the CEPT equivalent licence class, and the licensee's name, the callsign associated with the licence, the mailing address and 'main station address'. This is followed by the issue date of this particular licence, the original issue date of the first licence with this callsign issued to this licensee, and the licence number.

Pages 2 - 3 of the document explain in English, French and German the key details of the licence, intended to enable it to be interpreted in other countries as a UK amateur radio licence. Of importance is the statement: *"If this Licence is a Full licence* [as detailed on page 1 of the Licence - Ed] *then the Licensee shall also be authorised to operate in countries which have implemented CEPT Recommendation T/R 61-01 in accordance with Clause 16 of Section 2."* It should be noted, as said above, that this is only applicable when temporarily visiting a signatory country to T/R 61-01 and does not include cross-border remote operation, where other regulations may or may not apply.

It should be noted, also, that for amateurs visiting the UK and wishing and authorised to operate under T/R 61-01 the correct prefixes are M, MD, MI, MJ, MM, MU and MW, and not G, GD, etc. No provision exists in the UK Amateur Radio licence, issued by Ofcom, for reciprocal arrangements with other countries for holders of the Foundation or Intermediate licence. Overseas amateurs holding national licences below the UK Full-licence level have no reciprocal arrangements for operating when visiting the UK.

Within the licence the term UK implies the countries that make up the United Kingdom of Great Britain and Northern Ireland (that is England, Scotland and Northern Ireland) and the Crown Dependencies Guernsey, Jersey and the Isle of Man. We will use the same abbreviation in this book.

Section 2
1. Purpose
Section 2 of the licence document contains the 'Terms, conditions and limitations'.

Section 2 Clause 1 sets out the *purpose* of the licence. This is defined as being self-training, including technical investigations, and this is the major justification for radio amateurs maintaining their extensive frequency allocations. The following paragraphs expand on this by discussing the use of amateur radio in support of User Services. These are defined elsewhere in the document, but include bodies such as the Red Cross, local Emergency Planning Officers, Police, Fire and Ambulance. Radio amateurs are also authorised to help in international disaster communications. The clear message is that amateur radio is considered a public service, and is encouraged to stand up and be counted when there is a specific community need.

2. Location
Clause 2(1)(a) specifies where your station may be set up. The licence definitions (within Clause 17) enable you to operate from an alternative address, a temporary location, whilst mobile, and as maritime mobile, in addition to your main station address, which for most is their home. However, you will need to change your callsign if you operate from a different part of the British Isles by changing the 'Regional Secondary Locator' prefix to your callsign, or add one if necessary. For example, a Welsh station that would normally be GW8xxx would become GM8xxx when operating from Scotland, whilst M3xxx would need to become MJ3xxx with the addition of the J when operating from Jersey.

A subtlety of the ITU Radio Regulations as described earlier in this chapter means that for holders of the UK Intermediate Licence the callsign when operating from England requires the Regional Secondary Locator E to be used, thus 2Enxxx, where n is a numeral. This of course changes to 2Wnxxx when operating from Wales, 2Inxxx from Northern Ireland, etc.

In terms of operation from vehicles and other locations Clause 17 on pages 11 and 12 provides the core definitions and interpretation, along with note (d) to the licence that recommends certain suffixes on page 13. Whilst the four

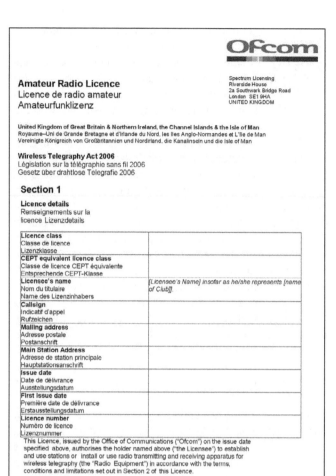

The first page of the UK Amateur Radio Licence

suffixes are optional the wording of the licence recommends that /P is used when operating from a temporary location that doesn't have a postal address (otherwise it would be regarded as an "alternative address" and signified by the use of the /A suffix), /M is for operation using radio equipment fitted into a vehicle, a vessel on inland waters, or carried on the person, ie a pedestrian, and Maritime Mobile operation is designated by using the suffix /MM.

Operating from a vessel on water is slightly different with the latest licence as the term 'territorial seas' has been introduced which relates to the area of waters up to 12 nautical miles from the UK coast. The significance is to do with the authorisation of the frequency bands that are permissible in the UK, which apply within the territorial waters (such as 50 - 52MHz and 70 - 70.52MHz) but do not necessarily apply on the high seas (in other words beyond the UK territorial seas). Clause 9(5) refers to such restrictions on frequency bands for high seas operation.

Ofcom's licence conditions are that Maritime Mobile only applies to operation from a vessel at sea, referring to territorial or high seas. In contrast, operating on inland or internal waters such as rivers or canals is Mobile. This distinction allows Mobile operation on vessels on inland waters by holders of the Foundation and Intermediate licence.

Note should be made that operation is prohibited from all forms of aircraft or other airborne vehicles, for example drones or balloons (tethered or untethered). Ofcom are aware that low power telemetry data can be sent from balloons and other airborne platforms using low power licence exempt equipment. However, provision for this falls outside the amateur licence.

For advice on these and other more subtle issues, and the most up-to-date guidance, refer to the Ofcom website.

3. Operators and qualifications

There follows a significant section, Clause 3, on who may operate an amateur radio station. In essence, this allows not only the licensee, but other authorised users under his/her direct supervision, to operate the station.

The clause sets out the privileges afforded Full and Full (Club) licence holders to allow non-licensed persons to operate the station when undergoing a 'Recognised Foundation Training Course'. Given that radio operating, like driving or flying, is not something you can actually learn from a book, this is very much to be welcomed. Reference to the clause is also important as it deals with the conditions for non-licensed persons to convey messages.

If the licence is a Full or Full (Club) Licence, the licensee may also allow a non-UK person holding a current amateur radio licence issued by any other country, or a holder of an Radio Amateurs' Examination Pass Certificate, to operate the station. It is up to the licensee, however, to assure himself that the person concerned is suitably qualified and not subsequently disqualified, for example by having had his licence revoked.

It is also worth noting that the licence applies to the licensee and not to the station. This is different to the situation that exists in some countries where a different distinction is drawn and the licence can be used from the licensee's address without the licensee being present.

The final paragraphs of this clause refer to the situation where the licence concerned is held by the individual on behalf of a club, when the station may indeed be used by another, properly qualified club member in the absence of the licensee. This is an important condition when considering remote operation, see the commentary on clause 10 below.

4. Variation and revocation;
5. Modification, restriction and closedown

Clauses 4 and 5 cover variation to, and revocation of, the licence; and modification, restriction and closedown procedures respectively.

Sometimes Ofcom will wish or need to vary or revoke a licence. A licence may be varied, with a "Notice of Variation" to the licence, to change for example the bands available to Amateur Radio licensees, or other aspects of the licence's terms and conditions.

Hopefully none of us ever has to face being closed down, but it is as well to be aware of the circumstances under which this might happen, and how it should be dealt with. Except when at sea, where the vessel's master has authority to close you down, a person authorised by Ofcom may require the Radio Equipment, or part of it, to be modified or restricted in use, or temporarily or permanently closed down. This will only occur if, in the reasonable opinion of the person

authorised by Ofcom, either a breach of the Licence has occurred and / or the use of the equipment is causing Undue Interference to the authorised use of other radio equipment. Ofcom offer guidance on their website of the revocation process that they must follow in these circumstances.

In the 2015 licence revision, clause 4(2)(g) of the licence addresses an issue that on occasion arises when a rift occurs between a club and the individual who holds the club licence. Readers are referred to Ofcom's guidance on the process than has been put in place to help in these unfortunate instances.

Clause 4(6) has been introduced in the 2015 licence for the 2.3 and 3.4GHz bands and there are additional mandatory requirements in separate Ofcom guidance for these bands.

6. Changes

With the 'lifetime licence' there is the requirement to ensure that details such as the Licensee's name, Main Station address (or mailing address if different from that recorded in the licence) are kept up-to-date. Perhaps not strongly brought out in this clause is the additional need to provide telephone contact information for operation on 5MHz, see Notes to Schedule 1, note (g)(x) on page 21 [of the licence - Ed]. A suitable (mobile) phone number can be lodged with Ofcom via your account on its online licensing portal if /P operation is planned on 5MHz (note, too,that /M operation is not permitted on 5MHz).

A further reminder to all readers who hold UK amateur licences that whether or not your details have changed, you need to revalidate your licence at least every 5 years, which can be done on the online licensing portal. [12]

7. Equipment

The uniqueness of amateur radio in comparison with most other forms of wireless communication is that holders of UK Intermediate and Full Licences (as well as the Club and Reciprocal variants) are permitted to operate equipment that they design and build so long as it complies with the licence. If we use commercial equipment, like most other spectrum users in our region of the world, the equipment that we use is constrained by technical standards enshrined in the European Commission's Radio Equipment Directive (2014/53/EU). Whilst there are some important restrictions in the licence to militate against causing undue interference to other users of the radio spectrum our licence gives us significant latitude for homebrew equipment. In our enjoyment of amateur radio we need to respect that, as it is the very foundation on which amateur radio flourishes. Understandably, holders of the UK Foundation Licence are restricted to commercial equipment or kits that conform to a particular standard, called the Interface Requirement, IR 2028.

8. Access and inspection

As a licensee you are required to allow "any person authorised by Ofcom" to be granted access to your station on request, in order to inspect your licence and equipment.

The RSGB's training manuals for the three main classes of UK Amateur Radio Licence.

Other than under extreme circumstances, such a request would only be made at "reasonable times" and, in practice, you would almost certainly be contacted beforehand to make an appointment, for example if a neighbour has suffered interference and a station inspection therefore became necessary. Note that all Ofcom field officers carry an identification card.

9. Limitations

The next section (Clause 9) is headed 'Limitations'. This is quite extensive. Paragraph 9(2) reiterates the obvious point that amateurs are only allowed to operate within the frequency bands, power limits and types of transmission specified in their licence. It might be worth pointing out that, in some instances, these and other limitations within the licence may be overcome through a Notice of Variation (NoV), for example to be able to operate general reception propagation beacons, gateways or repeaters. However, these NoVs are issued on an individual basis.

Some situations need a particularly convincing case to be made on a Special Research Permit (form ofw306) [14] to Ofcom both for the need to operate outside the normal restrictions of the licence and also of the way in which the additional privileges will be managed. In the case of a high power permit, for example, are there likely to be any repercussions in terms of interference to nearby electronic devices or issues about non-ionisation radiation hazard (see Notes to Schedule 1 (e) on page 21)?

10. Unattended and remote control operation

In the licence there is a distinction between 'unattended operation', which is where the location of the licensee is different from the location of the station, and 'remote control' where the licensee is again at a different location, but can switch between transmit and receive, change bands, tune, etc. Clause 10(3) of the licence clearly states that this privilege only extends to operating their own station remotely; the

implication is that other licensed amateurs generally are not permitted to operate your remote station.

The control links for unattended and remote control are limited to wireless links for holders of Foundation and Intermediate licences, whereas holders of the UK Full Amateur licence and its variants (Club, Reciprocal, etc.) subject to the ISP policy may also use Internet links.

As a point of general guidance on remote operation the callsign used must be the callsign of the station (transmitter) location, including, where appropriate, the relevant Regional Secondary Locator. One would not use a callsign signifying the current location of the operator. For example, if the holder of a UK Amateur Full Licence is physically in France but is operating their own station located in Scotland, the callsign would be the UK callsign of the station, including the RSL 'M'.

It should be noted that, even where unattended operations are allowed, there are geographical restrictions in a number of cases, principally within frequency bands which are shared in certain parts of the country with other users.

This clause also permits the licensee to control Radio Equipment remotely, for example over the Internet. However, it specifically prohibits the installation of equipment capable of remote control operation for general unsupervised use by other amateurs. There are additional conditions and limitations applicable to Beacons specified in Schedule-2.

Anyone intending to operate any sort of unattended or remote-controlled transmitter should study this section of the licence with care as there is significant complexity to be understood and complied with in order to be compliant with the relevant UK legislation. A check for the latest guidance on the Ofcom website is also recommended.

11. Messages

Clause 11 deals with the sort of communications which may be exchanged via amateur radio. Most of this section is self-explanatory. The use of abbreviations and recognised codes is permitted, recognising that amateurs make wide use of both, to overcome language barriers and to save transmission time (for example on Morse and data modes such as JT65). However, codes intended to hide the meaning of the communication (in other words, any form of encryption) are not allowed. There is nothing, incidentally, to prevent you holding QSOs in languages other than your own.

The 2015 revision of the licence included a new provision for exceptionally carrying messages on behalf of User Services - fire, ambulance, St John Ambulance, etc. Clause 11(2) refers to an exception for 1(2)and 1(3) for such circumstances, but permits no other occasions and the requirements to clearly identify the amateur station apply regardless.

This section also makes it clear that amateur radio is about communication with specific other stations, and is not intended as a broadcast medium. A specific exception is the GB2RS callsign used for the weekly news broadcast which is enabled by a licence variation (NoV).

12. Log
As a statutory requirement a station log only needs to be maintained when specifically requested by Ofcom, or when undertaking exceptional activity such as supporting a User Service under Clause 11(2). The other occasion when you might need to maintain a log is if you are operating Maritime Mobile and the master of the vessel has specifically requested you to keep a log.

Of course, as a part of amateur operation you may wish to maintain a log to keep track of your contacts, submit contacts for awards, contests, etc. Although not required by Ofcom it may prove helpful to maintain a log of your operating. Should, for example, a neighbour complain about interference to wireless or electrical systems in their house, you might be able to prove quite quickly that it is unlikely to be related to your amateur radio station. Of course, too, if there is some correlation between the interference and your operation it might quickly narrow the problem area for you and the Ofcom field engineer to a specific band, mode, etc. Speed may help put you on better terms with the complainant.

13. Identification
The 2015 licence is more general in terms of identification - it requires the station to be clearly identified at all times, the callsign to be transmitted as frequently as is practicable during transmissions in voice or another appropriate format. Whilst this is the statutory requirement, the RSGB supports the IARU *Ethics and Operating Procedures for the Radio Amateur* [15] that lays out best practice for when to send your callsign. Identifying at least once every 15 minutes (and on repeaters more often) is recommended. This does not conflict with the UK licensing requirements, but helps to ensure compliance as it generally avoids any ambiguity. Operating on the 5MHz band includes a specific licence requirement to identify by speech mode at least once every 15 minutes.

14. Recorded or retransmitted messages
While it is relatively uncommon to hear amateurs recording and retransmitting messages, Clause 14 makes it clear that there is no restriction in recording and retransmitting a message to an amateur with whom the licensee is in direct contact or which is intended for retransmission to a specified amateur.

Care must be taken to avoid confusion as to who is actually controlling the transmission and whose message is being retransmitted at any given time. Often it's simply a case of an amateur recording his Contest CQ call transmission and playing it back to save effort, but this clause can also refer to certain amateur data mode transmissions or personal cross-band usage. What is very clear, though, is that any retransmitted message must have originated from a licensed amateur. We are not allowed to send messages originated by non-amateurs (nor breach other conditions such as not broadcasting).

15. Fees
This is a change in the 2015 revision of the licence that brings the amateur licence in line with other licences that Ofcom issue. Ofcom advise us that this is an administrative change and that currently there are no plans to re-introduce a charge for our amateur licences.

16. Operation by the Licensee in CEPT countries
Clause 16, deals with operation abroad under the terms of CEPT Recommendation T/R 61-01 as discussed at the beginning of this section of the chapter. Two points made before are that firstly, operation under T/R 61-01 is only permitted by holders of a Full UK licence. Full (Temporary Reciprocal) and Full (Club) licensees along with Intermediate and Foundation licence classes are excluded. Secondly, the licensee must be a temporary visitor only and not a resident of the relevant host country.

17. Interpretation
Clause 17 defines such terms as "Amateur", "Callsign", "CEPT", "Club", "Mobile", "Radio Equipment" etc as they are to be interpreted within the licence document. Generally, terms given with initial capital letters in this chapter of this book (such as "Regional Secondary Locator") are those defined in Clause 17 of the licence document.

Notes to the licence
Following the 17 main clauses of Section 2, the UK Amateur Radio Licence has a series of notes which are mainly recommendations. This starts with *Note (a)* that the bandwidth used should be such as to ensure the most efficient use of the spectrum.

Note (b) recommends that if phonetics are used on voice modes, the phonetic alphabet contained in the ITU Radio Regulations ("Alpha, Bravo, Charlie", etc) should be used.

Note (c) states that if the Radio Equipment is used solely by a Club, separate club Regional Secondary Locators may be used instead of those in Clause 2(2) of the licence. (The club Regional Secondary Locators are 'X' for England, 'P' for Guernsey, 'T' for the Isle of Man, 'H' for Jersey, 'N' for Northern Ireland, 'S' for Scotland, and 'C' for Wales.) Note that there is no obligation to use these: the ordinary Regional Secondary

Locators may be used by club stations if that is preferred. Although the original intent when club Regional Secondary Locators were introduced was to identify club stations when greetings messages were being passed to third parties, they may now be used at any time (but only by Club stations). A common example is when clubs operate Special Event Stations, or when training Foundation licence candidates on air.

The use of suffixes after the complete callsign is no longer obligatory in the UK, but *Note (d)* recommends that "/A" is used when operating from an Alternative Address, "/P" from a Temporary Location, "/M" while Mobile, and "/MM" if operating Maritime Mobile.

When giving the location of the Radio Equipment, five means of doing so are recommended in *Note (e)*.

The remaining *Notes to the licence* refer to communication links for unattended or remote operation, a statement that it is an offence to send any message which is "grossly offensive" or of an "indecent, obscene or menacing" character, and finally a reminder that the licence will be revoked unless Ofcom is informed at least every five years of any change to the licence details or that they remain unchanged.

The Schedules

Finally in Section 2 of the UK Amateur Radio Licence are two Schedules. Schedule 1 consists of the Parameters for each of the licence classes: Foundation, Intermediate and Full. The Parameters consist of the frequencies, status of allocations to the Amateur Service and Amateur Satellite Service (whether Primary, Secondary or Not allocated) and the maximum power permitted for each licence class.

There are some important *Notes to Schedule 1* that as well as referring to terminology used in the frequency schedule, contain important points in relation to 472kHz and 5MHz allocations. The sharing arrangements in both these bands are such that care is needed in our amateur usage to avoid interference to primary users and indeed a co-secondary user in the case of 472kHz. In this respect, on 5MHz aerial heights are limited to 20m above ground level, real care has to be made in keeping transmission within the frequency segments and no mobile operation is permitted. Uniquely, communication with cadet stations is permitted on 5MHz.

Schedule 2 consists of additional restrictions which apply to the Unattended Operation of Beacons.

REFERENCES
[1] International Telecommunication Union (ITU), Place des Nations, CH 1211 Geneva 20, Switzerland. www.itu.int/
[2] Office of Communications (Ofcom), www.ofcom.org.uk/
[3] International Amateur Radio Union (IARU), Box 310 905, Newington, Connecticut 06131 0905, USA. www.iaru.org/
[4] http://life.itu.int/radioclub/rr/art25.htm
[5] *RSGB Yearbook*, RSGB, (published annually), available from www.rsgbshop.org
[6] *RSGB Prefix Guide*, available from www.rsgbshop.org
[7] CEPT Recommendation T/R 61-01 www.erodocdb.dk/Docs/doc98/official/pdf/TR6101.PDF
[8] European Communications Office: www.cept.org/
[9] *World Licensing and Operating Directory*, ed Steve Telenius-Lowe, RSGB, available from www.rsgbshop.org
[10] OH2MCN: www.qsl.net/oh2mcn/license.htm
[11] Radio Society of Great Britain (RSGB) website: http://rsgb.org
[12] Ofcom Licensing Portal: http://licensing.ofcom.org.uk/radiocommunication-licences/amateur-radio/amend-validate-apply/ or search with the keywords "amateur licence validation".
[13] Sample copy of the UK Amateur Licence http://licensing.ofcom.org.uk/binaries/spectrum/amateur-radio/guidance-for-licensees/nov/licence.pdf or search with the keywords "Sample amateur radio licence effective 7th April 2015".
[14] Ofcom application form for a Special Research Permit http://licensing.ofcom.org.uk/binaries/spectrum/amateur-radio/apply-for-a-licence/ofw306.pdf or search with the keywords "ofw306".
[15] *Ethics and Operating Procedures for the Radio Amateur*: www.iaru-r1.org/index.php/documents/Documents/Ethics-and-Operating-procedure-for-the-Radio-Amateur-(Edition-3)—2011/ or search using the title.

SETTING UP AN amateur radio station is a task which can vary from choosing a hand-held transceiver and reading up on its facilities to building an extensive and competitive station with multiple towers and antennas. There are some aspects which are common, others which you will only face as you become more ambitious. This chapter is intended to walk you through some of the decisions and steps involved, not in a technical way (there are plenty of books about designing and building antennas, for example), but by way of some practical advice. Of course, you will learn a lot with time.

Like most hobbies, it is likely you will start small, perhaps with second-hand equipment, but as time goes on you will want to build on what you already have.

GOALS

You will probably want to start by taking a look at the dealer advertisements, catalogues and websites, imagining yourself with the latest transceiver and maybe a substantial array of antennas in the garden. In practice, the starting point should be to ask yourself, "what is it I want to achieve?" Of course, if you are newly licensed, this may be easier to ask than to answer.

Although you may have done some listening on the bands, or visited another amateur's shack, you probably won't know at this stage exactly which bands are likely to appeal to you, or whether your interests are more likely to lie with chatting to friends around town or chasing contacts with remote islands around the world. Do you see yourself operating on voice, or might you fancy trying out CW or data modes? Do you plan to make your computer an integral part of your station, for logging and other purposes? You can probably see where this line of reasoning is going, because the equipment and antennas you need for one are going to be rather different to what you need for the other. Nowadays it's getting easier to cover all the bases. Many modern transceivers, unlike their predecessors, cover a wide range of bands from 160m through to UHF, for example. And some facilities, such as a linear amplifier, can easily be added later. On the one hand, there is little sense in spending large amounts of money on facilities which you are unlikely ever to use. On the other hand, to give just one example, if you have just gained a licence with limited frequency and power privileges, does it make sense to buy a transceiver limited to those frequencies and power levels, or are you planning to upgrade in the near future?

If you are an SWL (listener) without a transmitting licence, but you intend to take the exams later, buying a transceiver rather than a communications receiver may be just the incentive you need to crack on and gain your licence. If you do buy a transceiver without having a transmitting licence, though, you should make sure that it is not capable of transmitting, even accidentally, for example by ensuring no microphone or Morse code key is connected to the equipment.

Do you want a compact radio for portable operating, perhaps, or maybe nowadays you are looking for something that can be hidden in a cupboard and operated via a software interface on your computer.

CHOOSING EQUIPMENT

The heart of most amateur radio stations is the transceiver. Nevertheless, some amateurs prefer to use a separate transmitter and receiver, for instance those who enjoy building simple QRP (low-power) transmitters, people who experiment on LF or microwave frequencies, those who enjoy using 'classic' valve equipment, or perhaps those who use a state-of-the-art software-defined radio (SDR) receiver with their transmitter.

If your motivation for becoming a radio amateur is to be able to make contacts using equipment you have constructed yourself, then the choice of transceiver may be obvious. There have been some excellent designs in amateur radio publications in recent years, for example in the *RSGB Radio Communication Handbook* [1]. For those interested in building low-power equipment (from the very simple to the quite sophisticated) the GQRP Club [2] is the place to look. The RSGB has also published *The Low Power Sprat Book* [3], a compilation of the best from the first 150 issues of the GQRP Club's journal, *Sprat*, which contains numerous circuits for simple receivers and low power transmitters and transceivers.

There is a wide selection of kits you can buy, ranging from basic, easy to put together, kits offering limited facilities, power and frequency coverage, to top of the range transceivers with specifications at least as good as anything you might buy commercially.

However, if you do decide to follow the commercial route, the choice nowadays is quite overwhelming, and even modestly-priced radios boast a huge range of features. A lot of debate has centred on the design compromises between offering additional features and focusing on good, basic RF performance. To a large extent that debate is now irrelevant. To all intents and purposes, most transceivers offer both to a level at which you are unlikely either to push its RF performance to the limit or to want additional features. Of course, the usual basic rule applies, in that you are likely to get what you pay for. A low-priced radio, perhaps designed primarily for mobile operation, may start to show its limitations if you use it in your home station with a large Yagi antenna. But that's not a fault of the radio because it is being used outside its original design brief. Given, though, that performance and reliability can largely be taken for granted nowadays, your choice is just as likely to be driven by ergonomics, in other words whether you are comfortable with actually operating the set. This is an area which is very much a matter of personal preference, and can only really be answered by using the equipment concerned.

WHERE TO BEGIN?

None of this answers the question about where you should start. There's a lot to be said for trying out a transceiver in your home station before you lay out large amounts of money, just as you would want to test drive a car before entering in to a binding contract. If a friend can lend you a transceiver to use at home, so much the better, as you can then see whether it suits your requirements or whether you need something different. A dealer is unlikely to offer you this facility but most do the next best thing, which is to allow you to try out different transceivers at their premises. Another solution is to buy second-hand, which minimises your financial exposure, especially as you can probably sell it on in due course for close to what you paid. But this does have disadvantages. You are unlikely to be buying the latest model and, unless you buy second-hand from a recognised dealer, there is always the risk that you may be sold a pup.

Transceivers are like cars, in that they tend to fall into fairly clearly defined classes though, again like cars, manufacturers occasionally try to break the mould by trying to package things differently in terms of bands, facilities, or perhaps output power. However, it's worth a general discussion based on the most popular classes of rig.

VHF / UHF Hand-held Equipment

The starting point for many amateurs is a hand-held VHF / UHF transceiver, or HT ('Handy Talkie') as it's referred to in many parts of the world. This will usually cover one or more of the VHF and UHF amateur bands, using FM, perhaps also offering a general coverage receiver allowing you to listen to

the VHF broadcast bands and the like. Most use rechargeable batteries, and offer a range of facilities for repeater operation, memory storage of your popular channels, scanning, etc. They should be rugged for portable use, some even boast of being waterproof. All will come with a small whip or 'rubber duck' antenna. In some cases this can be removed to allow you to connect the transceiver to a car-mounted or even base-station antenna, but receive performance may suffer if it becomes overloaded with incoming signals. Prices range from under £30 for an 'entry-level' Chinese-made radio, to several hundred pounds for a multiband, fully-featured model.

The TYT TH-UV6R, an entry-level Chinese-made hand-held FM transceiver available for under £30. This one offers 5W output power and is dual-band!

Yaesu's FTM-400DE dual-band mobile transceiver which incorporates their 'System Fusion' digital voice system.

VHF / UHF Mobile Equipment

The next category of VHF / UHF transceiver concerns those which are intended for mobile operation. These will usually be of a similar size to a car radio, intended to be fitted into the dash, or perhaps boot-mounted with a remote dash-mounted front panel. Their facilities will be very similar to those described above for hand-held radios, but power output will normally be significantly higher, DC power will be drawn from the car battery, and there will be an antenna connector for connection to an external antenna mounted somewhere on the car body. Of course, there is nothing to stop one of these transceivers being used in your home station. However, for home use you may also want SSB and CW capabilities, for chasing longer-distance contacts when the bands are open. Some mobile transceivers offer alternate modes.

In the past it was typical to find a range of VHF / UHF transceivers designed specifically for home use, with a full range of facilities including SSB, CW and data modes, selectable filters, dual-band working for satellite operation, and much else. In recent years many of these have been withdrawn from the market, being replaced by a new generation of combined HF / VHF / UHF transceivers at similar prices. Some of these transceivers feature a spectral display (sometimes called a 'bandscope' or 'pan-adapter') which can be left on your favourite band allowing you to see immediately when there is a band opening as signals start to appear on the display.

HF / 6m Mobile / Portable Equipment

The entry point nowadays for HF equipment consists of a range of small, light-weight transceivers designed primarily for mobile or portable operation, although many amateurs use them quite satisfactorily from their home stations too. They operate from 12V DC so can be powered either from a car battery or, in the home, from a mains power supply unit capable of providing around 20A. Almost all these transceivers cover all bands from 160m to 6m, and some include 2m and 70cm as well. Just about all will offer general coverage HF receive capability, and many also have DSP filtering and much else.

It is worth mentioning at this point that very few commercial transceivers, whether VHF only, or combined HF / VHF, cover the 4m band as, until recently, this band has only

The Icom IC-7100 transceiver is unusual in that it includes coverage of the 4m band.

A modern SDR transceiver. This one can be used with or without a separate computer.

been available in a handful of countries, so it hasn't been worthwhile for manufacturers to include it. One exception is the Icom IC-7100, which does include the 4m band on its versions sold in the UK and Europe.

HF Base Station Equipment

Base station HF transceivers cover a very wide range of price and specification. Prices start around the £500 mark and go up to several thousand pounds for the latest generation of HF / VHF / UHF radios incorporating dual receivers, large LCD displays, multiple filter options, built-in ATU, 200-watt power output, and a huge range of menu-selectable options so that the owner can set them up exactly to suit his operating preferences. The lower-priced radios will usually require an external power supply, and will generally offer a more limited range of user options.

Software-Defined Radios

Software-defined radio (SDR) has made many inroads to the amateur radio market in recent years. Here features such as detection, mixing, demodulation and filtering are carried out by software, either embedded in the radio itself or by means

of an external computer, rather than by the traditional means using hardware.

SDR receivers are available, as are SDR transceivers, both at QRP (typically 5-watt) levels up to 100-watt transceivers with specifications as good as, or better than, any traditional 'hardware-defined radio'.

It is worth checking that your chosen transceiver is 'future proofed' in the sense of, for example, being able to add new bands if and when they become available, or downloading new software (many modern transceivers allow the operating software to be upgraded via an Internet download).

Given that all modern transceivers are hugely more capable than their predecessors of even 10 or 15 years ago, the final choice may well come down to price and usability. The latter is very much a case of personal preference. The layout and functions of the controls, the styling of the display, the general appearance and colour, all these may come into play in your selection, just as they might in choosing a car. But it is also sensible to get hold of product literature and read some independent equipment reviews, for example those by Peter Hart, G3SJX, published frequently in *RadCom* as well as reviews by the ARRL in their magazine, *QST* [4]. A compilation of over 10 years of Peter Hart's reviews can be found in a new book, *Hart Reviews* [5]. You can also find user reviews on the Internet at sites such as *eHam* [6].

Kenwood's top-of-the-range HF / 6m transceiver, the TS-990S.

BUYING EQUIPMENT

If you decide to buy a new transceiver, by all means shop around for the best price. But remember that you may need back-up, in the case of failure under warranty or later. Check that your dealer has suitable facilities. Nowadays it is often tempting to order over the Internet, perhaps from abroad, but do bear in mind that you may not get the same warranty with such equipment and it may also have a different specification (US mains voltage is 110V, as against 230V in Europe. VHF and UHF band limits, repeater shifts and channel spacings also vary from country to country).

Buying Second-hand

Many dealers offer a wide range of second-hand transceivers, usually from equipment that has been traded in. This will usually be offered with a limited warranty of a few months. Alternatively, large numbers of transceivers exchange hands privately, typically after being advertised in the amateur radio press but increasingly via Internet sites, either privately run or commercial (such as *eBay*). When buying privately, always take the usual precautions. Understand exactly what is being advertised, preferably go and see it, try it on the air, and maybe take another, more experienced amateur along for a second opinion. The RSGB's *Rig Guide* [7] is a ready source of key data about many of the transceivers sold in recent years, as is G3SJX's *Hart Reviews* [5].

Wherever you buy second-hand equipment, you will want to understand exactly what condition it is in (a scratched case, for example, may suggest that the rig has not been properly looked after, but it may also provide a bargain if the scratch is unimportant to the buyer) and exactly what options are fitted (eg an additional CW filter might cost you up to £100 to buy, if not already fitted). In some cases it is also important to know the serial number: as with most equipment, transceivers go through design upgrades during their lifetime and early models may have known problems that were eliminated later on.

Many amateurs, when they buy second-hand equipment, look for it to be in pristine condition and with the original box and packaging. If you expect to resell the equipment later, these aspects may be important in your purchase decision, although what matters is that the equipment does the job it was intended for; outward appearances are really of less importance. A transceiver with a few scuff marks may well be telling the tale of a good life, with plenty of field days, DXpeditions and other travels behind it!

MODIFYING EQUIPMENT

While most modern amateur radio equipment is of a high standard, and will do the job far better than its predecessors of, say, 20 or 25 years ago, that is not to say that equipment from earlier generations is unsuitable for use today. Many amateurs get pleasure from renovating and then using older equipment, though if you do choose to go this route, it is important to check the quality of the signals you are radiating, to ensure that there are no spurious emissions and no serious distortion of the audio.

Although modern transceivers undoubtedly have better performance than some of their predecessors in terms of parameters such as third-order intercept point and dynamic range (which affect the ability of the receiver to handle both strong and weak signals in close proximity), probably the main change that you might want to bear in mind from a usability point of view is that almost all modern transceivers have a computer interface.

The most popular models have attracted post-release modifications and improvements. For example, the Kenwood TS-940S was transformed by a simple phase-noise modification developed by one of the UK amateur radio retailers. Several other models from around that period also benefited from modifications developed and introduced by UK dealers. The Yaesu FT-1000D, still used by many amateurs, can be improved by a simple modification to reduce key clicks and another to reduce distortion caused by the noise blanker circuit. Its successor, the FT-1000MP, can be fitted with new first-IF roofing filters to improve receive performance on SSB, data modes and CW, at the expense of FM operation which is of less interest to some operators. These are all examples of how a competent transceiver can be improved even further.

However, you may well be reluctant to delve inside your transceiver for several reasons. Modifications made during the warranty period may render the warranty invalid. Modifications may also reduce the resale value of the radio at a later date, although most of those mentioned can be removed without affecting the transceiver in any way.

BUILDING YOUR OWN

Many amateurs are in the hobby because they enjoy the technical challenge of building equipment. The earliest radio amateurs had to build their own equipment because, quite simply, there was no alternative. After WWII a huge amount of surplus equipment came on to the amateur market at affordable prices, and many amateurs went along this route.

The Yaesu FT-1000MP was one of the most popular transceivers from the mid-1990s and is still used by many amateurs today. There were several versions produced: the one pictured here is the 'FT-1000MP Mark-V Field'.

The Elecraft K3 is a high-end transceiver that is available in kit form for the owner to assemble.

The 1960s was the era of kit building, with Heathkit dominating the market. By going the kit route, the metal-bashing had already been done, and most of the work was in soldering the various components into place. As affordable ready-built transceivers started to become available in the 1970s interest in kit building waned. Circuitry became more complex and unless you really were an experienced builder, it was difficult to match the performance of commercial equipment with something home-built. By the 1980s the reaction to this was an interest in home-construction of simple equipment for QRP operation.

Interestingly, the tables have turned again, with a number of kits now available for what are very sophisticated transceivers. By far the best-known examples are the products from US company Elecraft. The performance of their K3 transceiver is on a par with the best of the ready-built transceivers. Elecraft has also released a tiny portable transceiver kit, the KX3, for QRP operation, as well as a 500-watt linear amplifier, the KPA500. All three of these can be built without substantial amounts of test equipment. So once again, building your own appears to be a very real option for those who want to have the satisfaction of making contacts with equipment they have put together themselves.

OTHER EQUIPMENT

There is a plethora of other items you may want for your shack, either when starting up or at some later stage. Unless your antenna or antennas have an impedance of close to 50-ohms at all the frequencies you are likely to want to use, you will need some sort of antenna matching device, usually called an ATU (antenna tuning unit). Most modern base-station HF transceivers, and also some mobile / portable ones, have a built-in automatic ATU. However, they are often limited in the range of impedances they can match and may be thought of more as 'line flatteners' as typically they can match an SWR of up to 3:1, ie impedances from about 17 ohms up to 150 ohms or so. If you plan to use an antenna such as an end-fed wire, or a doublet with open-wire feeder, the impedance is likely to be very high on some bands and therefore an external ATU, capable of matching a much wider range of impedances than the built-in one in your transceiver, will be a necessity.

Another piece of equipment to be considered is a linear amplifier to boost the power of your transceiver. This might be a small, solid-state unit to boost a low-power transceiver to the 100-watt level. Or it may be a high power, possibly valve-based amplifier, to boost the 100 watts typical output of many HF transceivers to whatever your licence allows (400 watts PEP for UK Full licensees, but typically 1000 watts in many parts of the world, and 1.5kW in the USA and some other countries depending on licence class).

There is also a wide range of test equipment you might like to have, especially for measuring and setting up antennas, such as an antenna analyser. There may be data interfaces for DSP-based multimode operation. Power supplies for your transceiver or ancillary equipment. Specialist equipment for the microwave or LF bands, not covered by the main equipment manufacturers. Microphones, headphones and Morse keys, of course. And so on. Much the same advice applies to choosing and buying these items as to transceivers.

It is worth mentioning, though, that many of the ancillary items that would have been found in the shack in the past may no longer be necessary. Data terminals have largely been replaced by a combination of computer sound card and software. Most transceivers incorporate a keyer, SWR measurement and sometimes even antenna selection.

A 13.8V 25A power supply unit: almost essential for any station.

One of the popular range of Acom valve linear amplifiers, covering the HF bands plus 6m.

(left) The Rig Expert AA-54 antenna analyser, a very useful piece of test equipment for anyone building or simply installing antennas.

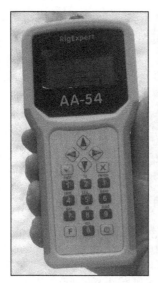

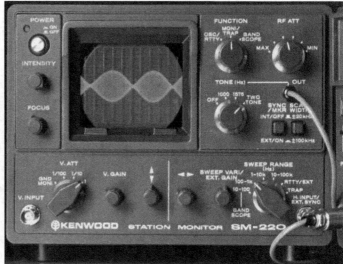

(right) A Monitor Scope is a handy tool for ensuring a good quality transmission

One particularly useful accessory, though, is a Monitor Scope, whereby you can keep an eye on the quality of your CW waveform and check whether you are overdriving your transceiver on SSB.

EQUIPMENT FOR VHF / UHF, MICROWAVE AND LF

Many commercial transceivers cover frequencies up to the 70cm band and, in a few cases, 23cm. A few models, such as the popular FT-847, specifically cater for the specialist requirements of satellite working.

Serious VHF and UHF DXers generally consider that, while commercial equipment is adequate for day-to-day operating, it falls short of their demanding requirements. Many, therefore build much of their own equipment, perhaps opting for transverters for the higher bands, which can work with a fully-featured HF transceiver, to get the best of both worlds.

This is even more true for the microwave bands, where there is very little commercial equipment available either to use directly or to adapt, although some specialist suppliers offer kits and modules. High-specification designs appear in specialist publications such as the respected *DUBUS* magazine [8], often with provision made for readers to be able to source the necessary components. The UK Microwave Group [9] is also a valuable source of information and parts.

Similar considerations apply at the other end of the spectrum - 136kHz and 472kHz - where, with a few exceptions, it is a case of 'roll your own'. Again, a number of suitable designs have appeared in the literature in recent years and the best are collected in the RSGB book *LF Today* [10].

SETTING UP YOUR SHACK

Unless you are planning to confine your amateur radio activity to portable or mobile operations, one of your first priorities will be to set up an operating location or 'shack'. In the days when an amateur radio station consisted of one or more racks of valve equipment, the shack would almost inevitably be one room, set aside specifically for that purpose. Nowadays that need not be the case. Most modern transceivers would not look out of place in the corner of the living

room, and take up relatively little space. But there are several practical considerations to take into account, largely determined by the amount of equipment you are likely to be using and the type of operating you plan on doing. The main factors, each needing to be considered in choosing a suitable location, are:

- Accessibility, privacy and security
- Acoustics and acoustic noise
- Comfort
- Position relative to the antenna
- Power
- Telecommunications
- Space

Accessibility, Privacy and Security

If you want to be able to check the bands at frequent intervals, it's not helpful to have to walk to a shed at the bottom of the garden every time. If, on the other hand, you plan to be active in 24-hour contests or even to invite friends to operate your station in such events, then it may be best to select a shack location which is remote from the rest of the household. Wherever your shack, though, there is a responsibility to ensure it is both safe and secure. Your equipment is valuable, it can potentially cause interference to other services if accessed and operated by an unqualified person and, given that it involves high voltages and RF, may cause injury to perhaps a child or elderly person.

Taken together, these factors suggest that, in most cases, your station should be set up in a separate room from the rest of the household, ideally one which can be locked and one which is not overlooked by neighbours or passers-by. Of course, in practice it may be necessary to use the same room for other purposes too, such as a study or general hobbies room, in which cases other users of the room need to be made aware of the radio equipment and asked to leave it well alone.

Acoustics and Acoustic Noise

Data modes and Morse operation can be almost silent, especially if headphones are used when operating. Phone operation is another matter. It can be very disturbing to other equipment either. Electronic equipment can easily be damaged by condensation or by overheating and most amateur radio equipment is designed for use in normal domestic environments, unlike military equipment which is usually designed (at great expense) for much wider environmental extremes.

You need to be aware of how the equipment itself will affect the environment. In a busy radio environment, such as a contest, where several items of equipment may be operating simultaneously (one or more computers, transceiver, linear amplifier, etc), this equipment will itself generate substantial amounts of heat, helping to raise the shack temperature. In the UK few homes have air conditioning and, in the extreme, it may even be worth investing in some sort of portable A/C device for use on such occasions.

The operating chair should be chosen with care, as you could be spending many hours in one position, and back pain is unfortunately much easier to acquire than to eradicate. Many amateurs choose an office chair, which can be adjusted for height, angle, etc. Equally important, though, is the position of the equipment relative to the operator (you). You will need to be able to reach items such as the computer keyboard, main tuning control (and other controls) of the transceiver, Morse key or microphone, antenna rotator controller and other items without undue strain. What might work fine for the casual operator may lead to fatigue and discomfort after several hours. Factors to take into account include the height of the main operating desk, and the reach to the main items of equipment. Unfortunately most home office furniture, as sold in DIY stores, isn't deep enough to take a full-size transceiver and computer keyboard, and still leave room to rest your arms comfortably. The main alternatives are good quality office furniture (which can often be bought second-hand for affordable prices) or building your own operating desk.

Finally, but by no means to be forgotten, your shack should have suitable access to bathroom facilities. Those who have undertaken 24-hour Field Day operations from remote spots will understand the importance of this recommendation!

Position Relative to the Antenna

Usually there will be more flexibility in siting the shack than in siting the antenna. Therefore the location of the antenna may be important in determining the best location for the shack. You need to consider both the length and geometry of the feed lines and, possibly, rotator cables. Feeder loss, especially at VHF and UHF, can be very substantial and although you can go some way to countering this by using more expensive cable, it is always best to keep feeder lengths to a minimum if at all possible. On the lower bands this is less of an issue, but even on the 12 and 10m bands feeder losses over 50m or so can be several decibels, depending on the quality of the cable used. There are also good reasons for running cables underground or, at least, close to the ground, if at all possible. This helps to reduce the potential for unwanted radiation from the feeder and unwanted pick-up by the feeder of local noise. It is also worth mentioning that an upstairs shack brings problems of effective earthing, which can lead to equipment becoming 'hot' in the

A shack in the garden may allow closer proximity to antennas; important on VHF / UHF where cable losses can become an issue.

members of the household, especially at night when they are trying to sleep and there are very few other noises around. With the windows open at night, or if operating from a garden shed, the sound can carry not only through your own house but to neighbours' ears as well. The watchword is to be considerate, using sound insulation to deaden the effects, which will also help to reduce echo on your transmitted signal. Judicious use of heavy curtains, acoustic tiles on the walls, suitable carpets and perhaps double-glazing can all help in this respect. Remember, also, that your rig has a microphone gain control, so it isn't necessary to shout at the microphone as some operators do, especially in the heat of chasing some rare DX!

Comfort

For occasional operating, comfort may not be a big issue, but can be of paramount importance when sitting in the same operating chair for hours on end, perhaps operating a contest. Temperature, humidity, draughts, the operating chair, and the positioning of the equipment relative to the operator all have an impact. Ideally your operating shack should be kept at a temperature between 19 and 24 degrees C (65 - 75 degrees F) summer or winter, especially when in use. Loft spaces and garden sheds, for example, can be subject to much greater extremes of temperature, which is not only uncomfortable for the operator, but does nothing for the

RF sense, and may exacerbate any EMC problems (such as TV breakthrough). See 'Siting the Antenna' later in this chapter.

Power

Obviously it is necessary for the shack to have adequate electricity supplies. Not only should the circuits be able to supply the sort of current you expect to be drawing but, ideally, there should be enough individual sockets to cater for the number of appliances you will be connecting. In practice this is rarely the case. A well-equipped shack may easily have a dozen or more items which require direct connection to mains power (HF transceiver, linear amplifier, VHF transceiver, 12V PSU for ancillary equipment, rotator, computer, table lamp, etc) and this can result in the use of several trailing leads with extension sockets, which are untidy and potentially dangerous. Ideally, when setting up your shack, time should be taken to wire in enough sockets in a professional way.

For safety reasons a clearly marked mains master switch which will cut off all power to the room should be installed. All members of the family should be made aware of its existence and told to use it in an emergency situation.

Continuity of power may also be an issue, both for the shack computer and for the transceiver. An Uninterruptible Power Supply (UPS) is useful, and can keep a low-power station on the air for several hours in the event of a power failure. Some amateurs also ensure they have generator power available in the event of mains failure, but this requires great caution in ensuring that the generator is never directly connected to an unisolated mains circuit. There are other important issues with generators such as fuel safety and proper ventilation.

Telecommunications

Most shacks nowadays will require access to a phone line and / or the Internet. In many ways, the latter is better provided by way of a wireless LAN from an access point elsewhere in the house, as wireless LANs appear to be less susceptible to RF breakthrough than wired (UTP) networks. If the phone network is provided by overhead distribution this can be a problem, especially if those overhead spans are close to your antennas. This is more a factor when considering antenna location, but in any case you may need to plan for the installation of filters on the incoming telephone line.

Space

When planning a shack, it is obviously a good idea to consider not only the immediate needs, but how the amount of equipment might expand as time goes on. If you expect to be engaging in home construction this is likely to require a bench in its own right (but such work doesn't necessarily have to take place in the shack, of course). Many amateurs have been highly innovative in their use of space, managing to squeeze large amounts of equipment into tiny spaces, for example under the stairs, by judicious use of custom-made shelving. Do allow space for ventilation, though.

It is also important to consider rear access to equipment. One of the recurring irritations is having to disassemble much of the station in order to wire in one more rear connection, perhaps for a new data modem. In an ideal world, we would all be able to walk to the rear of our operating tables to do this sort of work. In practice, this rarely seems to be possible!

DEVELOPING YOUR STATION

Later, once you have actually spent time on the bands, you will start thinking about upgrading your station. The usual experience of operators new to a particular band is that you will hear much more than you can work, either because your antenna system is limited or because you are running modest power levels, or both.

The first step is always to improve your antenna system, because this will have the dual benefit of improving both transmit and receive capabilities. It is indeed surprising that many amateurs upgrade a perfectly good transceiver to a newer model, while still choosing to use a compromise antenna such as a half-size G5RV or a small trap vertical. Improving your antenna system will allow you to work QRP stations and, especially on the low bands such as 160 and 80m, DX stations that you might otherwise not be able to hear at all.

If local noise is a problem - and unfortunately this is becoming more and more of an issue in the UK and elsewhere - you can improve your receive ability by installing specialist receiving antennas (especially for the low bands, for example with a Beverage, if you have space, or a K9AY loop if you don't). One of the modern noise cancelling devices may also be of help.

Having improved your antenna systems as much as you can, you might still find that you can hear more stations than you can work, and that is perhaps the time to think about increasing your power output, by building or buying a linear amplifier.

On the VHF, UHF and microwave bands, where the challenge is to extract every last fraction of a decibel out of the system, your focus will also be on the quality of feeder you use as well as the need to site a receive preamplifier and perhaps your power amplifier at or close to the antenna.

No matter what the frequency band or bands or interest, any improvement to transmit or receive capability can be useful and the very best stations will have optimised both.

If you take up a particular speciality such as contest operating, there will be other changes and additions you want to make to your station. For example, as a contester you may want a second transceiver in order to be able to look for multipliers on one transceiver while calling CQ on the other. This may then dictate the use of external band-pass filters to avoid interactions. If you decide to go in for satellite operation, you will not only want a transceiver that can handle the special requirements, but you may need to modify your antenna system to track elevation as well as azimuth heading.

And so, as with most hobbies, there is always room for improvement, as moving forward in one aspect of your station brings you face to face with its limitations in another area. Rest assured, you are unlikely ever to be finally satisfied!

STATION LAYOUT

Assuming a suitable site for the shack has been found, the next question is how the equipment shall be arranged in the most convenient manner. Obviously this depends upon the type of operation envisaged, and the quantity of equipment to be accommodated, but there are some basic rules common to most situations.

In general, the equipment should be arranged so that all controls in frequent use are within reach of the comfortably-seated operator, without any need to bend very far forward. Similarly, it should be possible to read meters and displays accurately without straining to one side or peering. Units which generate appreciable heat should not be stacked on top of one another, and care should be taken that any ventilation holes in the cabinets are unobstructed. Solid-state transceivers may have cooling fins on the rear of the cabinet, which should have unobstructed air flow. No room-heating radiator should be located in the vicinity.

Sufficient clearance behind the equipment should be allowed for the connecting leads, especially if large-diameter coaxial cable is in use. Adequate lengths of cable should be used to connect equipment together, so as to permit the sliding forward of any unit for inspection or adjustment while it remains connected to the rest of the station. Any strain in connecting leads will lead to failure sooner or later.

The transceiver is the most important item of electronic equipment in an amateur radio station, and it is recommended that the rest of the operating area be built around it. It should be placed on a large firm table which allows plenty of space in front for a logbook, scrap pad and any other material, and so positioned that its tuning knob can be turned easily with the elbow resting lightly on the table. These days, most frequently a computer is an integral part of the station, and its location is also vital in deciding where everything goes. There are two aspects. The monitor needs to be easy to see without straining your neck. Monitors are designed to be at desk height. However, you will also need to be able to see the display on your transceiver. It is therefore tempting to mount the computer monitor above the transceiver, but this can lead to neck fatigue after long periods of operating. Similarly, you will need access to both the keyboard and the main transceiver controls. One solution it to have the keyboard on a pull-out tray, fixed below the operating desk. Unfortunately, very few office desks or computer tables have enough depth for a transceiver and a computer keyboard, and some amateurs resort to building their own operating table. The advent of affordable LCD monitors is a big step forward, as they require very much less space on which to stand. They are also easier on the eyes during long periods of use.

Opinion varies as to whether the transceiver should be placed to the left or right of the operator or dead centre. Possibly one could get used to it placed in any of these positions. If, however, the set is placed to the left, the right-handed operator can tune the set with the left hand, leaving the right free to write notes, type at the keyboard and operate the key or microphone. Some CW operators deliberately train themselves to send with the left hand, so that the right hand is available for all other activities.

It may be found convenient to tilt the transceiver slightly so that its tuning dial is more easily visible, or so that its controls are more easily operated. Some transceivers have extensions already fitted to the front pair of rubber feet for this purpose. If there is still insufficient tilt, packing can be inserted under the front rubber feet of the set. Such packing should not obstruct ventilation holes, and should provide a firm mounting. A scrap length of wood about 150mm wide should be suitable, with a strip of foam rubber on top to deaden vibration.

Other equipment such as an antenna tuning unit, linear amplifier and computer may be positioned either side of the transceiver as convenient, preferably in a U-shaped layout as this ensures all displays are facing the operator. The power / SWR meter, monitor oscilloscope and clock are best arranged on a shelf above the operating position, but low enough to be easily viewed. All equipment which does not need to be adjusted or monitored while routinely operating, such as a low-pass filter or frequency meter, does not really belong to the operating area, and can be positioned elsewhere in the shack to save space. Conversely, equipment which you will need to adjust while operating, such as rotator controllers and antenna switches, should be within easy reach.

A suggested line-up on the table in front of the electronics is (from left to right) microphone, logbook / keyboard, scrap pad and Morse key, but the operator will no doubt have individual preferences. The main thing to ensure is that these items can be used with the minimum of effort. Over time, you will find what works and what doesn't and probably end up moving items around. So it is best to anticipate the need for flexibility when designing and setting up your operating position.

The best place for maps and lists constantly in use is the wall immediately above the operating position, but if this is not possible the material can be laid out on the table and a thin sheet of Perspex placed on top to keep it clean and in position.

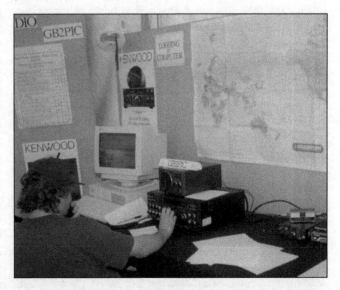

Maps and lists can be conveniently pinned up above the operating position, or perhaps underneath a glass top to the desk.

Last, but not least, a comfortable chair with adequate back support should be chosen, for this will allow the operator to concentrate properly on the job without any fears of aches and pains when a long operating session is over. Office chairs, with height and other adjustments are popular for this purpose. Those with castors allow you to move easily to the edges of your operating table if you need to reach other equipment in a hurry. Some contesters choose specially-designed ergonomic chairs to avoid back pain as a result of prolonged operating periods.

One of the potential problems you will face is noise and vibration from cooling fans, both in your transceiver and linear amplifier, and in your computer. For prolonged operating, noise-cancelling headphones can be beneficial in reducing the scale of the problem. It is also worth noting that vibration from fans can easily be carried through walls and floors, especially if the operating bench is fixed directly to the wall, for example. Sitting equipment on some sort of flexible matting can help to reduce vibration, and therefore minimise any nuisance to the rest of the household.

ROUTING ANTENNA CABLES

One of the unique problems faced by radio amateurs is how to bring cables into the shack from outside. This is something you need to plan carefully, as it is best to anticipate future requirements right from the start. Think about how many cables you are likely to need to bring in, and plan accordingly.

One solution is to drill the shack wall to take a standard piece of PVC drain pipe (about 7cm diameter). This is sufficient to accommodate, for example, low-loss feeder (such as H100) from four antennas, two rotator control cables, a control line for a remote antenna switch, and a couple of small diameter coaxial cables for back-up purposes.

The drainage pipe can be continued underground to the base of the antenna mast or tower. Draw strings should be left in place so that cables can be pulled in or removed as required. An alternative is to run cables above ground, in which case they should be attached to posts or the house wall at regular intervals, with other members of the household familiar with their location so that they are not likely to be damaged, during gardening work, for example.

CHOOSING ANTENNAS

The choice of antenna is governed by many considerations. There are technical considerations about the performance required and the frequencies to be covered. Initially you may want to have a multi-band antenna, but later you may want to specialise in one or two bands and have an antenna that does not have the compromises that a multi-bander has. There may also be physical constraints to do with the site, especially on the low bands where a half wavelength (the typical starting point for most antennas being a half-wave dipole) may be more than the available space. Or you may be planning on a mast or tower which has limited weight or wind-loading capabilities. And last but by no means least, there may well be planning constraints, restricting the sort of antennas which can be erected at your location.

It is also worth bearing in mind that any sort of directional antenna will need to be rotated, unless you want to use it only in one direction. This adds to both the cost and the complexity, though anyone who has upgraded from a vertical or dipole antenna to a multi-element Yagi or other antenna with significant amounts of gain will testify to the huge impact this will make to your station's capabilities, both on receive and transmit.

Commercially-made antennas for most bands are available from a wide range of suppliers. Nowadays it is reasonable to expect an antenna to have the gain specified, as most are designed using sophisticated computer modelling to arrive at an optimum combination of gain, front-to-back ratio and pattern. The main difference between two antennas of similar design and claimed performance is likely to be in the mechanical construction, both in the quality of the materials used (are the fasteners and mounting hardware made of stainless steel, for example?) and the way it is all put together. For portable operation you would be looking for something lightweight and easy to erect. For home station use, you would want an antenna which will survive the worst the weather can throw at it at your location.

VHF and UHF antennas are almost all of aluminium construction, though many collinear verticals are encased in weatherproofing material to protect the more delicate loading and matching components.

While the larger HF antennas are of similar construction, one of the joys of the HF bands is that a wide range of antennas can be constructed from wire, starting with simple dipoles, loops and verticals. A resonant antenna such as a half-wave dipole is easy to build and should work first time. It can be built for minimal expense (a few metres of wire and some insulators), and will be almost invisible when erected.

If you decide to buy an antenna, most of the major dealers can help you to decide what is most suitable for your location. Buying second-hand is fine, of course, but bear in mind that antennas will have been exposed to the weather, so will have suffered deterioration. Trapped antennas are particularly prone to weather damage, so check out the condition before parting with your money. A trap may look fine externally but, on removing the cover, you may find that the connections are heavily corroded. Also ensure that any antenna comes with full instructions as it will almost certainly be broken down for transportation, and you will need to know how to put it back together on site.

One of the best investments you can make is in the antenna feedline. Why spend a lot of money on a good transceiver and a high-gain antenna, and then throw away power in the

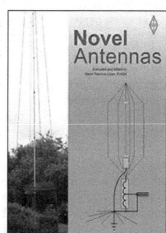

The RSGB and the ARRL publish a wide variety of useful books on antennas, such as this one.

feedline? Always use low-loss cable, remembering that the higher the frequency the greater the losses will be.

For further discussion of antennas, turn to one of the many excellent antenna books. Antenna experimentation remains one of the most popular aspects of the hobby, because there is no ideal solution and every location has its own challenges. Suggested books include *Building Successful HF Antennas* [11], *Successful Wire Antennas* [12], *RSGB Antenna File* [13], *Antennas Mastered* [14], *Stealth Antennas* [15] and *Novel Antennas* [16]. All these books, and many others, are available from the RSGB Shop [17].

SITING THE ANTENNA

For maximum efficiency, the antenna should be sited as high as possible, away from the ground, buildings and other obstructions. The advantages of even a hill-top site will not be realised unless this is done. For this purpose distances and heights should be thought of in terms of wavelengths rather than metres or feet, and the various publications describing particular antennas often give useful information on their performance at varying heights. Transmitting antennas should be kept away from metalwork, such as iron drainpipes. This can influence the directional properties of the antenna, and can also lead to radiation of harmonics of the transmitted signal if the metalwork contains joints capable of acting as metal-oxide diodes (the so-called 'rusty bolt effect'). Transmitting antennas should also be located as far as possible from TV antennas and their feeders to avoid electromagnetic compatibility problems (see later). TV feeders usually run vertically, and are therefore particularly prone to RF pick-up from vertical transmitting antennas.

Unfortunately TV equipment is not the only category susceptible to high RF field strengths. Hi-fi equipment, domestic radios, amplified external computer speakers, electronic organs and solid-state switching circuits can all be adversely affected. Similarly other domestic equipment can also radiate interference. Electric motors, thermostats and fluorescent lighting are frequent culprits.

If the antenna is fixed in position and thereby unable to rotate, it may be advantageous to position it so that equipment susceptible to RF (or generating interference) is in a position of minimum antenna gain. This is particularly important where high transmitter powers or high-gain antennas are in use.

The safety and social aspects of the antenna site should not be forgotten. Antennas such as dipoles have high RF voltages at their ends when transmissions are being made, and it should not be possible for children or animals to reach up and touch them. While you are not likely to be in the vicinity yourself when you are transmitting, as you will be in the shack, others may not be aware that you are on the air.

The aesthetic aspect is more a function of the type of antenna used than its location, but it may sometimes be better to have an antenna located lower than optimum to avoid antagonising neighbours or drawing attention to the presence of a radio station.

By far the best book on antenna design, location and installation is *The ARRL Antenna Book* [18], though there are many other excellent publications on the subject.

TRANSMITTER CHECKS AND ADJUSTMENTS

Clause 7 of the UK licence stipulates that "the Licensee shall conduct tests from time" to ensure that the licence requirements concerning non-interference to other telecommunications can be met.

Adverse comments made on the air concerning modulation quality (including that of CW signals) should be treated with concern, and the fault or incorrect adjustment traced before further transmissions are made. Most amateurs tend to be uncritical of other stations' signals out of politeness, and therefore when comments are made it is often the case that something is quite seriously wrong.

If available, the manufacturer's handbook should be carefully consulted for details of adjustments and tuning up procedure, and the operator should be fully conversant with these before putting the transmitter on the air.

Most test gear required is either inexpensively obtainable on the second-hand market or easy to construct at home. See the RSGB *Radio Communication Handbook* [1] and also *Test Equipment for the Radio Amateur* [19]. Regular use of test equipment is not only the mark of a responsible operator, but also one who is sure that his transmitter really is giving peak performance in those DX pile-ups!

SETTING UP AN AMATEUR TV STATION

An amateur TV station need be only as complex as the individual desires. Many stations employ no more equipment than a camera, transmitter, receiver and, of course, a TV monitor. This basic system is adequate for normal communications and has the advantage of being easy to use and maintain. The block diagram of such a basic amateur TV station is shown in **Fig 1**. Amateurs who do not wish to put together a complete TV station often set up a simple receiving system in order to 'eavesdrop' on ATV pictures in their area. This can be very rewarding, especially if they live in a high-activity area, and particularly when lifts in propagation conditions occur. Looking in on a local ATV repeater is a common pastime for many stations. In addition, they can often still participate via the 2m talkback channel.

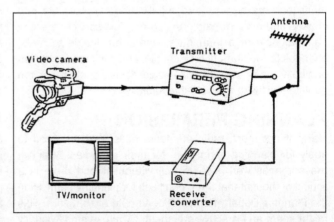

Fig 1: Block diagram of a basic fast-scan amateur TV station.

The television station of Arthur, G4CPE.

Various clubs exist to promote the hobby the largest being the British Amateur Television Club (BATC) here in the UK [20]. A free e-magazine from *CQ-DATV* is downloadable from [21]

Equipment

ATV equipment may either be purchased from a range of suppliers, surplus equipment sales, amateur rallies, magazine sales, or it can be constructed in the shack.

The pictures may be produced in a wide variety of ways. The simplest solution is to use a home video camera that provides a regular audio and video output that can be connected directly to the ATV transmitter. A more complex solution is to use several cameras, separate microphones, video recorders etc that can be individually switched to the transmitter. More complex still is to use a proper video and audio mixer fed either directly into the transmitter or into a recorder to make reasonably professional programs.

Most of the equipment required to achieve this is available from surplus equipment sales and other used equipment sources. In addition some kits are available, for instance at [22].

STATION NOTEBOOK

Right from the start, to get into the habit of maintaining a station notebook. In this you might record the routing and labelling of your various antenna feeders, a note of antenna SWR curves (when they change it is a sign that something may be wrong), details of modifications to any of the equipment (and maybe a note of serial numbers, plus date purchased and amount paid), and so on. This sort of data can be invaluable at a later date, when you decide to make changes to the station, for example, and can't recall why you originally made a particular design decision. It's never too early to start with this valuable habit.

PLANNING PERMISSION

Many, if not most, radio amateurs never see the need to apply for planning permission for their antennas. After all, the antennas work just as well without it and there is a school of thought that if you don't ask for planning permission the Planning Department can't be tempted to say "no". This might seem an attractive argument if you use small visually unobtrusive wire aerials, but if you have aspirations of any-

thing more substantial you are likely to fall foul of the local Planning Department if you do not have planning permission.

Urban Myths

Unfortunately holding an amateur radio licence in the United Kingdom does not convey any special 'rights' under planning legislation to have an antenna and there are a number of urban myths circulating regarding the need for planning permission. Amateur radio masts and antennas are generally treated as residential development, exactly the same as a garage or conservatory, and will require planning permission unless they come under one of the following categories:

• *Temporary* - Present for a total of calendar 28 days in a year or less.

• *De minimalist* - The visual impact is too small to be a concern to the planning process. There is no legal definition as to what is *de minimalist* and it is left in the first instance to the interpretation of the Planning Department, but it has been successfully argued that a single wire dipole can be classed as *de minimalist* when it uses existing structures such as a tree to support it.

• *Permitted Development* - The Town and Country Planning (General Permitted Development) (Amendments) (No 2) (England) Order 2008 permits certain alterations and / or improvements to existing dwelling houses without the need for planning permission. Although no references are made in this Order to amateur radio antennas and masts, some radio amateurs have successfully argued under Part 1, Class A of the Order that an antenna, mast or pole to the rear of, and attached to, a dwelling house is an "enlargement, improvement or alteration of a dwelling house", provided the antenna or mast does not protrude above the ridge of the roof. Similarly it has been successfully argued that a free-standing mast up to 3m in height to the rear of the property is also Permitted Development. There is currently no legal ruling on whether this type of installation is actually covered by the provision of this Order and it is left in the first instance to the interpretation of individual Planning Departments, but it is known that some Planning Departments do accept this argument whilst others do not. Your are therefore advised to seek the opinion of your local Planning Department before proceeding with any intended works under this Order. Some planners will seek to limit the size of antennas attached to masts under this Order, but it should be noted that the size restrictions for antennas in this Order apply only to satellite and microwave antennas. The Order gives no guidance on HF or other antennas. Similar legislation exists in other parts of the UK.

• *Mobile installation* - The legal position regarding mobile masts is uncertain if the mast is used for more than 28 days per year in one location. Some radio amateurs have successfully argued that mobile masts are plant and do not need planning permission, whilst others have failed and had enforcement notices served on them. The degree of permanence is the deciding factor, but if it is continually kept in the one location in an upright position or it is not able to be moved off site it is difficult to claim it is a mobile installation.

- *Four-year rule* - If your house is not a listed building and you have had your antennas and masts present and unchanged for four years or more, no enforcement action can be taken against you. You may be required to prove that the installation has been there for four years or more, but this need only be a letter of confirmation from your immediate neighbours or a receipt if it was commercially installed. A Certificate of Lawfulness for your antennas and mast can be obtained from the Planning Department after four years if you want one but there is no legal requirement to do this.

Applying for Planning Permission

Each local authority will have its own planning permission application forms, but they generally follow a similar style. They will typically require you to a complete a Householder's Planning Application form, site location plan(s) and development plan(s) showing the dimensions of the proposed antenna and / or mast and the distances to your property and the boundary with neighbouring properties. The number of copies and scale for these plans will be specified by the Planning Department in its planning pack. The drawings need not be professionally prepared as long as it is clear what your proposals are and they are to the specified scale. Generally the Department will want you to give details of the proposed antenna and will not accept vague descriptions that will allow significant change without applying for fresh planning permission. If you forget to show the antenna your planning permission will be for the mast only, without any antennas.

You will also need to complete a neighbourhood notification form detailing your 'notifiable neighbours'. This is usually those who share a boundary with your property or directly face any part of your property from across the road. It is worth discussing your proposals with them before making your submission: in that way when the official notice comes through their door it will not be a surprise. If you have breakthrough issues get these resolved first as, although EMC is not part of the planning process, experience has shown they will just object on other grounds, usually visual amenity which is extremely subjective.

Before formally submitting your planning application, ask if you can discuss the submission with your case officer. Minor changes at this stage may alleviate any concerns he / she may have, giving your application a better chance of success.

If you are an RSGB member you can also request a letter of support for your proposed antenna or mast to be sent to your Planning Department by the RSGB [23].

Refusal to Grant Planning Permission

Sadly not all planning applications are successful and there is sometimes no apparent reason why one Planning Department will grant planning permission for an antenna and mast in one area and another in a neighbouring area will refuse planning permission for a near identical installation.

You will have been told why your application was refused. Usually it's on the grounds of visual amenity: consider if the Planning Department has a valid point. To a radio amateur a large beam is a thing of beauty and a joy to own, but what do

A good outcome: 18m Versatower and beam at the station of Paul Cort-Wright, G3SEM, on the edge of a conservation area. Planning permission was originally refused but was won on appeal.

your neighbours think? Does it overly dominate the area? The Planning Department has to weigh up the rights of all involved, not simply take sides. You will usually be able to resubmit a revised application free of charge if it is less than 12 months from the original application. If appropriate, reconsider a less ambitious proposal.

If, however, you believe the Planning Department has treated your application unfairly you have the right of appeal to the Planning Inspectorate (England and Wales) [24], the Planning Appeals Commission (Northern Ireland) [25] or The Directorate for Planning and Environmental Appeals (DPEA), (Scotland) [26]. The appeal must be made within six months from the planning decision and is usually made in the form of 'Written Submission'. No charge is made for the appeal, it is simply a matter of filling in the appropriate form and submitting your evidence in writing. It is also possible to submit your planning appeal electronically, but all documentation must be supplied in an electronic form. Full details are available on the appropriate website. To be successful you must state why you believe the original decision was unsound. Simply saying you disagree or that it will curtail your operations as a licensed radio amateur is not enough. You must establish that the Planning Department has failed to comply with planning law, policy or guidelines, or has sought to impose a different standard on your application than it has done for others.

The RSGB's Planning Advisory Committee can assist members in the preparation of a planning appeal. If you require assistance, contact RSGB HQ and put you will be put in contact with your nearest Committee member.

If your appeal is not upheld and you have not used up your free resubmission, you can submit a revised proposal free of change if it is still less than 12 months from the original application.

Enforcement Notices

The Planning Department are likely to take enforcement action against you in two circumstances:

1. Where you have erected an antenna or mast which, in the Planning Department's opinion, requires permission and you have not obtained it; or

2. Where the Planning Department alleges that you have breached a condition attached to the planning permission they have issued (for example to keep the mast down when not in use).

The first is the most common. If you have not already submitted an application and had it refused, the Planning Department will normally write to invite you to submit an application. It is usually worth doing so unless you want to argue that you have permitted development rights for the antenna or they are *de minimalist*.

The Planning Department may serve on you a Planning Contravention Notice. This requires you to give certain information as to ownership or to attend the Planning Department's Offices at a specific date and time to give details of your installation and why you believe it does not need planning permission (for example, because it's permitted development or *de minimalist*). You must comply with the Notice: if you fail to do so you may be prosecuted.

If the Planning Department is not satisfied with your explanation they may elect to issue you an Enforcement Notice. The Planning Department can only do this if they can give reasons why they would not consider granting planning permission, and they may have to justify their decision to the Planning Inspectorate.

If an Enforcement Notice is issued it will set out what the Planning Department want you do. Usually this will require you to remove the antenna and / or mast. Should you be served an Enforcement Notice you have two choices:

1. To comply: remove the offending antenna, mast etc or
2. To appeal.

You must appeal within 28 days of receiving the Notice, or at least before it becomes effective. Details on how to appeal are available from the Planning Inspectorate, Scottish Government and the Northern Ireland Planning Appeals Commission websites.

If the notice relates to a breach of conditions, the Planning Department may serve on you an ordinary enforcement notice (against which you can appeal as above), or alternatively a Breach of Condition Notice, against which there is no appeal.

Failure to comply with an Enforcement Notice quickly leads to legal action being taken against you, so don't ignore them. If the Planning Department considers that the antenna / mast has a severe environmental concern which requires immediate action they can apply to the Court for an injunction. If such an injunction is granted, you must comply or you will be held 'in contempt of court'.

Tenancy Matters

As well as requiring planning permission, tenants will generally require the permission of their landlord to erect antennas on their property. Many Council tenants think having been granted planning permission by the Council it also includes landlord's permission. This is not always so and you should check. Private tenants must always obtain permission from their landlords before erecting any antenna to ensure they are not breaking their tenancy agreement.

Unfortunately permission is sometimes withheld even though planning permission was given. General information on how to complain about tenancy matters can be found at the Housing Ombudsman Service website [27]. This is an independent website and the RSGB cannot accept responsibility for any errors or omissions in the advice given.

SAFETY PRECAUTIONS

Safety is of paramount importance and every precaution should be taken to ensure that the equipment is perfectly safe, not only for the operator himself but also for the other members of the household or visitors. Double-pole switches should be used for all AC supply circuits, and interconnected switches should be fitted to home-constructed equipment so that no part of it can have high voltage applied to it until any valve heaters and low-power stages have been switched on. This precaution may not only save the life of the operator, but also protects the transmitter against damage.

Linear amplifiers using valves should have a microswitch fitted so that the EHT is switched off when the cabinet is opened. Where interconnecting plugs and sockets are used for high voltages, ensure that the female connector is connected to the supply unit, and the male to the unit to be supplied. It should be possible to turn off power to the entire station by operating one master switch, located in a very prominent position, and all members of the household should know that in the event of an emergency this must be switched off before anything is touched.

The antenna may require the provision of a lightning conductor in the immediate vicinity, or the use of lightning arresters. The most satisfactory type of arrester is the gas-filled type fitted in an adequately insulated mounting which includes a parallel air spark gap. Arresters for coaxial cable are also available. Lightning protection should always be located outside the building, providing as direct a path to earth as possible: "lightning doesn't go round corners!" Great care should be exercised before touching feeders which have been disconnected before a thunderstorm as they may hold a dangerous charge for a considerable time after the storm. Further information on lightning protection is given in [1].

Mains Voltages

An often-overlooked precaution concerns the current carrying capability of the mains supply to the station. An amateur station fully equipped with ancillary apparatus can draw quite a heavy current from the supply, and when assembling the equipment it is important to calculate the current that will be drawn when everything is in use and to check that the house wiring will carry this amount. If there is any doubt, new wiring should be installed.

It is most important that every amateur should develop a strict code of safety discipline for use when handling his

Safety Recommendations for the Amateur Radio Station

1. All equipment should be controlled by one master switch, the position of which should be well known to others in the house or club.

2. All equipment should be properly connected to a good and permanent earth (but see box on PME later in this chapter and Note A).

3. Wiring should be adequately insulated, especially where voltages greater than 500V are used. Terminals should be suitably protected.

4. Transformers operating at more than 100V RMS should be fitted with an earthed screen between the primary and secondary windings or have them in separate slots in the bobbin.

5. Capacitors of more than 0.01uF capacitance operating in power packs, modulators, etc (other than for RF bypass or coupling) should have a bleeder resistor connected directly across their terminals. The value of the bleeder resistor should be low enough to ensure rapid discharge. A value of 1/C megohms (where C is in microfarads) is recommended. The use of earthed probe leads for discharging capacitors in case the bleeder resistor is defective is also recommended. (Note B). Low-leakage capacitors, such as paper and oil-filled types, should be stored with their terminals short-circuited to prevent static charging.

6. Indicator lamps should be installed showing that the equipment is live. These should be clearly visible at the operating and test position. Faulty indicator lamps should be replaced immediately. Gas-filled (neon) lamps and LEDs are more reliable than filament types.

7. Double-pole switches should be used for breaking mains circuits on equipment. Fuses of correct rating should be connected to the equipment side of each switch in the live lead only. (Note C.) Always switch off before changing a fuse.

8. In metal-enclosed equipment install primary circuit breakers, such as micro-switches, which operate when the door or lid is opened. Check their operation frequently.

9. Test prods and test lamps should be of the insulated pattern.

10. A rubber mat should be used when the equipment is installed on a floor that is likely to become damp.

11. Switch off before making any adjustments. If adjustments must be made while the equipment is live, use one hand only and keep the other in your pocket. Never attempt two-handed work without switching off first. Use good-quality insulated tools for adjustments.

12. Do not wear headphones while making internal adjustments on live equipment.

13. Ensure that the metal cases of microphones, Morse keys etc are properly connected to the chassis.

14. Do not use meters with metal zero-adjusting screws in high-voltage circuits. Beware of live shafts projecting through panels, particularly when metal grub screws are used in control knobs.

15. Antennas should not, under any circumstances, be connected to the mains or other HT source. Where feeders are connected through a capacitor, which may have HT on the other side, a low resistance DC path to earth should be provided (RF choke).

16. Antennas must be designed with due allowance for wind loading. For this, guidance from the antenna manufacturer is necessary and British Standard (BS) CP3 Chapter 5 for guyed masts and BS 8100 for self-supporting masts should be consulted.

17. Certain chemicals occur in electronic devices which are harmful. Notable amongst these are the polychlorinated biphenyls (PCBs) which have been used in the past to fill transformers and high-voltage capacitors and beryllium oxide (BeO) which is used as an insulator inside the case of some high-power semiconductors. In the case of PCBs, the names to look out for on capacitors are: ARACLOR, PYROCHLOR, PYRANOL, ASBESTOL, NO-FLAMOL, SAFT-KUL and others. If one of these is present in a device, it must be disposed of carefully. The local Health and Safety Authority will advise. In the case of beryllium oxide, the simple rule is DON'T OPEN ANY DEVICE THAT MAY CONTAIN IT.

Note A. - Owing to the common use of plastic water main and sections of plastic pipe in effecting repairs, it is no longer safe to assume that a mains water pipe is effectively connected to earth. Steps must be taken, therefore, to ensure that the earth connection is of sufficiently low resistance to provide safety in the event of a fault. Checks should be made whenever repairs are made to the mains water system in the building.

Note B. - A 'wandering earth lead' or an 'insulated earthed probe lead' is an insulated lead permanently connected via a high-power 1k resistor or a 15W 250V lamp at one end to the chassis of the equipment; at the other end a suitable length of bare wire with an insulated handle is provided for touch contacting the high-potential terminals to be discharged.

Note C. - Where necessary, surge-proof fuses can be used.

radio equipment. It should be the rule never to work on equipment which is plugged into the AC supply if this can possibly be avoided. However, there are occasions when this is unavoidable and under these circumstances the following precautions should be followed:

- Keep one hand in a pocket.
- Remove metal bracelets or watch straps.
- Never wear headphones.
- Be certain that no part of the body is touching an object which is earthed and use a rubber or similar non-conductive covering over concrete floors.
- Use insulated tools.

Before working on equipment of any kind, plugged into the mains or not, it is vital to make sure that all filter capacitors are fully discharged as these are capable of retaining what could be a lethal charge for a considerable time. Use an insulated screwdriver to short each capacitor in turn. The vast majority of shocks sustained from electrical apparatus are derived from the 230V mains line lead. Every year there are 100 or more deaths in the UK due to electrocution, mostly as a result of accidental contact with mains voltage. There is evidence to suggest that because of the different physiological effects, those who receive shocks from voltages of more than 1000V have a better chance of survival than those subjected to severe medium-voltage shocks. Voltages as low as 32V at high current have been known to cause death - as the jingle says: "It's volts that jolts but mils that kills".

The danger of electrocution is increased where the victim's skin resistance is lowered by dampness or perspiration, or where he grips an extensive area of 'live' metal while in good contact with earth. It is against this second possibility that particular care is needed in amateur stations.

It is wise to ensure that all mains plugs are of the non-reversable (three-pin in the UK) type and to test any equipment connected to the mains supply with a neon-screwdriver before working on it.

Also, check all three-pin supply sockets in the house to see whether they have been correctly wired; all too often this is not the case. A three-pin plug with the 'earth' contact at the top should have the 'neutral' contact on the bottom left, and the live 'line' contact on the bottom right - these directions apply when looking at the back of the plug for wiring purposes (see **Fig 2**). Correct colour coding of leads in the UK is: 'live' brown; 'neutral' blue; 'earth' yellow and green. It is very important to note that this coding may not apply to the wiring on some imported equipment, and the manufacturer's instructions should be very carefully studied before plugging into the supply. The use of modern fused plugs is recommended.

An even greater hazard, because it is seldom anticipated, can arise under fault conditions on equipment fitted with a double wound (ie 'isolating') transformer of the type so often used in amateur equipment. It is by no means unusual or unknown for the primary winding to short circuit to the screen between the primary and secondary, the core, or to

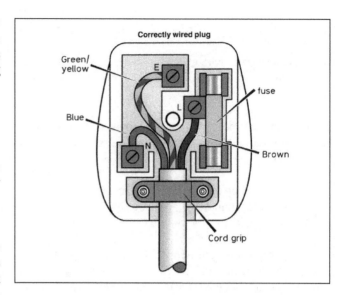

Fig 2: The correct wiring for three-pin plugs in the UK. The fuse should be of the correct rating for the equipment being powered. To test that a socket is correctly wired, a lamp should light when connected between 'L' and 'N' or 'L' and 'E', but not when connected between 'N' and 'E'. A neon bulb will glow when touched against 'L'.

one of the secondary windings, so that the chassis of the equipment becomes 'live'. Such equipment will often continue to operate quite normally and can thus represent a very real danger over a considerable period. The best safeguard against this danger is to ensure that the screen between the primary and the other windings, the core and the chassis are all effectively earthed.

The earth connection must be of very low resistance otherwise the supply fuses may not blow. These fuses should be of the minimum practicable rating - it is no use having a 50 ohm resistance to earth and a 10A fuse - if this should be the case the size of the electricity bills may be surprising, but the hazard is likely to remain undetected!

Another source of danger is the electric tool which has developed a fault and which has a 'live' casing. This can happen, for example, with soldering irons and electric drills. A very careful check should be kept on the leads to all such tools, and any 'tingles' felt when they are in use must be investigated immediately.

Many amateurs fit extra power sockets in their stations and the control arrangements may call for quite a lot of semi-permanent AC wiring and switching. In the UK these should always conform to the high standards laid down in the IEE Wiring Regulations. These are rather formidable reading for the non-professional but a number of books giving sound advice on modern wiring practice, based on the IEE recommendations, have been published and can often be obtained from local libraries. In most countries overseas, similar regulations exist and operators in these areas are recommended to obtain copies or seek the advice of the supply authorities.

Another problem is the use of protective multiple earthing (PME) in some UK houses (see panel later in this chapter). Finally, taking the worst possible event into consideration the

Always wear a safety belt when working at heights!

operator and members of his household are advised to familiarise themselves with the procedures for the treatment of electric shock.

It is often not realised that low-voltage, high-current equipment can also have dangerous aspects. Transceivers can have power supply requirements of some 20 - 30A at 12V. It is vital that suitable cable is used to connect any external power supply and that all electrical connections are of low resistance, otherwise there could be a fire risk. There is also a considerable personal danger through hot or molten metal if the user inadvertently short-circuits such a power supply - the resultant current through, say, a wedding ring could cause severe burns. It is a wise precaution to have a fire extinguisher of the type suitable for use on electrical equipment in the shack. The best type is that which directs a stream of carbon dioxide gas on to the burning area; the powder and Halon types may be used but are liable to cause further damage to electrical equipment with which they come into contact.

Antenna and Tower Safety

A word, too, about working on antennas. Firstly, in siting antennas do ensure that they are well clear of power cables and cannot fall across power cables in the event of structural failure. Many UK amateurs use tilt-over masts and towers, which avoids having to climb them to work on antennas. Never try to climb a telescopic tower when it is extended, a potentially lethal activity.

If you have a fixed tower, or need to climb a telescopic tower when retracted, always use a good-quality climbing belt, wear a safety helmet and, if at all possible, have a friend or relative nearby in case of injury. In the USA and other countries where fixed towers are more common, there are all too many climbing accidents each year, most of which would have been avoidable if proper safety precautions had been observed.

If your antennas are roof or chimney-mounted, again care should be taken when doing installation or maintenance work. Of course, you can always employ a professional antenna installer but, sadly, most TV antenna installers have little understanding of the particular requirements of radio amateurs, so the usual solution is to do the work ourselves. If you don't feel competent to handle the job, it may be that an amateur at your local club is willing to step into the breach.

A further comment regarding wind-up towers is perhaps appropriate at this stage. Be aware of the manufacturer's specifications. If the tower is unguyed, you will need to know the wind loading of your antenna(s) and rotator, and be prepared to lower the tower if strong winds are forecast. The guying of towers is a specialist subject which it is not intended to cover here. Be aware, though, that many failures of amateur towers have been due to twisting, due to the antenna itself not being balanced with respect to wind loading. Simple three-point guying cannot prevent this, and additional precautions may need to be taken.

SECURITY AND INSURANCE

Many amateur stations contain easily portable equipment worth thousands of pounds. Sometimes this is located in a shack remote from the house, possibly on view to the passer-by. It is not surprising that an amateur station can attract attention of the wrong sort, and some elementary precautions should always be taken.

Make a note of the model number, serial number and distinguishing features of each item of equipment and keep this somewhere in the house (not in the shack) where it is unlikely to be seen by an intruder. Make sure the shack is secure by checking (and using) the locks on windows and doors. Consider fitting a burglar alarm, especially if a separate shack in the garden is in use.

If in doubt on these matters, seek the advice of the crime prevention officer at the local police station. When going on holiday, let the police know.

Equipment left in cars is at particular risk. Never leave hand-held transceivers (or any other valuables, for that matter) lying around on the seats of cars. Keep them with you or, if this is not convenient, locked up in the boot. Remove mobile transceivers when the car is left parked outside the house. Make sure the car is fitted with an alarm. If the worst comes to the worst, make it difficult for the thief. Give the details of the theft and the equipment to the local radio club(s) and the RSGB (or appropriate national society) as well as the police and insurers. The local radio shops should also be warned, particularly any dealing in second-hand equipment.

The existing household insurance should be checked to ensure that the equipment is covered and the cover should be increased if necessary. General household insurers do not always understand the special requirements of amateur radio.

One story, apparently not apocryphal, is of the amateur who had specialist microwave band equipment stolen and was offered a voucher for a replacement microwave (oven) by his insurance company! Do, therefore, ensure that your insurance company fully understands what it is covering, with a list of equipment, replacement values, serial numbers and other relevant information.

While every amateur will try to construct and maintain his station so that it is completely safe for himself and any others who may visit it, there is always the possibility that an accident may occur. Owing to a component failure a visitor may receive an electric shock, or an antenna or mast may fall and injure someone or damage property. Such an occurrence can result in a legal action, which could result in the award of very substantial damages against the person held to be responsible for the accident. This risk can, and should, be insured against, either by an extension to the existing house-holder's comprehensive policy or by taking out a separate public liability policy if only fire insurance is held. The annual premium for this will be quite a small amount and readers cannot be too strongly urged to consult their insurance advis-ers over this matter.

Insurance is also important for special event and DXpedition operations. The same considerations apply.

EMC:
DEALING WITH BREAKTHROUGH

Traditionally the most troublesome problem in amateur radio was interference to radio and TV equipment, not so much because of technical difficulty but because of the social implications. When TV in the UK moved to UHF, the biggest difficulty, harmonics of HF transmissions interfering with weak TV signals in Band 1, ceased to be a problem.

As domestic radio and electronic devices proliferated and higher powered rigs became more affordable, the focus moved to interference caused by the fundamental transmis-sion getting into neighbours' radio and electronic equipment. The term 'breakthrough' is used to describe this phenome-non, emphasising that it is a shortcoming on the part of the equipment being interfered with, and not a transmitter fault Breakthrough can affect almost any type of electronic equipment but the most commonly reported problems are to Radio, TV, audio players, telephones and security sys-tems.

There are two ways of combating breakthrough.

- By ensuring that the station is designed and operated with EMC in mind. The term good radio housekeeping has been coined to cover this.
- By increasing the immunity of the affected equipment by using ferrite ring chokes and similar devices.

Good Radio Housekeeping'

Most good radio housekeeping rules apply to reception as well as transmission, so we can kill two birds with one stone. By far the most important factor in preventing both breakthrough and pick-up of local noise, is the antenna and its siting. The aim is to site the antenna as high as you can, and as far as possible from your own house and from neigh-bouring houses (**Fig 3**).

Many amateurs are persuaded by social pressures into using low, poorly sited, antennas only to find that break-through problems sour the local relations far more than fears of obtrusive antennas would have done. It is probably true to say that many objections to planning applications for antennas are rooted more in fear of interference than in concern about the appearance of the antenna system. This is unfortunate since improvised 'covert' antennas are much more likely to give rise to interference problems than one which is well designed and well sited.

HF Antennas

The question of which antenna to use is a perennial topic and the last thing that anyone would want to do is to dis-courage experimentation, but there is no doubt that the use of certain types of antenna are more likely to result in break-through than others. It is simply a question of 'horses for courses'; what you can get away with in a large garden, or on HF Field Day, may well be unsuitable for a confined city location.

A similar argument applies to interference from local man-made noise, but it is important to note that at HF the ambient noise is tens of dB greater than thermal noise, even where there is no man-made noise. This is due to cos-mic, ionospheric and atmospheric sources and is the reason why relatively poor antennas can be effective for HF recep-tion, provided they are well away from man-made noise sources.

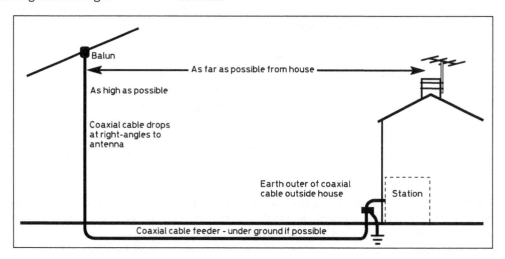

Fig 3: Good radio house-keeping - a balanced antenna well away from the house.

Where EMC is of prime importance, the antenna system should be:

- Horizontally polarised. TV down leads and other household wiring tend to look like an earthed vertical antenna as far as HF is concerned, and are more susceptible to vertically polarised radiation. For similar reasons vertical antennas also tend to pick up more local noise
- Balanced. This avoids out-of-balance currents in feeders giving rise to radiation which has a large vertically polarised component. Where a balanced antenna is fed with coaxial feeder, a balun should be used.
- Compact, so that neither end comes close to the house and consequently to TV leads and mains wiring. Antennas to be careful with are the extended types such as the W3DZZ trap dipole or the G5RV because, almost inevitably, in restricted situations one end is close to the house.

On frequencies of 14MHz upwards, it is not too difficult to arrange an antenna fulfilling these requirements, even in quite a small garden. A half-wave dipole or small beam up as high as possible and 15m or more from the house is the sort of thing to aim for.

At lower frequencies compromise becomes inevitable, and at 3.5MHz most of us have no choice but to have one end of the antenna near the house, or to go for a vertical antenna which can be mounted farther away. A small loop antenna is another possibility, but in general any antenna which is very small compared to a wavelength will have a narrow bandwidth and is likely to have a relatively low efficiency.

Many stations use a G5RV or W3DZZ trap dipole for the lower frequencies but have separate dipoles (or a beam) for the higher frequencies, sited as far down the garden as possible.

The arrival of VDSL 'broadband' internet access (see below) has added another complication in that it would be preferable to avoid proximity to overhead telephone lines and in particular to avoid configurations where the antenna runs parallel to the telephone line.

VHF / UHF Antennas

The main problem with VHF and UHF is that large beams can cause very high field strengths. For instance, 100W fed to an isotropic transmitting antenna in free space would give a field strength of about 3.6V/m at a distance of 15m. The same transmitter into a beam with a gain of 20dB would give a field strength, in the direction of the beam, of 36V/m the same distance away. Again, it comes down to the fact that if you want to run high power to a high-gain beam, the antenna must be kept as far from neighbouring houses as possible and, of course, as high as practical.

Operation in Adverse Situations

The obvious question arises as to what to do if your garden is small (in relation to the wavelength in use) or non-existent, or domestic conditions make a simple wire tuned against ground the only possibility. First of all, and most important, don't get discouraged: many amateurs operate very well from amazingly unpromising locations. It is really

a question of cutting your coat according to your cloth. If there is no choice but to have antennas very close to the house, or even in the loft, then it will almost certainly be necessary to restrict the transmitted power. It is worth remembering that it is good radio operating practice not to use more power than is required for satisfactory communications.

So far as breakthrough is concerned, not all modes are equally 'EMC friendly', and it is worth looking at some of the more frequently used modes from this point of view:

SSB: This is one of the least EMC-friendly modes, particularly where audio breakthrough is concerned.

FM: This is a very EMC-friendly mode, mainly because in most cases the susceptible equipment sees only a constant carrier turned on and off every minute or so.

CW: This is the old faithful for those with breakthrough problems because it has two very big advantages. First, providing the keying waveform is well shaped with rise and fall times of about 10ms or so, the rectified carrier is not such a problem to audio equipment as SSB. Secondly it is a very 'power efficient' mode, so that it is possible to use much lower power for a given contact.

Data: Generally the data modes seem be EMC-friendly. Some data modes rival - or even beat - CW in their ability to 'get through' with minimum power. These modes open up new horizons to amateurs living in difficult locations.

Earths

From the EMC point of view, the purpose of an earth is to provide a low impedance path for RF currents which would otherwise find their way into household wiring, and hence into susceptible electronic equipment in the vicinity. As

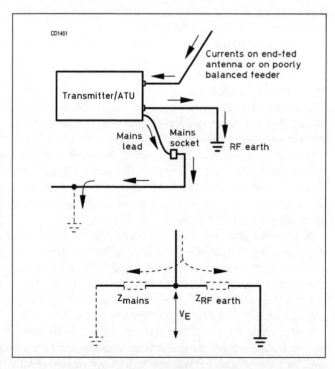

Fig 4: Earth current divides between RF earth and mains. The current down each path will depend on the impedances. The transmitter earth terminal will be at V_E relative to 'true' earth potential.

WARNING
Protective Multiple Earthing (PME)

Many houses, particularly those built or wired since the mid-1970s, are wired on what is known as the PME (or TN-C-S) system. In this system the earth conductor of the consumer's installation is bonded to the neutral close to where the supply enters the premises, and there is no separate earth conductor going back to the sub-station.

With a PME system a small voltage may exist between the consumer's earth conductor, and any metal work connected to it, and the true earth (the earth out in the garden). Under certain very rare supply system faults this voltage could rise to a dangerous level. Because of this supply companies advise certain precautions relating to the bonding of metal work inside the house, and also to the connection of external earths.

WHERE A HOUSE IS WIRED ON THE PME SYSTEM DO NOT CONNECT ANY EXTERNAL (ie radio) EARTHS TO APPARATUS INSIDE THE HOUSE unless suitable precautions are taken.

A free leaflet, *EMC 07 Protective Multiple Earthing,*can be downloaded from the RSGB EMC Committee web site [24].

If in any doubt, consult a properly qualified electrician.

---

shown in **Fig 4**, the RF earth is effectively in parallel with the mains earth path.

Good EMC practice dictates that any earth currents should be reduced to a minimum by making sure that antennas are balanced as well as possible. An inductively coupled ATU can be used to improve the isolation between the antenna / RF earth system and the mains earth. The impedance of the mains earth path can be increased by winding the mains lead supplying the transceiver and its ancillaries on to ferrite cores to form a common-mode choke.

Antennas tuned against earth at the transmitter should be avoided since these inevitably involve large RF currents flowing in the earth system. If this type of antenna must be used (for instance for space reasons or on the LF bands), arrange for it to be fed through coaxial cable and a remote automatic ATU so that the antenna earth is effectively separate from the earth system in the house.

The minimum requirement for an RF (EMC) earth is several copper pipes 1.5m long or more, driven into the ground at least 1m apart and connected together by thick cable. The connection to the station should be as short as possible using thick cable or flat copper strip / braid.

Where the shack is installed in an upstairs room, the provision of a satisfactory RF earth is a difficult problem,and sometimes it may be found that connecting an RF earth makes interference problems worse. In such cases it is probably best to avoid the need for an RF earth by using a well-balanced antenna system - but don't forget lightning protection.

An increasing number of houses in the UK are being wired on the TN-C-S system using Protected Multiple Earthing or PME (see the sidebar). RSGB Leaflet *EMC 07* explains PME and the special precautions which should be taken when connecting an earth to an amateur station in such installations. Leaflets are available on the RSGB EMC Committee web site [28].

Harmonics

Harmonics are much less of a problem than formerly, partly due to the closing down of VHF TV in the UK and partly to a greater awareness by home-constructors and commercial manufacturers alike of the importance of good design and construction. Notwithstanding this, if there is any doubt about the harmonic performance of a transceiver, a low-pass filter should be used. Care should be taken where harmonics can fall into broadcast radio or TV bands, in particular:

- The second harmonic of the 472kHz band falls in the Medium Wave AM broadcast band.
- The harmonics of some HF bands fall into the VHF broadcast band, 88 - 108MHz, as does the second harmonic of 50MHz.
- The fourth harmonic from the 144MHz band could cause problems on TV channels 34 and 35 and the fifth on channels 52 and 53.

INTERFERENCE TO AMATEUR RECEPTION

While breakthrough causes the most problems so far as the relationship between an amateur and his (or her) neighbours is concerned, the most serious long-term threat to the future of amateur radio is the pollution of the spectrum by the increasing number of interference sources. Interference generated by motors and similar devices is still with us, but by far the most serious problem is the broad-band noise generated by digital electronic equipment.

Interference from Data Transmission Systems Using Existing Copper Infrastructure

The transmission of data over the mains wiring PLT or PLC
There are two types of PLT. Access PLT where an internet service is supplied to householders by feeding signals into the mains supply and In-house PLT where the internal house wiring is used to connect computers and similar equipment.

In the UK, Access PLT has never got beyond the trials stage. It is now generally assumed that it is no longer a practical proposition.

In-house PLT has established itself as an alternative to wireless links and is in common use. The modems are called Powerline Adapters (PLAs). Frequencies vary but 4MHz to 24MHz would be typical. All PLAs reduce their transmission power in the amateur bands by about 30dB this is known a 'notching' and seems to give reasonable protection. Without the notching, interference on the amateur bands would be intolerable. New standards are being developed to cover PLT, and the RSGB has representatives on the appropriate bodies.

Transmission of high speed data over the telephone lines
Many households in the UK have internet access by 'broadband' on the telephone lines. There are two systems in use. ADSL (Asymetric Digital Subscriber Line) and VDSL (Vert high speed Digital Subscriber Line).

ADSL has been in common use for a number of years and given little trouble, though there have been a few reported cases of breakthrough from amateur signals.

VDSL is a newer system which allows much greater speed and it is likely that it will become the standard system in the near future. There have been a number of reports of interference to the amateur bands from VDSL. The RSGB is actively investigating this and has requested amateurs to send in reports to the EMC forum. For further information see the RSGB EMC web pages [28].

Other Specific Sources of Interference
As well as emissions from faulty or non-compliant domestic devices there are a number of potential sources which are a cause of concern to the RSGB's EMC Committee. These include:

- Solar panels
- Wind farms
- High efficiency lights.
- Plasma TVs
- Rogue devices which are labelled as a genuine product (including CE mark) but where EMC Components have never been fitted.

To be able to discuss such problems with the appropriate authorities the EMC Committee needs information from members on the effects of emissions from any of these these sources. This can be done by posting to the RSGB EMC forum.

Reducing Interference
RFI on the HF bands from a specific device, such as a switch-mode PSU, is usually caused by RF currents on external leads. In such cases the RFI can often be reduced by winding the lead on to a ferrite ring or split ferrite core to make a choke.

In cases where it is not possible to deal with the interference at source it might be worth considering interference cancelling. For more information see the *Radio Communication Handbook* [1] and the EMC Committee Web Site [28].

The EMC Standards
The EU EMC Standards put limits on permissible emissions from all types of electrical equipment, but they are intended to protect relatively large signal services. They are not stringent enough to prevent all interference to amateur reception. Fortunately most products are well below the maximum limit for emissions, or may be near the limit only on a few specific frequencies, so in practice most Standards are a reasonable compromise.

EMC is a major factor in amateur radio and these notes give only a brief outline of how problems may be tackled. The RSGB EMC Committee publishes leaflets on arrange of EMC subjects including *EMC 04* and *EMC 09* on interference to amateur reception and *EMC 10* on interference to radio and electronic equipment. These leaflets can be found on the EMC Committee website [28]. The latest information on EMC issues can be found in the regular 'EMC' column in *RadCom*.

REFERENCES
[1] *Radio Communication Handbook*, ed Mike Dennison, G3XDV, and Mike Browne, G3DIH, 12th edition, RSGB.
[2] GQRP Club: www.gqrp.com
[3] *The Low Power Sprat Book*, ed Steve Telenius-Lowe, 9M6DXX (PJ4DX), RSGB, 2013.
[4] *QST* magazine: www.arrl.org/qst
[5] *Hart Reviews*, Peter Hart, G3SJX, RSGB 2015.
[6] *eHam* rig reviews etc: www.eHam.net/reviews
[7] *The Rig Guide*, ed Steve White G3ZVW, RSGB.
[8] *Dubus* magazine: http://www.dubus.org/
[9] UK Microwave Group: www.microwavers.org/. Also useful for advice and skeds is a Yahoo group: https://groups.yahoo.com/neo/groups/ukmicrowaves/info
[10] *LF Today*, a guide to success on the bands below 1MHz by Mike Dennison, G3XDV, RSGB.
[11] *Building Successful HF Antennas*, Peter Dodd, G3LDO, RSGB.
[12] *Successful Wire Antennas*, eds Ian Poole, G3YWX & Steve Telenius-Lowe, 9M6DXX / KH0UN (PJ4DX), RSGB 2012.
[13] *RSGB Antenna File*, ed Steve Telenius-Lowe, 9M6DXX (PJ4DX), RSGB 2013.
[14] *Antennas Mastered*, Peter Dodd, G3LDO, RSGB 2014.
[15] *Stealth Antennas*, 2nd edition, Steve Nichol, G0KYA, RSGB 2014.
[16] *Novel Antennas*, Steve Telenius-Lowe, PJ4DX, RSGB 2015.
[17] RSGB Shop: www.rsgbshop.org
[18] *The ARRL Antenna Book*, 22nd edition, ARRL (available from the RSGB Shop).
[19] *Test Equipment for the Radio Amateur*, 4th edition, Clive Smith, GM4FZH, RSGB 2011.
[20] The British Amateur Television Club, BATC, publishes a quarterly magazine, provides streaming video facilities, a forum, Facebook pages, components, equipment and runs a yearly convention. See: www.batc.org.uk
[21] From the UK, *CQ-DATV* a free monthly on line magazine. See: www.cq-datv.mobi
[22] ATV kits: www.minikits.com.au/
[23] http://rsgb.org/main/operating/planning-matters/advice-booklet/
[24] The Planning Inspectorate (England and Wales): www.planningportal.gov.uk/planning/appeals/planningappeals
[25] Planning Appeals Commission (Northern Ireland): http://www.pacni.gov.uk/
[26] The Directorate for Planning and Environmental Appeals (DPEA, Scotland): www.gov.scot/Topics/Built-Environment/planning/decisions-appeals/Appeals
[27] http://www.housing-ombudsman.org.uk/
[28] RSGB EMC Committee web site. Accessible via the RSGB web site, http://rsgb.org/main/

Computers in the Shack, and the Internet

THERE IS CERTAINLY NO requirement to have a computer (PC, tablet or smart phone) in your shack, and many amateurs continue to manage perfectly well without one. But for the majority, computers have become an essential element of a modern amateur radio station. They might be used for station management, datacomms, controlling an SDR receiver, looking up information on stations or countries, or any combination of these and many other applications. It is not at all unusual for an amateur station to have several networked computers performing a variety of functions.

This chapter isn't intended to cover programming or the various technical issues you might face in interfacing your PC to your transceiver and other equipment in your shack. Rather, it will provide an overview of the ways in which a PC can enhance the operating experience, with some suggestions for further reading and research. A more technical approach can be found in the *Radio Communication Handbook* [1].

The first PC-based application to find its way into many amateur radio stations was logging. Keeping a log book was not only a licence requirement, but can also be a pleasurable activity. Over the years it is a joy to be able to look back and use the log book entries as an *aide mémoire* to recall special contacts. But the reality is that if you are especially active, perhaps because you are a regular contester or simply because you have been licensed for a long time, those log books start to accumulate and it becomes harder and harder to keep track of what you have worked or to find a particular contact. This is where computers really come into their own. They are ideally suited for handling large quantities of data, allowing the user to index that data and retrieve it in a variety of ways.

Frankly, any popular spreadsheet or database program could serve well as a computerised log book, and all offer a variety of ways of searching for specific data. For example,

Station with integral PC, used for both logging and datamodes programs.

you might enter contacts into a spreadsheet in chronological order, but then sort the data alphabetically to be able to retrieve it. And if you are at all experienced in writing macros or programming in, for example, *VB*, then you can easily keep track of statistics such as countries worked.

However, you don't actually have to go to such trouble at all. There are many custom-made logging programs for both day-to-day logging and contest logging, some which you have to pay for and some of which are available as freeware or shareware (the benefit of the latter is that you can usually expect a higher level of customer support). The section below on logging and station management programs goes into more detail.

As well as handling data, the other thing that computers are particularly good at is undertaking calculations. So it wasn't long before programs became available for propagation prediction and for antenna modelling, both of which are computationally demanding. As personal computers have become more powerful, later versions of such software have become more and more effective. Propagation prediction will always be subject to the vagaries of the ionosphere, just as weather forecasting remains something of a black art, but antenna modelling has now reached the stage where in most cases the calculated parameters are as close to final performance as measurements allow.

Computers have also taken over the data modes, covered in Chapter 8. RTTY, SSTV, *WSPR*, *JT65* and many other data modes all lend themselves to the world of computers. The PC soundcard acts as the interface between the digital world appropriate to these modes and the analogue world of HF radio, where data is normally sent by modulating a carrier with audio tones.

Of course, the same approach can also be taken to voice transmissions, and many logging programs now provide such an interface, for example allowing the user to record incoming audio so that individual contacts or even a whole contest can be saved to the hard disc while, on the transmit side, CQ calls and other frequently-used phrases can be pre-recorded and played as required.

The distinction between transceiver and computer has become ever more blurred in recent years. While the PC can receive and generate audio tones, as discussed above, more and more of the circuitry in amateur transceivers is digital in nature.

The first commonly-implemented interface was for frequency readout and control. This is extremely useful in the logging environment. On the one hand, it means that you need never mis-log the band on which you make a contact, as the PC will automatically capture the frequency information from the transceiver. On the other hand, it can be extremely useful to control the transceiver's frequency from the PC, for example by capturing a spot from the Cluster system and moving the transceiver instantly to the frequency. But nowadays the level of interaction between PC and transceiver can be very much more than this, to the extent that several transceiver models can be remotely controlled in every respect over the Internet. This is ideal, of course, for anyone wanting to set up their station at, say, a remote rural location but operate it from their suburban home. There is more on remote operation later in this chapter.

In the last few years, the development of software defined radio (SDR) has really taken off, where, in simple terms, a high-performance soundcard in the PC provides the signal processing capabilities and the hardware SDR 'box' the RF amplification.

THE INTERNET

In many ways the real revolution has come through networking, especially in the context of the Internet. As in almost every other area of life, the Internet has opened up a plethora of opportunities for amateur radio, and new ideas are coming along all the time. As well as being an almost universal source of information, from circuit designs, equipment reviews, contest rules, and pretty much anything else you might need, the Internet's ubiquity allows many interactive applications which can enhance the pleasure of our hobby. The subject is one which could fill a book in its own right, so it is easiest here just to give a few examples.

Log keeping again comes to the fore. Many DXpeditions have taken to posting their logs on the Internet in something close to real-time, which has become very popular with DX chasers. In this case, the complete log with date and time is rarely if ever uploaded, but rather just the band and mode on which a contact has taken place. This allows the DXer to know that his QSO is a 'good' one and that the DX station has indeed copied (and logged, with no typing errors) his callsign correctly, thus dispelling the need to make an 'insurance' contact on the same band and / or mode.

Most contest organisers now encourage submission of contest logs via the Internet, for speed, security (logs are less likely to go astray than in the international postal system) and also because electronic logs lend themselves to computerised log-checking, speeding up and improving contest adjudication whilst reducing the burden of manual log checking. And for awards purposes the advent of the ARRL's *Logbook of the World* (LoTW) has already had a huge impact. Amateurs will undoubtedly still wish to collect traditional QSL cards, but will no longer have to subject them to the vagaries of the postal service in order to claim awards.

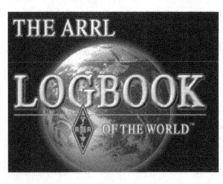

LoTW makes it unnecessary to submit physical QSL cards when applying for awards such as DXCC.

There have been several instances where contest stations have linked their logs directly over the Internet, the best example being in the annual IARU HF Championship, where each IARU member society is encouraged to run an HQ station which others can work for multipliers. There is no rule requiring this HQ station to be confined to a single site and it has become common practice to host different bands at different well-equipped contest stations around a country, and then link their logs by Internet so that each band position has access to the full HQ station log. It does not take too much of a leap of the imagination to see some contest organisers encouraging events in which all entrants are linked in some way, with running scores available in real-time. Amateur radio contesting would then become much more like other spectator sports, perhaps with non-participants logging on to see how the leaders are doing in the same way as watching a road race.

In those countries where the authorities allow linking of Internet and amateur radio, other possibilities emerge. This happened some years ago with the PacketCluster system, where European and North American Cluster networks, operating over VHF, UHF and microwave links, were linked across the Atlantic via a terrestrial data connection. Nowadays most Cluster nodes have an Internet connection as well as VHF / UHF access, and amateurs can access the system via a web interface or a Telnet session.

The development of VoIP (Voice over Internet Protocol) has allowed VHF and UHF nodes and voice repeaters to be linked together over the Internet making it possible, for example, for an amateur in California using a 2m handheld transceiver to talk with an amateur in the UK using a similar transceiver on, say, 70cm. See the chapters on repeaters and operating modes for more on this topic. To the purists this isn't amateur radio in the truest sense, but it is an interesting marrying of two technologies and, of course, relies on the amateur licensing system to permit a radio link at one or both ends of the connection.

TYPICAL STATION CONFIGURATION

Before discussing some of the uses of the PC in more detail, it is helpful to look at what a typical modern station configuration might be. **Fig 1** is illustrative only, and every station will have different requirements. Although the diagram looks complex it is by no means at the limits of what might be found in, for example, a state of the art expedition or multi-multi contest station. In fact, for single-operator two-radio contesting, the configuration would be rather more complex!

What is immediately apparent in Fig 1 is the large number of interfaces to and from the PC. Indeed, this is where the bottleneck was in the early years, with limited serial and parallel ports on most early computers. Nowadays that is really no longer an issue, the bigger problem being how to avoid earth loops and other EMC-type problems with all these interconnecting cables in a high-RF environment. Several items of equipment can be connected wirelessly, removing the need for wires and connectors and reducing the EMC hazards. Obviously the PC will have some sort of Internet connection, to gather information (Cluster spots, etc) and to dis-

Fig 1: A typical basic station set-up, showing how PC and other equipment are linked. There may also be a VHF radio and, perhaps, interfaces to antenna rotators and similar devices. A slightly more complex system might include a router and other computers as well as an Internet connection.

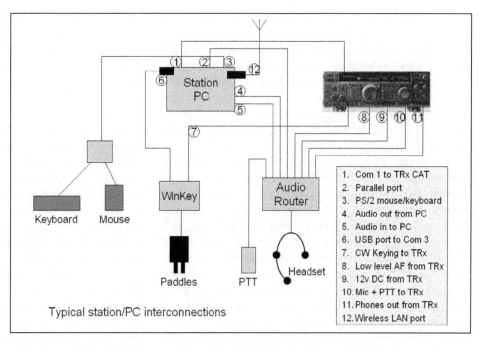

1. Com 1 to TRx CAT
2. Parallel port
3. PS/2 mouse/keyboard
4. Audio out from PC
5. Audio in to PC
6. USB port to Com 3
7. CW Keying to TRx
8. Low level AF from TRx
9. 12v DC from TRx
10. Mic + PTT to TRx
11. Phones out from TRx
12. Wireless LAN port

Typical station/PC interconnections

tribute information (sending logs, Cluster uploads, WSPR spots etc). There is likely to be a data link (RS-232 / CAT / CI-V) to the PC, for both-way sharing of frequency information, mode, maybe even data such as filters in use. There will be audio interfaces, for sending audio to the transceiver (CQ calls, etc for voice modes, tones for data modes) and for receiving audio from the transceiver (for recording voice and CW transmissions, for decoding data mode transmissions).

There may be a connection to the transceiver for direct FSK keying for data modes (not shown in the diagram, where it is assumed the interface will be an audio one). There may be interfaces to other, ancillary equipment, such as an antenna rotator, antenna switches and audio router (used to switch audio sources such as microphone and soundcard, and audio destinations such as soundcard and transceiver microphone input, depending on the mode in use). For CW, the computer will typically be used to generate standard messages and to produce transmitted text from keyboard input. Most CW operators still prefer to copy CW by ear, but many programs exist to decode received CW, although they usually fall down in the face of significant amounts of interference.

It is now relatively simple to network several computers using cables or wirelessly, allowing each device to be dedicated to a different application or group of applications, eg data modes, logging or controlling a software defined radio.

CHOOSING A PC FOR THE SHACK

What features do you need to look for in a PC for the shack? Any modern Windows-based PC (desktop, laptop or notebook) will run the sort of software you are likely to want to use in your day-to-day radio activities. There are also some amateur radio programs designed for computers running Unix or Mac operating systems and for the smaller 'smart' devices - phones and and tablets. More on these later.

One difficulty that may be encountered is that some of the popular programs intended for amateur radio use were written in the days of DOS-based PCs, and have not been fully migrated to the Windows operating system. The earlier operating systems were able to interact directly with the external hardware, which makes real-time activities such as generating CW relatively straightforward. Windows sits between the application and the hardware, deciding when each process can have its share of CPU time. As a result, when running multiple applications, CW can end up sounding distorted with erratic timing. Problems can also occur with other early programs, for example for RTTY or Packet. Similarly, some programs written for 16-bit versions of Windows may not be compatible with modern 32- and 64-bit operating systems.

As a result, some amateurs quite deliberately use an older PC in their shack, perhaps a previous-generation family PC that is no longer required. Others take the alternative route of using a modern PC, and discarding their earlier software, using only software that has been developed specifically for the up-to-date operating system. A third approach involves using a modern computer with some software that emulates an older PC. This can be useful but often throws up more problems than it solves.

In any case, there will be certain requirements for a PC that is to be of use for the various applications described in this chapter.

Let's look firstly at interfacing to the outside world. Is a network or direct Internet connection required? If so then you will need a telephone modem, Ethernet port or wi-fi adaptor. Maybe, as well as Internet, you want to interface to a Packet modem, en route to a VHF transceiver for packet radio, including PacketCluster access, which will probably require a serial (RS232) interface. Then there is an interface to the transceiver for band data, which may also require a serial port. Many programs allow you to use either a serial port or a parallel (printer) port for CW keying.

For data modes, you will need a soundcard, the transceiver interface being by way of the microphone input and sound output connections to that card. One way or another, it is easy to run out of ports, especially serial ports. There are add-in cards available for desktop PCs, to allow extra serial ports, though you will then need to consider addressing the various ports to avoid conflicts. Some of the earlier logging programs only recognised Com1 and Com2, but most can now be configured to Com3 and Com4 as well. Older laptop computers often come with only one serial port, but PCMCIA to serial port adaptors are available.

Many modern PCs, however, have moved away from serial ports entirely, and offer only USB ports. All is not lost, as USB to serial adaptors are available from most PC suppliers, and some amateur radio suppliers are now offering interface boxes for data communications and logging which are specifically designed to work with a USB interface. An advantage of USB is that expansion adapters are available to provide several ports from a single USB output, the best adapters being the ones that include their own power supply. The latest transceivers, rotators and other shack equipment are now equipped with USB interfaces, reflecting this overall trend.

One of the biggest challenges you will face in interfacing the PC to your radio equipment is simply that, with so many separate interfaces to be made, there is huge potential for earth loops, resulting in hum on your transmitted audio, and for RF from your transmitter getting into the PC and causing (potentially catastrophic) problems. There is no simple answer to this. The use of one common station earth, decoupling leads and installing ferrite beads on every line will help. You should also take care in the orientation of leads, keeping audio leads well clear of RF leads, for example. Network cables are notorious for RF pickup, and wi-fi appears to be a more reliable alternative for networking in the shack. Audio circuits (eg from soundcard to transceiver) should usually be routed through isolating transformers or opto-couplers to permit various earthing points to be isolated from one another, avoiding earth loops. There is more on this in Chapter 8.

Many amateurs believe the ideal solution is to use a laptop PC. The self-contained nature of these, and the rigorous EMC standards they must meet because they may be used in aircraft and other critical environments, means that generally they are far less likely than desktop PCs either to generate

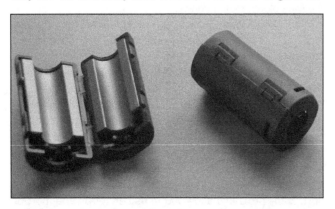

The use of clip-on ferrite chokes is recommended to reduce or eliminate interference from laptop PC's switched-mode power supplies.

interference, or themselves be affected by RF. Most will, of course, accept a full-size keyboard and external mouse and, indeed, an external monitor, though as soon as you start adding these peripherals there is a risk of the very problems starting to re-emerge that you selected the laptop to avoid.

Incidentally, some older PC monitors were particularly bad at generating spurious emissions which can affect your reception of amateur signals. Modern TFT screens are a welcome step forward in this respect.

Another common source of problems is the switch-mode power supply and here laptops seem to be more of a problem than desktop computers, because the power supplies are generally smaller and less well screened. Liberal use of clip-on ferrite chokes is recommended or, in the extreme, replacing the switch-mode PSU with a traditional linear power supply for use in the shack.

One other benefit of a laptop, as against a desktop PC, is that it will have internal batteries, useful if the power goes down. Some amateurs solve this problem by having an uninterruptible power supply (UPS) in the shack. A good one will also provide enough capacity to keep your transceiver on the air for an hour or two as well, maybe enough to finish that midweek contest while the rest of the family sit in darkness!

In contrast, the benefit of a desktop PC is that you can add additional cards, as required, for example, a terminal card for data modes. Nowadays, it is possible to add a complete transceiver with all the interfacing being done by mouse and keyboard through suitable control software, though the limitations on current from the PC's power supply and on power dissipation on a PCI card mean that any power amplifier will have to be external to the PC.

STATION MANAGEMENT BY PC

Programs that used to be termed 'logging' are now better described as 'station management'. While logging is the underlying function, most do very much more than this. There may be a number of underlying databases in addition to the log itself (or, more accurately, the logs themselves, as many amateurs keep several logs, perhaps for expeditions they have undertaken, or other callsigns they hold), for example, a database of IOTA islands, one for DXCC entities, several 'name' databases for club members, previously-worked stations, etc, and whatever else is appropriate to the operator's specific interests. Above these databases sits the management program, through which the operator can undertake a huge range of functions, of which logging contacts is just one.

It is possible that a large percentage of QSOs may not be logged through the main station management program at all. For example, because most contests have unique rules, there is no universal contest logging program. The popular contest logging programs cater for the most popular events (CQ WW, ARRL, IARU, etc). But specialist contest logging programs have been developed for other events, those for the RSGB IOTA Contest, European Sprint Contests and the ARI (Italian) contest being good examples. These handle the QSO data requirements and the unique scoring system for the contests concerned. However, nowadays there is a standardisation of data formats which allows data to be exported and imported easily between programs. So, usually, logs generated by another program can be imported to your main station management program for later manipulation. That manipulation may be the generation of statistics ("how many countries have I worked on each band this year?"), the processing of QSL requests including the printing of labels or perhaps award handling (for example generating a file of recently-confirmed IOTA islands, which can then be used as a basis for the annual update).

As well as data manipulation, the logging program will almost certainly handle the interfacing to your transceiver(s), and probably most of the other interfaces described in the previous section. It will provide useful data as you tune around the bands (beam heading, sunrise and sunset times for stations heard and worked). It may well have built-in maps and / or propagation charts or interface seamlessly to other programs which handle these functions. It may work with online or CD-based callbooks to allow you to access addresses of stations worked or their QSL managers. It will almost certainly allow you to see Cluster spots, either off-air or from the Internet, identify whether, for example, they are for a new country and allow you to move your transceiver to the frequency of the spot with a single mouse click or press of a function key. Some can be configured to send an alert to a handheld VHF transceiver if a 'new one' appears, so you needn't miss the DX even when you're in the garden! The program will no doubt handle the other data provided by the Cluster network (WWV, Announces and Talks, etc) in both directions. It will probably allow you to generate and send off an update to your *Logbook of The World* submission. And it will almost certainly handle the data modes for you, either in itself or by way of an integrated interface to another program (for example, many station management programs hand off RTTY to the popular *MMTTY* program on the basis of "why reinvent the wheel?"). This, in fact, is the real clue as to how station management programs will continue to evolve in future. As soon as a new idea or application comes along (new data mode, *LoTW*, etc), it is likely to be served in the first instance by some sort of stand-alone program. But very quickly it will be brought into overall station management, either by integrating with one of those stand-alone programs or by writing new code within the station management program itself.

Of course, you may not choose to go the route of having everything integrated at this level. You may decide to mix and match, to find the best program for each individual requirement. For instance, you may use a popular station management program for everyday logging, awards tracking, QSLing and analysis, but for contest logging a variety of programs, according to the particular contest. After the contest, the program should be able to import the log into the main station log. With the adoption of Cabrillo as the format for most contest entries and of ADIF as an interchange format between logging programs, it is almost certain nowadays that any program will be able to export one or both of these, and any good station management program will be able to import the result, so there should be no problem.

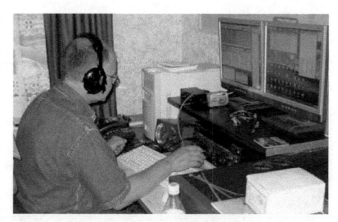

Using two monitors to display all the required windows. Here G4RCG is operating from the station of G3LZQ.

In a contest environment it may be useful to have a second PC running *Geoclock* or some similar program, showing a map of the world with the daylight / darkness split. Of course, this could run on the logging PC, but it is very easy for the screen to become so 'busy' that it is hard to keep track of what is going on. It may be useful to supplement the main station computer with a small network of cheap second-hand PCs. Alternatively, it is possible to run one computer but with two screens with, for example, data modes software running on one screen and other useful station management windows open on the second screen.

Regardless of whether the applications are integrated into a single station management program, or quite separate, there are certain attributes that you, the user, will want to look for when selecting suitable software for your shack. The following sections look at each of the main applications in turn.

Station Logging

The UK licence no longer requires the licensee to keep a log, except in certain specific circumstances (see Chapter 2), and there will be those amateurs who go on the air but who do not bother to log their contacts. However, a majority of active operators will want to keep a log for their own interest, even if it is not a legal requirement.

Over and above the basics of date, time, frequency band, mode, etc, you will no doubt want to be able to enter additional data, such as name, location, QSL sent and received, and so on.

Then, as has already been described, there are the interfaces to radio and PC, perhaps to external databases, and useful additional features, either directly or by way of integration to other programs. And, of course, the ability to import and export data, especially via the Cabrillo and ADIF formats.

Beyond that, selection of a logging program is very much a matter of personal preference. For instance, you might prefer a logging screen that shows the last 10 contacts or thereabouts, with those and the QSO entry field looking very similar to a line in a conventional logbook. Not all logging programs take this approach. Some use pop-up windows for QSO entry, for example.

Mark	Date	Time on	Callsign	Freq	Mode	RST se	RST rc	Name	QTH	IOTA	QSL sent	QSL rcvd	DXCC	CQ z	State	LoTW
	04/01/2015	14:50	M1MST	28.000	SSB	59	59						223	14		
	28/03/2015	21:04	M3BNN	28.500	SSB	59	59						223	14		
	08/01/2015	16:16	M3DFW	28.000	SSB	57	59						223	14		
	29/03/2015	12:31	M3DFW	21.200	SSB	59	59						223	14		
	08/01/2015	15:55	M3IFG	28.000	SSB	58	59	Frank	Nr Manchester				223	14		
	09/01/2015	15:47	M3NFL	28.000	SSB	55	59	Neil					223	14		
	29/03/2015	21:25	M3NFL	21.200	SSB	59	59						223	14		
	09/01/2015	15:07	M3SMK	28.000	SSB	57	59	Stewart	Manchester				223	14		
	29/03/2015	13:21	M4D	21.200	SSB	59	59						223	14		
	29/03/2015	22:42	M4D	7.100	SSB	59	59						223	14		
	28/03/2015	12:11	M4U	28.500	SSB	59	59						223	14		
	08/01/2015	16:24	M5CBS	28.000	SSB	56	57	Mike	Swindon				223	14		
	21/03/2015	16:04	M5E	28.400	SSB	59	59						223	14		
	28/03/2015	01:40	M5E	14.200	SSB	59	59						223	14		
	28/03/2015	15:58	M5E	28.500	SSB	59	59						223	14		
	26/01/2015	14:58	M5GUS	18.068	SSB	55	59	Gus	Truro				223	14		

Territory: England
Name: Gus
QTH: Truro

Notes:
<EMPTY>

The AALog main logging screen. This station logging program developed in Russia by Alexander Anipkin, RZ4AG, is one of the more simple to configure, yet allows tracking of a number of awards, QSLing functions and the import and export of files in various formats. The log can be sorted by date, band, mode or - as here - alphabetically by station worked.

Look out for potential problems with callsign entry. A station operating as G3XDV/VP9 might not be recognised as a Bermuda callsign as some logging programs will only do so if the callsign is (incorrectly) entered as VP9/G3XDV. Some logging programs have callsign fields which are too short for some perfectly valid amateur callsigns. The advent of much longer callsigns for temporary special event stations means that we are now faced with callsigns that are maybe 15 characters long, whereas some logging programs accept as few as 10 characters in the callsign field.

Another aspect to bear in mind is that not all logging programs recognise all amateur bands. Some are designed primarily for HF use, some specifically for VHF use. Even those covering all bands may not, for example, recognise the 70MHz or 136kHz bands, given that they are only available in certain countries. Neither will all programs offer the sort of facilities you may want for, say, satellite, meteor scatter or moonbounce (EME) operation, where you may need to record cross-band operation or specialist types of signal reporting.

Similarly, your choice of logging program may be influenced by specific awards you like to chase. Most logging programs will track DXCC entities, and have fields for common data such as locator and IOTA reference. Others will have general purpose index fields where you can log state, county, etc.

The other requirement which can be important is to be able to have several log files for different callsigns (G3XDV, GJ3XDV, G3XDV/VP9, etc). Be aware that not all logging programs allow this, or you may need to pay an additional registration fee for each callsign.

For the reasons described above, some programs generate CW themselves but others, recognising that Windows can adversely affect CW timing, support an interface to an external keyer. Some for example, offer support for the increasingly popular WinKey kit from K1EL, others for proprietary keyers.

Some station logging programs also offer contest logging facilities (see below), which are in some cases quite comprehensive. Others feature simply the ability to track serial numbers and generate a Cabrillo file but without scoring

capabilities. Whether the facilities will meet your requirements will depend on how serious a contester you are, and which contests you like to enter.

It's really a case of checking out the various programs to see which best suits your particular needs. The good news is that most can be tried out free of charge. Usually this is done by imposing a limitation on the numbers of contacts that can be logged. When you pay the registration fee, you are issued with a password which opens up the program to unlimited use.

Contest Logging

Contest logging programs came into widespread use even before station logging programs as contests lend themselves well to computer support. Before this, contesters were faced with a lot of complex tasks even while the contest was in progress, the best example being the need to keep real-time 'dupe' (duplicate) sheets, to avoid calling the same station a second time on any particular band. With serious contesters making maybe 3000 QSOs or more in a weekend, this was a nightmare. Then there was the further nightmare after the contest of having to make a copy of the log, in whatever format the organisers required, along with scoring the whole thing. Using a computer for these labour-intensive routine tasks frees up the operator(s) for the actual operating, thinking about strategy, and other added value activities.

Contest logging programs normally dispense with the peripheral facilities offered by station logging programs (awards tracking, QSL management, etc) to focus on the aspects you will need specifically for contesting. A good place to start is the SD ('Super Duper') suite of contesting programs developed by EI5DI [2], very much with RSGB contests in mind. The programs handle logging (of course!), scoring for all RSGB events and many of the major international contests (CQ WW, ARRL, etc), Check Partial and Super Check Partial (ie checking a partial call against QSOs you have already made and, with Super Check Partial, checking a partial call against a database of tens of thousand of active contester callsigns), and CW keying both direct from the program itself and also via an external *WinKey*. There is, of course, an interface to the radio for capturing frequency information. The program allows editing and rescoring after the contest (sometimes it's quicker just to make paper notes during a contest if you have mistyped something, for example, and fix it later) and, of course, generation of the required files for the actual submission.

Interestingly, the *SD* approach is to have different programs for HF (*SD*) and VHF contests (*SDV*). The popular *Writelog* takes a slightly different approach which is to have core code and a published API (Application Programmers Interface) so that third parties can write add-ons to support a wide range of contests.

SD is essentially designed for the single-operator and, like some other programs, offers full support for SO2R (single-op, two radio). Other contest programs have facilities for networking to allow multi-operator contesting with multiple transmitters and hence multiple PCs. In some cases the networking is via IP, so there is nothing to prevent those multiple PCs being scattered throughout the country (or even the world!).

In recent years GR2HQ (formerly GB7HQ), the RSGB HQ station in the IARU contest, has operated from sites throughout the British Isles. All the stations have been connected through the Internet using a bespoke program called the *StarSoftware* DXpedition management suite [3] (originally developed for the Five Star DXers Association D68C Comoros Islands DXpedition). The main server, known as *StarServer* - the application that does all the work - was located at *StarLog* 'Mission Control Centre' at the station of G3WGV, in Cumbria, even though none of the transmitting stations was at that location.

A feature that many operators look for is full integration with the Cluster network, to allow the acquisition of Cluster spots, with one-key QSY to work a multiplier that appears on the Cluster network.

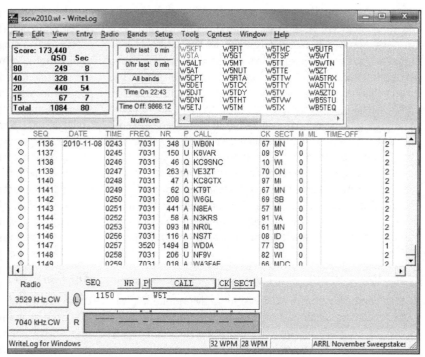

The main screen of the *Writelog* contest logging program.

Some contest programs have been developed for specific contests, an example being the program developed by DL2NBU to support the European Sprint contests. This is a case where the contest format is slightly unusual and it was important for the organisers to ensure that a suitable program was available in order to make participation as easy as possible. Another example of a specialist contest format is the Worked All Europe contest, with its concept of exchanging QTCs (data from previous contacts).

Contesters will have their favourite programs, and are generally reluctant to change as some of these programs require a fairly steep learning curve (preferably before the contest rather than during it!) In some cases the contest rules will suggest certain programs which fully support that contest, in other cases it is a matter of making enquiries, for

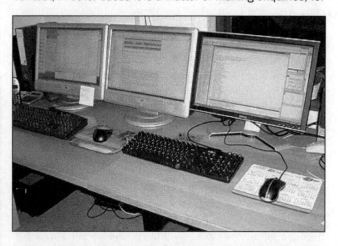

G3WGV's *StarLog* Mission Control station for GB7HQ in 2008. Two computers are driving three 20" wide screen displays. Everything is on a large UPS (bottom left) which keeps the ensemble going for about two hours without mains power.

Using *SD* in a CW contest. EI5DI's '*Super Duper*' suite of contest logging programs has proved very popular.

example via one of the contest reflectors on the Internet, to see what other contesters recommend. Given the ability to interface some contesting programs to the Internet, it is interesting to speculate where this will lead. It is quite possible that serious entrants to some contests may be required to have a permanent connection open, with scores updated and published as the contest proceeds and your score at the moment the contest finishes deemed to be final.

Already, of course, the fact that by far the majority of contest entries are submitted in standard electronic format means that the adjudicators can themselves use a variety of software tools to aid in crosschecking and the compilation of final scores. This makes the creation of results timelier and more accurate, while relieving the adjudicators of the chore of manually checking many tens or hundreds of thousands of QSOs.

QSLing

QSLing can easily become a chore for active amateurs, with lots of incoming cards that aren't always wanted. But it is a matter of courtesy to reply, as many will be from newly-licensed amateurs who are keen for a card. After all, we were all there once upon a time. The availability of software to handle QSL management makes the whole process a lot easier. After all, the QSO details are already in your log, so it's then just a case of indicating which ones you need printed out for QSLing. Many logging programs have the facility built in, but here are also some popular stand-alone programs including *BV* by DF3CB. Most of these allow multiple QSOs to be printed to labels for sticking on to your standard QSLcard, and will usually print them ready sorted into alphabetical order so that there is no more work to do before dropping them in the mail to the QSL bureau. Typically there will be features such as printing cards separately for direct and bureau QSLing, options to print immediately or later, options to QSL other contacts with the same station and, of course, options to print to various size labels, either single or multiple contacts.

Related to QSLing, it is worth mentioning here that files for both *eQSL* and *Logbook of The World* (see Chapter 10) can be generated from ADIF files, so most logging programs can handle these without difficulty. Some logging programs provide full integration with LoTW, so that they will also track the credits you already have for your various DXCC awards, downloading this information from your *LoTW* record.

Awards Tracking

As has already been mentioned, most logging programs will keep track of DXCC entities worked as a matter of course, along with data for other popular awards. The matter of identifying a DXCC entity isn't entirely straightforward, of course. No logging program knows automatically where an E51, FO, VP8 or even a GB station is located, as examples, because all of these country prefixes are used for multiple DXCC entities. But once you allocate a callsign to a specific entity, the logging program will track it. It is worth noting that, for this purpose, most logging programs use a unique 'country number' as the identifier. The ARRL has introduced

country identifiers for *LoTW* purposes, and these have now become the *de facto* standard for logging programs.

There is no single way for logging programs to track other awards data. Some have general purpose index fields which you can use for various purposes. For example, *TurboLog* [4], popular in the UK, allows you to use the same index file for several purposes: "S-PA" would indicate "State, Pennsylvania", while "OC-001" would be recognised as a valid IOTA reference. You can then sort and output the various data according to the relevant identifier. Some programs are specifically designed to cater for individual awards programs, US county hunting for example. If you have a favourite award that you follow, it is worth seeing which program suits it best. *TurboLog*, for example, also has the capability of generating your annual update file for the IOTA awards and tracking those island groups you already have credited.

Rig Control

There are many transceiver control programs available and, again, most station and contest logging programs allow at least basic data (frequency, in both directions) to be exchanged with the popular transceivers. Specialist programs go much further, allowing you to control a very wide range of parameters, storing your favourite settings and memory frequencies, etc. This opens up a whole range of new opportunities to control your transceiver remotely from the comfort of your armchair while the rig is in an outdoor shack or, more significantly, remotely across the Internet (see later in this chapter).

CW Generation and Decoding

Mention has already been made of the issues surrounding the generation of good-quality CW under various operating systems. The solution increasingly being adopted is the use of an external CW keyer, such as the popular and inexpensive *WinKey* by K1EL. Such keyers work as stand-alone keyers in their own right or can act on behalf of the logging program, responding to input from keyboard, stored messages associated with function keys, etc.

The inexpensive *WinKey* external keyer kits are popular for generating accurate CW from a computer.

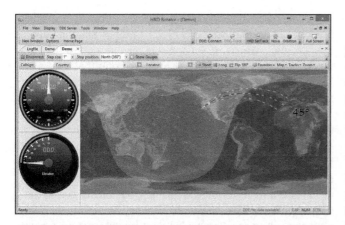

Rotator from Ham Radio Deluxe can steer an antenna to a given location. Elevation control is included so the program can integrate with satellite tracking software.

With some programs, you can even choose to send Morse with your paddle and the PC captures the callsign directly into the logging program. This only works if your code is accurate, of course!

There are many programs for receiving CW, though none has yet reached the capability of a good human operator. Most require clear, well sent CW, without interference from noise or other signals. Nevertheless, some software writers have experimented, with a degree of success, in developing programs which will run a CW contest entirely without operator intervention!

Data Modes, Including SSTV

Data modes software falls into various categories. On HF, the most popular modes nowadays are RTTY (emulating the mechanical teleprinters of old), *PSK31* and *WSPR*, though *PacTOR*, *MFSK*, *Clover*, *PSK63*, *Opera* and many others are also to be found. There are programs available to support all of these, from basic terminal emulators to full-featured data programs with waterfall displays for tuning, logging facilities and, for RTTY, contesting programs which also provide the features required by the major RTTY contests. A popular RTTY program is *MMTTY* by JE3HHT; this can be used standalone, but the interface specification is available to allow it to be integrated into other logging packages (as several do).

Apart from packet radio, VHF data modes software tends to focus on specialist weak signal applications, such as meteor scatter and moonbounce. Best known is the WSJT suite of programs ('Weak Signal' by K1JT), including *FSK441* and *JT6M* for meteor scatter (the latter optimised for 6m use), *JT65* for EME and extreme troposcatter, and *EME Echo* for checking your own return path to the Moon.

Several SSTV programs are available, including *MMSSTV* from the same stable as *MMTTY*.

The whole topic of data modes is covered in much more detail in Chapter 8.

Databases

Many logging programs have facilities for accessing external databases, either resident on your hard disc, on CD or via the Internet. Local examples might include a club membership list, giving a ready *aide mémoire* of names and locations. Or you might have one of the popular CDs holding a national or international callbook. Via the Internet you might want to access addresses or QSL information, for example via the popular qrz.com site. Some programs allow you to enter a callsign and the search a number of these resources sequentially to find the data you are looking for.

Peripheral Control

Nowadays there is scope for controlling a wide range of station peripherals via your PC. Examples include your antenna rotator and remote antenna switches. Software is available that will control the azimuth and elevation rotators of satellite antennas to track the satellite of choice, and for moonbounce similar software can be used to track the Moon.

Some software will control external audio switching devices to route microphone, soundcard, etc to transceiver, back to soundcard, etc. For example, when a CQ message is being pre-recorded you would want your microphone routed to the soundcard, whereas when operating phone you would want it routed direct to the transceiver. But when you then want to use the recorded CQ, you would want the soundcard output directed to the microphone input. Commercial switching devices are available to undertake this role.

DSP

Just as our transceivers often feature DSP, so it is also possible to have software on your PC which will take audio, via the soundcard, and act on it with whatever software-defined filter characteristics you have chosen. For instance, you might want to work on some recorded QSOs, to improve their clarity. Another use for software of this kind is in displaying very low-speed CW (QRSS) signals, for example. There are many suitable programs available, the most comprehensive being *Spectrum Laboratory* (*SpecLab*) [5].

INTERNET APPLICATIONS

The preceding discussion has focused on the sort of applications you may want to run locally on your shack PC. But, as has already been pointed out, this is only part of the story. The Internet takes the value of your PC to a whole new level, opening up a huge range of opportunities for data access, especially now that broadband 'always-on' acess is commonplace. Some examples are communication with other like-minded amateurs, posting Cluster spots, and viewing maps. This section will cover some of the broad areas in which the Internet can be useful, but you will only discover the ways in which it will benefit you when you start to explore it yourself.

Cluster Access

For many DXers and contesters, the great benefit of the Internet is in offering real-time access to the Cluster network (formerly PacketCluster). The Internet provides a more reliable link into the Cluster network then when a VHF packet link was used.

There are two ways of seeing Cluster information. One is via one of the many web pages which collect that information

DX Summit displays Cluster spots in your web browser.

```
Telnet cluster.cdxc.org.uk
14255.0  JW/M1ACB   15-Jul-2015 1655Z                         <M0NKR>
24901.2  LU1VT      15-Jul-2015 1655Z                         <DF5AU>
14141.0  UA4VDV     15-Jul-2015 1655Z  tu                     <RX3DLH>
7161.0   EA5RCK     15-Jul-2015 1655Z                         <EC7TL>
14244.0  PA1H/P     15-Jul-2015 1655Z  paff-088               <EA4SE>
7065.0   AM410DCU   15-Jul-2015 1654Z  10 Aniversario EURAO   <EA4AMQ>
14038.0  W5MPZ      15-Jul-2015 1654Z  Trinity Site 70 yrs    <W5CBP>
7067.0   EA4EQ      15-Jul-2015 1654Z  D.Pueblos de España    <EA1HQ>
14255.0  JW/M1ACB   15-Jul-2015 1654Z  Svalbard EU-026        <M0BLF>
14003.0  CR6R       15-Jul-2015 1654Z  iota  eu-167           <EA1DRL>
50125.0  W7GNE      15-Jul-2015 1653Z  DM43>DN27              <W7GJ>
14085.0  PD5SS      15-Jul-2015 1653Z  RTTY                   <IK8GVS>
7065.0   AM410DCU   15-Jul-2015 1653Z  10 Aniversario EURAO   <EA4AMQ>
28090.0  LU9DPT     15-Jul-2015 1653Z  RTTY CQ CQ SUMER FRIENDS RAS<LW6DLS>
14226.0  OH5C/P     15-Jul-2015 1653Z  TNX QSO                <F4ESV>
14215.0  9M2TO      15-Jul-2015 1652Z  splx wkd 100W only gud prop <ON8ON>
14170.0  CT7/F8BBL  15-Jul-2015 1652Z  LAURENT NR PORTO       <DF5QF>
14226.0  OH5C       15-Jul-2015 1652Z  tnx fer qso            <HB9FUX>
14244.0  PA1H/P     15-Jul-2015 1652Z  PAFF-088               <EA5HOX>
14011.9  RN3ZDD     15-Jul-2015 1652Z  CQ                     <VE7SV>
10123.2  SP0WFF     15-Jul-2015 1652Z                         <IZ2QXG>
21020.0  PP5BK      15-Jul-2015 1652Z                         <HA6VH>
10108.0  UE4OSA     15-Jul-2015 1651Z  tnx QSO                <UY0TF>
14070.6  ON15BWP/P  15-Jul-2015 1652Z  tnx QSO                <F4BAL>
18071.0  JW/M0VFC   15-Jul-2015 1652Z  1st call vibroplex 1947 fb o <F8DGY>
```

Accessing the Cluster by _Telnet_.

from around the world and bring it together into one place. The best-known is undoubtedly _DX Summit_ [6], now operated by the OH8X 'Radio Arcala' team. Anyone can access sites such as this, of course, and you can input data to the system too, whether you are a licensed amateur or an SWL.

The alternative, offering exactly the same interactive capabilities as if you were connecting via packet radio, is to use _Telnet_ access. _Telnet_ is a communications program that comes bundled with your PC's operating system and, in this case, allows you to connect to any Cluster node throughout the world that has a suitable Internet interface. You will be asked to log on to the Cluster node with your amateur radio callsign, in the usual way. In practice, most amateurs will access Cluster over the Internet either through a _Telnet_ client bundled with their logging program or through a program such as _DX Telnet_ which has been developed for amateur use, and can be downloaded from the Internet (there is a charge). It is designed specifically to handle the various commands and information associated with the Cluster network.

Newsgroups and Reflectors

There are many discussion groups and reflectors on the Internet of interest to radio amateurs. They deal with specific manufacturer's equipment, including possible modifications,

as well as contesting and DXing, popular software, operating modes, bands and specialisations (meteor scatter, moonbounce, etc). Whatever your particular interests within the hobby, there will be a reflector or newsgroup that caters for it, and maybe several. Some are geographically-based but most are of universal appeal.

While some would regret that since our hobby is about communications, using the Internet to communicate with other amateurs is a retrograde step, others would argue that having this extensive access to other amateurs actually stimulates the hobby. For example, if your transceiver has developed a fault, or you are having trouble configuring that weak-signal software, there will be many amateurs out there able and willing to help who, without the Internet, you might never come across. Users of new modes or the less active bands (eg microwave or LF) will find opportunities for skeds, and newcomers can soak up information and ask advice from experienced operators

News Bulletins

Related to the above, there are many newsletters and bulletins you can subscribe to, some free and some for which you have to pay. In Chapter 9, reference is made to some of the DX bulletins which are available, but there are subscription services for awards information, QSL information, and much more. Indeed, any subject that might have spawned a printed magazine or newsletter in the past will almost certainly have an electronic equivalent nowadays.

Club Log

Club Log [7] is a free, web-based application by Michael Wells, G7VJR, that uses a large database to analyse amateur radio log files, which are uploaded by DXers all over the world. The idea of _Club Log_ is to produce statistics from this combined resource of information in a clear and flexible interface that DXers will find useful. There is a great deal of information that can be mined and analysed in a standard ADIF file. _Club Log_ offers the following facilities and much more: band-mode league tables, log search tools, DXCC analysis, 'Most Wanted' lists, propagation charts, DX Cluster filtering, QSLing tools, callsign checking and DXpedition log hosting.

The driving principle of _Club Log_ is to store as many contacts as possible, as this makes the reports and statistics more meaningful and representative. Since launching in 2007, _Club Log_ has expanded at great speed, and contains hundreds of millions of QSO records. You can read more and register for a free account on the website [7].

Websites

The worldwide web certainly is ubiquitous. Many individual amateurs have their own web pages, often reflecting their own specialist interests within the hobby. Many clubs and almost all national radio societies have web pages. Both the RSGB and the ARRL, for example, have extensive sites for public consumption, but with further information reserved for paid-up members (for example, offering early access to contest results, equipment reviews, etc). Almost all suppliers

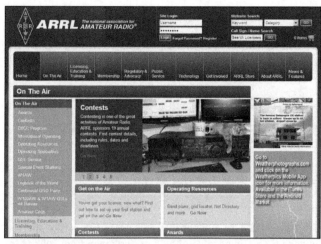

Dave Gould, G3UEG, operating the first fully remote controlled station in the UK.

Both the ARRL and the RSGB have extensive web sites combining much free information with additional material exclusively for their members. The top picture shows the start of the ARRL's operating section, and below that is the RSGB's front page promoting the members-only *RadCom plus* magazine.

of amateur radio equipment and software have web sites. Contest organisers, DXpeditions, special event organisers also have a web presence, as you would expect. Many DXpeditions post logs and pictures while the DXpedition is still in progress. The Internet is also your gateway to the ARRL's *Logbook of The World*, discussed later in Chapter 10.

Obviously there is a huge amount of technical information available if you are interested in home construction, antenna design, propagation studies, etc. There is a vast amount of material that you can download, from published articles, to software, manuals for equipment you have bought second-hand, and so on. And, talking about buying second-hand, there are many sites where you can buy, sell and swap equipment. Truly, if you have a need for it, someone has probably already made it available on the web.

VoIP

The Voice over Internet Protocol, already mentioned, is the means by which amateur radio voice nodes (including some repeaters) are interconnected via the Internet, allowing world-wide communications from low power hand-held and mobile transceivers. VoIP is discussed in more detail in Chapter 13.

Station Remote Control

The technology now exists to operate an amateur radio station remotely over the Internet and many amateurs are already doing so. Such remote operation can be advantageous for those who, for example, have planning restraints at home but may have a weekend house where they can set up more effective antennas. For example, in the USA, Ron Lago, AC7DX, has used a Yaesu FT-1000D transceiver and Henry 3K linear amplifier to an 18-element array on 10m (6-over-6-over-6), a 6-element monobander on 15m, 4-element long-boom Yagis on 17m and 20m, 2-elements on 40m and a 4-square vertical array on 80m, all remotely operated from his condominium in Eugene, Oregon.

In the UK, the licence has, since December 2006, permitted remote control of equipment over the Internet, or by a wireless link (see Chapter 2).

Dave Gould, G3UEG, received special permission to work on remote operation as far back as 1999, and he wrote up his results in a series of articles in *RadCom* [8]. A more recent two-part article by Dave Pick, G3YXM, on remote operation has also been published in *RadCom* [9].

A number of transceivers now have the capability for remote operation specifically built in to the design. and come ready equipped with a suitable interface. A broadband Internet link offers great flexibility and it can usually be left permanently open. The new generation of SDR equipment is also eminently suitable for remote control over the Internet. A receive-only remote station might pose less of a technical challenge, especially when using some data modes.

SOFTWARE-DEFINED RADIO (SDR)

A fairly recent reason to have a computer in the shack is to control a receiver. It has been possible to use computer software to control all the functions of a radio since the late 1990s, giving a much wider range of functions, memories and customisation than are available on a 'conventional' front panel.

Later, the appearance of software defined radios (SDRs) at affordable prices made computer control essential. Although a handful of SDRs are completely self-contained, the vast majority require a PC to provide all of the front panel controls and varying degrees of signal processing.

Software defined radio is a generic term and covers a wide range of receivers - and nowadays some transceivers - where the wideband signal from the antenna is digitised and then processed in software and passed to a computer. The tuning, filtering and demodulation is carried out in software either in the receiver itself or the computer, depending on the sophistication of the receiver's hardware.

It is possible to buy a very cheap SDR on a USB stick, designed to receive broadcast radio and TV stations on a computer, and this might be a useful way to get used to the way an SDR works. However, these are likely to have a low dynamic range - the higher the number of 'bits' per sample at the digitising stage, the greater the dynamic range of the receiver and the better its ability to receive weak signals in the presence of strong ones. More expensive (and better) options are available up to very sophisticated radios such as the Perseus. The cheaper radios will need additional front-end filtering. Given a high-enough sample rate and good rejection of unwanted signals, an SDR can outperform a high-end analogue receiver.

The greatest advantage of a software defined radio is its flexibility. By using the software provided with the radio, or a free program such as *HDSDR*, a front-panel appears on the computer screen. This will include one or more panoramic

The **Afedri SDR is inexpensive and not much larger than a tobacco tin but is capable of high performance from 100kHz to 30MHz once the appropriate front end filters are added.**

displays showing the signals received in the narrow bandwidth of the audio output but also the band either side, perhaps extending a few kilohertz to more than a megahertz depending on the radio. In addition the display shows all of the radio's controls which can be adjusted by using the computer's keyboard and mouse.

The number of modes receivable and the level of customisation of selectivity, gain and AGC is likely to be greater than available on all but the most expensive analogue radios.

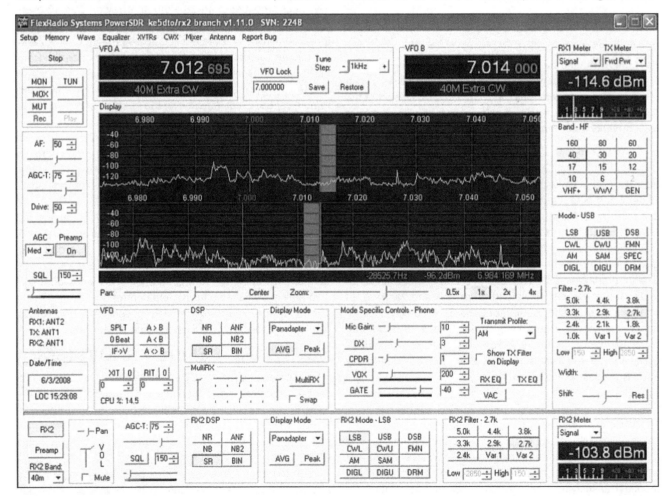

The comprehensive control panel of a FlexRadio software defined radio using the *PowerSDR* software.

The ANAN-100 is a 100W SDR transceiver covering all HF bands and 6 metres.

Additionally it is possible to make a digital recording of not only the audio output but also the full RF bandwidth as well.

SDR transceivers, such as the FlexRadio series, feature wide coverage receivers and either a low power or 100W transmitter.

It is possible to combine the qualities of an SDR receiver with your own transceiver by taking an output at the analogue radio's IF and diverting it to the SDR. Some modern transceivers provide an IF output for that purpose.

CW SKIMMER

CW Skimmer [10] is a an innovative software tool written by Alex Shovkoplyas, VE3NEA, and which was released early in 2008. It uses the processing power of your PC to decode many CW signals in parallel. The simplest way to implement *CW Skimmer* is to connect it to the audio output of your receiver. Full details of how to do this can be found at [11].

However, to get the full benefit of *CW Skimmer*'s facilities, you can connect it to your radio's IF or to an SDR to allow it to 'see' signals over a much larger bandwidth, perhaps the entire CW section of a band.

When decoding CW callsigns, *Skimmer* uses a very sensitive and specialised detection process which is fortified with a list of valid callsign patterns. It uses this to improve its copy of callsigns in the noise. *CW Skimmer* has been demonstrated decoding over 700 signals in parallel!

Uses for Skimmer

CW Skimmer hunts continuously for CQ calls and for stations sending '599'. This information is displayed against the waterfall display as a real-time band plan. *CW Skimmer*'s band plan is linked to the radio with CAT, and any callsign that has been decoded is clickable. DXers will know that hearing a station send '599' is a clue as to the listening frequency of a DX station running split. Clicking on the callsign tunes your radio (via a serial connection) - potentially giving you an edge in the pile-up.

CW Skimmer also has a basic DX Cluster server built in, providing a traditional Telnet interface to access a list of stations heard calling 'CQ' or 'TEST'. Skimmer cleverly uses the comment of the DX spot to tell you the CW speed and signal strength heard. The purpose of providing a DX Cluster server is to allow CW Skimmer to integrate with your logging software or contesting software, which probably already offers Cluster integration.

An alternative and popular use for the built-in cluster is to run a so-called 'reverse beacon', which means sending the spots off to a website so everyone can see what your station is hearing. Check the Reverse Beacon Network (RBN) website [12] and you may be surprised to find your own CQ calls have been picked up by a *Skimmer* station somewhere in the world.

Last but not least, *CW Skimmer* can be used to record all of the CW activity on the band, and can be used later to play

(right) A CW Skimmer display showing a contest, in wideband mode.

(pictured below) CW Skimmer showing a 3kHz wide audio stream

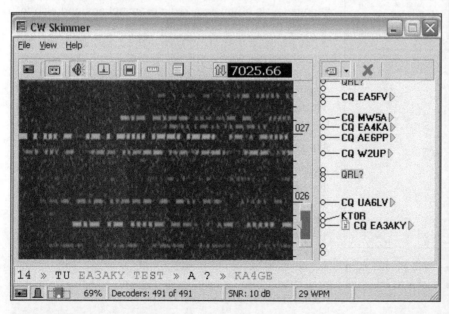

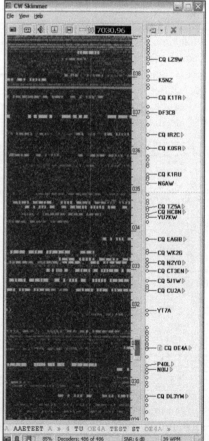

back the entire range of signals heard. One thing to know is that this software is not perfect, so it's good to check everything you hear or see, just as it is with the DX Cluster.

OTHER APPLICATIONS

The other applications you will want to use will vary according to your interests. Antenna modelling and design, terrain modelling in respect of antenna gain and radiation patterns, circuit design and layout, and many others may be applicable. The list is endless, but as this is an operating manual, we will concentrate on those that might be of particular use to those whose main interests lie in radio operating.

Ionspheric Propagation Prediction and Greyline Calculations

There is a huge selection of propagation prediction programs nowadays, though most are based on a handful of propagation prediction 'engines', ie specialist software developed for the purpose. A good example is *IONCAP*, developed initially by the US government and put into the public domain. Various software authors have written user-friendly *Windows*-based front ends for the underlying engine.

Most of the propagation prediction programs available nowadays are very competent, taking account not only of the two ends of a propagation path, but also intermediate reflecting points en route. Beware that propagation forecasting is rather like weather forecasting: anything but an exact science. As most amateurs will know, there are many anomalous events at work in the ionosphere which can enhance or adversely affect a propagation path. Most programs, for example, assume a traditional model for the launch of signals into the ionosphere and for intermediate reflections. But in practice effects such as chordal hop and ionospheric tilting at dawn and dusk can affect this traditional model, leading to unexpected propagation paths. So always use with care.

Greyline propagation and dawn / dusk enhancement on the low bands requires knowledge of sunrise and sunset

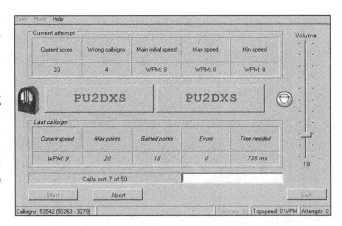

Rufz **CW training program.**

times and the location of the terminator (the boundary between daylight and darkness). Many logging programs calculate sunrise and sunset whenever a prefix is entered. Several programs are available which show a world map, or part thereof, superimposed with the terminator.

Software is also available for beacon monitoring, for example for keeping track of the NCDXF beacon chain on HF or for monitoring beacon transmissions on the VHF bands. Whatever it is you want to do, and whichever beacons you wish to monitor, there is almost certainly software available to do the job.

QSO Recording

With the huge capacity of modern hard discs, it is now quite realistic to record a whole contest, particular DX QSOs of interest, or even every contact you make, especially if you then transfer them to CD. Some logging programs allow you to associate the recording with the QSO details, for easy recall at a later date. The various datacomms programs also offer recording facilities, including capturing images with the SSTV programs.

Training Programs

There are plenty of programs available for preparing for the various levels of amateur radio examinations and also for learning CW. Taking this a stage further, one popular genre of programs is that of QSO simulators, especially for CW. This is an ideal way of building your operating skills, especially contesting skills, away from the cut and thrust of an actual on-air event. The German *Rufz* [13] is a popular CW contest simulator, and there are programs from G4FON [14] and others.

Mapping programs

EI8IC [15] offers, free of charge for home use, a range of on-line maps of the world, with overlays of country prefix, IOTA reference, zone, etc. These are very handy to have available in the shack, especially if you don't have room on the shack wall for a large world map. *DX Atlas* [16] is an excellent tool for propagation analysis (linked to *IonoProbe*), greyline indication and a wide range of maps with various projections. There is a charge to register the software, but a 30-day free trial is available.

```
Circuit 1: KK_AUS                Distance: 6689mi        Date: 10 Sep 2009
Tx: Kota Kinabalu   5.97   116.06   Bearings: 112  273   SSN: 6
Rx: Austral         -23.00 -149.00  Path: Short Path      TxAntenna: ISOTROPIC
FSet:amateur2       Min.Angle: 1deg Noise:-150dBW/Hz CCIR RxAntenna: ISOTROPIC
Appr PCLoss PredConf.82% Required S/N:3dB RxBW:3.0kHz   %Days:90  Power:1000 W
Mode: 3F          FIELD STRENGTH
===============================================================================
UT  MUF  OUF   θMUF θOUF  1.8  3.5  7.0 10.0 14.0 18.1 21.0 24.9 28.0
00 26.2 20.9   -5   -4    ..   ..   ..   ..  -18   -6   -4   -4   -7
01 25.7 21.0   -6   -5    ..   ..   ..   ..  -20   -7   -5   -5   -8
02 24.8 20.7   -6   -5    ..   ..   ..   ..  -20   -7   -5   -7  -10
03 24.2 20.2   -6   -5    ..   ..   ..   ..   ..   -7   -5   -7  -10
04 23.8 19.9   -5   -4    ..   ..   ..   ..  -13   -4   -4   -7   ..
05 23.3 18.2   -4   -2    ..   ..   ..   ..   -7   -2   -2   -6  -11
06 23.0 16.9   -2    2    ..   ..   ..   ..   -1    2    0   -5  -11
07 21.9 16.1   -1    5    ..   ..   ..   ..    5    4    1   -6  -13
08 20.3 15.0    1    8    ..   ..   ..   ..    8    4    0   -9   ..
09 19.5 14.9    2   10    ..   ..   ..   13   11    5   -1   ..   ..
10 19.4 15.6    3   10    ..   -8   14   16   13    6   -1   ..   ..
11 18.9 15.2    3   11    ..    1   16   17   13    5   -2   ..   ..
12 17.9 14.4    4   11    ..    5   17   17   12    3   -4   ..   ..
13 15.6 12.5    4   11    ..    5   16   15    8   -2   ..   ..   ..
14 13.7 10.6    4   11    ..    4   15   13    3   ..   ..   ..   ..
15 12.4  9.7    4   11    ..    4   14   10    0   ..   ..   ..   ..
16 12.0  9.4    5   11    ..    4   14   10   -2   ..   ..   ..   ..
17 14.1 11.6    4   10    ..    5   15   13    5   ..   ..   ..   ..
18 13.8  9.9    1    6    ..   ..   ..    6    1  -11   ..   ..   ..
19 11.9  8.7   -4   ..    ..   ..   ..   ..   -8   ..   ..   ..   ..
20 11.3  8.3   ..   ..    ..   ..   ..   ..  -14   ..   ..   ..   ..
21 14.2 11.3  -12   ..    ..   ..   ..   ..  -12   ..   ..   ..   ..
22 23.6 20.6   -5   -3    ..   ..   ..   ..  -10   -3   -3   -6   ..
23 27.8 22.2   -4   -1    ..   ..   ..   ..  -15   -4   -1   -2   -4
```

Propagation prediction table showing predicted field strength (in dBuV) between two places on Earth for each hour of a specific day, on each band.

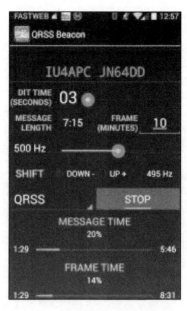

(right) A cheap *Windows* tablet computer running *SDR#* , together with a £10 SDR dongle, makes a portable receiver.

(left) QRSS Beacon is an *Android* app that generates a QRSS, FSK/CW or DFCW audio signal to plug into your transmitter.

OTHER OPERATING SYSTEMS, TABLETS AND SMART PHONES

This chapter has been written assuming that the main station computer(s) run the ubiquitous *Windows* operating system. It is likely that most stations will have at least one *Windows* computer, but other options are becoming more popular and amateur radio programs have been developed for a variety of platforms. Most have been specially written but others are versions of programs already popular with *Windows* users.

Users of Apple Mac computers have had amateur radio software for some time. Programs for logging, satellite tracking, datacomms and much more are listed at various web sites, including *machamradio* [17]. *DX Zone* [18] and *QSL.net* [19].

There is a large following for the *Linux* operating system, and it also has many specially written amateur radio programs of all types, as well as versions of some popular *Windows* applications. Some useful web sites listing soft-ware include *Hamsoft* [20] and *DX Zone* [21]. A description of using the *Ubuntu* variant of *Linux* can be found on the ARRL web site at [22].

Both Mac- and *Linux*-based computers will also run virtual machines or emulators which allow *Windows* programs to work. These are quite resource hungry and require a powerful machine, but it gets over the problem that some desired programs will only run on *Windows*.

Recently, handheld computers, either tablets or smart phones, have become popular. They can be useful for amateur radio where size or weight can be important, such as when operating portable, or even to check propagation (for instance) whilst travelling to your shack. These devices are relatively new and amateur radio programs - usually referred to as applications (abbreviated to apps) - are often in the development stage. The situation is complicated by the various operating systems used, such as *Apple iOS*, *Android* and *Windows*, and their numerous versions.

A search in the app store of your operating system should reveal apps for licence and Morse training, datacomms, callsign directories, satellite prediction, rig control and much more. Some useful suggestions for several operating systems can be found at [23]. An article on using a cheap *Windows*-based tablet for amateur radio is at [24].

A hand-held device can also be useful to access the web and email to avoid disturbing the main station computer, or when backpacking on a SOTA expedition.

A reported drawback with using these small devices is the limited number of hardware connections to the outside world. It remains to be seen whether tablets and phones will replace full-sized PCs; in any case they will certainly continue to be handy additions.

CONCLUSION

The overall conclusion, from this chapter, must be that, far from taking away from amateur radio, computers and the Internet have done a huge amount to enhance our hobby, and there is still a long way to go. Amateur radio is, by its nature, a technical hobby, concerned with the advancement of communications. Many amateur developments (packet radio, APRS) have found their way into the professional and commercial sphere and we should in no way feel threatened when this becomes a two-way traffic.

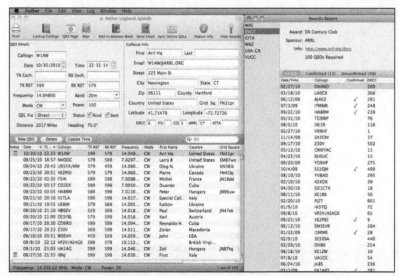

Aether is a logging program written for the Mac OS X operating system.

REFERENCES

[1] *Radio Communication Handbook*, RSGB.
[2] *SD* logging programs by EI5DI: www.ei5di.com
[3] http://starsoftware.g3wgv.com/
[4] *Turbolog*: www.turbolog.de
[5] *Spectrum Laboratory*: www.qsl.net/dl4yhf/
[6] *DX Summit*: www.dxsummit.fi
[7] *Club Log*: www.clublog.org
[8] 'There's a remote possibility...', David Gould, G3UEG, *RadCom*, August - October 2005.
[9] 'Remote operation', Dave Pick, G3YXM, *RadCom*, October - November 2009.
[10] *CW Skimmer*: www.dxatlas.com/CwSkimmer
[11] www.dxatlas.com/CwSkimmer/Files/Skimmerintro.pdf
[12] Reverse Beacon Network site: www.reversebeacon.net

[13] *RUFZ* pile-up trainer: www.rufzxp.net
[14] G4FON Koch Morse trainer: www.g4fon.net
[15] EI8IC maps: www.mapability.com/ei8ic
[16] *DX Atlas*: www.dxatlas.com
[17] www.machamradio.com/
[18] www.dxzone.com/catalog/Software/Macintosh/
[19] www.qsl.net/ah6rh/am-radio/mac/
[20] http://radio.linux.org.au/?sectpat=All&ordpat=title
[21] www.dxzone.com/catalog/Software/Linux/
[22] www.arrl.org/ubuntu-linux-for-hams
[23] http://swling.com/blog/2014/01/the-best-amateur-radio-and-shortwave-apps-for-ios-and-android-smart-phones/
[24] http://www.essexham.co.uk/news/linx-windows-tablet.html

VERY FEW AMATEUR STATIONS are equipped for all the allocated bands. To be so equipped would require a mountain of equipment and a rather impressive collection of antennas. Even the most experienced amateurs would probably admit to focusing their interests on specific bands or groups of bands. But one of the joys of the hobby is the sheer variety of operating experiences to be gained from exploring the many different bands and modes available to us.

There is a lot to be said for spending a few years on certain bands, and then re-equipping your station to explore a completely different part of the spectrum. For example, enjoy the wide open spaces of 28MHz (10m) when the sunspot cycle is at its peak, then concentrate on the low bands during sunspot minima. Or take some time away from the HF bands and try operating the VHF, UHF or microwave bands from suitable hilltop sites - or vice-versa. One way or another, there is scope for a lifetime of interest.

This chapter sets out to give a flavour of the various amateur bands, with some hints and tips about the types of propagation you might expect to find, specific issues about band planning and, where appropriate, some advice on equipment and antennas. What you will certainly find, as you spend more and more time on the air, is that each band has its own 'character' in terms of propagation and activity.

A little history is perhaps in order here. In the UK, as in most parts of the world, the first HF bands to be allocated to amateurs were 1.8, 3.5, 7, 14 and 28MHz (160, 80, 40, 20 and 10m). It is no coincidence that these are harmonically related. Before the days of synthesisers, many transmitters used to have crystal control or an oscillator running on one of the lower bands, and this frequency was progressively doubled to generate RF on the higher bands. 21MHz (15m) was a later addition, and is three times the frequency of the 7MHz

(40m) band. Similarly, the harmonically-related microwave bands were allocated to the amateur service at the 1947 World Administrative Radio Conference (WARC).

At the 1979 WARC, amateurs were given allocations at 10, 18 and 24MHz (the 30, 17 and 12m bands). These new HF bands are relatively narrow compared with the earlier HF bands. They have the benefit of slotting neatly between the existing bands, offering some valuable propagation opportunities, for example 24MHz (12m) is often open when 28MHz (10m) is closed. But because of their narrow bandwidth, there is international agreement that they should not be used for contest operating and the IARU also recommends restricting operation on 10MHz (30m) to narrow-band modes (CW and data modes). For those who prefer to avoid contest operations, these bands therefore offer a valuable refuge. Because of their genesis, these three bands are still often referred to collectively as "the WARC bands".

More recently, UK amateurs gained a temporary allocation at 73kHz (now withdrawn), and permanent allocations at 136kHz, 472kHz, and 11 narrow bands of frequencies between 5258.5 and 5406.5kHz (the so-called 60-metre 'band'), all of which are allocated to UK radio amateurs on a Secondary basis (the 472kHz and 5MHz frequencies are allocated only to Full licensees; the 136kHz band is also available to Foundation and Intermediate licensees).

The pattern elsewhere in the world is much the same, though it is worth noting that a small number of countries have yet to release the WARC bands to their amateurs, despite it being over 35 years since that conference decision. It should also be noted that even the more historic bands aren't universally available. Many amateur bands are shared with other services, and in some countries this is a more significant issue than in others.

A word about the various USA licence classes. Whereas in the UK all licence classes (Foundation, Intermediate and Full) have access to the whole of each band that is allocated to them, in the USA that is not the case. There are also three licence classes in the USA: Technician, General and Extra (also known as Amateur Extra). The Technician licensee is granted all VHF / UHF amateur bands plus CW only on 80, 40 and 15m, and 10m using CW, SSB and data modes. The General class licence offers all VHF / UHF amateur bands, all frequencies in the 160, 30, 17, 12, and 10m bands and significant segments of the 80, 40, 20 and 15m bands. Finally, the Extra class licensee is authorised to operate on all frequencies allocated to the Amateur Service in the USA, although it should be

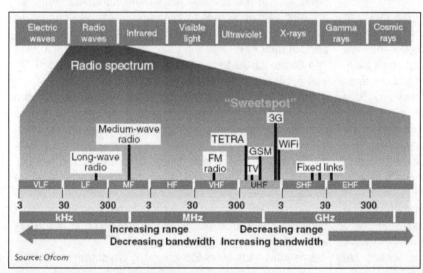

Radio waves are only part of the electromagnetic spectrum. Radio amateurs have allocations across the radio spectrum.

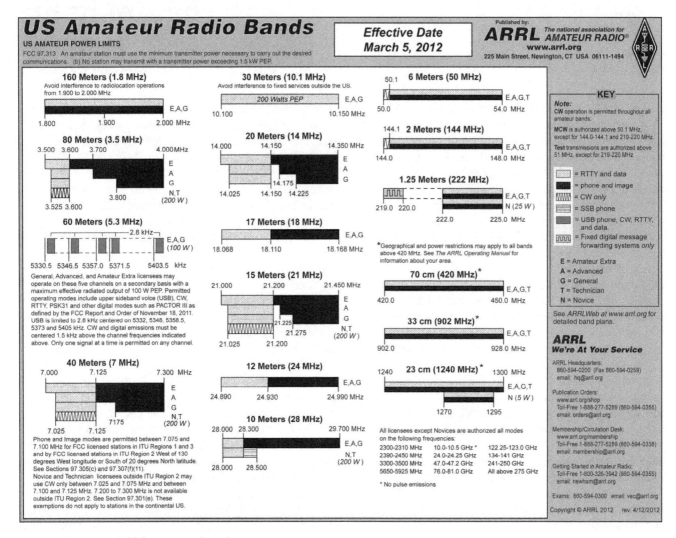

Fig 1: ARRL table of US frequency allocations.

noted that all US licence classes - including Extra - have restrictions to the frequencies on which they are permitted to use certain modes. In the USA, the 5MHz (60m) 'band' consists of five spot frequencies, which are not, however, available to Technician class licensees.

The situation is complicated somewhat by the fact that before 2000 licences were also being issued in two further licence classes - Novice and Advanced. Although no new Novice or Advanced licences have been issued since then, those already in existence remained unchanged and amateurs have been able to renew them. Some frequency privileges remain for these existing Novice and Advanced licensees. The frequencies allocated to each licence class are summarised in a chart compiled by the ARRL (reproduced here as **Fig 1**) and are described below when discussing each of the amateur bands. A colour version of this chart may be downloaded as a PDF from the ARRL website [1].

Above 30MHz, the official dividing line between HF and VHF, amateurs have progressively been allocated more bands, extending into the microwave spectrum. National allocations vary, although most of the major bands are available in most countries. For example, at the 1979 WARC mentioned above, amateurs also gained a number of new primary microwave bands above 24GHz.

The 50MHz (6m) band, though, has only become available across most of Europe in recent years, and is still not allowed in some European countries. For a long time the UK has enjoyed, along with a few other countries, the 70MHz (4m) band, and in the last few years more European countries are also gaining access to this band. These two bands are sufficiently 'different' from other VHF bands to warrant a book of their own - and such a book, *Six and Four* (subtitled The Complete Guide to 50 and 70MHz Amateur Radio) [2], was published by the RSGB in 2013.

The 220MHz and 900MHz bands, popular in the USA, are unfortunately unavailable in Europe. Although there is less need for countries to co-ordinate VHF allocations on an intercontinental basis as the risk of mutual interference is very low, for amateurs it is nevertheless advantageous if their VHF and UHF allocations coincide, as this allows long-distance contacts to take place via, for example, satellites or moonbounce. On HF it is very important, as propagation on most bands can be world-wide, at least at certain times of the day and certain periods of the solar cycle.

Amateur bands allocated in the UK are shown in **Table 1,** together with the names they go under in day to day amateur radio parlance. The table also shows the official designations of the various parts of the radio spectrum.

Spectrum (kHz, MHz, GHz)	Official designation	Amateur bands (kHz, MHz, GHz)	Wavelength (metres)	Informal usage (see Notes below)
3 - 30kHz	VLF (Very Low Frequency)	Nil		"VLF"
30 - 300kHz	LF (Low Frequency)	136kHz	approx 2200m	"VLF" or "LF"
300 - 3000kHz	MF (Medium Frequency)	472kHz	630m	"LF"
		1810kHz	160m	"LF", low bands, 'Topband'
3 - 30MHz	HF (High Frequency)	3.5MHz	80m	"LF", low bands
		5MHz	60m	(11 narrow frequency bands)
		7.0MHz	40m	"LF", low bands
		10.1MHz	30m	'WARC bands'
		14.0MHz	20m	"HF"
		18.068MHz	17m	'WARC bands'
		21.0MHz	15m	"HF"
		24.89MHz	12m	'WARC bands'
		28.0MHz	10m	"HF"
30 - 300MHz	VHF (Very High Frequency)	50MHz	6m	VHF, 'Six', "The magic band"
		70MHz	4m	VHF, 'Four'
		144MHz	2m	VHF, 'Two'
300 - 3000MHz	UHF (Ultra High Frequency)	430MHz	70cm	UHF, 'Seventy'
		1240MHz	23cm	"Microwaves"
		2310MHz	13cm	"Microwaves"

NOTE 1: There can be some confusion over the terms VLF, LF, HF, etc as used by radio amateurs to describe the amateur bands. This has come about because for many years the lowest-frequency amateur band was 1.8MHz so the 1.8, 3.5 and 7MHz bands were known informally as "the LF bands" or simply as "LF", to differentiate them from 14, 21 and 28MHz, which were known as "the HF bands". Officially all these are HF except for 1.8MHz which is an MF band. Later when 73kHz and 136kHz were allocated the new bands were known as "VLF" in order to differentiate them from the so-called "LF" bands. In fact, 136kHz is the only true LF band
The 136kHz band is often grouped with the newer 472kHz (MF) band and described as "LF", and in recent years 1.8, 3.5 and 7MHz have become known instead as "the low bands" and this is the preferred term in this book.
NOTE 2: The spectrum between 3 and 30GHz (3000 - 30,000MHz) is referred to as 'SHF' - Super High Frequency - though all amateur bands above 1GHz are usually referred to simply as "Microwaves".

(above) Table 1: The radio spectrum and the main amateur bands within it.

The UK band plans are deliberately not given here because they are subject to change. They are published on the RSGB website [3], and annually in the *RSGB Yearbook* [4] and in *RadCom* (usually in the February issue). The IARU also produces band plans and the latest version of the Region 1 plan can be found on their website [5]. The centres of activity specified in the IARU Region 1 HF band plan are shown in **Table 2**.

LF AND MF

136kHz (2200m) Band; 472kHz (630m) Band

These two bands are considered together, as they share many characteristics and are both considered to be 'enthusiasts' bands, requiring a specialist technical approach.

(right) Table 2: Centres of activity etc as identified in IARU Region 1 HF band plan.

QRP Centres of Activity:
1836, 3560, 3690 (SSB), 7030, 7090 (SSB), 10116, 14060, 14285 (SSB), 18086, 18130 (SSB), 21060, 21285 (SSB), 24906, 24950 (SSB), 28060, 28360kHz (SSB).

QRS (Slow CW) Centres of Activity:
3555, 14055, 21055, 28055kHz.

Digital Voice Centres of Activity:
3630, 7070, 14130, 18150, 21180, 24960, 28330kHz.

Image Centres of Activity:
3735, 7165, 14230, 21340, 28680kHz.

Emergency Communications Centres of Activity:
3760 (Region 1), 7110 (Region 1), 14300 (Global), 18160 (Global), 21360kHz (Global).

Priority for Intercontinental Operation:
3500 - 3510, 3775 - 3800, 7175 - 7200, 14195 ±5kHz (Priority for DXpeditions).

The 135.7 - 137.8kHz LF band has been available to all UK amateurs for several years. Following a period when MF operation (initially at 501 - 504kHz) was available only by Special Research Permit, the 472kHz band has now been made available to all Full licensees, UK Foundation and Intermediate licence do not include this allocation.

Both bands are licensed on the basis of non-interference to other users of the spectrum. In the case of 472kHz the licence goes much further by saying the station "may not claim protection from other wireless telegraphy or electronic equipment".

136kHz is unsuitable for day-to-day 'ragchewing'. There is no phone operation (the band is too narrow) and no contest operation. The power limit in most countries is defined by Effective Radiated Power (ERP), limited to 1W. This may not sound much, but may actually require substantial transmitter power to generate, as antennas are inevitably going to have very low efficiency. After all, a full-size quarter wave vertical would have to be over 500m high!

Given that the band is just 2.1kHz wide, it is clear that the use of wideband modes is out of the question, but this would also be precluded for simple technical reasons; the reduced size of the antenna means that it will inevitably have a high Q and therefore a very narrow bandwidth. Early operations on the band were mainly using traditional CW, albeit at fairly low speeds, and it proved possible to make contacts up to ranges of 1500km or so. To achieve greater distances, amateurs have turned to very low speed CW (QRSS), using PC software and, increasingly, to specialist data modes which take advantage of the PC's ability to integrate signals over an extended period of time and, in doing so, recover them from the noise. Beacon-based modes such as *Opera* and *WSPR* are popular.

Any station in another country could be considered as 'DX' on 136kHz but, to put a figure on it, most LF operators would feel very satisfied with an 800km+ CW contact. Propagation on 136kHz is more stable than on 160m with long distances,

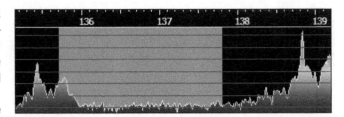

The 136kHz band (the light rectangle) has strong utility stations just outside its edges, whose sidebands spill into the amateur band.

such as G to SV, being possible in broad daylight using the Op32 mode. Darkness does bring considerable signal enhancement but with it often comes a similar increase in noise. Some of the best DX QSOs have been made in the early mornings when the atmospheric noise has died down and the local noise is still low. On many occasions the Atlantic has been crossed on this band during the hours of darkness using computer-assisted slow CW modes. Occasionally, signals have been received between Europe and Japan, South America and even Australasia.

Almost all European countries now have a 136kHz allocation, although some are by special permit, and most have some activity. Canadian stations have full access to the band and can make two-way QSOs. The first transatlantic contacts took place in 2001 between Canada and the UK. A few South American countries, including Argentina and Brazil, have the band and New Zealand stations may use a huge 130 - 190kHz at 5W EIRP. At the 2007 WRC, a proposal for a world-wide secondary allocation of 135.7 - 137.8kHz to the Amateur Service was approved, opening the way for more countries to allocate the band. Many more have since done so.

A notable exception is the United States. Since 1999, the FCC will issue 'Part 5' experimental licence which allow tests to be carried out on fixed frequencies, and several of these stations have successfully crossed the Atlantic on 136kHz. At the time of writing, attempts are ongoing to have this band added to the US licence(s).

Since the availability of MF allocations many of the regular 136 operators have moved up and 136 activity has dropped. On 472kHz there is some normal-speed CW operation and ragchews do take place. Additionally, activity can always been found on computer-based modes such as Opera and WSPR.

The power limit for 472kHz is 5W EIRP. Note that this is actual radiated power as on 136kHz, but is based on an isotropic radiator (the 'I' in EIRP), Again, although this seems a low figure, antennas will be relatively inefficient and many stations don't get anywhere near this level. A transmitter power of several hundred watts would probably be required to do so with an average antenna system.

Many countries, worldwide, have allocated 472kHz on a similar basis, though some have restricted power levels. At the time of writing, Russia and the USA are major exceptions. As with 136kHz, some US stations have special permits for this band.

Propagation on 472kHz is more akin to 160m than 136kHz, with large differences between day and night time

The comprehensive LF/MF station of Gary Taylor, G4WGT.

signals. During daylight hours a well equipped station can work a two or three hundred kilometres on regular CW. At night the band is alive to signals from all over Europe but with deep QSB. Strangely, transatlantic propagation doesn't seem as reliable as on 136kHz, An Australian station has been received in France using WSPR but this has proved to be very difficult to repeat.

As in the early days of 136kHz, most newcomers to 472kHz use normal CW as this is easiest to do. Computer-assisted modes are popular as operators try to increase their range, but QSB tends to be faster and deeper than 136 which can cause problems with very slow modes.

Many HF transceivers are able to receive on 136kHz and 472kHz, though not necessarily very well so a preamplifier may need to be constructed. Dedicated receivers, including Software Defined Radios (SDRs), may have better sensitivity but may need additional front-end selectivity.

At the time of writing, no HF transceiver has full transmit capability on these bands, but some provide a very low power output to drive an external amplifier. So it will be necessary to build a dedicated transmitter or, alternatively, some sort of converter to work with your existing transceiver. Several suppliers are now offering kits for LF/MF equipment.

When designing your station consider the ERP required; a station with a large antenna may need 50 to 100W to achieve a useful radiated power but someone with a small antenna may need to run much more power to achieve the same result. If you plan to use the low-speed modes, remember that the sent characters are much longer than on normal CW, so your transmitter needs to be designed with this in mind.

Most stations use Marconi antennas - inverted-L or T - so a good earth system is essential and earth stakes or radials should be used in conjunction with any existing underground metalwork such as water pipes.

Important as radiating a good signal may be, no DX will be worked unless it can be heard. Reception is undoubtedly the most challenging aspect of LF operating. The main enemy of the LF DXer is noise - local noise from switching power supplies, etc, QRM from nearby broadcast transmitters and atmospheric noise.

Atmospheric noise (QRN), due to distant lightning, is often bad during the summer months and can make the bands difficult. This is the main reason that most DX is worked between October and April. Some computer-assisted modes can still be effective in the presence of moderate QRN.

Other noises can usually be reduced by the use of directional receive antennas such as active loops. It must be borne in mind, however, that the transmit antenna will re-radiate the noise which it picks up. It is therefore often necessary to throw the transmit antenna off-resonance whilst receiving on a loop.

When choosing a receiver for these bands, consider the following points:

• It must have very good selectivity. Strong signals just a few hundred Hertz away will desensitise a receiver without a

135.700 - 136.000	Station tests
136.000 - 137.000	CW (avoiding the Intercontinental slot at 136.172kHz)
136.169 - 136.175	Intercontinental QRSS (Europe transmitting)
137.400 - 137.600	WSPR2 (set dial to 136.000kHz USB)
137.600 - 137.625	WSPR15 (set dial to 136.000kHz USB)
137.450 - 137.550	Opera32 (set dial to 136.000kHz USB)
137.660 - 137.740	QRSS3 and QRSS10
137.774 - 137.780	Intercontinental QRSS (N America and Russia transmitting)

Table 3: Activity by frequency on the 136kHz band (subject to change).

CW	Often around 472.5kHz, though can be heard all over the lower half of the band.
WSPR	Set dial to 474.2kHz USB (for signals between 475.6 and 475.8kHz).
ROS	Set dial to 476kHz USB
QRSS	Around 476.175kHz. Also around 478.900kHz.
Opera	Set dial to 477.0kHz USB (for signals between 478.45 and 478.55kHz).

Table 4: Activity by mode on the 472kHz band (subject to change).

good narrow CW filter. DSP-equipped sets can work well but there's no real substitute for a narrow filter as near to the first mixer as possible.

• Stability and frequency accuracy must be of a very high order. Most modern transceivers are surprisingly good and can be relied upon to be within a few Hertz of the indicated frequency and to stay there. Remember that when using QRSS (very slow speed CW) to work DX it is possible to miss the DX station altogether if you are just a few Hertz out of calibration. Any drift will make a very slow CW signal difficult to read.

• Receiver sensitivity is often poor below 1.6MHz and front-end selectivity usually non-existent. Connecting the average transceiver to a large aerial and tuning to the LF bands will often yield nothing but broadcast intermodulation and noise. A selective preamplifier will solve these problems. If all your efforts with a 136kHz receiving system have been successful, the German transmitter at 138.8kHz should be an S9+ signal, whereas the daytime band noise should be about S3 in a 250Hz filter. On the 472kHz band in the absence of signals you should hear a quiet(ish) background with no broadcast breakthrough.

Table 3 shows a band plan which has been adopted by 136kHz operators. While not mandatory, by failing to observe it not only will you upset other band users, but you are unlikely to make any contacts. There is no official band plan for 472kHz yet, but activity can be found on the frequencies shown in Table 4. Both bandplans are subject to change as modes and activity patterns develop.

Given the specialist nature of both these bands, most UK amateurs active on them are 'members' of the RSGB LF Group which is a Yahoo group. This is the place to learn about forthcoming activity and new narrowband modes, or to ask for skeds. It is also where you can ask questions on LF matters, no matter how simple or complex, with the assumption that you will get replies from experienced, knowledgeable and friendly people. To join, simply go to the Group's web site [6]. Another good source of information is *LF Today* [7].

THE LOW BANDS

1.8MHz (160m) Band

160m is often called 'topband' because for many years it was the lowest-frequency (and thus the highest wavelength) band allocated to radio amateurs. Almost every country has a 160m frequency allocation, though allocations and power limits still vary significantly from country to country and it can be quite difficult to keep track of them (see **Table 5**). Generally in ITU Region 1, the allocation begins at 1810kHz, whereas in Regions 2 and 3 it starts at 1800kHz, though this is by no means universal.

In broad terms, activity on the band divides between local rag-chewing, especially during daylight hours when range is limited to no more than 80km or so, and DXing which, because of the nature of the band, takes place during the hours of darkness. In the UK, most local operation takes place above 1900kHz, whereas DX activity stays largely within the bottom half of the band.

As far as local activity is concerned, 160m continues to be favoured for many club and special-interest group nets. While it cannot support nationwide nets during daylight hours, it is ideal for a club with members in and around a particular town, maybe within a circle of 35km or so diameter. This part of the band is also popular with those indulging in a little nostalgia, for example by operating AM with restored valve equipment. Most, though by no means all, major contests include 160m, and the band is also used for a number of small local and national contests. There is increasing use of data modes, including those such as *Opera* and *WSPR* which allow transmissions to be received at very low signal levels.

It is difficult to define 1.8MHz DX in terms of distance, but 3000 to 5000km would generally be considered to qualify. 160m propagation is not dissimilar to that experienced on the medium-wave broadcast band, with little sky-wave propagation during daylight hours, but with long-distance working possible throughout the hours of darkness. In years gone by, achieving DXCC (100 entities, or 'countries', worked) on 160m would have been considered an almost unattainable goal. However, a substantial increase in activity which, combined with improvements in antennas and receiver technology have led to scores of 200 DXCC entities or more becoming relatively commonplace. A few of the most dedicated 160m DXers have now exceeded the 300 country level. A well-equipped UK amateur prepared to lose sleep in the cause of 160m DXing could nowadays expect to work 100 countries or more in a season, and large contest stations have been able to work DXCC in a single weekend. Even with 10W, many stations with good antennas have worked all continents.

DX propagation on 160m requires that the whole path lies in darkness, though there can be significant signal enhancement at dawn and dusk due to ionospheric tilting. For example, the path between the UK and Australia often opens for about 10 - 15 minutes before and after Australian sunrise. Such openings will not occur every day, and openings can be very short (just two to three minutes) with signals peaking at good strength and then falling away very rapidly indeed. To some extent, propagation will depend on ionospheric activity.

Australia	1800 - 1875	Advanced licensees only
Canada	1800 - 2000	
Japan	1810 - 1825	CW only
	1907.5 - 1912.5	CW & data only
New Zealand	1800 - 1950	
Russia	1810 - 2000	
UK	1810 - 1850	400W PEP
	1850 - 2000	32W PEP
USA	1800 - 2000	

Table 5: Some 160m allocations around the world.

In particular, signal paths through the auroral zone will be subject to strong attenuation when auroral activity is high. In the northern hemisphere, signals from the north also arrive at much lower wave angles than those from the south. To achieve these wave angles with a horizontal antenna would require antenna heights of 250ft or more, so vertical antennas are generally favoured by 160m DXers.

On shorter paths (eg Europe to North America), the path can be open for several hours, although signals may still peak around sunset in North America and around sunrise in Europe. Having said this, peak time for paths between Europe and Central America is often around local midnight at the mid-point of the path, and therefore around 0200 or so European time. North-south paths, such as those between Europe and South Africa, frequently peak around midnight European time.

In broad terms, DX working during the winter period tends to be more productive for stations in the northern hemisphere due to the longer hours of darkness and lower static levels. However, the converse is that this is the worst period for activity from the southern hemisphere, and European DXers are increasingly recognising the need to be alert during the summer for activity from southern Africa, South America and even Australia. Because of the uncertainty surrounding 1.8MHz propagation, and the way in which signal strengths can vary significantly over a short period, successful 1.8MHz DXing demands regular monitoring of the band, often at unsociable hours.

As mentioned above, 1.8MHz DXers typically use some sort of vertical antenna, which may be an inverted-L, a loaded vertical, or perhaps a shunt-fed tower. All such systems require an excellent earth system if reasonable efficiency is to be achieved. Details of suitable antenna systems can be found in many references, for example [8], [9]. As ground-wave communication is more effective with vertically polarised antennas, the use of a vertical antenna will also enable good daylight distances to be achieved on 160m in addition to the DX capability.

The main limitation with vertical antennas is that they are more prone to noise pick-up than horizontal antennas. Serious 160m DXers therefore use separate receiving antennas. This may be a small tuned loop, designs such as the K9AY loop and 'EWE' antennas or, if space is available, a Beverage antenna. None of these is suitable for transmitting purposes, but all can give significant signal to noise enhancement on received signals.

Receiver performance is important on 160m, not so much in terms of absolute sensitivity but more in respect of being able to receive weak DX signals in the presence of very strong local signals on adjacent frequencies. Good intermodulation performance is therefore crucial.

Many DX stations and DXpeditions will operate 'split frequency', and in some cases split-frequency operation is essential due to differing frequency allocations. For example, although they now have an allocation lower in the band, some Japanese stations continue to transmit between 1907.5 and 1912.5kHz, listening around 1830kHz for European stations. The ability to operate split is therefore important.

Most DX operation takes place on CW, and good-quality narrow CW filters make reception of weak signals that much easier. SSB DX working is, however, becoming more common as station improvements compensate for the inherent disadvantages of the mode (wider bandwidth and lower average power, resulting in significantly poorer signal-to-noise ratio than with CW, all other factors being equal).

Over the years, increasing levels of activity and competition have taken away some of the 'exclusiveness' previously felt by 160m enthusiasts. Activity in the major contests can be especially frenetic and, although these provide an opportunity

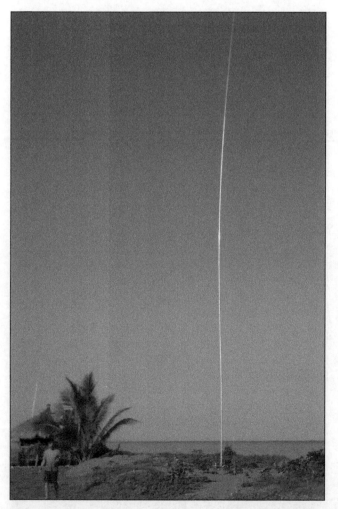

A vertical antenna is recommended for the 160m band, both for DX and local ground-wave working. This is a 26m (87ft) vertical used on the 4W6A (Timor-Leste) DXpedition in 2011.

for the newcomer to increase his tally of DX, they can be somewhat intimidating. Better, perhaps, to cut your teeth on working relatively common DX, for example UK to USA or Asiatic Russia, from where there is plenty of activity.

The IARU Region 1 band plan restricts SSB operation to frequencies above 1840kHz (which, given that LSB is used, means that the carrier frequency should be no lower than about 1842.5kHz), and the majority of CW activity takes place below 1840kHz. Because of the narrowness of the band, this split tends to be treated with flexibility in the major contests, but most Region 1 stations adhere to it at other times to the benefit of all users.

Although 160m frequency allocations have been brought much more into harmony than was previously the case, there are still differences from country to country. The one band segment which is common to most users is 1810 to 1850kHz, which is why most DX activity takes place in this part of the band.

On CW, operating speed is very much dependent on conditions. If signals are strong each way, there is no reason why normal speeds of operation should not be used. Some stations advocate slower speeds when signals are weak, though often it is better to operate at normal speeds but with several repeats in the hope that at least one transmission will be heard through the noise or fading. Remember that band openings can be of short duration so, in fairness to other operators, contacts should be completed in the shortest possible time. Equally, it is unreasonable to work a rare station several times, on consecutive nights for example, when others are trying to make a first contact.

Most rare stations and DXpeditions nowadays will make at least some effort on 160m, although some are more prepared than others to cope with the more demanding operating and lower rates of making contacts, compared with the other HF bands. In some cases it can be productive to work a rare station on one of the higher bands and make a schedule for a 160m contact, but not all DX operators will be prepared to do this. In any case, do not waste their time unless you feel there is a good chance of making a contact at the time and on the frequency agreed.

Unfortunately there are few reliable propagation indicators for European stations on 1.8MHz, but activity is high enough nowadays for the presence and strength of DX stations to be used instead (the signal strengths of local and semi-local stations provide no guide at all to DX conditions). Careful listening can provide clues, and the occasional directional CQ at what ought to be an optimum propagation peak (for example a grey-line propagation path) can sometimes yield a call from a rare DX station.

Although significant parts of 160m are now primary amateur allocations, UK amateurs are still restricted to lower power levels above 1850kHz and must avoid interference to other non-amateur band users. In the segment 1810 - 1830kHz there continue to be non-UK commercial users and, again, amateurs should exercise restraint and avoid interference to these other services.

1.8MHz has always been regarded as a specialist DX challenge. The late Stu Perry, W1BB, the first amateur to gain DXCC on the band, took many years to achieve his goal. Even though DX working on the band is now much more commonplace, 1.8MHz remains the most challenging of the 'HF' bands, requiring persistence and perseverance to achieve competitive results. *DXing on the Edge - The Thrill of 160 Meters* by Jeff Briggs, K1ZM, [10] captures something of the unique flavour of the band.

3.5MHz (80m) Band

80m is very much a mainstream band for all aspects of the hobby. It is popular for local and national nets and for those wanting to have 'rag-chew' type contacts both around the UK and with nearby countries in continental Europe. For UK stations wanting to improve their French or German language skills, 80m is an ideal band. It is increasingly popular for data modes enthusiasts, too. The 80m band is used for many national contests and is included in most of the major international events, too. It is also a magnet for those who want a real challenge in DXing (compared with the relatively easy pickings on, say, 20m).

With so much going on, the band inevitably gets rather crowded at times, so a degree of flexibility and understanding is required of its users. This is a most useful band for local and near-European working during daylight hours and for longer-distance contacts after dark. In winter, particularly during the years when solar activity is low, it is an excellent DX band, capable of providing world-wide communications. In summer, transequatorial contacts with Oceania, the Pacific and Africa are possible and there are openings to other parts of the world, but summer static can be a limiting factor. Particular attention should be paid to the possibility of 'greyline' paths (see Chapter 6).

In Europe and some other parts of the world the band is allocated to amateurs on a shared basis, with military and commercial stations and specialised point-to-point services taking many of the available frequencies. This sharing can result in high levels of interference. While many countries allow their amateurs to operate between 3500 and 3900kHz or even 3500 to 4000kHz, Europe (including the UK) uses 3500 to 3800kHz. In North America, where the band extends to 4000kHz, the higher-frequency part of the band which is mainly used for phone is known as "75 meters". Some other countries, such as Russia, Australia and Japan have restricted allocations on 80m, which DX operators need to be aware of. **Table 6** shows the 80m allocations for some key countries, illustrating the sort of differences which occur.

80m is an ideal band for daytime nets and 'rag-chews'. Distances up to a few hundred miles are typical, which makes it very suitable for contacts around the UK. As a result, the band is very popular with clubs and other special-interest groups, as it provides reliable communications, with most participants able to hear each other comfortably. When using the band for such activity, though, it is necessary to be aware of the impact on other users who may be trying to work DX, especially in the CW and SSB DX segments of the band (see below). For example, in the winter the Scandinavian countries enjoy almost round-the-clock DX opportunities as they are in almost permanent darkness, but signals from the

UK can be much louder than the DX signals. So, while the DX is inaudible in the UK, UK stations may inadvertently be preventing the Scandinavians from working DX.

Turning now to DX working, on CW the bottom 30kHz is used, with the lower 10kHz being most favoured, in accordance with the IARU Region 1 band plan. As the USA restricts the use of the 3500 to 3525kHz segment to Extra class licensees, it is necessary to monitor above this segment for contacts with American amateurs who do not hold the higher licence.

As with other bands, DXpeditions and 'rare' stations often use split-frequency working, listening for calls in a specified frequency or band of frequencies away from their transmit frequency.

The majority of DX working on phone is in the upper 20kHz of the European band (3780 - 3800kHz), although the band plan actually allows the upper 25kHz for this. When the band is open, DX contacts should be given priority in this segment and no local contacts should take place to allow faint DX signals to be heard. Local contacts in this DX 'window' should be avoided whenever the band is capable of supporting DX traffic to / from anywhere in Europe. In practice this means around the clock in December and January and from two

USA 80m allocations
Novice and Technician classes:
 3525 - 3600kHz: CW only (200W maximum)
General class:
 3525 - 3600kHz: CW, RTTY / data
 3800 - 4000kHz: CW, Phone, Image
Advanced class:
 3525 - 3600kHz: CW, RTTY / data
 3700 - 4000kHz: CW, Phone, Image
Extra class:
 3500 - 3600kHz: CW, RTTY / data
 3600 - 4000kHz: CW, Phone, Image

Australia 80m allocations
Foundation class:
 3500 - 3700kHz: SSB, AM and hand-keyed Morse only.
Standard class:
 3500 - 3700kHz: All modes <8kHz bandwidth
Advanced class:
 3500 - 3700kHz: All modes <8kHz bandwidth
 3776 - 3800kHz: All modes <8kHz bandwidth

Japan 80m band allocations (NB revised 5 January 2015)
 3500 - 3520kHz: CW only
 3520 - 3535kHz: CW, data
 3535 - 3575kHz: CW, phone / image, data
 3599 - 3612kHz: CW, phone / image, data
 3680 - 3687kHz: CW, phone / image
 3702 - 3716kHz: CW, phone / image
 3745 - 3770kHz: CW, phone / image
 3791 - 3805kHz: CW, phone / image

Table 6: Some important 80m allocations.

hours before sunset to two hours after sunrise for the rest of the year.

Just as for CW working, the USA phone-band allocations are based on the class of licence held, and General class licensees are not allowed to work on phone below 3800kHz. For contacts with these stations it is necessary for European stations to work split frequency, ie non-USA stations below 3800kHz and USA stations above this frequency. At peak times when this band is open there can be substantial interference from many stations working in a relatively small segment and it can be productive for European stations to operate below, say, 3750kHz and nominate the frequencies where they are listening for calls from North American stations.

Many DX operators are chasing the five-band DXCC and five-band Worked All Zones awards, as well as band-countries for the ARRL's DX Challenge. This means that very substantial pile-ups of stations occur whenever a rare country appears. Some of these operators work split-frequency (particularly on CW), but in the past on SSB the trend was to use the list system (see Chapter 9). Many operators dislike the list system and it is now not as common as it once was on 80m, with more DX stations having adopted split-frequency working.

With simple antennas at moderate heights it is possible to take advantage of mid-winter conditions and work into North America and other parts of the world during the hours of darkness. For more consistent DX working, some form of low-angle antenna is required, often a vertical operated against ground. While a quarter-wave vertical is capable of excellent performance, being omni-directional and vertically polarised means it picks up more man-made noise and atmospheric static than a horizontal antenna. A further disadvantage is that it provides no directional discrimination against interference from amateur and non-amateur signals. Many amateurs who have plenty of ground area available use a vertical antenna for transmission in conjunction with highly directional low-angle receiving antennas such as a Beverage or K9AY loop.

Another popular antenna for 80m is the sloping dipole, which is basically a vertical dipole mounted from a single support and sloped at an angle of approximately 45°. To reduce the height of the support mast, the lower half of the dipole is often bent so as to run parallel with the ground. Sloping dipoles exhibit some directivity towards the slope and radiate at the low vertical angles suitable for long-distance working. It is possible to use more than one sloping dipole mounted from the same support mast, and to phase the feed lines to enhance the directivity characteristics and to provide electrical rotation of the polar pattern. Vertical antennas radiate little or no high-angle signals; they do not therefore perform well under daylight conditions when high-angle radiation is required. Many serious 80m DXers use phased arrays of vertical antennas, including 4-squares, though these can be complex to adjust and require a lot of real estate. The results, however, can be outstanding.

Horizontally-mounted dipoles and simple wire antennas radiate at too high a vertical angle for serious DX working unless the support height is at least a half wavelength above ground. As few amateurs have the facilities to erect antennas in excess of 40m high, recourse is made to other configu-

rations that work satisfactorily at lower support heights. The pulled-out single quad and delta-loop, particularly when corner-fed for vertical polarisation, have found favour with many operators and support heights of 13 - 15m have been proved to be effective for DX working. Although smaller non-resonant loops have been suggested by the late Les Moxon, G6XN, and others in *RadCom*, it is probably easier to use a full-wavelength loop and extend the horizontal sides to make up for the shorter vertical sections of the loop.

The Five-Band DXCC and Worked All Zones awards and the ARRL DX Challenge have increased the number of countries active on 80m and it is now relatively easy to achieve quite high country scores. A substantial number of operators have been able to contact in excess of 200 countries and there are some who have more than 300 countries confirmed for 3.5MHz CW and SSB working. A low-angle antenna system, a good receiver and an amount of single-minded persistence are needed, but for the newcomer to amateur radio and the operator who wishes to try a new band, DXing on the 3.5MHz band can be most rewarding.

Returning to more local working on 80m, including, for example, participation in the RSGB's AFS and Club Championship contests, the aim is to have a high-angle signal, quite the opposite of what has been discussed above for DX working. Fortunately, this is relatively easily achieved by using a low dipole. In this context, 'low' means anything less than about a quarter-wave above ground, which at 3.5MHz is still about 70 feet! But if you have sufficient horizontal space - and a half-wave dipole is anywhere between 37.5m (123ft) and 40.7m (134ft) long, depending on which end of the band it is designed for - an antenna even 3 or 4m above ground will perform well for local working.

If you do not have sufficient horizontal space available, a good compromise antenna for this band is the quarter-wave inverted-L, with an approximately 10m long horizontal wire connected to the top of a 10m vertical section. Although this is primarily a vertical antenna, the horizontal wire will contribute a considerable horizontal component to the signal, making it a good compromise for both local and DX working, especially for those without the space for a full-size half-wave dipole.

Numerous antenna designs for 80m, both for local and DX working, can be found in references [11] to [16].

It is worth a final note on antennas for 80m, which is that the band is very wide in percentage terms. Not only does this mean that propagation at the high end of the band can sometimes be noticeably different from that at the low end, but it can also present challenges for antenna design. Even full-size antennas may not cover the whole band, and antennas that are reduced in size through, for example, inductive loading, are likely to have a bandwidth which limits them to one very specific area of the band.

A number of solutions have been proposed over the years, but the best advice is to consider where your main interests lie, whether CW or SSB, and install an antenna optimised for that end of the band. With luck, you will be able to use it throughout the rest of the band via a suitable antenna tuning unit.

5MHz (60m) Band

Note that although referred to as a 'band', the 5MHz or 60-metre band is in fact made up of a series of eleven separate narrow bands, rather than a continuous band of frequencies. These frequency segments are allocated on a secondary basis to holders of a UK Full Amateur Licence. The maximum power output on 5MHz is restricted to 100W from the transmitter and 200W eirp from the antenna. Mobile operation is not permitted.

The UK 5MHz frequency allocation is shown in **Table 7**. Further restrictions apply to radio amateurs using 5MHz frequencies which are specified in a note to the licence (see sidebar opposite).

Unlike other amateur bands there is no IARU band plan for 5MHz, but operation in the band largely follows the standard convention of CW at the bottom of the band and SSB at the top. Exceptions to this may occur on certain spot frequencies which are also available to other countries, and contacts may be made on these frequencies using any mode. Upper sideband should be used for SSB operation at 5MHz to preserve compatibility with other services.

AM operation is permitted provided the maximum bandwidth does not exceed 6kHz. AM activity can often be found at 5317kHz.

It is important to ensure that the transmitted spectrum lies completely within the allocated frequencies and the highest USB frequency that can be used in each segment is shown in the table.

Lower limit (kHz)	Upper limit (kHz)	Notes on current usage
5258.5	5264.0	CW activity, 5262kHz QRP. 5258.5kHz international use
5276.0	5284.0	5278.5kHz international use. Emergency comms centre of activity
5288.5	5292.0	Beacons on 5290kHz. WSPR
5298.0	5307.0	All modes. Highest USB frequency 5304kHz
5313.0	5323.0	All modes. AM 5317kHz. Highest USB frequency 5320kHz
5333.0	5338.0	Highest USB frequency 5335kHz
5354.0	5358.0	Highest USB frequency 5355kHz
5362.0	5374.5	Digital modes activity. Highest USB frequency 5371.5kHz international use
5378.0	5382.0	Highest USB frequency 5379kHz
5395.0	5401.5	Highest USB frequency 5398.5kHz
5403.5	5406.5	Highest USB frequency 5403.5kHz international use

Table 7: UK 5MHz frequencies and recommended usage (see text).

Note (g) to Schedule 1 of the UK of the UK licence

Where Radio Equipment is being used in the 5MHz band, the following specific terms and conditions will also apply:

(i) When operating double sideband, the maximum bandwidth shall not exceed 6kHz;

(ii) Notwithstanding the maximum peak envelope power expressed in the table, above, the maximum radiated power must not exceed 200 Watts eirp;

(iii) The antenna height shall not exceed 20 metres above ground level;

(iv) The Licensee must not cause interference to the use made of the 5MHz band by the Ministry of Defence ("MoD") and must close down any apparatus that operates in the 5MHz band if he or she becomes aware that such use is causing undue interference to the MoD's use of the band;

(v) Communication may be established with military or military cadet organisations by transmitting and receiving only in the 5MHz band;

(vi) Particular care must be taken to ensure radiation does not take place outside the specified frequencies within the 5MHz band;

(vii) Where the Licensee intends to operate within a "net" (a network), the Licensee shall observe the following requirements in relation to the transmission of his or her Callsign:

(a) The Licensee shall transmit the station Callsign when he first joins the net and on leaving it;

(b) subject to sub-clause (c) below, whilst participating in the net, the Licensee shall not be required to transmit the station Callsign when making contact with other participants;

(c) where the Licensee's transmissions have been other than in speech mode for at least fifteen minutes, the Licensee shall transmit his call sign when next he transmits speech.

(viii) The Licensee shall operate the Station only at the Main Station Address or at a Temporary Location within the United Kingdom.

(ix) At a Temporary Location within the UK, the Licensee shall give the location of the Station every 30 minutes to an accuracy of at least 5km by a generally used identifier as indicated in Note (e) to the "Notes to the licence";

(x) The Licensee shall only operate the Station to the extent that the Licensee can be contacted on a telephone which is located in close proximity to the Station.

(xi) In this footnote, "the 5MHz band" means the radio spectrum between 5.2585MHz and 5.4065MHz.

UK amateurs are subject to additional restrictions when using 5MHz frequencies.

The Amateur Radio Operating Manual

Note that the segment from 5403.5 - 5406.5kHz is only 3kHz wide, therefore it should be considered as a single channel. 5403.5kHz is a popular frequency shared by many countries, so it will frequently be busy.

Experimental beacons operate around 5290kHz. With the exception of WSPR from 5288.5 - 5289.0kHz, it would be helpful if operators do not transmit in this narrow segment.

As with the WARC bands at 10, 18, and 24MHz, there should be no contest activity on 5MHz.

The 5MHz band is the only band in which radio amateurs are permitted to carry out communications with non-amateur stations, ie with "military or military cadet organisations". These stations will identify with callsigns of a different format to amateur calls and they use a concise operating procedure. They are unlikely to give operator names or locations but will often exchange information on equipment and antennas. Whilst military stations may be heard on any frequency around 5MHz, amateur stations must never attempt to contact military stations outside the frequency allocations in the table.

Activity from stations outside the UK can be found on 5MHz, although many countries are limited to a few spot frequencies. The more common frequencies are marked in Table 6 "for international use". Operators should be considerate when selecting a frequency for intra-UK operation that their chosen frequency does not prevent operation on a known international spot frequency. For example, selecting a USB frequency 0.5 or 1kHz above or below the indicated frequency for international use will unnecessarily prevent a contact on the international frequency, and while the UK stations can change frequency, the international stations may not have that ability. A good rule of thumb is to use the common frequencies of 5278.5kHz, 5371.5kHz, 5398.5kHz, and 5403.5kHz.

The status of 5MHz varies considerably from country to country. Many countries still have no allocation at all, whereas in Norway radio amateurs have the complete band from 5260 to 5410kHz allocated on a Secondary basis.

In the USA, General, Advanced, and Amateur Extra licensees may operate on the five channels shown in **Table 8** on a secondary basis with a maximum effective radiated output of 100W PEP. As from January 2012, permitted operating modes include upper sideband voice (USB), CW, RTTY, PSK31 and other digital modes (as defined by the FCC) such as PacTOR III. USB is limited to 2.8kHz centred on 5332, 5348, 5358.5, 5373 and 5405kHz. CW and digital emissions must be centred 1.5kHz above the channel frequencies indicated. Only one signal at a time is permitted on any channel

Most amateurs who operate on 5MHz do so with their normal SSB transceivers, many of which can be modified for coverage outside the usual amateur bands. Modification details can often be found on the Internet or, if you are uncomfortable with modifying your transceiver, you should ask the original dealer to make the modification on your behalf.

Transatlantic contacts now take place quite regularly, propagation being somewhere between what would be experienced on 80m and what would be expected on 40m.

Centre frequency	USB 'dial' frequency
5332.0kHz	5330.5kHz
5348.0kHz	5346.5kHz
5358.5kHz	5357.0kHz
5373.0kHz	5371.5kHz
5405.0kHz	5403.5kHz

Table 8: USA 5MHz channel frequencies.

5MHz lends itself well to intra-UK contacts during the hours of daylight, but offers scope for effective long-distance working at night, even with simple antennas and low power. Over 60 DXCC entities are believed to have authorised some form of amateur operation on 5MHz and two-way contacts have been made between many of them and the UK.

7MHz (40m) Band

The widely differing propagation conditions that exist on 7MHz during a 24-hour period, and the differences between winter and summer conditions, make this a very useful band for both local and DX working. In many ways there is a similarity to 3.5MHz, with signal attenuation through ionospheric absorption being the main limiting factor for DX working. Another common factor is the 'greyline' openings that take place.

In ITU Region 2 the band is 300kHz wide, 7000 - 7300kHz, but in ITU Regions 1 and 3 it is only 7000 - 7200kHz. However, some countries in Region 3 including Australia, New Zealand and Papua New Guinea also have access to the whole 300kHz.

Agreement to make 7100 - 7200kHz a world-wide Primary amateur allocation was reached at the World Radio Conference in 2003 and officially came into effect in 2009, although the UK and many other countries granted amateurs access well before this date. There are still a few countries that do not allow radio amateurs to operate between 7100 and 7200kHz.

Prior to 29 March 2009, 7100 - 7200kHz was a broadcasting band in ITU Regions 1 and 3 and while almost all the broadcast station have now moved to frequencies above 7200kHz, a small number of broadcast stations can still be found operating within the amateur band.

As with all bands, CW stations can be found at the lower-frequency end of the band and DX stations, including DXpeditions, often operate in the lowest 10kHz of band. However, as the USA restricts the use of the 7000 to 7025kHz to its Extra class licensees, it is necessary to look above this segment for contacts with all other American licence classes. DXpeditions often use split-frequency working on both CW and SSB, listening for calls in a specified frequency or band of frequencies away from their transmit frequency.

Because of the varied conditions that are found on the band, many operators regard 7MHz as the key to making a winning score in the RSGB Commonwealth Contest and other multi-band CW events.

The IARU Region 1 band plan that came into effect in 2009 shows 7175 - 7200kHz as "priority for intercontinental operation" on SSB.

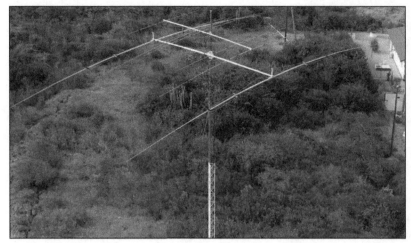

40m beams may be large, but their use is becoming more and more common. This is a Force 12 240N 2-element Yagi with linear loaded elements.

During daylight hours, ionospheric absorption on 40m is high and the skip zone is very short or non-existent, thus limiting communications to local contacts up to a few hundred kilometres. For this reason the band is ideal for contacts around the British Isles and the nearer countries in mainland Europe and daytime activity includes regular nets, special event stations and general 'rag-chewing'. Around sunset, there are long-haul greyline openings and, because attenuation is less than on 3.5MHz, these are longer in duration and signals are stronger than on the lower frequency. After dark, the skip zone lengthens and good medium-distance contacts are possible with North and South America, Asia and Africa.

In every respect, therefore, 40m is very much a mainstream band, with a high level of participation in all aspects of the hobby. This is especially true during the years of low solar activity, when the higher bands are closed and 40m comes into its own as a band for all purposes.

The existence of high-power broadcast stations on nearby frequencies (7200 - 7450kHz is allocated to Broadcasting in Regions 1 and 3, and 7300 - 7400kHz in Region 2), means that receiver-generated spurious signals can cause cross-modulation problems, leading to high levels of interference, particularly at night. Receiver performance is therefore critical and the use of front-end attenuators and / or passive pre-selectors helps to alleviate the problem.

Rotary directional antennas and phased vertical arrays including 4-squares are becoming commonplace with DXers as, apart from providing extra gain, the directional pattern helps to reduce interference. While low-angle radiation is desirable, dipoles, loops and other horizontal antennas are very popular and are capable of providing good DX performance. Ground planes, base-fed verticals and 'slopers' are also widely used.

For local working with Europe, a simple dipole is more than adequate. At the sort of heights typically possible in a suburban location (30 to 40ft), it will generate mainly high-angle radiation, perfect for working across distances up to a few hundred miles.

US phone operation commences at 7125kHz for Advanced and Extra class licensees, and at 7175kHz for the General class.

Many US stations operate between 7200 and 7300kHz and some may be listening for DX contacts below 7200kHz, so it can pay dividends to listen right up to 7300kHz when wishing to work the USA and other countries in North and South America on SSB. However, finding a clear listening frequency in what, in Europe and Asia, is a broadcast band, can be difficult at times. Matters improve around dawn as the UK starts to lose propagation to Europe and the US can be heard more easily.

The US 40m band allocations appear as **Table 8.**

HIGH FREQUENCY (HF)

10MHz (30m) Band

30m is an interesting transition band, exhibiting characteristics of both the low bands and the higher-frequency bands. Allocated for amateur use at the 1979 World Administrative Radio Conference (WARC), almost all countries now permit their amateurs to use 10100 - 10150kHz on a shared basis, though a few administrations have yet to release the band for amateur use and some allow only spot frequencies. In the UK, the 10MHz band is allocated on a Secondary basis for all three licence classes: Foundation, Intermediate and Full.

The IARU has recommended that contests and phone operation be excluded and therefore most operation is on CW and data modes, especially RTTY and PSK31. There are exceptions: 10120 - 10140kHz may be used for SSB transmissions

---

Novice and Technician classes:
  7025 - 7125kHz: CW only (maximum power 200W)

General class:
  7025 - 7125kHz: CW, RTTY / data
  7175 - 7300kHz: CW, Phone, Image

Advanced class:
  7025 - 7125kHz: CW, RTTY / data
  7125 - 7300kHz: CW, Phone, Image

Extra class:
  7000 - 7125kHz: CW, RTTY / data
  7125 - 7300kHz: CW, Phone, Image

NOTE: Stations licensed by the Federal Communications Commission (FCC) in ITU Regions 1 and 3, or in ITU Region 2 West of longitude 130° West or South of latitude 20° North, are permitted to use Phone and Image modes between 7075 and 7100kHz. In practice, this allows all US-licensed stations except those in the continental United States and Alaska (eg those in Hawaii, Guam, Puerto Rico, the US Virgin Islands, etc) to use 7075 - 7100kHz as well as their allocations shown in Table 8. US Novice and Technician licensees outside ITU Region 2 may use CW only between 7025 and 7075kHz and between 7100 and 7125kHz. 7200 to 7300kHz is not available to FCC-licensed amateurs outside ITU Region 2.

Table 9: US 40m band allocations.

in the area of Africa south of the equator during local daylight hours, and in Australia SSB is permitted by the band plan between 10115 and 10140kHz. SSB may also be used in the 10MHz band during emergencies involving the immediate safety of life and property, but only by stations actually involved in the handling of emergency traffic.

In the USA, the band is open to General, Advanced and Extra class licensees, but only using CW, RTTY and other data modes and with a power restriction of 200W PEP. American amateurs must also "avoid interference to fixed services outside the US".

Contacts on the 10MHz band count for a number of awards such as IOTA, DXCC, Commonwealth CC, WAB and IARU Region 1.

Propagation reflects the characteristics of the adjacent 7 and 14MHz bands. In daytime the skip shortens as the MUF rises but a skip zone generally persists all day except under exceptional sunspot maximum conditions. Absorption is lower than on 7MHz. Under night-time conditions propagation can become world-wide as absorption falls, being best towards the dark sector and being enhanced at the onset of sunset or sunrise. Greyline effects are very noticeable, offering world-wide propagation between, for example, the UK and the Far East or South Africa. A real-time greyline map, eg [17], is a most useful aid.

During periods of sunspot minima long-range propagation can persist all day, allowing propagation between the Far East and the UK in the mid-afternoon (UK time). Under very low sunspot conditions the MUF may not rise much above 10MHz at any time of day.

Long-path propagation, especially to Australia and New Zealand, occurs most mornings under undisturbed conditions. This path starts around UK sunrise and can extend for up to two hours afterwards. The closure of this long path is often signalled by a short enhancement of Central American signals, followed by rapid closure of both paths.

A major problem for radio amateurs on 10MHz is the commercial activity. This confines most amateur activity to a series of narrow 'slots' which tend to move under the pressure of commercial stations. Most DXpeditions make an effort to operate on 30m, and it is remarkable to note the long hours the band is open to many parts of the world. The characteristics of the 10MHz band mean that it is suited to antenna and propagation experimentation. Compact directional antennas for reception and a better understanding of the many propagation modes will allow good DX results to be achieved by the average CW amateur. Given the excellent propagation characteristics and other virtues of the band, it really does offer a strong motivation to become proficient in CW.

The band is also popular with QRP operators, and many designs have been published for self-build QRP transceivers for the band.

It took some years after the 1979 WARC before manufacturers started to incorporate 10, 18 and 24MHz into linear amplifier designs. However, many earlier valve linear amplifiers will work effectively on those bands by adjusting the tune and load controls accordingly. Most use a low-pass filter

as the input circuit, so always set the linear band switch to the band above (14MHz for 10MHz operation, 21MHz for 18MHz operation, etc). The main thing to check before running substantial power is to ensure that there is no unexpected resonance in the anode choke. Such a resonance would result in excess heat and possible damage. As far as antennas are concerned, because a half-wavelength is just 45ft or so, many operators will be able to erect a dipole at or near this height and enjoy good low-angle propagation. Vertical and loop antennas can also be very effective. Some amateurs also press their 80m dipoles into service (10.1MHz is the third harmonic of 3.37MHz, so an 80m dipole cut for the low part of the band can work as a one-and-a-half wavelength antenna through an ATU).

14MHz (20m) Band

This is the amateur band which carries the main load of inter-continental communications throughout the whole of the sunspot cycle. There are very few days even at sunspot minima and in the middle of winter when propagation is not available for at least some time into each continent. A result of this is that for much of the time the band is very congested, and this situation is made worse by the ITU Radio Regulations footnote which permits stations of the fixed service in some countries to use the 14250 - 14350kHz segment on a shared basis with amateurs. The IARU Region 1 band plan recommends that 14000 - 14099kHz be used for CW use, with the area 14070 - 14099kHz also being used for data communications. There are several RTTY, PacTOR and other mailboxes in the data modes area of the band, which can occasionally lead to problems with real-time data modes activity. In the USA only stations with Extra class licence are allowed to use 14000 - 14025kHz. Particular care should be taken to avoid causing interference to the beacon chain on 14100kHz.

DXpedition stations often tend to use CW frequencies which are multiples of 5kHz above the lower band limit but rarely go above 14050kHz, and 14025kHz is perhaps the most widely used. Most listen for replies a few kilohertz above their transmitting frequency and usually announce their tuning procedure.

The part of the band below 14150kHz is not available to phone stations in the USA and is therefore often used by non-USA stations working each other or by non-USA stations working split frequency and listening in the US band for callers (this is often helpful when interference is heavy).

At the lower end of the segment there are very often nets of French-speaking stations - including those from Canada and elsewhere as well as in France itself. Many Russian-speaking stations can also be found operating below 14150kHz. Spot frequencies have also developed on 20m SSB as unofficial 'meeting places' for amateurs speaking certain languages, eg Chinese on 14270 and Greek on 14285kHz.

The IARU Region 1 band plan lists 14195kHz ± 5kHz as 'Priority for DXpeditions' but in practice DXpeditions on SSB tend to use any convenient and vacant frequency. 14260kHz is the most popular Islands on the Air (IOTA) expedition frequency. SSTV signals from all over the world

Novice and Technician classes:
No allocation
General class:
14025 - 14150kHz: CW, RTTY / data
14225 - 14350kHz: CW, Phone, Image
Advanced class:
14025 - 14150kHz: CW, RTTY / data
14175 - 14350kHz: CW, Phone, Image
Amateur Extra class:
14000 - 14150kHz: CW, RTTY / data
14150 - 14350kHz: CW, Phone, Image

Table 10: US 20m band allocations.

will be found around 14230kHz (see Chapter 8). 14300kHz is listed in the IARU band plans as the 'Global Emergency Centre of Activity'. Except for the few major contests, contest activity tends to stay below 14300kHz, allowing room for non-contest activities.

In the USA 14150kHz to 14175kHz is reserved for those who have Extra class licence. The Advanced class phone section commences at 14175kHz and the General class at 14225kHz. There are many USA-based nets to be found in the General potion of the band, ie between 14225 and 14350kHz. **Table 10** shows the full US 20m band allocations.

There are no special equipment issues on 20m. However, it is probably true to say that there is a higher percentage use of gain antennas (Yagis, quads, etc) on this band than on any other, because it is the primary band for reliable DX working. This can be intimidating if you are struggling with a vertical antenna or a simple dipole. However, a well-sited half-wave dipole mounted in the clear 35ft or more above ground, while it will never beat a multi-element rotatable array, can still be an excellent performer.

18MHz (17m) Band

Allocated for amateur use at the 1979 World Administrative Radio Conference but only released for service some years later, this band is now very popular with some excellent DX around; most DXpeditions provide operation on it. Propagation is similar to the 14 and 21MHz bands, and the band is a useful 'half-way' house, particularly at sunspot minimum when 18MHz might be open for long-distance DX working at times when 21MHz is effectively closed.

The IARU Region 1 band plan recommends that the segment 18068 - 18095kHz is reserved for CW use only, with the area 18095 - 18109 for data modes and CW. Phone operation is found from 18111 - 18168kHz. Data modes activity continues to increase on the band, especially as the data modes sub-band on 20m tends to get rather busy. In the US, the band is available to General, Advanced and Extra class licensees.

The main limitation of the band is its narrow width. If a DXpedition is operating on, say, 18145kHz and listening on 18150kHz, that takes out a significant part of the band. Nevertheless, many UK amateurs find this an extremely reliable band for keeping long-distance schedules with friends or relatives in the US, Southern Africa or even Australia / New Zealand.

All modern equipment incorporates 18MHz as a matter of course. As far as antennas are concerned, a full-sized dipole at a half-wave high is very achievable for most amateurs and will work well. There is also a wide range of commercial antennas available which cover this band and these days most DXers use some sort of gain antenna.

21MHz (15m) Band

This is a favourite band with many HF operators, with more space than the crowded 14MHz band, and significantly more reliable than 28MHz except perhaps at sunspot maxima. The IARU Region 1 band plan recommends that the segment 21000 - 21149kHz be reserved for CW, with the area 21070 - 21149kHz also used by data modes. On CW, contest stations usually operate in the first 50kHz of this segment, although in the bigger contests they may spread up to and even above 21100kHz. DX on CW, although fairly evenly distributed in the first 75kHz or so, tends to be heaviest around 21025kHz, this being a popular frequency for DXpeditions. It is also the upper limit of the CW frequency allocation exclusive to the Extra class licensees of the USA.

All other US licence classes (Novice, Technician, General and Advanced) may

Although physically quite a large antenna (10m x 10m in size), the 5-band Spiderbeam is light enough in weight to be mounted on push-up masts at heights of up to 35 or 40ft. With separate wire elements for each band, the performance of the Spiderbeam approaches that of a 4-element monoband Yagi on 10m, 2-ele on 12m, 3-ele on 15m, 2-ele on 17m and 3-ele on 20m.

THE AMATEUR BANDS

use CW on 21025 - 21200kHz (General, Advanced and Extra licensees may also use RTTY and data modes). When conditions are good this part of the band becomes very crowded and is therefore one of the simplest indicators of propagation into North America.

Moving up the band, SSB signals commence around 21151kHz. As it is outside the USA phone allocation, 21151 to 21200kHz is often used by DX stations particularly wishing to work Europe, including Canadians, Central and South Americans, the Caribbean, Asia etc. When DX propagation is poor but short skip is possible this part of the band is used for inter-European working. The USA phone segment commences at 21200kHz and when conditions are good very strong signals are heard from USA Extra class licensees who have the exclusive use of the first 25kHz in their country. The Advanced class phone section starts at 21225kHz and the General class at 21275kHz. IOTA activity is centred on 21260kHz and SSTV operators centre their activities on 21340kHz. The segment 21250 to 21350kHz is usually very crowded at weekends and tends to attract high-powered stations. Stations with more modest means are therefore advised to operate in the 21350 to 21450kHz segment when working into the USA. **Table 11** shows the US 15m band allocations.

Over the years both US and non-US DXpedition stations have tended to use 21295kHz for their operations, but some DXpeditions operating from areas other than those controlled by the USA seem to favour frequencies around 21195kHz and 21245kHz for this purpose, announcing their listening frequencies for various areas from time to time.

As with 20m, there are no special equipment issues for 15m. One benefit that some amateurs take advantage of is that this band is the third harmonic of 40m, so antennas designed for 40m such as the half-wave dipole or quarter-wave vertical can easily be pressed into service, often with good results.

Many 15m operators will be using triband Yagis or even high-gain monoband antennas: while a full-size Yagi for 20m is beyond the scope of many suburban plots, a three-element Yagi for 15m is no bigger than a typical triband trapped Yagi, and has less weight and wind resistance by virtue of having no bulky traps. The difference in performance between a trapped antenna and a no-compromise monoband antenna is one that can only be fully appreciated when you have experienced it first hand.

Novice and Technician classes:
 21025 - 21200kHz: CW only (maximum power 200W)
General class:
 21025 - 21200kHz: CW, RTTY / data
 21275 - 21450kHz: CW, Phone, Image
Advanced class:
 21025 - 21200kHz: CW, RTTY / data
 21225 - 21450kHz: CW, Phone, Image
Extra class:
 21000 - 21200kHz: CW, RTTY / data
 21200 - 21450kHz: CW, Phone, Image

Table 11: US 15m band allocations.

24MHz (12m) Band

Allocated for amateur use at the 1979 World Administrative Radio Conference, this band can be very quiet during periods of low solar activity. However, it is well worth checking the various beacons on the band, as there can often be propagation but no activity. At such times a CQ call can be a very good idea. 12m can provide communications on days when the 28MHz band is quiet, and so should not be overlooked: for example there have been occasions when Pacific DXpeditions were workable for hours at a time on 24MHz from the UK, whereas 28MHz opened only briefly and, on some days, not at all. 12m also benefits from Sporadic E propagation in the June / July time period each year, with strong short-skip signals from around Europe.

The IARU Region 1 Band Plan reserves 24890 - 24915kHz for CW operation, with CW and data operation from 24915 - 24929kHz. Phone operation takes place from 24931 - 24990kHz. In the US, the band is available to General, Advanced and Extra class licensees.

Modern equipment incorporates 24MHz as a matter of course. Because antennas for 12m are relatively small in size, it is well worth thinking about some sort of gain antenna such as a two-element Yagi or quad. The cheap mass-produced 27MHz Yagis, designed for CB use, can be modified to achieve a low-cost, lightweight and effective antenna for 24MHz. A two-band quad for 10 and 12m can also be made from garden canes for just a few pounds.

28MHz (10m) Band

The 28MHz band is on the borderline between HF and VHF. Of course the delineation between HF and VHF, specified by definition at 30MHz, is man-made and nature draws no such firm division. It is this location in the spectrum which gives the band, sometimes described as 'the band of surprises', the variability which is one of its attractions. As at VHF, high power is by no means necessary to operate long ranges. It is generally accepted that if a path exists at all then 10W, say, on CW and little more on SSB will achieve satisfactory communications. Indeed, contact with almost all the USA call areas has been made with as little as 200mW. Even a simple ground-plane antenna performs well, especially for the Sporadic E (Es) or short-skip conditions which can produce good coverage of Europe from the UK during the summer (May to September, peaking in June and July). It will be seen that these features, coupled with the wide frequency range available, make it a very good band for relatively simple and inexpensive stations.

The band is much more dependent on solar activity than 14 and 21MHz, but it is to be regretted that the majority of operators desert it during the years around sunspot minimum. Those who continue to use it through these periods are often surprised at the paths which appear from time to time. To work 100 countries during the lean years can be a stimulating challenge. While, as in the lower HF allocations, propagation from the UK tends to swing from the east in the morning to the west in the afternoon, paths to many parts of the world will often exist simultaneously and WAC (Worked All Continents) in five minutes is by no means a rare feat.

Although generally propagation requires daylight over most of the path, DX contacts may still be made during the hours of darkness. Stations operating from close to the equator regard this as commonplace. For example, from West Africa there is often a long-path opening to Japan which extends through much of the night. It may well be that the few contacts recorded from the UK under these conditions would be increased in numbers if operators checked the band at times when experts say there will be no signals and also transmitted a CQ call. The same suggestion holds good also for the years around sunspot minimum.

As an aside, evening propagation to the southern states of the USA can sometimes happen when the operators at both ends point beams to the South Atlantic. Frustration occurs when the distant station does not realise this is necessary and turns to the direct bearing, and then considers the contact lost. Apart from E and F-layer propagation, the band performs in a similar manner to that of 50 and 144MHz and signals can be ducted over quite long distances under 'lift' conditions. Extended ground-wave contacts over distances of several hundred miles are commonplace via ducting.

The IARU Region 1 band plan for the 28MHz band follows a similar pattern to those for the other HF bands. That is to say, the lower frequencies from 28000 - 28070kHz are reserved for CW, with 28070 - 28190kHz for shared CW and data use. 28190 - 28225kHz is reserved for the IBP (International Beacon Project) beacons and operators are

Novice and Technician classes:		
28000 - 28300kHz: CW, RTTY / data (max power 200W)		
28300 - 28500kHz: CW, SSB (max power 200W)		
General, Advanced, Extra classes:		
28000 - 28300kHz: CW, RTTY / data		
28300 - 29700kHz: CW, Phone, Image		

Table 12: US 10m band allocations.

asked to keep these frequencies clear of any two-way contacts. The remainder of the band, 28225 -29700kHz, is available for both CW and phone, though, as might be expected, CW operation is centred on the portion below 28190kHz. A small 10kHz band centred on 28680kHz is recommended for SSTV working. AM and FM operation, including FM repeaters, can be found above 29MHz.

In the USA, the FCC permits all licence classes, including Novice and Technician licensees, to use 28000 - 28300kHz for CW, RTTY and other data modes. Novices and Technicians may also use 28300 - 28500kHz for CW and SSB, while all other licence classes (General, Advanced and Extra) may use 28300 - 29700kHz for CW, phone and Image modes. Because no USA stations may transmit on phone below 28300kHz, during years of high solar activity non-American phone operators tend to operate either below 283000kHz or well up the band, eg 28900kHz and upwards, to avoid USA interference. Towards sunspot minimum, random phone operation tends to be conducted between 28450 and 28550kHz. **Table 12** shows the full US 10m band allocations.

Above 29MHz, the IARU Region 1 band plan was modified in 2011 and again in 2014, which resulted in changes to the frequencies recommended for FM operation. Transmissions in the segment 29000 - 29200kHz now have a permitted bandwidth of 6kHz (previously it was 2.7kHz) and FM simplex operation should take place between 29110 and 29290kHz, with 10kHz-spaced channels (previously FM simplex channels were found at 29520 - 29550kHz and 29610 - 29650 kHz). The number of FM repeater channels was increased from four to eight, numbered RH1 - RH8 and an FM simplex 'parrot' repeater frequency was introduced: 29610kHz (input and output). A deviation of ±2.5kHz should be used, with 2.5kHz as the maximum modulation frequency.

The revised IARU Region 1 10m FM band plan can be found in **Table 13**.

29600kHz is also the FM simplex calling frequency in the USA, and there are 29MHz FM repeaters with outputs at 29620, 29640, 29660 and 29680MHz (inputs are 100kHz lower in each case). Increasing numbers of DXpeditions are including some activity on 10m FM, and it is remarkable how well the mode can

If you think the Spiderbeam is too large for your garden, a much smaller alternative is the Hexbeam. This design offers two monoband elements on each band from 20 to 6m inclusive.

29110kHz	Simplex channel
29120kHz	Simplex channel
29130kHz	Simplex channel
29140kHz	Simplex channel
29150kHz	Simplex channel
29160kHz	Simplex channel
29170kHz	Simplex channel
29180kHz	Simplex channel
29190kHz	Simplex channel
29200kHz	Simplex channel
29210kHz	Simplex channel
29220kHz	Simplex channel
29230kHz	Simplex channel
29240kHz	Simplex channel
29250kHz	Simplex channel
29260kHz	Simplex channel
29270kHz	Simplex channel
29280kHz	Simplex channel
29290kHz	Simplex channel
29520kHz	Repeater input RH1
29530kHz	Repeater input RH2
29540kHz	Repeater input RH3
29550kHz	Repeater input RH4
29560kHz	Repeater input RH5
29570kHz	Repeater input RH6
29580kHz	Repeater input RH7
29590kHz	Repeater input RH8
29600kHz	FM simplex calling channel
29610kHz	Simplex 'Parrot' Repeater (input & output)
29620kHz	Repeater output RH1
29630kHz	Repeater output RH2
29640kHz	Repeater output RH3
29650kHz	Repeater output RH4
29660kHz	Repeater output RH5
29670kHz	Repeater output RH6
29690kHz	Repeater output RH7
29690kHz	Repeater output RH8

Table 13: IARU Region 1 recommended 10m FM channels between 29100 and 29700kHz.

work when the band is open. But the existence of repeaters means that there is scope for working over extended ranges even when propagation is at an ebb.

Most multiband transceivers include FM and the availability of synthesised FM CB equipment that can be easily converted for 29MHz operation has encouraged many mobile operators to use the band both for DX and local working.

Although there are no frequencies specifically recommended for AM operation on 10m, it remains a popular mode, particularly for transatlantic communications at times of solar maximum, and these AM transmissions should now take place at 29000 - 29100kHz.

It is worth noting that at 28MHz, losses can be high if you have a long run of coaxial cable. The difference in loss between 50m of, say, the popular UR67 / RG213 and the more expensive H100 or H103 is probably 1dB or so, not huge but worth having. But using UR43 / RG58 cable would result in a further 2dB or so of loss, which is starting to be significant. If you have longer feeder runs, it is even more important to invest in low-loss cable.

The smaller size of antenna elements for this band allows the construction of compact, efficient installations. Gain antennas are easy to construct, perhaps by building a light-weight quad. Cheap 27MHz 3 and 4-element CB Yagis can easily be modified to provide a lightweight, low-cost and effective 10m antenna. Those who do have high-gain antennas on 10m, perhaps a 5 or 6-element monoband Yagi, find the band full of surprises at sunspot maximum, for example being able to work long-path to the Pacific during the evening or to the US West Coast around dawn.

THE VHF / UHF BANDS

The term 'VHF' (Very High Frequency) applies to frequencies between 30 and 300MHz, and 'UHF' (Ultra High Frequency) means 300MHz to 3GHz, although in amateur practice frequencies above 1GHz are normally termed 'microwaves' (see Table 1). The ITU VHF / UHF allocations for Region 1 are 144 - 146MHz and 430 - 440MHz. Most Region 1 countries permit 144 - 146MHz operation but there are several with restricted 430 - 440MHz Amateur Service allocations.

Notwithstanding ITU allocations, national administrations may permit amateur service operation in additional bands. Starting with the UK in the 1980s, amateurs in the majority of Region 1 countries have now been granted permits to operate in the 50 - 52MHz (6-metre) band. Also originating in a UK-only allocation, several countries now permit operation on the 70MHz band on some basis, either permanent or temporary.

Amateur allocations in Regions 2 and 3 are broadly similar to those in Region 1, with the addition of an ITU allocation between 50 and 54MHz. In Region 2 the bands 220 - 225MHz and 902 - 928MHz may also be allocated for amateur use. It should be noted that many of the amateur bands above 30MHz are shared with other services.

The four VHF / UHF bands of particular interest to UK amateurs are those at 50, 70, 144 and 430MHz, commonly referred to as 'Six', 'Four', 'Two' and 'Seventy' respectively.

Because of the wide variety of activities taking place on VHF and UHF, the band plans are necessarily much more complex than those for the HF bands. The main aim of the band plans is to separate incompatible transmission modes, and so let everyone get on with the business of communicating by his or her chosen method. Although the band plans are, as on HF, purely voluntary arrangements (in the UK, at least), there are good reasons for observing them at all times. Calling CQ on CW on 145.7MHz is quite legal within the terms of the amateur licence, but is very unlikely to result in a contact, and certainly will not make any friends. Similarly, the beacon sub-band may seem completely empty and an ideal spot for a contact, but even a short transmission there could well cause serious annoyance to somebody many miles away who is intently listening in the noise for a distant beacon. There is room on the bands for all of the many activities, provided a little care, consideration and respect for the interests of other operators are shown. The band plans act as a guide in this. For example, by having specific calling frequencies for data communications, operators can concentrate their listening and calling on known frequencies, and avoid interference both to and from other modes. All VHF / UHF users are recommended to keep a copy of the band plans to hand near the rig.

Novice class:	
No allocation	
Technician, General, Advanced and Extra classes:	
50.0 - 50.1MHz:	CW only
50.1 - 54.0MHz:	CW, RTTY / date, Phone, Image

Table 14: US 6m band allocations.

50MHz (6m) Band

The 6-metre band sits at a very interesting point in the radio spectrum, behaving for much of the time as any other VHF band but, for short periods during each sunspot cycle, enjoying the benefits of E and F-layer propagation, enabling world-wide DX contacts to take place. It is probably true to say that 6m is the only band where every type of propagation is observable and usable. Meteor scatter propagation is reliable on an almost daily basis for those with the right equipment and software, Sporadic E propagation, especially during the summer months, brings the band to life with contacts throughout Europe and beyond, and some well-equipped stations even achieve EME ('moonbounce' or Earth-Moon-Earth) contacts on the band (see Chapter 9).

Almost all European countries now have access to 6m, as do most other countries around the world. In some cases access is by way of a special permit, rather than as a basic part of the licence, so that the authorities can withdraw permission at short notice if problems occur with other services. All US licensees except for those with the Novice licence (which is no longer issued) have access to a 4MHz-wide band at 6m, from 50.0 to 54.0MHz (see **Table 14**). It should be noted that frequency allocations in some countries are more restricted than in the UK. French stations, for example, can be found on SSB only above 50.2MHz.

In the UK, the band is effectively divided into two halves. 50 to 51MHz is allocated on a primary basis and 51 to 52MHz is a secondary allocation, with a lower power limit for Full licensees (100W compared with 400W for 50 - 51MHz). Foundation and Intermediate licensees may use their full licensed power - 10W and 50W respectively - over the whole band.

Many operators never stray outside the lower 250kHz of the band, where the majority of SSB and CW operation takes place. Beacons are located in the bottom 80kHz of the band, giving an early warning of a rising MUF, though many 6m enthusiasts also monitor commercial frequencies below 50MHz for the first indication of possible band openings. The band segment 50.1MHz to 50.3MHz is the 'DX window', with an inter-regional calling frequency at 50.110MHz,

and 6m DXers tend to be very protective of these arrangements, getting upset if intra-continental contacts take place within this segment or if any QSOs at all take place on the calling channel (as with all calling channels, the intention is that stations move away as soon as communication has been established). Day to day SSB activity in Region 1 should centre on 50.150MHz. The problem, of course, is that the band can get very busy indeed when there is a good Sporadic E opening, and stations inevitably start to spread themselves further and further from that frequency.

Higher in the band, there is a certain amount of FM activity, simplex and via repeaters, and there are allocated datacomms channels. The Region 1 Meteor Scatter reference frequency is 50.2MHz, but JT6M meteor scatter operation typically takes place on or around 50.230MHz.

The 6m DXer lives a rather different life to either an HF DXer or 2m / 70cm DXer. Unless he ventures into the specialist areas of meteor scatter or EME, there will be long periods when there is nothing much to chase. But during those periods of the year when propagation is enhanced and there are DXpeditions to be worked (most 6m DXpeditions are timed to coincide with the Sporadic E season), he cannot afford to be away from the radio, because band openings can be fleeting. It's no good working even 10 minutes from home and being able to drop everything to rush back to the radio if a DX spot appears. By the time you get there the opening could well have disappeared. So 6m DXers either organise their lives to work from home, or schedule their annual holidays for June and July, getting those painting and gardening jobs done, but being ready to drop everything the moment the band opens. It is different again, of course, when F2 propagation is expected. This is likely to be optimum in the autumn and early spring during sunspot peaks but, again, there will only be certain days when the MUF goes above 50MHz, so there are long periods when nothing much happens, then all hell breaks loose when the band opens: this is both the joy and the frustration of the band.

6m is available on budget HF radios such as the FT-450D . . .

. . . as well as the top-of-the-range transceivers such as the IC-7851.

The various propagation modes are discussed in detail in Chapter 6, but it is worth mentioning that, from the UK, double-hop, and even triple-hop, Sporadic E is a remarkably consistent phenomenon around early July each year, and allows contacts into the Middle East and to North America. It is not unusual to work North American stations in the early hours of the morning when the higher HF bands are completely dead. Stations closer to the equator are well served with trans-equatorial propagation (TEP), the level of ionisation at equatorial latitudes remaining high almost constantly. UK stations are often frustrated to see Cluster spots for DX being worked by Italian and Greek stations that is totally out of the question at more northern latitudes. TEP sometimes extends as far north as the southern half of the UK, usually around March and October. What we do benefit from in the UK, though, is Auroral propagation, which can provide some useful openings to other countries in northern Europe.

The good news is that, with so many countries now active on 6m, achieving DXCC (100 countries worked and confirmed) is realistic for anyone with a reasonable location and antenna and 100 watts or so to play with. Even in years of low solar activity, a European station who is alert to what is happening on the band could expect to work perhaps 60 or 70 countries in a year, and have DXCC within five years or less; the more serious and better-equipped operators do somewhat better. However, the leading scores (and several UK DXers now have over 200 DXCC entities on the band) are achieved only by being active through at least a couple of solar maxima.

As far as equipment for 6m is concerned, most HF transceivers now have this band included as standard. This goes for both 'mobile' transceivers and the medium to top-end 'base station' equipment. Some models are particularly popular with 6m operators because they have a spectral display which is an excellent way of monitoring the band for openings. The alternative approach is to use a dedicated 6m transceiver, though fewer of these are now available, or to transvert from another band. There are also several linear amplifiers marketed for 6m, while some HF amplifiers also cover the band. In addition, modification details are available for several older HF amplifiers, now available at low prices, for

converting them to 6m use. The good news, though, is that when Sporadic E propagation is in evidence, signal strengths are usually high and an output of 100 watts is more than adequate.

A number of contests take place on 6m each year (see Chapter 11), sponsored particularly by the RSGB and by the UK Six Metre Group (UKSMG) [18], a body well worth belonging to if you start to take 6m operating seriously. Even if you don't consider yourself a contester, these events generate activity on what might otherwise be a dead band and, unlike in HF contesting, QSO rates are usually low enough that there is time for a brief chat with other stations worked, should you so wish.

Antenna systems vary enormously, from a dipole in the loft (fine when Sporadic E signals are loud) to long-boom Yagis and, for the really serious players, stacked Yagi arrays. There is no doubt that, at times, every last decibel of performance can be critical and at these times those amateurs with a hilltop location, high power, a first-rate receiver, the lowest-loss feeder and a stack of Yagis will be able to work DX that others simply won't hear. But the varying nature of 6m propagation means there are other times when that very same amateur, with his top-of-the-range station will sit in frustration listening to band noise while it is you, just 20 miles away and with your modest set-up, who is working the DX.

A Voluntary Operating Code of Practice for Six Metre Operators has been formulated by the UKSMG in conjunction with other national 6m groups including JAROC, HARDXA, SixItaly, DRAA, LABRE-SP and SSA, and is available at [19].

70MHz (4m) Band

UK amateurs have had use of this band since the 1950s. It is at 70.0 - 70.5MHz and is available on a secondary basis on condition that no interference is caused to other services either inside or outside the UK. The power limit is 160W for Full licensees (50W for Intermediate and 10W for Foundation licensees).

It is unfortunate that because the 70MHz band is available in relatively few countries its full potential has not been recognised, though this is gradually changing with several European countries gaining access to the band in recent years. Not all these countries have full or permanent access to the band: in some cases it is on a time-limited experimental basis, while in some other countries access is by a limited 'special licence'. The situation is fluid, and it is always a good idea to check the latest situation, for example via the 70MHz website [20] or the IARU Region 1 website [21].

In addition to those whose authorities permit them to transmit, there are operators in other countries who have suitable receiving equipment and who are interested in cross-band working. Most commonly frequencies around 28885kHz are used for talk back, but other bands have also been employed, with 6m / 4m working becoming quite popular (propagation often being similar). There have been a few 70 to 144MHz cross-band contacts from the UK to the European mainland by meteor scatter, where the more modest power and antenna gains in use on the lower band are compensated by the greater propagation efficiency. Meteor

The UK Six Metre Group (UKSMG) website is a focal point, bringing together announcements, a calendar of 6m events, 6m spots from the Cluster network and other related information.

scatter contacts also take place, and skeds are usually co-ordinated via the ON4KST chatroom [22] as well as the Cluster network.

The ultimate cross-band achievement is a 50 to 70MHz contact with stations on the other side of the Atlantic. A few such contacts were made by F2 propagation during solar maxima, but what is believed to be the first 50 / 70MHz cross-band contact between Europe and North America via multiple-hop Sporadic E took place in June 2007, at solar minimum, between G7CNF and VE9AA. When arranging cross-band skeds, care should be taken over the choice of the 70MHz frequency as this band may be used for other purposes in various parts of the world. The advice of the distant station should be sought on this point.

One of the brakes on 4m activity in the UK up to now has been the availability of suitable equipment. FM and digital voice transceivers are available commercially and many surplus PMR sets can easily be converted for the band. This has led to an increase in FM activity in some parts of the country, especially where local clubs have run a project to modify such equipment for members in order that the club net can run on 4m. The band is also used for data modes.

However, SSB and CW operation has relied largely on home-built transverters operating in conjunction with an HF or 2m transceiver. This situation is slowly changing. The version of the Yaesu FT-847 transceiver sold in the UK had limited 4m capabilities and, as more countries gain access to the band, manufacturers are starting to take 70MHz more seriously. Recently, The Elecraft KX3 has been available with a 4m transverter installed. Also, the Icom IC-7100 HF-70cm mobile includes the 4m band in its European version. A new company, Noble Radio [23] produces a 4m single band transceiver running up to 15W of CW and SSB. A 300W all-mode amplifier is available from HA1YA [24].

FM activity takes place with vertical polarisation and most users have a quarter-wave or other vertical antenna. SSB and CW operation is best accomplished, especially if you are chasing DX, with a horizontal rotatable Yagi, 4- or 5-elements being a convenient size for most locations.

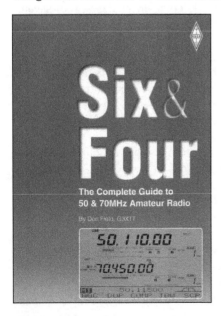

The definitive guide to operating on the lower VHF bands, *Six and Four*.

4m 300W all-mode amplifier made by Mechanics & Electronics Inc.

The most recent development on this band is that Ofcom have agreed the use by radio amateurs of an extra mega-hertz at 70.5 to 71.5MHz for digital experimentation. Use will be permitted only via a Special Research Permit on a non-protection, non-interference basis, and is not available in Scotland. Further details are on the RSGB web site at [25].

144MHz (2m) Band

This has long been the most popular of the amateur VHF bands. On a day to day basis it is used for FM and various data modes, and under good conditions it is possible to make CW and SSB contacts from the UK deep into Europe, to North Africa and down to the Canary Islands in the North Atlantic. When an opening of one sort or another occurs the high level of activity ensures there will usually be someone on the other end of the path keen to make a contact.

As well as the normal CW, SSB and FM, many specialist communications techniques and propagation modes are in regular use, and this is reflected in the complexity of the usage part of the band plan. The summary below is only intended as a guideline; band users are advised to study the full band plan [3].

The bottom 35kHz has traditionally been devoted to moon-bounce (EME) and it is still important that this region be kept clear unless the Moon is well below any European horizon. It is in regular use by stations using high-gain antennas and sensitive receivers to copy weak signals which may be inaudible on most normal equipment.

The CW-only segment extends up to 144.110MHz, with a calling frequency at 144.050MHz. Most CW activity takes place between 144.035 and 144.075MHz, and during openings, especially of the auroral type, there are usually many good DX contacts to be made in this part of the band. In particularly intense auroras the entire CW exclusive section can become quite congested. There is a CW activity period from 2000 local time every Monday evening. The calling frequency for random meteor scatter CW contacts is 144.100 and MS activity can extend to 144.126kHz. From 144.110MHz to 144.150MHz, CW is shared with narrowband data modes, including PSK31 and those used for EME. Datamodes extend to 144.180MHz and are shared with both CW and SSB.

The most popular DX mode is SSB for which the calling frequency is 144.300MHz. To avoid overcrowding, a substantial change of frequency is recommended once contact has been established on 144.300MHz. When activity is high, such as during openings and contests, the concept of a calling frequency tends to be dropped and stations may be heard calling CQ anywhere from 144.150 to 144.350MHz or higher. In these circumstances contacts are made in a similar manner to those on the HF bands. Cross-mode CW / SSB working is rare but can prove useful in getting through interference.

The SSB and CW segment continues up to 144.400MHz, the higher frequencies being more popular for local SSB working and nets, such as those involving Worked All Britain enthusiasts. The bottom 500kHz of the band includes several meteor scatter and field-aligned irregularity calling frequencies and working segments, which should be avoided by stations not participating in such activities.

The beacon band falls between 144.400 - 144.490MHz, and most European countries have one or more beacons in this region, as shown in the *RSGB Yearbook* [4]. These beacons are used by keen DXers to help evaluate propagation conditions, and by careful monitoring often give a valuable forewarning of an impending opening. This section should be regarded as strictly 'out of bounds' for transmitting. Personal WSPR beacons are found just HF of the DX beacon band, no more than 500Hz either side of 144.492MHz.

The non-channelised all-mode segment runs from 144.500 to 144.794MHz and it is here that many specialist communication modes, including RTTY, fax and SSTV, are to be found. Each of these modes has a specific calling frequency which should be avoided by other operators. The sub-segment 144.794 to 144.990MHz is designated for data modes, mostly the DX Cluster network and packet radio.

The top megahertz of the band contains allocations for FM simplex, digital voice, repeaters, satellite and ISS communications, which are dealt with in Chapters 12 and 13.

Equipment considerations for the 2m band were discussed in Chapter 3. For FM and digital operation, a wide range of transceivers is available, from small handhelds, through sets designed for car installation to fully-fledged base stations. SSB and CW DX operators also have a choice of equipment but will be more demanding in terms of RF performance and will want to ensure that their entire station is optimised. For receiving, a masthead pre-amplifier may prove valuable if a long cable run is involved. On the transmit side, many serious DXers use linear amplifiers, in which case it is especially important to check that the transceiver is properly adjusted, to avoid causing problems to other band users.

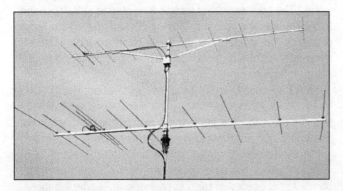

The G0HCE 2-4-6m Yagi group antenna.

Antenna systems for FM operation usually consist of a vertical antenna, probably 5/8-wave, mounted well in the clear. For DXing, a horizontal Yagi of probably eight elements or more is typical, with some stations opting for large, stacked arrays.

In 2014, Ofcom announced that in order to encourage amateurs to experiment and test new communications schemes and systems the frequencies from 146 to 147MHz, would be available for a year via a Notice of Variation on a temporary basis to Full licence holders only. Further details can be found in a December 2014 *RadCom* article [26].

430MHz (70cm) Band

This used to be very much an enthusiasts' band, most of the equipment being home-built, but now there is a wide selection of excellent commercial equipment available, from all-mode transceivers through high-power amplifiers to antennas. Although path loss, which is frequency dependent, is greater than on the lower bands, this is compensated for by the higher antenna gains in common use. Most terrestrial DX contacts are made by tropospheric propagation, although the better-equipped stations complete auroral and meteor scatter contacts. Sporadic E mode does not exist at 430MHz, the highest reported Sporadic E frequency being in the 220MHz region in the USA. The anatomy of the DX section, 432.000 - 432.990MHz, is very similar to that of 144MHz, with CW, SSB, all-mode and beacon sub-bands, as well as special allocations for moonbounce and data modes. Many of the comments in the preceding section apply equally to 430MHz. Operating practice is also similar to that on 144MHz.

A common practice during lifts is for operators who are interested in 144MHz, 430MHz and perhaps 1.3GHz to call on the lower band and announce that they are "QRV on 70cm" (or 23cm, or both). If the other station is interested, a frequency on the higher band is agreed. This procedure has the advantage of allowing beam headings to be accurately determined, which is particularly useful when the narrow beamwidths in common use on the higher bands are considered. More and more new technology is appearing on the market place these days with DSP (digital signal processing) being just one new addition - DSP is extremely useful for weak-signal working on any VHF / UHF band.

The FM segment of the band is used for simplex contacts, repeater contacts, both conventional FM and digital voice, as well as data modes. There are many 70cm FM repeaters in the UK, and the data modes section is busy. Some amateur television activity also takes place on the band, though most is now on 23cm or above.

In the UK the primary user of this band is the Ministry of Defence and as Secondary users the Amateur and Amateur Satellite Services generally enjoy a peaceful co-existence. There are, however, increasing pressures on this band and users should be aware of local restrictions that may exist. These can be found in the current band plan [3].

The equipment issues are much the same as for 2m, except that frequency stability is even more important and, of course, feeder losses are significantly higher on both transmit and receive. This latter may necessitate, for example, siting a receive pre-amplifier and remote power amplifier close to the antenna.

FM antennas usually consist of some sort of phased vertical, suitably weatherproofed. Many suitable vertical antennas are commercially available. DX operation uses horizontally-polarised Yagi antennas, typically of 18 elements or more. As on 2m, serious DXers use stacking to achieve greater gain. For moonbounce or satellite operation, it will be necessary to be able to adjust antenna elevation as well as azimuth.

THE MICROWAVE BANDS

1.3GHz (23cm) Band

The 1.3GHz band is the lowest-frequency 'microwave' band but exhibits some of the characteristics of both the VHF / UHF bands and the higher bands. Propagation losses are higher than on 430MHz, and unless efficient equipment is used results can be rather disappointing. Nevertheless, many dedicated 1.3GHz operators have made contacts of well over 1500km and some have worked over 100 locator squares. However, with the exception of over-water super-refraction paths (West Coast USA to Hawaii, or across the Great Australian Bight), longer paths are easier via the half-million mile Earth-Moon-Earth path!

Uses include amateur satellite Mode L operation where the Earth-to-space uplink is in the 23cm band and the space-to-Earth downlink is in the 70cm (433MHz) band. The band is popular for ATV and there are growing numbers of analogue and digital ATV and speech repeaters in this band. There are also quite a few propagation beacons (between 1296.800 and 1296.990MHz) which help to indicate when tropospheric propagation is present or even just to provide confidence that the receiver is working correctly.

There are only a few current commercial multimode trans-ceivers that cover the 1.3GHz band. These include the Kenwood TS-2000X and the Icom IC-910X. For serious DX work some form of power amplifier (HPA) is essential and raising the power output to 50 - 100W will effect a useful improvement in transmitter range under average conditions. Most serious DX operators use solid-state amplifiers located close to the antenna or use very low loss coaxial cable runs. As with the lower bands, a good antenna system is of great bene-fit. Small antennas, such as corner reflectors or a single, short, Yagi, will have insufficient gain for other than local operation.

Serious operators use multiple,stacked Yagi arrays or dishes greater than 2m in diameter. Since coaxial cables can be

The TS-2000X is a multimode, multiband transceiver that covers the bands from 1.8MHz all the way up to 1300MHz (with the exception of 70MHz).

considerably lossier at 1.3GHz than on lower frequencies, the best quality cable you can afford should be used. For example, an 11m run of RG-214 cable will have a loss of 0.78dB at 144MHz, 1.52dB at 432MHz but almost 3dB at 1.3GHz. This means that only half of the power generated by the PA will reach the antenna - and your receiver noise figure will be degraded by 3dB too. So-called 'low-loss' UHF TV cable should not even be considered at 1.3GHz! Andrew Corporation (Andrew) Heliax feeder is a good choice for this or any other microwave band below 10GHz, although mounting the receive preamplifier(s) and power amplifier stage(s) at masthead will allow the use of less expensive coaxial cable, eg Ecoflex 10. Most stations employ masthead pre-amplifiers and these are always of great benefit regardless of the feeder losses involved.

The IARU Region 1 band plan is quite detailed. As far as DX activity is concerned, most operation is around 1296.200MHz, referred to as the narrow-band centre of activity. Two points are important, however. The segment 1296.000 to 1296.025MHz should be left clear for moon-bounce operating, and no transmissions should be made in the beacon segment (1296.800 to 1296.990MHz). Contrary to the practice on the lower bands, almost all activity, local or DX, SSB, CW or FM, is horizontally polarised, although some vertically polarised FM operation is used in some areas.

The 2.3GHz (13cm), 3.4GHz (9cm) and 5.7GHz (6cm) Bands

These three 'intermediate' microwave bands are considered together since activity is relatively low compared with 1.3 and 10GHz. Although transmitter power output levels generally drop with increasing frequency the ready availability of suitable ex-commercial, surplus, solid state, high power amplifiers, using either LDMOS transistors or power GaAs FETs, means that transmitter output power levels of several hundred watts are now common at 2.3GHz and 20 - 50W at 3.4GHz. At 5.7GHz power levels tend to be below 25W using solid-state power amplifiers. Travelling Wave Tube Amplifiers (TWTA) are still used and are preferred for some high-power EME. Low noise preamplifiers, using HEMT devices, enable system noise figures below 2dB in terrestrial systems and below 0.5dB in EME systems for all three bands.

At 2.3GHz, using tropospheric scatter or aircraft scatter propagation, distances up to around 600 - 800km for terres-trial contacts are possible, beyond which the EME path is easier! The corresponding terrestrial distance at 3.4GHz and 5.7GHz bands is a little less although the increasing efficiency of rain scatter propagation on these bands may occasionally allow operation to beyond 750km during some of the bigger summer thunderstorms.

Loop-Yagi antennas are practical up to about the 3.4GHz band. Beyond this, dimensions and constructional tolerance become too critical to make them worthwhile. Consequently, above 3.4GHz, parabolic dish antennas predominate.

The availability of higher power amplifiers, together with very low noise pre-amplifiers, has opened up the middle bands to DX operation from even moderate home locations. Consequently the amount of portable operation in Europe (and particularly in the UK) has noticeably declined in recent years. Elsewhere portable and 'rover' operation seems to be as popular as ever.

Amateur TV on 2.4GHz is popular due to the availability of low-cost video sender based equipment modules, and a significant number of amateur TV repeaters are located within the band. The Comtech modules mentioned in Chapter 3 are also available for 13cm, and they provide an inexpensive means of frequency-agile operation. However, most licence-free 2.4GHz videosenders have at least one channel within the amateur 13cm band, and as a licensed amateur you can increase the power and antenna gain. A simple and cheap power amplifier is a 'WLAN booster' or amplifier, often available at 0.5 or 1W power output (check your favourite online auction site). You may have to change the input/ output sockets to standard SMA, but apart from that they work straight out of the box and some even include a preamp. (As they're intended for WLAN, which shares the same band as video senders, they may not be effective at other parts of the 13cm band). Increasing interest in digital TV means that the band should see further growth in ATV operation. There is some ATV operation in the 3.4 and 5.7GHz bands, although understandably this is at a relatively low level at present. 5.7GHz video senders are beginning to appear,and are being pressed into service for ATV use.

These bands are increasingly being used in amateur satellite communications, as described in Chapter 14, as well as for other experimental work including EME.

The 10GHz Band

10GHz (3cm) has, for many years, remained a very popular microwave band. Initially this is because very simple, low-powered, wideband FM (speech) transceivers are very easy and inexpensive to construct. These systems are based on surplus intruder-alarm Doppler units, used as the receiver local oscillator / mixer and the transmitter at power levels in the range 1mW to 40mW. The techniques are simple and serve as an admirable introduction to microwave operation over short distances from fixed locations, or longer line-of-sight paths when operated portable.

In recent years the much greater effectiveness of narrow-band techniques has tended to overshadow wideband operation. Several manufacturers offer kits and ready-made

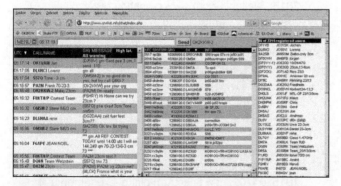

The ON4KST chat facility can be used to set up skeds on any band or group of bands, including microwaves [part of a photo from www.ok2kkw.com/vusc4win_eng.htm].

transverters for the 10GHz band and even the most inexperienced kit builder should be able to put these together to produce a highly-effective narrowband system. When combined with a small dish antenna of typically 60cm diameter a very potent station,capable of tropospheric scatter ranges of more than 200 - 300km with 1W RF output can be produced. Rainscatter can increase this to over 500km. The world record for 10GHz terrestrial tropospheric DX is over 2000km.

Using solid state GaAs FET amplifiers transmit powers up to 20W are within the grasp of many home-based stations and 5 - 10W is very common. System receiver noise figures are usually below 2dB. Dish antennas of up to about 1.2m diameter are routinely used by home based 10GHz stations. Radio amateurs seem to have few difficulties pointing these dishes to with a degree or so of the partner station.

Coupled with enough antenna gain (say a 2.4 or 3m dish), EME contacts are routinely possible at the 20 to 100W power level. The narrow beam-width of such a dish means that accurate antenna pointing becomes very important. However, it is possible to track the Moon using 'Moon noise' as a powerful aid. This is possible because the diameter of the Moon is comparable with the beam width of the dish and so the Moon 'fills' the dish aperture with noise that is higher than the surrounding cold sky. The receiver noise output level can rise several dB when pointing at the Moon with a low noise receiver system and a 3m dish.

10GHz is fairly popular for ATV, either using simple Gunn-diode based transmitters or by multiplying up from a lower frequency such as a 2.4GHz transmitter operating just out of band. The Comtech 13cm transmitters mentioned in Chapter 3, suitably re-programmed, are ideal for this. Commercial x4 multipliers are readily available, and suitable for ATV. Receiving 10GHz ATV is usually achieved using a modified commercial satellite ATV LNB with the local oscillator re-tuned to 9GHz so the output is in the 23cm band. Replacement 'pucks' (dielectric resonant oscillators) are available,and these are quite simply substituted for the original one in the LNB. As LNBs usually contain two identical amplifier strips (one each for H and V polarisation), some amateurs have experimented with hacking out one of the preamplifier stages to use as QRP power amps for multipliers that have a low power output.

The 24GHz Band and Higher

These bands lie in a region of the spectrum where atmospheric gas (including water vapour) absorption can be very high. With the current generation of amateur radio equipment this tends to limit tropospheric propagation range to around 150 - 200km. However, relatively long-distance terrestrial communication is possible from time to time on the 24 and 47GHz bands by either super-refraction (eg over the North Sea) or by forward rain scatter and, of course, worldwide by EME.

A typical amateur radio 24GHz system consists of a 1 - 3W GaAs FET power amplifier, sub-2dB noise figure HEMT preamplifier (usually about 3dB system noise figure) and 30 - 60cm diameter dish antenna.

G4AET (front) and G8CUB operating on 76GHz from Winter Hill [photo: G8ACE].

The effect of the gas absorption is that it is necessary to add a few tenths of a dB per km to the normal propagation losses. Over a 100km path this might mean an additional 20 to 30dB to the tropospheric propagation loss. It is unlikely that amateurs will ever be able to develop the sort of power levels necessary to achieve ranges on 24GHz and above similar to 10GHz. However,that may be an overly pessimistic comment, given the ability of radio amateurs to find ways of achieving the seemingly impossible! Greater frequency stability, digital modes and DSP may provide the answer. Already these have been exploited by the likes of WA1ZMS to achieve remarkable distances at 241GHz and above.

Contacts have been made in the UK on all amateur microwave bands up to 141GHz and it seems likely that contacts on the higher allocations may be made in the next few years.

Talk Back for Microwave Contacts

In the past it has been usual to make initial contact with a station on a lower band, such as 2m, 70cm or 23cm, by calling CQ or maybe by previous arrangement (sked). Calling CQ directly on bands above 23cm tends to be unproductive due to the very directive antennas that are necessary to achieve long range. The probability of two antennas, each with a beamwidth of less than 10°, being initially aligned for successful communication is rather low. All that has changed with the advent of the popular logging and chat web facilities like the ON4KST chat pages [22]. Here everyone is 'equal' and even stations located in remote areas of Europe can make their presence known to the community and contacts can readily be organised. Big stations no longer dominate.

The ON4KST chat facility, in particular, has been responsible for a dramatic increase in amateur microwave activity in Europe in the last few years. As a consequence of this the use of 144MHz talk back has reduced. Since man made noise levels on 144MHz have increased noticeably in recent years, particularly in urban areas, some home stations have had to abandon 144MHz for talk back operation.

A further drawback of 144MHz for talk back is that the very different propagation modes experienced on 144MHz and, say, 10GHz, can often mean that signals on 10GHz are stronger than on 144MHz, even at distances of over 300km! However, it is unlikely that 144MHz talk back will disappear completely and for sheer simplicity it is hard to beat the effectiveness of a simple 2m talk back system for the shorter operating range usual on 24GHz and above.

REFERENCES

[1]   ARRL chart of USA amateur frequencies: www.arrl.org/graphical-frequency-allocations

[2]   *Six and Four (The Complete Guide to 50 and 70MHz Amateur Radio)*, Don Field, G3XTT, RSGB 2013. Available from www.rsgbshop.org

[3]   UK band plans: http://rsgb.org/main/operating/band-plans

[4]   *RSGB Yearbook*, ed Mike Browne, G3DIH, RSGB (published annually). Available from www.rsgbshop.org

[5]   IARU Region 1 (for band plans etc): http://iaru-r1.org

[6]   http://uk.groups.yahoo.com/group/rsgb_lf_group/

[7]   *LF Today - a guide to success on the bands below 1MHz*, 3rd edition, Mike Dennison, G3XDV, RSGB 2013. Available from www.rsgbshop.org

[8]   *ON4UN's Low-Band DXing*, 5th edition, John Devoldere, ON4UN, ARRL. Available from www.rsgbshop.org

[9]   *The ARRL Antenna Book*, 22nd edition, ARRL. Available from www.rsgbshop.org

[10] *DXing on the Edge - The Thrill of 160 Meters*, Jeff Briggs, K1ZM, ARRL 1997. Available from www.rsgbshop.org

[11] *Building Successful HF Antennas*, Peter Dodd, G3LDO, RSGB. Available from www.rsgbshop.org

[12] *Successful Wire Antennas*, eds Ian Poole, G3YWX and Steve Telenius-Lowe, 9M6DXX / KH0UN (PJ4DX), RSGB 2012. Available from www.rsgbshop.org

[13] *RSGB Antenna File*, ed Steve Telenius-Lowe, 9M6DXX (PJ4DX), RSGB 2013. Available from www.rsgbshop.org

[14] *Antennas Mastered*, Peter Dodd, G3LDO, RSGB 2014. Available from www.rsgbshop.org

[15] *Stealth Antennas*, 2nd edition, Steve Nichol, G0KYA, RSGB 2014. Available from www.rsgbshop.org

[16] *Novel Antennas*, Steve Telenius-Lowe, PJ4DX, RSGB 2015. Available from www.rsgbshop.org

[17] Grey Line Map: http://dx.qsl.net/propagation/greyline.html

[18] UK Six Metre Group: www.uksmg.org

[19] www.uksmg.org/content/code.htm

[20] 4m band: www.70mhz.org

[21] IARU Region 1: www.iaru-r1.org

[22] ON4KST chat rooms: www.on4kst.com/chat/start.php

[23] www.nobleradio.eu/

[24] www.ha1ya.hu

[25] http://rsgb.org/main/blog/news/gb2rs/headlines/2015/04/02/new-spectrum-digital-experimentation/

[26] '146-147MHz: A New Frontier for Amateur Innovation' by John Regnault, G4SWX, *RadCom*, Dec 2014.

The Amateur Radio Operating Manual

Propagation

A MAJOR PART OF the fascination of amateur radio as a hobby lies in the tremendous variety of communication paths provided by the amateur bands. This caters for a wide range of interests, from regular schedules across town or across the world to the search for contacts with rare and exotic DX stations and a variety of competitive activities and contests. In all these aspects, satisfaction and competitive success benefit from a thorough knowledge of the possibilities presented by the various propagation modes which will be encountered on the bands.

This chapter discusses the propagation mechanisms of most interest to amateurs, but is by no means intended to be a technical treatise on propagation. Rather, its focus is on how our operating is affected by, and needs to take account of, the various propagation mechanisms. There are many excellent textbooks dealing with propagation at a more detailed level, though it is certainly worth bearing in mind that propagation mechanisms which are of little interest to the professional world, because of their unpredictability and sporadic nature, may be of huge interest to amateurs. One of the great pleasures of amateur radio is finding an unexpected propagation path, and making contacts over that path, whereas such anomalies are anathema to professional communicators because, as often as not, they actually serve to disrupt normal communications. A good example is Sporadic E, of great interest to amateurs on 6 metres and, occasionally, 2 metres, but extremely disruptive of VHF band television (where that still exists) and FM radio broadcasting, as well as other services using those frequency bands.

The historical divide between HF and VHF, at 30MHz, is a recognition that this is normally the highest frequency at which ionospheric propagation can take place, allowing long-distance communications. Frequencies above 30MHz were considered line-of-sight (or a little beyond that). In practice, of course, nature is never so simple. The 11-year solar cycle, onto which are superimposed both annual and daily cycles, determines that the maximum usable frequency for ionospheric propagation varies widely and, at times, can rise to well above 30MHz. In addition, over the years both amateurs and professionals have discovered, explored and learned to use a wide variety of other propagation mechanisms which were little known, if at all, when that early divide was set in place.

What follows, therefore, is a discussion of the main propagation mechanisms that you will encounter in day to day amateur radio operating, with hints and tips on how to exploit them to advantage. The discussion inevitably refers to the frequency bands on which these propagation mechanisms are likely to be encountered. For further information on each band, refer to the previous chapter. It should also be mentioned that, on occasion, more than one propagation mechanism may be at work at the same time, for example a combination of ionospheric propagation and Sporadic E. In some cases, it may not even be possible to determine what mechanism is at work to make a particular contact possible. Often it is only possible to do so after combining information about a large number of contacts taking place during a specific period. There is much still to be understood and bodies such as the RSGB's Propagation Studies Committee [1] set out to gather data and add to the fund of knowledge which exists. A world-wide network of amateur propagation beacons exists in most of the bands - from the low bands to high microwave - in order to provide enhanced data for propagation studies in addition to alerting amateurs to propagation opportunities.

GROUND-WAVE PROPAGATION

The starting point with radio propagation is that radio waves are just one component of the electromagnetic spectrum. Like other elements of that spectrum (visible light, X-rays), radio waves will travel in straight lines unless something acts to divert them from that path. That something could be a change in the density of the medium (think of light waves being refracted as they enter or leave water), or a strong magnetic or electric field when in the presence of free electrons. Even when travelling in a straight line, although the waves will theoretically go on for ever, they will be attenuated by the medium they are travelling through. However high the gain of the antenna they are propagated from, they will diverge with distance, reducing in strength according to the inverse square law. Although a coherent beam of light from a laser, for example, can remain concentrated over extended distances, there is no straightforward way of achieving this with the wavelengths involved in radio frequencies except in the microwave bands where parabolic reflectors can be used to focus the radiated energy into a 'beam', much like light, that may only be a few fractions of a degree wide. But however high the gain of an antenna, the radiation will gradually spread out.

Which brings us back to line-of-sight propagation. All frequencies, from VLF through to the highest microwave frequencies, will propagate line of sight from the transmitting antenna just as light does (which, after all, is what "line of sight" actually means). Some very impressive distance records have been set on the microwave bands by stations on mountaintops with no intervening obstructions.

Without going to those extremes, the distance achievable by ground-wave propagation will vary according to the terrain and conductivity of the ground and the nature of any obstacles (such as buildings, vegetation and hills). The distance will also vary with frequency. The higher the frequency, the greater the attenuation as signals travel close to the Earth. All other factors being equal, a 160m ground-wave signal, for example, will travel farther than an 80m signal before attenuation renders it inaudible at the receiver. At LF this advantage continues with 630m ground-wave outstripping 160m and 2200m being even better. It is difficult the distinguish the ground-wave from skywave, and significant amounts of sky-wave are present even in daytime at LF.

Other factors can come into play, for example in the microwave region where some bands are more affected by water absorption with the result that a rain storm can severely affect ground wave communications. However, in practice, radio waves will usually travel about one third farther than a geometric line-of-sight, mainly as a result of variations of refractive index with height causing bending around the Earth.

More locally, mechanisms such as diffraction over the tops of hills or reflections from hills and large metal objects (gas-holders, grain silos and the like) may come into play. To put a figure on something which is difficult to quantify, ground wave contacts on the low VHF bands are likely to be over distances up to 40 or 65km, this figure reducing for the higher frequency bands. However, this can be countered to an extent by using high gain antennas. On 2m, for example, it is easy to achieve 10dB gain over a dipole so, while ground wave communications with an omni-directional antenna (such as a mobile whip) might be only 10 to 15 miles, from a good home station with a Yagi well in the clear, and the same at the other end of the path, reliable contacts might be achieved over 150km or more. By the use of active repeater stations, much greater distances can be achieved, especially if they are on high spots. Hence the networks of hilltop repeater stations on the VHF and UHF bands in most countries but, even more so, the various amateur satellites which achieve exactly the same result but from a much greater elevation (more about repeaters and satellites later in this book).

Diffraction

It is worth a brief mention here of the way in which radio waves can travel beyond line of sight through diffraction over hilltops and other objects. **Fig 1** shows what happens. In practice, the effect depends upon the size of the object concerned. Waves with wavelengths much shorter than the size of the object will be reflected from the object (in this case a hill). Waves with wavelengths much larger than the size of the obstacle will pass virtually unaffected and hence continue in a straight line. However, waves with intermediate wavelengths curve around the edges of the obstacles by a process called diffraction, allowing the radio signals to propagate behind obstacles. This will typically happen in the VHF region of the spectrum, on the 4m band and above.

IONOSPHERIC PROPAGATION AT LF, MF, AND HF

People first started to get really excited about the potential for radio communications when it was realised that radio waves could propagate over much greater distances than could be accounted for by ground wave. It didn't take long before the mechanisms for this were explained. It was clear that signals

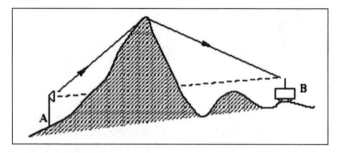

Fig.1: Diffraction over a hilltop.

were being reflected or, more accurately, refracted within the higher atmosphere in a region which became known as the ionosphere. The ionosphere has been studied extensively over time and we now know a lot more about the mechanisms involved and have identified several layers of ionisation, discussed in detail in any propagation textbook.

Ionospheric propagation became the backbone of international communications and broadcasting for many decades, and amateurs were lucky to hold on to their HF allocations over this time. Nowadays the situation has changed. International communications is almost exclusively by undersea cable and by satellite. Although HF is certainly still used for international broadcasting, satellites and, increasingly, the Internet are becoming the more important media. But for amateurs the joy of making long-distance contacts via the ionosphere remains as great as ever.

Ionospheric propagation due to direct solar activity is useful on all amateur bands up to 50MHz, though 6m openings are infrequent and occur only when solar activity is at a maximum. However, from the UK it is easy to get only a partial impression. Stations nearer the equator often continue to benefit from ionospheric propagation on the high bands when they are closed at higher latitudes. The corollary of this, though, is that absorption on the lower 'HF' bands can be much higher close to the equator whereas stations at high latitudes, for example in Scandinavia, can often be heard working the Pacific on these bands at times when this is out of the question for stations closer to the equator. These thoughts should be borne in mind when reading the remainder of this section, which describes the ionospheric propagation very much from the perspective of the UK. Of course, other parts of the world at similar latitudes will experience similar propagation.

Even within the UK there can be significant differences in propagation. It is not unusual for stations in the Channel Islands and southern UK to be working DX on 28MHz which is inaudible in the north of England and Scotland, as the MUF at those higher latitudes is somewhat lower. Conversely, in the winter months, sunrise in the Orkney islands, for example, is significantly later than in London, with stations in that northern location being able to work Pacific DX on the low 'HF' bands that would be impossible from the more southerly latitude.

There are also some sporadic (occasional and short-lived) ionospheric effects, discussed later in this chapter, which can lead to ionospheric propagation on some of the higher VHF bands.

Ionospheric propagation depends on the build-up of charged particles high in the rarefied upper fringes of the atmosphere where wave and particle emissions from the Sun arrive with sufficient intensity to ionise the air (what little there is of it) - in other words to split the molecules into positive ions and negatively-charged electrons. This layer of ionised air then behaves almost like a semi-silvered mirror as far as radio waves are concerned, causing some of them to be returned to Earth. However, the higher the frequency of those radio waves, the higher their energy, and at any given time there will be a frequency above which all radio waves will pass through the ionosphere into space. That frequency (the Critical Frequency, when applied to waves travelling perpendicular to the Earth's surface) will vary according to the level of ionisation. And the level of ionisation will vary according to the amount of energy being received from the Sun. And the energy received from the Sun varies constantly.

There are several superimposed cycles involved here:
• Diurnal: variations within the day due to the varying altitude of the Sun in relation to a particular path as the Earth rotates.
• Seasonal: variations from month to month, again due to alterations in mean solar altitude and the duration of daylight. This effect is very similar to the seasons we experience due to the incidence of sunlight. Higher latitudes will receive less energy from the Sun than latitudes close to the equator.
• Solar: changes from day to day in the intensity and mix of the solar radiations responsible for ionisation in the upper atmosphere. These changes can be considerable over quite short periods of time as well as showing longer-term trends, of which the 11-year cycle is the best known (or more strictly a 22-year cycle, but this is not relevant to the present discussion).
• Geomagnetic: variations in ionospheric behaviour caused by alterations in the intensity and shape of the Earth's magnetic field. The magnetic variations are themselves caused by certain solar emissions.

It is important in the context of radio propagation to note that ionisation takes place at different levels within the ionosphere, corresponding to the D, E and F layers. Long-distance radio propagation above 1MHz relies mainly on the higher, F layer (which, at certain times of the day, itself splits into two layers, the F1 and F2 layers, as shown in **Fig 2**). But to reach the F layer, the radio waves have to travel through the lower D layer, which absorbs but does not reflect the radiation. At times the E layer also absorbs energy, although at other times it can reflect signals (Sporadic E, 80m during daylight, etc).

Above a certain frequency, the radio waves will pass through all the layers of the ionosphere and will travel on into outer space without being reflected back to Earth. So solar energy affects two characteristics of the ionosphere:

(a) its ability to reflect HF waves of a particular frequency at a given time and angle of incidence;
(b) the absorption (attenuation) suffered by the waves passing through the lower regions of the atmosphere on the way to and from the reflecting regions.

Below 1MHz the situation is very different. At 136kHz and 475kHz the signal suffers some attenuation in the D-region, but is also returned by refraction in it. This occurs even in day-time. This is clear as the maximum strength of a station in daytime corresponds to mid-day at mid-path. After dark the situation changes, because the D-region ionisation decays, the attenuation is reduced and the signal reaches the lower E-region at an altitude of around 100km which is ionised both night and day. The refraction from this higher level doubles the hop-length on the ground leading to longer workable ranges.

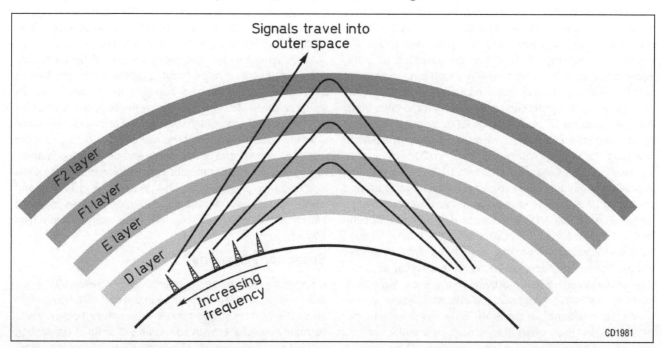

Fig 2: Propagation using the ionosphere at different frequencies.

Night-time propagation is subject to fading caused by the interaction of different signal paths, whose phases vary as the height of the refraction layer changes, at the receiver.

Both of these vary but not by any means always in step. Both reduce as frequency is increased, the absorption decreasing roughly with the square of frequency. In general, communications are possible over a given path at a given time if the frequency is low enough to be reflected and high enough not to be attenuated below the noise level at the receiver.

MUF and LUF

This leads to the concepts of Maximum Usable Frequency (MUF) and Lowest Usable Frequency (LUF). The MUF is higher than the critical frequency, mentioned above, as we are now concerned with radio waves impinging on the ionosphere at an oblique angle rather than straight up. For long-distance communications the ideal is to launch your signals at an angle low to the horizon, so that they will reflect over the maximum distance before returning to Earth.

Because it is impossible to predict the MUF in advance for a given path, for all the reasons explained above regarding hourly, daily and other variations, broadcast and commercial users generally plan to use a frequency safely below the MUF for their communications - the so-called Optimum Working Frequency (OWF) - and compensate for any additional absorption by using higher power than they might otherwise. Amateurs can often work very close to the MUF, as we are not looking for highly reliable communications but for the fleeting propagation opportunities where we can achieve long-distance communications with minimal power. The 10m band is well-known for providing world-wide communications with modest power and antennas at the right point in the solar cycle when the MUF often sits around the 30MHz mark.

The one limitation we do have as amateurs is that we are restricted to discrete frequency bands rather than being able to use any frequency in the radio spectrum. But our bands are close enough together that this is rarely a problem. The hour-by-hour change in MUF can be observed at work, especially in contests where there is a high level of amateur activity. Around dawn the higher bands will start to support propagation and signals can be worked from the east, firstly on 20m, then on 15 and finally on 10m (depending on the point in the solar cycle). Similarly, later in the day, the path to the west, to North America, will start on 20m as sunrise reaches the East Coast, then 15m and 10m will open later. Typically, the majority of the contesters will follow this upward move in MUF and then, later in the day as darkness sweeps across Europe, the MUF will start to drop at the European end of the path and the contesters will follow it down through 15m and 20m, before working through the night on the low bands. The same effects are taking place on other days, but it is not always so obvious if activity levels are low. Variations, such as long-path propagation, are discussed below.

The LUF is not as clear cut as MUF. It is very much a matter of absorption. Even when 10m is open in a major contest, you will still hear plenty of contest activity on 20m, with DX being worked. But the serious 20m contester, perhaps

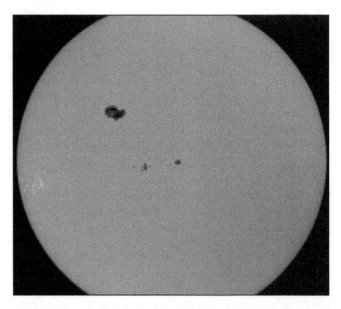

This photograph was taken approximately three years after sunspot maximum, on 14 January 2005. The large sunspot group is approximately seven times the Earth's diameter. A number of smaller sunspots can also be seen.

undertaking a single-band entry, will need a high-gain antenna and reasonable levels of power, probably up to the legal limit, to overcome absorption and achieve a high score.

Absorption on the lower bands is usually sufficient to prevent long-distance communications during much of the day but, again, with the right equipment and enough activity it is surprising what can be achieved. For example, a multi-multi contest team in the CQWW CW contest one November was able to work Japan on 40m over the long-path almost to midday and again by short-path from early afternoon onwards. But they did have a full-size 40m quad antenna on a high location. The combination of high gain and low take-off angle, along with plenty of activity from well-equipped stations at the Japanese end meant that the band openings could be 'stretched' at both ends of the day.

As far as day-to-day operations on the HF bands is concerned, the general rule of thumb is that the bands 14MHz and above are daytime DX bands, with the MUF typically falling below 14MHz at night, leaving the band dead. This may not be true at times of high solar activity or in mid summer or near the equator, when 14MHz can be open throughout the night. In contrast, the bands 7MHz and below are effectively night-time bands, day-time absorption being too high to allow long-distance propagation. This leaves the 10MHz band which, during years of high solar activity, behaves much as 7MHz and, during years of low solar activity, more like 14MHz.

Seasonal Variations

Even with unchanging solar activity, F2 layer MUFs are much higher in local winter than in the summer, being highest in the Northern Hemisphere in January / February and October / November with something of a dip in December. Around the equinoxes in March and September the distribution of MUFs in the two hemispheres is similar, and these periods tend to be excellent for world-wide propagation on all bands. Many major DXpeditions quite deliberately time their operations around the equinoxes to achieve best results.

Solar Variations

The various ionising radiations from the Sun are not constant in their effect. Since the sources of radiation are not evenly distributed over the Sun's surface there is usually a 27-day cycle of variation due to the Sun's rotation relative to the Earth. The daily count of sunspots has been the traditional measure of solar activity, but a more modern and somewhat more objective one is the power received on Earth at 2800MHz (the solar flux). On average the two vary together and are nearly linearly related. For practical purposes the relation:

R = 1.1 (SF -60)

where R = sunspot number and SF = solar flux

gives an answer sufficiently accurate for amateur purposes, enabling the WWV 18 minutes-after-the-hour broadcast of the daily solar flux value (SFU) to be converted to an approximate sunspot number if so desired (see below).

The most well-known aspect of solar variation is the approximately 11-year cycle of rise and fall in the 12-month mean of the daily sunspot numbers and solar flux - 'approximately' since Cycles 15 - 19 were all nearer 10 years while the start of Cycle 24 was delayed until January 2009 making Cycle 23 one of the longest cycles since records began. The average rise time is about four years. Cycle 24 is also unusual in having two peaks or maxima, the first in Jan 2012, and the seond higher peak now clear in April 2014. It is probable when the final values are averaged that the Smoothed Sunspot Number will be close to 79. Since the cause of this cyclic behaviour is not yet fully understood (there is even evidence that it is not always present, the last absence being in the 75 years from 1650AD), prediction of future trends is based on extrapolation from the past. For the amateur communicator it is important to remember that professional propagation predictions are based on forecasts of solar activity and that these are based on heavily smoothed data. While the ionosphere does not respond instantly to solar variations, its smoothing effect spreads over days rather than months, and generally the higher the mean solar activity, the greater the short-term fluctuations. For example, during the peak months from November 1957 to March 1958 the highest daily sunspot number was 342 and the lowest 90. Since forecasts have to be prepared well ahead of events one should always be on the look out for conditions which are outside the limits predicted.

There are also from time to time shorter periodicities within the 11-year cycle. On its downward slope one cycle had distinct subsidiary peaks at intervals of rather more than two years, and over the years 1975 - 1977 there was a fairly regular rise and fall with a period of approximately 120 days. Professional forecasts smooth out these variations and, since they perforce are based on data which is many months old by the time the prediction appears in print, they can even get 180° out of phase with them. The amateur, on the other hand, would like to know what band conditions will be like the next day, or for the following weekend's contest. As with weather forecasting there can be no certainty but a surprising amount can be done with relatively little effort.

Only those who have experienced a complete 11-year cycle can fully appreciate the impact it has on HF propagation. At the peak of the cycle, MUFs can climb above 50MHz, so that even the 6m band can enjoy world-wide propagation, with UK stations working into the Far East and the Pacific at times. Yet during the solar minimum 10m, 12m and even 15m can be dead for weeks at a time, enlivened only by summer Sporadic E or other anomalous propagation. Amateurs may still enjoy a certain amount of local activity on those bands,

 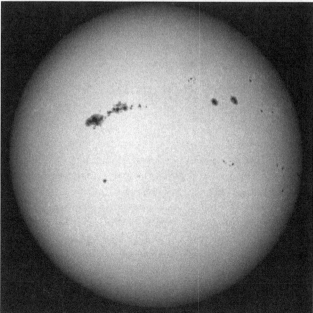

Left: A completely spot-free Sun, taken on 17 December 2008. Compare this with (right) the Sun during the last sunspot maximum.

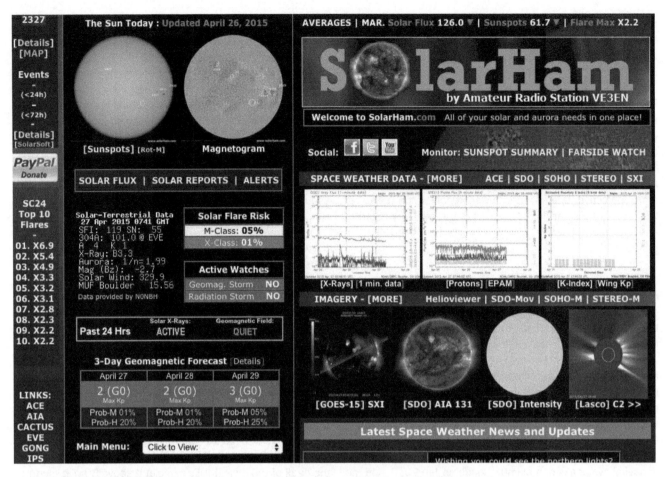

The *Solar Ham* site by VE3EN at www.solarham.com can provide you with the latest space weather data.

or perhaps use the FM repeaters on 10m, but global propagation will have to wait until the next sunspot peak.

It is not all bad news as absorption on the lower bands tends to be lower, again due to the lower levels of solar activity, so there are great opportunities to increase DX scores on those bands. 40m in particular comes into its own during sunspot minima, with excellent world-wide propagation. The most recent sunspot cycle peaked in January 2012 and again later and higher in April 2014, and in mid 2015 is headed down towards the next Solar Minimum.

PREDICTING IONOSPHERIC PROPAGATION

The 27-day (28 in the early stages of a cycle) solar rotation is a key factor in short-term prediction. Some amateurs keep a record of their own assessment of band conditions on this basis and know that similar conditions, both good and bad, can often be predicted 27 days ahead. The criteria to be used depend on individual interests. A useful one is the duration and penetration of the North American opening because there is plenty of activity and the path is a good indicator of general conditions.

The easiest way to get solar data nowadays is via the internet. There are many sites that can provide the solar flux index, A and K indices, including SolarHam [2] and the Space Weather Prediction centre [3]. Knowing the current data will help you understand what is going on in the ionosphere.

Paul Herrman, NONBH, has written a utility which allows the solar flux, A index, sunspot number and other data to be made available on websites. It can be found, for example, on the *DX Summit* site [4].

The web pages of NOAA (the National Oceanographic and Atmospheric Association [5]) are another excellent source and there is a good summary of data, collated from a number of sources, maintained by N6RT on the *qsl.net* website [6], which is well worth bookmarking.

The A-index is a measure of world-wide geomagnetic activity. In itself, a low value (15 or less) means a stable magnetic field and stable radio conditions, usually with low absorption. A low A-index with a high flux value means excellent conditions, particularly on the high bands. For good low band conditions look out for low flux values together with very low 'A'.

A 27-day plot of the A-index shows recurrent peaks due to persistent sources of particle emission from the Sun and coronal holes.

High peaks mean disturbed conditions, magnetic storms and possibly auroral effects, and if recurrent these can be predicted from the 'A' plots. However, an SID (sudden ionospheric disturbance) caused by a flare cannot be so predicted since it is a 'new' event and the rise in the A-index follows a day or two later when the effects of the flare disturb the magnetic field.

All that can be said is that such events are more likely to appear near a peak in the solar flux. 27-day calendars are also of importance in VHF auroral communications.

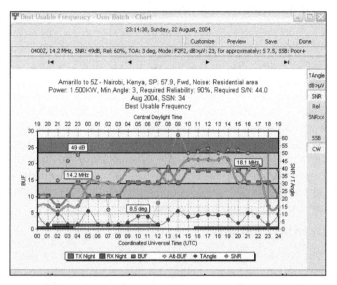

Fig 3: *WinCAP Wizard* **is one of many propagation prediction programs. This is a screen from** *WinCAP* **that suggests the best usable frequency for a particular path.**

The above should serve to show that with not too much effort an amateur can form quite a reliable view of the likely trend of radio conditions a month or more ahead, and with the help of current solar data be aware of what is happening more or less currently.

For those interested in the trend of the solar cycle, a three month running mean plot of the provisional sunspot number gives a good idea how things are going.

Since the geomagnetic field is affected by emissions from the Sun it also shows cyclic behaviour although this is not so clearly defined. Geomagnetic activity, ie the incidence and intensity of disturbances, ionospheric storms and auroral activity, certainly increases as the sunspot peak approaches but may continue to rise before reaching its own peak.

Nowadays there are many propagation prediction programs available for traditional ionospheric propagation, and these are dealt with in Chapter 4. *WinCAP Wizard* [7] is one such program which is based on the VOACAP prediction engine (see **Fig 3**).

GREYLINE PROPAGATION

Low band DXers are very familiar with greyline propagation, whereby long-distance DX is possible where signals can travel along the terminator, the division between daylight and darkness. At the equator, the greyline exists only for a very short period each day, as the Sun rises and sets very quickly, whereas at high latitudes twilight can exist for long periods during the winter months, allowing a wide range of DX locations to be worked on 40, 80 and 160m.

Computer software is available to calculate the times and bearings when this occurs, with some programs displaying a world map with the terminator and greyline superimposed. Many computer logging programs give sunrise and sunset times, but the visual display on a map has more impact in showing likely greyline paths at a glance.

Programs such as *DX Atlas* [8] and *Geoclock* [9] all have a map display which shows the terminator clearly. The DX.QSL.NET website [10] has a greyline map updated in real time every five minutes.

However, there is also a method of determining this involving a great circle map, an aid which no keen DX operator should be without. **Fig 4** shows the variation in the time of sunrise and sunset at London throughout the year together with the great circle bearing along which the dawn / dusk line lies at those times. Applying this data to a great-circle map (see Appendix 1 for a great circle map centred on London) will show which areas are in darkness and which lie along the zone of lowest absorption which is just inside the area of darkness. Remember that the dawn / dusk line is only a straight line on a great-circle map at sunrise and sunset.

Sunrise and sunset times are different elsewhere in the UK - typically 10 minutes later in Birmingham and as much as 40 minutes later in Glasgow and Belfast in summer - and the differences are not the same for sunrise and sunset. To make a table for your own location, borrow a copy of *Whitaker's Almanac* from the local library or find it on the web, for instance at [11].

It should be remembered that the standard great-circle map centred on London, while applying with sufficient accuracy to the whole of the UK in most cases, can be misleading with paths to the antipodes. While the bearing of ZL4 (the south of

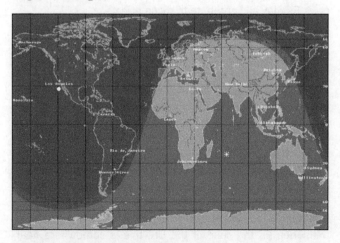

Geoclock **screenshot showing a classic greyline path: UK to Japan at 0730UTC in mid-December.**

'Greyline' map, showing areas of the world in daylight and darkness (essential information for the 1.8MHz DXer) on the http://dx.qsl.net website. It is updated in real time every five minutes.

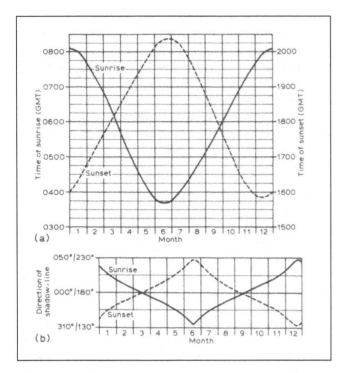

Fig 4: (a) Time of sunrise and sunset in London. (b) Approximate great-circle direction of shadow-line at local sunrise and sunset in UK.

New Zealand South Island) from London is 060° / 240°, it is 030° / 210° from Belfast. The corresponding values for ZL1 (north of the North Island) are 010° / 190° and 350° / 170° respectively. While these differences may seem small, they mean a completely different path for the two locations. The difference in sunrise and sunset times and the difference in bearings (which can impact whether the signals have to travel through the auroral zone) mean that a station in, say, the Orkney Islands will experience very different low-band propagation from a station in the Home Counties.

To summarise, DX can be worked throughout the year on the low bands although interference and noise level may make life difficult in the summer months. Basically the rules are simple. Most, or all, of the path must be in darkness and the best times, particularly for long hauls, are when much or all of the path lies just inside the area of darkness, a situation which occurs if it is near sunrise or sunset at both ends of the path. The latter condition cannot of course always be met, in which case there are two optimum times - around sunset at the western end of the path and near sunrise at the eastern end. With the shorter paths, eg to North America, the path is open between these times but with long hauls, eg to the Far East and Australasia, the openings can only be expected at these times.

ANOMALOUS PROPAGATION, DISTURBANCES AND BLACKOUTS

There are various ways in which band characteristics depart from the general pattern, as described in the preceding paragraphs, and the effect of those of most concern to amateurs are briefly described below.

Extended ('chordal') Hops

When transmitting in a direction in which there is a 'valley' in the MUF contours, the F2 ionisation gradient, though not steep enough to return your signal to Earth, may bend it sufficiently for it to follow the curvature of the Earth until it encounters a rising MUF on the far side of the 'valley', when it will be deflected downwards. This mode of propagation is most common between antipodes (points diametrically opposite to each other on the Earth's surface), where it is dawn at one end and dusk at the other, as there is a tilting of the ionosphere at these times (the charged layer rises in daylight, and falls after dusk). Such hops have low attenuation and can be very much longer than 4000km.

Ground Scatter

At certain times of the day and in certain directions the path attenuation may be low enough for quite strong signals to be scattered from the point of ground reflection both sideways and back along the transmitting path. This is useful to the amateur in three ways:
• If a beam antenna is used to determine the direction from which the back scatter from other UK or Continental stations is arriving, this is evidence of a good DX path in that direction.
• It can be used to contact stations that are in the skip zone if both beam towards the scatter source.
• When there is no normal path to, say, the USA it may still be possible to communicate if both stations beam towards West Africa or South America.

An interesting example of this can be seen in the evenings on 14 and sometimes 21MHz when there is no direct path to Australasia but a good path to South Africa. Good communication is then possible with the Australasian and UK stations both beaming towards South Africa. Whether the scatter occurs in Africa or in the South Polar Region is an open question.

In fact both the long and short paths to stations near the antipode sometimes show significant deviations from the great-circle route from 'over the pole' before the opening is fully developed to north of (LP) or south of (SP) the true direction as the path closes. Side scatter, ionospheric tilts and polar Es may all contribute to these effects.

Skip and Antipodal Focusing

When operating well below the MUF the various vertical rays from and to your antenna follow different vertical paths with different hop lengths When, however, the operating frequency is close to the MUF for the path, these rays tend to converge and this skip focusing can provide significant signal enhancement, equivalent to the difference between a typical dipole and a good beam antenna (6 - 9dB). This accounts for the signal peak which often occurs soon after an MUF-limited path has opened and shortly before it closes, and is the best time for the operator with low power.

Antipodal focusing is also an important mechanism. To the antipodes (in the case of the UK, this is somewhere near New Zealand) all directions are great-circle paths (so no need for a beam!) and therefore all signals arriving there will

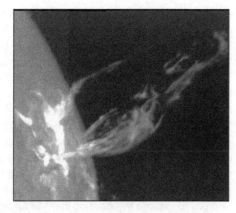

A solar mass ejection which can lead to a blackout in communications on Earth.

be cumulative in the distant receiver (although not all directions will necessarily be open, of course). This is one of the reasons the path from the UK to Australia / New Zealand is so reliable.

Disturbances and Blackouts

Events taking place in the Sun can cause major and minor upsets to HF communications in basically two ways. As already mentioned, a rise in certain emissions can cause daytime absorption to rise to high levels. On such occasions paths in a generally westerly direction which are normally open at a given time may show signals for a short time after opening, but signals will then fade to return after dark if the path MUF is still high enough. In extreme cases, usually associated with solar flares, the absorption rises suddenly to a high value and all daylight paths are 'blacked out'. Such a sudden ionospheric disturbance (SID) may last minutes or hours. Sometimes solar noise is high on 21 and 28MHz before the blackout, and MUFs may be abnormally high both before and after the disturbance. Particle radiation from flares or through coronal holes affects the intensity and shape of the Earth's magnetic field and therefore the shape of the MUF contours. These magnetic disturbances or 'storms' generally result in lower MUFs and higher absorption in high latitudes, particularly in the auroral zones. Under such conditions paths in northerly directions, notably to North America, may be badly affected while conditions to the south may even be improved. Disturbances resulting from persistent solar anomalies are predictable since they recur at 27-day intervals.

Again below 1MHz the effect of solar storms is very different. The solar flares which lead to a 'blackout' above 1MHz in day-time actually enhance propagation on the bands at 475kHz and 136kHz. Day-time signal strengths can be enhanced by 8 to 10dB by the radiation from a solar flare. Unfortunately these occurrences are difficult to use because they only last for a few minutes and there is no warning. In addition the enhancement is slightly less than is achieved normally on darkness paths.

Geomagnetic storms caused by the impact of clouds of plasma ejected from the solar corona, have a negative effect on LF darkness propagation. Hot electrons from the plasma captured in the Equatorial Ring Current are injected into the D-region and these give rise to attenuation in the same way the solar radiation generated electrons attenuate in daytime.

There is usually up to two days notice of these events, but good propagation does not return as the geomagnetic index Kp returns to quiet levels. The Ring current acts as a reservoir of hot electrons which are injected at the sunrise shadow edge. All is not lost because the Dst index (Disturbance storm time) is a measure of the quantity of electrons in the reservoir. Normal condition return as the Dst, which may be depressed to -200nT by the storm, returns to -20nT or above.

IONOSPHERIC VHF PROPAGATION

As mentioned in the introduction to this chapter, as well as the more conventional forms of ionospheric propagation, due to the various daily, seasonal and 11-year solar variations, there are other ways in which the ionosphere can be energised such as to reflect radio waves and therefore enable long-distance propagation. This section discusses the main mechanisms involved.

Trans Equatorial Propagation

Trans Equatorial Propagation or TEP, is peculiar to the bands between 50 and 150MHz. This mode allows contacts to be made over paths several thousand miles in length between stations on either side of the equator. The mode is much more common for those stations located in a band around the tropics; however, 50MHz will produce TEP propagation, particularly around the months of March and October, as far north as the UK. To date no TEP contacts have been made on 2m from the UK.

Sporadic E (E_S) Propagation

This is the name given to intense ionisation of the E-layer which happens sporadically. Patches of high ionisation can appear without warning and disappear as suddenly. In the UK area they are most likely in the daytime and from March to September, peaking in June and July, and can result in communication over ranges of 500 - 2000km at frequencies very much above the F2 MUF.

For the HF operator their effect is most noticeable on 24 and 28MHz where, as already mentioned, they not only give good contacts with Europe but may 'help' a DX signal into a region of higher F2 MUF, and can even be observed as very short skip propagation on 20m.

E_S can also help the DX operator. It is common throughout the year in daytime in equatorial regions and mainly at night in the auroral zones. The so-called 'M' reflection, involving a signal on its way down from the F2 region being 'bounced' back off the top of an E_S cloud, can help your signal cross an area of low F2 MUF and has low attenuation because the signal still only passes twice through the absorbing regions.

The current thinking on the causes of sporadic E is that it is probably produced by varying winds, known as wind shear, in the E region. These E region winds move charged particles, typically debris from meteors, and force this ionisation to converge into thin layers because of the effect of the Earth's magnetic field. This field is represented by the K index, which is usually '3' or less for a strong opening. Many years of observations show that E_S occurs in two peaks during the day, one late morning and a second, stronger peak, late afternoon or early evening.

Regarding the location of E_S, it is becoming apparent that turbulence in the lower atmosphere produced by weather features, for example jet streams, and thunderstorms, can propagate upwards to the E region, and cause the wind shear mentioned above.

An RSGB Forum [12] dedicated to Radio Propagation Questions contains a thread where daily charts of jet streams are uploaded. Use these to gauge where these weather triggers might be located.

E_S gives rise to propagation over distances from a few hundred to over 2000km at frequencies up to about 200MHz, so that it affects the 24, 28, 50, 70 and 144MHz bands. However, the ionisation has to be very intense for 144MHz propagation to occur such that on occasions when E_S may be observed continuously on 28MHz for several days, it may reach 144MHz for only a few minutes during this time.

Particularly in June and July, the 50MHz band is often full of E_S signals on a daily basis, sometimes supporting multi-hop propagation from the British Isles to the Eastern Mediterranean, the Middle East and across the Atlantic to North America. For example, there was a superb multi-hop E_S opening to North America in June 1994 when JY7SIX (Jordan) made a multi-hop contact with W4 at 9600km. This event occurred within about a year of sunspot minimum, so F-layer propagation can be discounted. Several rare DX stations located in the Caribbean have been worked from the UK during the summer months.

The 70MHz band is often open for lesser periods in these months but still provides a stepping stone and MUF monitor to 144MHz openings, particularly now that more countries have access to the band.

Typically, as the intensity of E_S increases and higher bands start to be affected, propagation distances on the lower bands start to shorten as higher-angle radiation is reflected. So, for example, when UK amateurs are able to work Italy on 2m, they will probably find themselves working near-in DX such as Germany and Luxembourg on 6m.

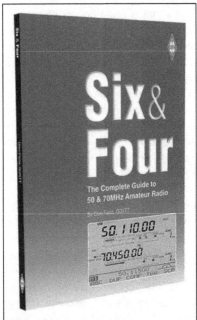

The most interesting E_S band is 144MHz and since openings can be very short, from a few seconds to at most a few hours, it is desirable to know when E_S is likely. This involves careful monitoring of

More about propagation on the low VHF bands appears in the RSGB book *Six & Four*.

signals in the approximate range 28 - 118MHz and a general-coverage receiver, preferably able to receive both AM and FM, is desirable. Most modern amateur transceivers with VHF capability allow scanning of frequencies over a wide range, perhaps aided by a panoramic display. (Do, however, bear in mind that it is illegal to listen to certain types of transmission which can be found in the 30 - 144MHz range.)

In the 28MHz band, European signals will always be audible when E_S is around. When ionisation is intense, signals are extremely strong and the shorter the distance, the more likely it is that higher frequencies such as 50MHz are affected. As a first step, use the beacon network on 10m and 6m to explore the development of an opening and, now that 4m is more widely available, you may find it possible to track the E_S all the way up to 2m.

The OIRT Eastern European broadcast band at 65.8 - 74MHz was a useful indicator of E_S propagation to this part of Europe, though many stations have now moved above 88MHz.

The VHF / FM Band II at 88 - 108MHz is used by most European countries for VHF / FM broadcasting. The sudden appearance of DX stations from Italy or Spain indicates that 144MHz may well open in those directions. In some cities in the British Isles several dozen FM stations are always audible and the appearance of a DX station may pass unnoticed. There can be some confusion since there may be local stations serving ethnic communities broadcasting in foreign languages (eg London Greek Radio on 103.3MHz).

Short-Path Summer Solstice Propagation (SSSP)

Short-Path Summer Solstice Propagation is the name being given to a particular type of long-distance opening that often occurs on 6m around the summer solstice. Steady signals have been observed from Western Europe, including the UK, to Japan, and from the Eastern USA to Japan, even at times of solar minima, eg during the summers of 2008 and 2009. Multiple-hop E_S has been the generally-accepted propagation mechanism, but the variable nature of E_S propagation and the large number of intermediate hops that would be required (given that the E layer is considerably lower than the F layer) makes it hard to believe that the signals could be so steady and subject to so little attenuation en route.

SSSP is described in more detail in *Six and Four* [13].

Auroral propagation

The natural phenomenon known in Europe as the northern lights has been studied and used as a propagation medium by amateurs for more than 50 years. Radio auroral events cause great excitement among VHF operators, who are able to work DX stations at distances far exceeding their normal tropospheric range. During strong events, stations located in southern England are often able to make contacts with Finland and Estonia by beaming their signals towards the auroral reflecting zones.

All auroral openings occur after a solar flare has released energy from the Sun. The *GB2RS* news bulletins in the UK and Internet news pages [14] often give details of sunspot activity and flares that are usually associated with these eruption holes on the disc of the Sun. A solar flare releases

The aurora of 21 January 2001 as seen 25 miles west of Aberdeen. Photo: Jim Henderson Photography.

tremendous amounts of energy across the entire electromagnetic spectrum from X-rays to radio waves. The Sun emits ionised gas continuously and this is termed the solar wind.

During flares, bursts of energetic charged particles stream outwards from the Sun and spiral towards the Earth via the solar wind. These particles are divided by the Earth's magnetic field and then follow the field lines to regions known as the auroral zones. These zones are oval shaped and typically (depending on particle energy) extend outwards from the poles to a radius of 23° on the night side of the Earth and to 15° on the daylight side. Visual auroral sightings indicate where the charged particles impinge on the Earth's upper atmosphere, ionising the E layer at a height of 110km. The number of auroral openings in any year is dependent on the solar activity. Some areas of the Sun can remain active for several weeks, causing repeats of events 26 to 28 days after the initial aurora. This is due to the period of rotation of the Sun and events like these are known as solar repeats.

A good and reliable indication of a forthcoming auroral event is known as pre-auroral enhancement and is familiar to HF band operators. This effect is particularly obvious during periods of poor propagation such as in the summer months at sunspot minimum. For example, if during a sustained period of mediocre conditions on 14MHz, the band suddenly becomes full of strong signals from Australia and New Zealand, it is likely that the following day HF band conditions will have collapsed and an intense aurora will be enjoyed by VHF operators on the 50, 144 and perhaps even 430MHz bands.

Shortly after the commencement of a magnetic storm the comparatively slow-moving particles ionise the E layers and align along the Earth's field lines. VHF radio signals beamed towards the auroral regions are reflected and refracted by the moving area of auroral ionisation. This moving reflector causes frequency shift and spreading, making all auroral signals sound distorted and difficult to copy. Morse signals are transformed into a rough hissing note and SSB voice transmissions vary from a growl to a whisper. The amount of frequency change on signals varies proportionately to the frequency band used; this effect is known as Doppler shift and can be as much as 1.5 - 2kHz higher or lower than the actual transmitted frequency on 144MHz. The frequency change is less on 6m, making auroral contacts on that band is somewhat easier. If the aurora is strong enough, a form of Sporadic E develops, known as auroral Es.

Some operators keep 27-day 'auroral calendars' on which they record both the visual and radio events. Many events repeat in 26 to 28 days, sometimes three or even four times, making this a useful method of predicting when an aurora may take place.

Meteor-scatter Propagation

Meteor scatter (MS) is a DX propagation mode which relies on reflecting signals off the brief ionised trail left by a falling meteor. These can last for up to a minute or more on rare occasions, but more usually for fractions of a second. This requires specialist operating techniques (see Chapter 9), relying mainly on signal-processing software. Meteor scatter is open to exploitation by most serious VHF operators; it should not be regarded as the province of a few specialists. However, it does require a higher level of station organisation and operational competence than random 'tropo' DX chasing.

Meteors are particles of rocky and metallic matter ranging in mass from about 10^{-10}kg to larger than 10kg. About 10^{12} are swept up by the Earth each day. At an altitude of about 120km they meet sufficient atmospheric resistance to cause significant heating. At 80km all but the largest are totally ionised (and generating trails of ionised gas), and this ionisation can be used to scatter radio signals in the range 10MHz to 1GHz. The level of ionisation required for 2m meteor scatter usually means that contacts can only take place during well-known meteor showers (which recur annually as the Earth orbits the Sun and passes through the same areas of cosmic particles). However, on 6m, meteor scatter propagation is possible most days, as there is a constant stream of cosmic debris entering the Earth's atmosphere.

Signal strengths associated with meteor scatter propagation, especially on 6m, can be quite high, and distances are comparable to those achievable with Sporadic E propagation.

NON-IONOSPHERIC PROPAGATION

The remainder of this chapter is devoted to long-distance propagation through means other than reflection off the ionosphere. Some of these occur naturally, some make use of more artificial mechanisms.

Tropospheric Propagation

In the early days of VHF it was thought that propagation was only possible over line-of-sight paths and at distances beyond this attenuation was rapid. However, experience in the early 1930s showed that this was not always so and sometimes much longer distances could be covered. These effects were soon related to atmospheric conditions and it was realised that radio waves were being bent back to Earth

The 6 metre EME antenna system of M0BCG, consisting of four 5-element Yagis.

by the troposphere, the lowest layer of the atmosphere, characterised by clouds and weather and in which temperature generally decreases with increasing altitude. Hence the term tropospheric propagation.

The relation between weather and tropospheric propagation is complex but in general it may be said that the main requirement is a temperature or a humidity inversion. Normally the temperature of the atmosphere decreases with increasing height above Earth, but in abnormal circumstances it may increase over part of the distance so that VHF waves which are normally lost in space are bent back to Earth, sometimes at a range of hundreds of kilometres.

Distances of up to 1500km or even 2000km may be worked by 'tropo'. Clearly the DX enthusiast will wish to forecast these conditions and the two essential aids are a weather map (synoptic chart) and a barometer or barograph. Good conditions are usually associated with stable weather patterns and this means areas of high pressure (anticyclones). Therefore, look for anticyclones on the map and a barometer reading high. It will soon be found that the appearance of a high pressure system does not produce good conditions, but when it starts to decline things may start to happen, especially if the anticyclone is short-lived. However, good conditions can occur when the atmospheric pressure is steady or even increasing. It must be added that anticyclones may form over the British Isles and decline without any significant effect on conditions. Conversely DX can appear when the weather map appears to be a series of depressions, though an opening under these conditions is usually short lived. A complete understanding would require a study of the atmosphere in great detail.

The Internet has made available a tropospheric propagation forecast by William Hepburn [15] this displays world wide plots of the likely ducting areas.

A quick check of signal strengths of the beacons on the bands of interest will usually give a clue to the state of conditions; especially useful on 144MHz where there are many beacons operating.

A comprehensive beacon list is published in the annual *RSGB Yearbook* [16]. It should be added that the beacons may be observed at enhanced strength when no other signals can be heard, either because there is no activity or because stations which are operating are beaming in other directions.

Some points to observe:

• All bands are not necessarily affected equally. It is possible for propagation to be enhanced at 144MHz but not at 432MHz and vice versa.

• Propagation does not vary uniformly. It can be good to, say, the south but poor to the north simultaneously.

• Skip effects are noticeable at times. It can be possible for a station 300km to the west to be working DX several hundred kilometres to the east which is quite inaudible. This is very frustrating and the only thing to do is to monitor carefully and hope for a change.

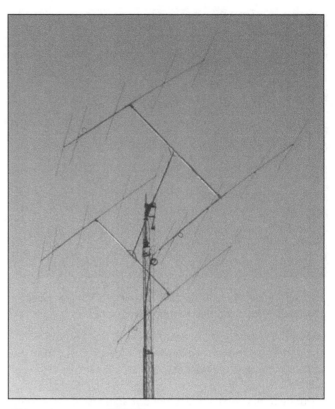

Moonbounce (EME)

Not strictly propagation in the conventional sense, but amateurs have, for many years, been using the Moon as a passive reflector of VHF signals. In theory, any frequency which is not reflected by the ionosphere but passes out into space can be used for moonbounce (also known as EME - Earth-Moon-Earth) communication. In practice, the lowest frequency band in use is 6m, where moonbounce is possible only when Sporadic E and other enhanced propagation is absent.

The 2m, 70cm and 23cm bands are also in regular use for moonbounce contacts. Path losses can be calculated with a reasonable degree of accuracy, allowing the station to be designed with sufficient antenna gain, transmit power and receive sensitivity to achieve two-way communications (depending on the station at the other end of the contact, of course). Modern software-based systems, discussed later in Chapters 8 and 9, have made EME accessible to many more amateurs.

Artificial Satellites

Again, not strictly propagation in the conventional sense, amateur satellites are, in effect, extremely well sited 'repeaters in the sky'.

Unlike the static terrestrial repeaters which are mainly in-band transponders, most of the artificial satellite-borne transponders are cross-band, for example VHF to UHF, UHF to microwave, and so-on.

Many are LEO (Low Earth Orbit) satellites and, as such, move relatively fast relative to the Earth's surface. Thus, amateur stations operating through such satellites must be capable of predicting accessible satellite 'pass' orbits to allow for antenna steering (if high gain beams are used) and correction for Doppler shift on the satellite signals.

The UO-Sat UO12 satellite.

Other satellites have been placed in highly elliptical orbits which minimise Doppler shift and antenna tracking problems when the satellite is at its most distant point from Earth (apogee). Modern software systems, like those mentioned in the EME section above, have made satellite predictions, Doppler correction and antenna steering available to many more amateurs.

There's much more on satellites in Chapter 14.

MICROWAVE PROPAGATION

Ionospheric propagation rarely, if ever, occurs above 1GHz. Indeed, the upper limit appears to be somewhere around the amateur 70cm band (432MHz). There are a few isolated reports claiming to have observed ionospheric propagation at 1.3GHz but these are largely unconfirmed and therefore doubtful.

Free-space transmission losses, measured in decibels, increase with the square of the frequency (in megahertz) as well as with the square of the transmission path distance (in kilometres). In addition, above about 23GHz, atmospheric absorption by water, water vapour and oxygen peak in certain frequency bands, adding greatly to the free-space losses. As a consequence, the total path loss on these bands can be very large, leading to significantly shorter ranges when the path is mainly within the troposphere.

All the tropospheric propagation modes observed at VHF and UHF also occur at microwave frequencies. It is becoming apparent, as more regular fixed-station activity takes place, that 'lifts' or 'openings' may occur more frequently than at VHF or UHF because the vertical extent of the tropospheric anomaly may be smaller to have the same effect. That is, the ability of a 'duct' of a particular thickness to propagate radio waves with low-loss (attenuation) is related to frequency (amongst other things). DX of over 1000km has been worked frequently during these events.

Most long-distance propagation is carried within elevated ducts. These tend to be between a few hundred metres and about 1km high. Elevated ducts can and do occur at higher

levels but these are harder to access and therefore of more limited use to most microwave enthusiasts.

Surface ducts can form over land and water due to various mechanisms such as night time thermal radiation and the movement of warm air over colder water areas such as large lakes (eg the North American Great Lakes) and shallow seas. Surface ducts tend not to extend to any great distance and usually tend to be no more than a few metres or tens of metres thick. They may only support the higher microwave frequencies.

A particular type of surface duct, which forms over shallow sea areas such as the southern North Sea, gives rise to what is known as super-refraction. Super refraction ducts form mainly, but not exclusively, in the spring and provide extremely high signal levels across the sea and to some extent up to about 30 to 50km inland depending on the height of the land. These inland areas are known as coastal zones.

Fig 5 illustrates some of the trans-horizon atmospheric propagation mechanisms, briefly discussed in the paragraphs above, and in the earlier section on VHF / UHF propagation modes. The principal difference between VHF / UHF propagation and microwave propagation is one of scale: the effectiveness of an atmospheric 'duct', or the forward scatter properties of the atmosphere itself and of hydrometeors (rain, hail, snow), are all functions of frequency. A shallow duct (such as a super-refraction duct over calm water in settled weather) which will not support VHF or UHF propagation may well act as a near-perfect 'waveguide' for microwave signals. Similarly, large raindrops, hail or snow, such as those typically associated with thunder 'cells', can provide a very effective, if short-term, scattering medium particularly in the 5.7 or 10GHz bands.

Microwave Scatter Propagation

Quite a lot has already been said about the various scatter propagation modes (such as ionospheric, tropospheric, meteor and auroral scatter) as observed and used at HF, VHF and UHF. All scatter propagation, regardless of the frequency in use, depends upon irregularities, for instance changes in the level of ionisation of the ionosphere in the case of HF and the lower VHF bands, or changes in the temperature, humidity and therefore Radio Refractive Index of the atmosphere in the case of the VHF, UHF and microwave bands.

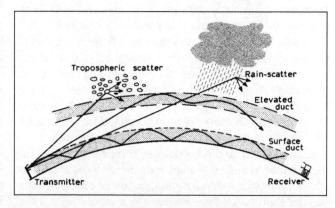

Fig 5: Trans-horizon propagation mechanism in the lower atmosphere.

Scatter propagation is always a 'dispersive' mode, in that a small proportion of the radio wave incident on the irregularities is scattered in the desired direction, depending on the angle of incidence of the radio wave. At an acute angle, back-scatter and absorption tend to predominate, whilst at an oblique angle forward scatter (or side-scatter, or both) tend to predominate. Rain scatter, in particular, shows marked depolarisation of the signal and unless there is secondary scatter from additional rain cells, horizontally polarised signals will not provide any significant side scatter. Forward scattered signals may provide a near T9 note, whilst back scattered signals may not be readable in SSB, due to the distortion, but switching to NBFM may well provide a perfectly readable signal, although it will exhibit a characteristic 'noise' not unlike that experienced with 70cm band FM mobile operation. Hydrometeor scatter is a relatively strong signal mode, especially during big thunderstorm events.

In the millimetre bands (above 24GHz) forward scatter DX is more likely with heavy snow than heavy rain because, at sub-zero temperatures, the loss due to water vapour absorption is minimised, ie the relative humidity is very low so that the mass of water in the atmosphere is low.

Microwave forward scatter signals may sound like auroral signals do on the VHF bands, because of the Doppler shift caused by the relative velocity of the scattering object.

Forward Troposcatter

Forward troposcatter which results from atmospheric irregularities, for example temperature, pressure and humidity cells, is a reliable, ever-present mode in the microwave bands and is much used professionally for beyond-the-horizon communications. To be reliable and cover the maximum link range (in commercial or professional terms) requires that a number of factors need to be satisfied. First, high transmit power, high antenna gain and low receiver noise. Second, the antennas of both stations need to be pointed accurately along the great circle path and radiate at as low an angle to the horizon as possible. This is in order that both stations can 'see' a common scattering volume of the atmosphere, the height of which largely determines the ultimate range of the link. It is also essential that both stations have good horizons, that is, an unobstructed horizon, as the path loss in a scatter link is so high, eg >300dB at 10GHz over a 1000km path, that additional losses caused by obstructions at either end of the path may shorten the link length by hundreds of kilometres.

Reliable forward troposcatter over long distances is practicable with amateur power levels, and ranges of 500 to 700km are regularly achieved by well-sited stations using power levels of several hundred watts and high gain antenna arrays (>20dBi) on the 1.3 and 2.3GHz bands. On the 10GHz band troposcatter allows ranges of up to about 400 to 500km to be regularly achieved with 10W and a 60cm diameter dish.

Aircraft scatter and reflection can increase the range on these bands to around 800km from aircraft flying at around 10 to 12km high. Although the duration of the reflections may be short (often lasting around one minute on 1.3GHz and shorter on the higher bands), with suitable techniques this can be enough to complete a contact. Sometimes it is necessary to wait for a second or third aircraft to complete the contact, leading to QSO times of up to 30 minutes and more, depending on the station's location with respect to the more congested airline routes. The longest ranges occur when the aircraft is located mid path to both stations.

Another propagation mode that may be useful to amateurs is the use of reflection from solid objects which are line-of-sight to both stations, but off the direct path. Such reflection is also a dispersive mode, since such solid objects are seldom either perfect reflectors or perfectly smooth as is a mirror to light. Similar considerations to troposcatter apply, although for minimum path loss, the reflecting object should be close to one end of the path. This is because the path loss is proportional to $1/(d1.d2)^2$, where d1 and d2 are the distances of station 1 and station 2 from the reflecting object. It can be seen that minimising either d1 or d2 will minimise the path loss.

A good example of reflection is provided by buildings and large metal structures located along a coastal zone, such as along the coast of the Low Countries. During a super refraction ducting event it is often possible to contact another station by both operators beaming towards a common point on the opposite coast that can be 'seen' by both stations. Often it is not possible to detect the other station by beaming along the normal great circle path. There have been numerous examples of this mode being used between the English east coast and Scotland (including the Scottish islands) to make seemingly impossible contacts on many of the bands between 1.3GHz and 10GHz.

Ephemeral Scatter

Ephemeral scatter occurs in the microwave bands due to a number of temporary, short-term, small-scale phenomena, such as rain, hail and snow (collectively known as 'hydrometeors'), aircraft, passing ships etc.

Passing ships are a rare phenomenon unless the amateur stations are using the super-refraction layer which forms low over extensive stretches of water (eg the North Sea, the Great Australian Bight, the Mediterranean, UK - Canaries, and California - Hawaii) under settled weather conditions. Large passing ships might conceivably aid (or possibly hinder!) such propagation by acting as slow-moving reflectors.

Extreme Propagation

Most if not all of the extreme microwave DX has resulted from a mixture of tropospheric propagation modes - super-refraction, combined with other forms of ducting and possibly refraction and reflection - across such stretches of water.

It can be seen, therefore, that there are several apparently conflicting factors affecting microwave propagation. On the one hand, settled weather conditions can lead to the formation of ducts and, on the other, turbulent, unsettled weather can enhance scatter modes. Again, at higher microwave frequencies, atmospheric water vapour absorption can increase attenuation and yet super-refraction layers over water (where the humidity is obviously high) can enhance propagation! It is these apparent contradictions which add to the fascination and challenge of microwave operation.

THE BEACON NETWORK

Propagation predictions are all very well but if you have just switched on your radio and want to work DX, it's obviously better to know what is happening right now, rather than what has been forecast. This is where beacons can help. On most bands there are beacons situated in strategic locations all over the world which can provide an excellent clue to band conditions, and these are proving valuable in both amateur and professional propagation research. A list of these beacons appears annually in the *RSGB Yearbook* [16].

Of particular interest to HF operators are the beacons operated by the Northern California DX Foundation (NCDXF) in cooperation with the IARU. These beacons operate on 14100, 18110, 21150, 24930, and 28200kHz. There are 18 beacons in the chain, although at the time of writing a few are off the air due to hardware problems. Each beacon transmits in turn at various power levels from 100 watts down to 100mW, with each transmission repeated every three minutes. A full transmission schedule can be found on the NCDXF website [17] from which it is also possible to download software for automated monitoring of the beacons.

Beacons on 10m all have their own frequencies in the 28190 - 28225kHz sub-band, and run continuously.

VHF beacons have already been mentioned and, as with the HF beacons, are an invaluable indication of propagation. Many DXpedition and DX stations also run interruptible beacons. This saves having to monitor a band continuously, but if you hear the beacon you can break the transmission and, hopefully, alert an operator at the DX end. However, never transmit on, or close to, a normal beacon frequency or in a beacon sub-band, even if you can't hear anything - your signals will cause severe interference to others straining to catch the faint signals.

In addition to formal beacons, there are several data modes that use temporary beacons (eg WSPR). It is possible to use these, together with various internet-based reporting systems (eg Reverse Beacon Network [18]) to spot DX openings in real time. More on these in the chapter on Operating Modes.

FURTHER READING

Many books are available on propagation, its relation to solar activity, and how to make forecasts, for example [19, 20].

REFERENCES

[1]   www.rsgb.org.uk/psc/
[2]   Solar Ham web site by VE3EN at www.solarham.net
[3]   The Space Weather Prediction centre at www.swpc.noaa.gov/products/station-k-and-indices.
[4   DX Summit: new.dxsummit.fi/
[5]   NOAA solar geophysical data: www.swpc.noaa.gov
[6]   N6RT propagation data: http://dx.qsl.net/propagation
[7]   WinCAP Wizard: http://sur.ly/o/taborsoft.com/AA001290
[8]   DX Atlas: www.dxatlas.com
[9]   Geoclock: http://home.att.net/~geoclock
[10] Reatime greyline map: http://dx.qsl.net/propagation/greyline.html
[11] www.sunrise-and-sunset.com/
[12] http://forums.thersgb.org/index.php?forums/radio-propagation-questions/
[13] *Six and Four*, Don Field, G3XTT, RSGB.
[14] http://rsgb.org/main/news/gb2rs/
[15] Hepburn forecast www.dxinfocentre.com/tropo_nat.html
[16] *RSGB Yearbook*, RSGB, published annually.
[17] NCDXF beacons: http://www.ncdxf.org/pages/beacons.html
[18] Reverse Beacon Network. www.reversebeacon.net/
[19] *The Shortwave Propagation Handbook*, George Jacob, W3ASK, and Theodore J Cohen, N4XX, CQ Magazine. [This is out of print but may be available second-hand from Internet shops or auction sites]
[20] *Radio Propagation - Principles & Practice*, Ian Poole G3YWX, RSGB 2004.

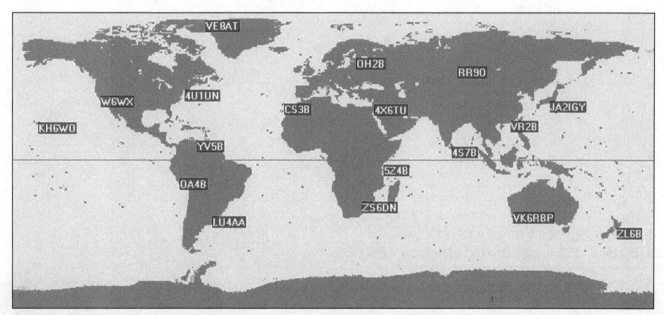

The callsigns and locations of the 18 beacons in the NCDXF beacon chain.

An Operating Primer

CHAPTER 1 COVERED some of the basics of amateur radio operation, and explained why a manual of this sort is necessary. This chapter covers operating in a greater level of detail, from making your first contacts to the point where you have achieved a high degree of proficiency. From that point on your operating interests are likely to migrate to one of the more specialist aspects, which are covered in subsequent chapters.

MONITORING THE BANDS

In days gone by, short-wave listening was by far the most common route into amateur radio. Most licensed amateurs would have started by spending time listening to CW or phone contacts taking place on the bands. While some still enter amateur radio this way, it is less common nowadays. There is no doubt that time spent monitoring the bands is time well spent, though. However detailed and comprehensive an operating manual such as this, it is no substitute for actually observing what happens on the bands and, in the fullness of time, making contacts yourself. 'Monitoring' in this context includes listening to phone and CW transmissions, but also decoding RTTY and / or other data modes using computer software.

By monitoring the amateur bands you start to get a feel for propagation, begin to recognise callsign prefixes, start to get used to some of the abbreviations in common use and, of course, get used to using your equipment in a live environment. You will hear good operating and bad operating and, hopefully, will learn to distinguish between the two. There is no requirement to keep a log of what you hear, though you may wish to make notes for future reference.

Monitoring also gets you used to what you will find where on each of the bands, a practical exercise to complement the theoretical knowledge of band plans which you will need to have before you start operating and, potentially, operate in an inappropriate part of the band. Monitoring also helps you to become familiar with amateur callsigns, a topic which confuses many newcomers and even many experienced operators. To help matters along, both band plans and callsign structures are covered in the following sections, before the discussion turns to making your first contact.

Even when you are ready to start transmitting, it is always helpful to have a listen around the band first. It will give you an idea of what propagation is like at that specific time. It will give you an idea of how busy the band is and whether, for example, there is a contest taking place or maybe some

Listening is the best possible introduction to amateur radio. Here Aidan, M6TTT (left), encourages SWLs Dan and Chris at the Dorridge Scout Group. Photo: Callum McCormick, M0MCX.

special event stations active. You may well also hear one or two stations calling CQ, and decide to call one of them. And if you decide to call CQ yourself, you will be better able to make a decision about what frequency to choose on which to do so. This advice applies to all bands, though is more applicable to HF operating, or to the VHF / UHF bands when they are 'open'. On the VHF (and higher) bands under normal circumstances, you will probably need to do no more than check the calling channel or local repeater, to ensure it is not already in use before making your CQ call.

BAND PLANS

At the outset, it is important that you are aware of the band plans applicable to the band(s) you intend to operate. Band plans come in two forms, mandatory and recommended. Mandatory band plans are those imposed by the licensing authority. In the USA, for example, the SSB section of each band is delineated by the FCC (US licensing body), as described in Chapter 5, whereas in the UK our licence doesn't specify which modes we use where in each band. Instead, we follow the recommendations made by the IARU, amateur radio's own international body (see Chapter 2).

However, that isn't to say that there is no mandatory band planning in the UK. Although Full licensees can use all of the UK allocation in each amateur band, the power limits differ, while Intermediate and Foundation licence holders have limitations regarding both frequencies and power limits. And even for Full licence holders,

it is important to be aware of specific notes in the licence schedule, for example the differing power levels permitted in different parts of the 160m band or the geographic restrictions applicable to the 431 - 432MHz section of the 70cm band.

CALLSIGNS

Most UK amateurs will be familiar with the callsign series used in the UK and will know immediately whether a station they contact is in England or Wales, for example, and the class of licence, Foundation, Intermediate or Full. But would you be able to do the same for callsigns that you hear from

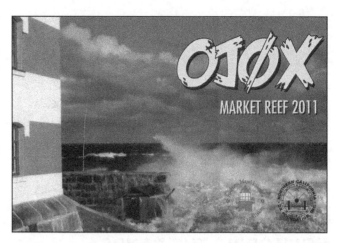

Don't ask why it is a DXCC entity, just accept the fact that it is! Yes, the tiny Baltic island of Market, with shared sovereignty between Finland and Sweden, is a separate DXCC entity.

outside the UK? This is an area that causes a huge amount of confusion, not helped by the daily appearance of new prefixes or unusual callsigns on the bands. Over the years, DXers and contesters develop a knowledge of callsigns that goes way beyond what you might find in most prefix lists. This section aims to help you make a modest start, but because this area is a moving feast, you will need to be observant to snippets which might appear in magazines or newsletters which will add to your knowledge.

At this point we need to make a definition and a distinction. In amateur radio parlance the word 'entity' is used to mean a place included in the ARRL DXCC list [1]. An entity could be a place that everyone recognises as a country, eg Hungary; it could be an island or group of islands such as the Balearic Islands (Mallorca, Ibiza etc) which, although part of Spain, are considered to be a separate entity; or it could be any number of other distinct geographical areas that have conformed to the ARRL DXCC list criteria. Note that many radio amateurs use the word 'country' interchangeably with entity: they might say that they have contacted, for example, 300 'countries' when what they actually mean is 300 entities. In this book the word entity is used to mean a place on the DXCC list: the word country is used in the more generally-accepted meaning of the word.

Take the three callsigns VP2EZZ, VP2MZZ and VP2VZZ. The suffixes are EZZ, MZZ and VZZ. All have the same prefix, VP2, although most amateurs would tell you that the prefixes are VP2E, VP2M and VP2V, for Anguilla, Montserrat and the British Virgin Islands respectively. Yes, there is a local agreement that suffixes starting with E are issued in Anguilla, M in Montserrat, and V in the Virgin Islands, but as far as the ITU is concerned the prefix VP2 is allocated to the British West Indies, and any sub-division of this is by local arrangement. Equally, a callsign with prefix VP8 could be in one of several DXCC entities, but the authorities in Port Stanley, who issue VP8 callsigns, don't make any local arrangements to distinguish between the Falklands, South Georgia, South Sandwich, etc, so it is impossible to tell from the callsign which of these DXCC entities a VP8 station is operating from.

Although part of the country of Spain, the Balearic Islands count as a separate entity from Spain for the ARRL DXCC award.

You cannot tell from the callsign whether an E5 station is in the DXCC entity of the South Cook Islands or the North Cook Islands. Most are in the South Cooks, but this DXpedition was from Manihiki in the North Cooks - a much 'rarer' entity.

The simple fact is that ITU-recognised countries do not map on to amateur radio entities. In some countries the national licensing authority will play ball with the amateur community and set aside certain callsign blocks for specific DX entities. In other countries the licensing authority will see absolutely no need to go down that route, and amateurs have to use other methods to keep track of who is operating from which DXCC entity. E5 is the prefix for the Cook Islands, for example, but the North and South Cook Islands count as separate entities for DXCC purposes. Experienced amateurs will know that there is more activity from the South Cooks than from the North Cooks, so if an E5 station appears on the bands there is a high probability that it is from the South

Cooks. An expedition to the North Cooks is such a rare event that it will almost certainly have been well publicised in advance and you will be alert to the fact.

Even when you are able to determine the DXCC entity, there is then a matter of call areas within that entity. The best-known example is the USA. US callsigns used to be allocated by state. An amateur with a callsign starting W2, K2, AA2, etc would be in New York or New Jersey. An amateur with a W6, K6, AA6, etc callsign would be in California. If he operated from elsewhere in the US, he would have to sign an appropriate designator. NK1G, operating from Montana, would become NK1G/7 or, from Hawaii, NK1G/KH6. This is no longer the case.

Callsigns can be allocated to US amateurs irrespective of their location, and no portable designators are required. This applies even to US possessions offshore. So KH6XYZ may be operating, not from American Samoa, but from mainland USA or, perhaps, even from somewhere like the US Virgin Islands. He may never have lived in American Samoa, even when the licence was issued. Similarly, NK1G could actually be operating from Hawaii or Alaska. In practice, most amateurs will use some designator, on a voluntary basis, to indicate their DXCC entity, but generally won't bother to indicate which part of the mainland USA they are in.

Apropos of which, experienced DXers will know that a station signing with a KG4 prefix and a two-letter suffix is in Guantanamo Bay, whereas a station signing with a KG4 prefix and a three-letter suffix is in mainland USA, probably in the '4' call area (but not necessarily!) Most stations with KG6 callsigns are in the California area, but a few KG6 stations are in Guam, with callsigns preceding the allocation of the KH2 prefix to Guam. Confusing, isn't it?

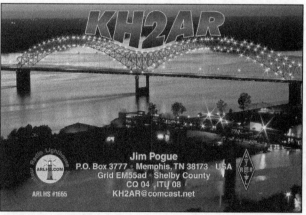

QSLs from some American stations that are not located where you might expect them to be: Jim, KJ4WKD, operates from Connecticut in the '1' call district, N1LVO is in Florida (the '4' call district), whereas KH2AR operates from Memphis, Tennessee, although his prefix indicates Guam in the Pacific.

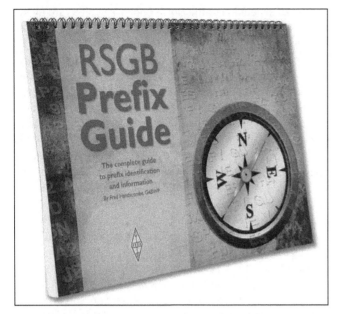

The *RSGB Prefix Guide* is the best source of detailed information on callsign prefixes available anywhere.

In contrast, in Japan the number in the callsign indicates in which part of Japan an amateur is located, and Japanese amateurs will always sign a portable designator if they are operating away from the address where the callsign was issued. All nice and clear! The same is true in certain other countries with discrete call areas, such as Brazil.

Generally, none of this is too important, other than in those contests where the call area is a multiplier, but it does make life confusing. Contesters, probably more than other amateurs, get to be good at knowing whether a callsign is or isn't possible. In the UK, if we logged the callsign G2XDV, we would quickly realise when looking at the log afterwards that this was an error, as G2 callsigns never got as far as the second part of the alphabet - they were issued before WWII, and after the war all new callsigns were issued from the new G3 series. Similar local knowledge applies to specific prefixes and suffix blocks in many other countries of the world, and gradually you will come to know what is and isn't possible. Contest and expedition operations often use a so-called Super Check Partial (SCP) facility as an add-on to their computer logging. This is a database of active callsigns, built up from previous contest or DXpedition logs. If the operator hears a callsign that doesn't appear in the SCP database, it may simply be a newly-issued licence or newly-active amateur, but it may also be that the operator has miscopied the call.

By far the best source of detailed information on callsign prefixes available anywhere is the *RSGB Prefix Guide* [2] illustrated on this page.

YOUR FIRST TRANSMISSIONS

Before making your first transmission, you will want to ensure that your station is working correctly (transceiver and antenna) and that you know how to operate it, at least at the basic level.

You should check the antenna SWR using an antenna analyser of some sort, or by running very low power and ensuring that you find a clear frequency on which to make your checks with an SWR meter. Of course, if you do not use a resonant antenna, you will also need to be familiar with how to use your antenna tuning unit (ATU). Some can give false indications, so do carefully follow the tuning instructions in the manual.

As far as the transceiver is concerned, the first step is probably to run it into a dummy load and determine whether everything appears to be working correctly. Remember that most dummy loads are not rated for continuous power, but for 10 or 15 seconds at a time. If you are using an ATU, it should be adjusted for minimum SWR and maximum forward power with the transceiver's drive at a low level. Power can then be increased to the desired level and the adjustments repeated.

It is most important that any tune-up signal radiated by the antenna should not cause interference to stations already using the band, and a careful check of the chosen frequency should first be made. In particular, any temptation to tune up on the frequency of a DX station before calling should be very firmly resisted for obvious reasons!

When near a band-edge, care must be taken to ensure that the transmission does not accidentally occur outside the amateur band. Allowance should be made for sidebands, calibration accuracy and (in the case of home-made or old-fashioned valve PA transmitters) frequency drift. Narrow-band FM carriers should be at least 10kHz within the limits of the band in use.

Establishing Contact

The basic principles behind establishing and conducting a contact have already been discussed in the opening chapter. There are two accepted ways of establishing contact with another amateur station. The first method is to put out a general call ('CQ' call) to all stations and to hope that another station responds. The second is to call another specific station by prior arrangement (known as keeping a schedule or 'sked') or after the other station has just finished a contact or made a CQ call.

Calling a specific station which has just finished a contact or made a CQ call has the advantage that you know who is likely to reply, and the signal strength of that reply. This is important on the HF bands because likely fading can be taken into account to determine whether a contact can be sustained.

Another factor is that any rare or distant (DX) station on the band is probably already having a contact and would not reply to a CQ call.

When calling a specific station it is good practice to keep calls short and to use the callsign of the station called only once, followed by your own callsign pronounced or keyed carefully and clearly (particularly when signal strengths are not good or in the presence of interference). The calling procedure should be repeated as required until a reply is obtained or it is clear that someone else is in contact. Break-in operation on CW is very useful, because if properly adjusted it will be possible to listen between characters and know what is happening at all times.

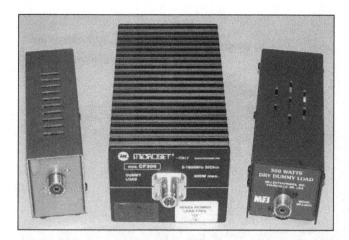

Three 300W dummy loads: the Vectronics DL-300M, the Microset CF-300 and the MFJ-260C.

This basic procedure may be summarised as follows:

1. Listen - to find out exactly what is happening on the frequency.
2. Be patient - wait until any other station already in contact has finished.
3. Make calls short - give the callsigns once or at the most twice.
4. Listen carefully - between characters on CW if possible.
5. Be ready to stop transmitting if the station being called replies to someone else.
6. Do not answer directional calls unless in the category of station being called.
7. If unlucky, be patient! Wait for another chance and call again.

This procedure may be made more 'snappy' if that is the operating style of the station being called, for example if it is a DXpedition station. Then it would be normal just to give your own callsign once, always using phonetics on SSB (see 'Procedure' under 'Telephony Operation' below). There are exceptions to the general rules on establishing contact, for example when joining an existing net, or using a repeater.

If activity on the band is low a CQ call may be useful. When this is transmitted just as 'CQ' it can be answered by any other station. If the call is 'CQ DX' this limits replies to calls from distant (DX) stations. The definition of DX varies from band to band, and also on conditions (see Chapter 9). Make sure this is understood before making (or especially answering) a CQ DX call.

If it is desired to make contact with a particular country a directional CQ call can be made, such as 'CQ VK', which means that only replies from Australia will be answered. Before making a CQ call it is important to find a frequency which appears unoccupied by any other station. This may not be easy, particularly in crowded band conditions. Listen carefully - perhaps a DX station is on the frequency which is difficult to hear. If you are using a beam antenna, rotate it to make sure.

If after a reasonable time the frequency still seems clear, ask if the frequency is in use before transmitting the CQ call (on CW this can be done by transmitting 'QRL?' or just '?'). If two or three CQ calls produce no answer it may be that

interference is present on that frequency for distant stations and a new frequency should be sought.

Each CQ call should be short with a break to listen for replies. It may then be repeated as often as required. A long CQ call without a break is poor operating technique - interference may be unwittingly caused to stations which were already on the frequency but which the caller did not hear in the initial check, and moreover stations intending to reply to the call may become impatient and move on to another frequency.

CQ calls on VHF / UHF should include details of your location (or locator) so that those stations using a beam antenna can work out the rough bearing and swing their antenna round before answering your call.

Summarising, the important points in making a CQ call are:
1. Find a clear frequency - check that this is so.
2. Keep calls short as possible and listen frequently.

Conducting the Contact

If contact has been established on a special calling channel, the frequency should be vacated as soon as possible, and the contact completed elsewhere.

After the usual greetings it is customary to exchange details of signal strength, name, location and information on the equipment being used, the latter often consisting only of the model of transceiver, the antenna and, if not immediately obvious, the power in use.

Often on the VHF / UHF bands the height above sea level (ASL) of the location is also given, along with the Locator, while HF operators usually mention the local weather and radio conditions. The locator is also often exchanged during LF and MF contacts.

A contact limited to exchanging such information (quite common on the HF bands) is often known, somewhat disparagingly, as a 'rubber stamp' contact. Yet many amateurs deserve great credit for learning enough of a foreign language (such as English) to enable them to do this. They may not be familiar with other words and expressions, certainly not colloquialisms, and if a contact goes beyond the basic details with a foreign-language amateur it is always wise to use the simplest words possible (including the use of Q codes on telephony). A further point is that in poor conditions it may be necessary to keep the whole contact short in case fading or interference occur. The good operator takes all these factors into account when expanding on a basic contact.

On VHF / UHF contacts tend to be much less formal due to the usual absence of language difficulty, and 'rubber stamp' contacts are rare except under good conditions when DX contacts are possible.

On both HF and VHF / UHF it is good operating practice to use the minimum amount of RF power output consistent with 100% copy at the other station. Any reports of better than S9 received suggest that too much power is in use and should be reduced if possible to avoid interference to other band users.

Concluding the Contact

It is customary in a final transmission for an operator to express some gratitude for the contact, and to convey best wishes to the other person, with often a hope that another contact may be made at a later date.

After concluding the contact, both stations will listen carefully for callers, and what happens next depends on which station was using the frequency or channel prior to the contact. This station has some claim to the frequency, and it is usual and polite for the other station to move off elsewhere after the contact. However, this convention may be modified to suit the circumstances.

Good operators move off a frequency where they have been fortunate enough to be called by a rare or DX station, to enable others to contact it. No band is so crowded that it is not possible to find another frequency (though occasionally it may seem that way!)

Abbreviations and Procedure Signals

For the newcomer, some of the terminology and abbreviations used on the air can be confusing. Not only will you hear other amateurs using technical terms to describe their equipment and antennas, but you will run across both abbreviations and codes. Both originate in the world of CW operation, where it speeds things up. The Q codes, which you will also hear used on telephony, originate in the world of commercial radio activity, and have very specific meanings (Incidentally, it is because these Q codes are so widely used, that no UK callsign suffix starts with the letter Q, in order to avoid confusion. This is not the case in all countries, however.)

If you look in any commercial list of Q codes you will see that the full list is very extensive. Each Q code can be used in two ways, either to give information or to ask a question. Thus the code 'QTH', for example, is defined officially as meaning "My position is", which would normally be followed by latitude and longitude or some other recognised method of giving a location. Sent as "QTH?" it would obviously mean, "What is your position?" In amateur usage, it also refers to location, either in the context of QTH Locators, commonly used on the LF and VHF / UHF bands, or simply to say, "My QTH is London" or whatever.

A list of the more informal meanings attributed by amateurs to Q codes appears at **Table 1**. An extract from the full Q code list, showing those most commonly used in amateur operation, appears at **Table 2**. Obviously, Q codes specific to the world of flying, or other specialist activities don't find application in amateur radio. Neither do the Z codes used in military communications. There is no need for you to learn all the Q codes, but you will certainly come across the abbreviated list in Table 1 on a daily basis as you operate on the amateur bands.

Abbreviations and procedure signals are found mainly on CW and, to an extent, on RTTY and other data modes. Abbreviations are exactly that in most cases, "HR" for "here" or "TU" for "thank you" for example. Some are slightly more obscure, but obvious when you think about it, "BCNU" for "be seeing you" and "XYL" for wife ("ex-young lady"). If you are familiar with the sort of the abbreviations in common usage on text messaging with mobile phones, you will probably take to most amateur abbreviations very quickly!

Although most of the abbreviations are obvious derivations of English words, they are well understood throughout

QRG	Frequency
QRM	Interference from other stations
QRN	Interference from atmospheric noise or from nearby electrical apparatus
QRO	High power
QRP	Low power
QRT	Close(d) down
QRV	Ready; active on air; activity
QRX	Stand by
QSB	Fading
QSL	Verification card; confirm contact
QSO	Radio contact
QSX	Listening frequency
QSY	Change frequency
QTC	Message
QTH	Location
QTR	Time

Also some 'unofficial' Q codes:

QRPp	Very low power
QRSS	Very slow speed CW
QSLL	Card sent in receipt of yours
QTHR	Address is correct in the current RSGB Yearbook (used in the UK only)

Table 1: Informal use of the most common Q codes.

the amateur community and even used by overseas amateurs who may well not be aware of the English word(s) from which they derive.

Procedure signals (sometimes called "prosigns") are used to facilitate contacts, for example by indicating that you are listening for calls, passing the transmission to a specific station or closing down your station. "CQ" ("seek you") is, of course, also widely used in voice transmissions. **Table 3** lists the most commonly used abbreviations and procedure signals.

Signal Reports

The other element of a contact which you will come across from the very start is the exchange of signal reports. It is very rare for a contact to take place without this, though there are many amateurs nowadays who would question why we even bother.

Signal reports date from the earliest days of amateur radio, when every contact was a major achievement, and many contacts were made under some degree of difficulty, with poor copy at one or both ends, either because of weak signals, badly-adjusted or drifting transmitters, or any one of many other possibilities. Nowadays most of those problems are consigned to the past, with most signals of good quality and readable, at least on the main HF bands, even when they are quite weak.

Signal reports are based on the RST code, shown in **Table 4**. Due originally to W2BSR, it covers Readability (R) of the signal on a 1 - 5 scale, strength (S) on a 1 - 9 scale, and tone (T), also on a 1 - 9 scale. The latter applies to CW and data modes transmissions, but not to voice.

QRA	What is the name of your station? The name of my station is . . .	QSO	Can you communicate with . . . direct (or by relay)? I can communicate with . . . direct (or by relay through . . .)
QRB	How far approximately are you from my station? The approximate distance between our stations is . . . kilometres.	QSP	Will you relay to . . .? I will relay to . . .
QRG	Will you tell me my exact frequency (or that of . . .)? Your exact frequency (or that of . . .) is . . . kHz (or MHz).	QSR	Shall I repeat the call on the calling frequency? Repeat your call on the calling frequency; did not hear you (or have interference).
QRH	Does my frequency vary? Your frequency varies.	QSS	What working frequency will you use? I will use the working frequency . . . kHz (Normally only the last three figures of the frequency need be given).
QRI	How is the tone of my transmission? The tone of your transmission is . . . (amateur T1-T9).	QSU	Shall I send or reply on this frequency (or on . . . kHz (or MHz)) (with emissions of class . . .)? Send or reply on this frequency (or on . . . kHz (or MHz)) (with emissions of class . . .).
QRK	What is the intelligibility of my signals (or those of . . .)? The intelligibility of your signals (or those of . . .) is . . . (amateur R1-R5).		
QRL	Are you busy? I am busy (or I am busy with . . .). Please do not interfere.	QSV	Shall I send a series of Vs on this frequency (or . . . kHz (or MHz))? Send a series of Vs on this frequency (or . . . kHz (or MHz)).
QRM	Are you being interfered with? I am being interfered with.		
QRN	Are you troubled by static? I am troubled by static.	QSW	Will you send on this frequency (or on . . . kHz (or . . . MHz)) (with emissions of class . . .)? I am going to send on this frequency (or on . . . kHz (or MHz)) (with emissions of class . . .).
QRO	Shall I increase transmitter power? Increase transmitter power.		
QRP	Shall I decrease transmitter power? Decrease transmitter power.	QSX	Will you listen to . . . (callsign(s)) on . . . kHz (or MHz)? I am listening to . . . (callsign(s)) on . . . kHz (or MHz).
QRQ	Shall I send faster? Send faster (. . . words per minute).	QSY	Shall I change to transmission on another frequency? Change to transmission on another frequency (or on . . . kHz (or MHz)).
QRR	Are you ready for automatic operation? I am ready for automatic operation. Send at . . . words per minute.		
QRS	Shall I send more slowly? Send more slowly (. . . words per minute).	QSZ	Shall I send each word or group more than once? Send each word or group twice (or . . . times).
QRT	Shall I stop sending? Stop sending.	QTC	How many messages have you to send? I have . . . messages for you (or for . . .).
QRU	Have you anything for me? I have nothing for you.		
QRV	Are you ready? I am ready.	QTH	What is your position in latitude and longitude (or according to any other indication)? My position is . . . latitude . . . longitude (or according to any other indication).
QRW	Shall I inform . . . that you are calling him on . . . kHz (or MHz)? Please inform . . . that I am calling him on . . . kHz (or MHz).		
QRX	When will you call me again? I will call you again at . . . hours (on . . . kHz (or MHz)).	QTQ	Can you communicate with my station by means of the International Code of Signals? I am going to communicate with your station by means of the International Code of Signals.
QRY	What is my turn? (Relates to communication). Your turn is Number . . . (or according to any other indication). (Relates to communication.)		
		QTR	What is the correct time? The correct time is . . . hours.
QRZ	Who is calling me? You are being called by . . . (on . . . kHz (or MHz)).	QTS	Will you send your callsign for tuning purposes or so that your frequency can by measured now (or at . . . hours) on . . . kHz (or MHz)? I will send my callsign for tuning purposes or so that my frequency may be measured now (or at . . . hours) on . . . kHz (or MHz).
QSA	What is the strength of my signals (or those of . . .)? The strength of your signals (or those of . . .) is . . . (amateur S1-S9).		
QSB	Are my signals fading? Your signals are fading.	QTV	Shall I stand guard for you on the frequency of . . . kHz (or MHz) (from . . . to . . . hours)? Stand guard for me on the frequency of . . . kHz (or MHz) (from . . . to . . . hours).
QSD	Is my keying defective? Your keying is defective.		
QSI	I have been unable to break in on your transmission or Will you inform . . . (callsign) that I have been unable to break in on his transmission (on . . . kHz (or MHz)).	QTX	Will you keep your station open for further communication with me until further notice (or until . . . hours)? I will keep my station open for further communication with you until further notice (or until . . . hours)
QSK	Can you hear me between your signals and if so can I break in on your transmission? I can hear you between my signals, break in on my transmission.		
		QUA	Have you news of . . . (callsign)? Here is news of . . . (callsign).
QSL	Can you acknowledge receipt? I am acknowledging receipt.		
		QUM	May I resume normal working? Normal working may be resumed.
QSN	Did you hear me (or . . . (callsign)) on . . . kHz (or MHz)? I did hear you (or . . . (callsign)) on . . . kHz (or MHz).		

Table 2: International Q code (extract).

55	best success	ES	and	PWR	power
73	best regards	FB	fine business	R	received
88	love and kisses	FER	for	RCVR	receiver
AA	all after . . . (used after a question mark or RPT to request a repetition)	FONE	telephony	RPRT	report
		FQ	frequency	RPT	repeat (or I repeat or Repeat . . .)
		FREQ	frequency	RX	receiver
AB	all before . . . (see AA)	GA	good afternoon (or go ahead)	SA	say
ABT	about	GB	goodbye	SED	said
ADR	address	GD	good day	SIGS	signals
AGN	again	GE	good evening	SK	end of work
ANI	any	GLD	glad	SKED	schedule (prearranged transmission)
ANT	antenna	GM	good morning		
AR	end of transmission	GN	good night	SN	soon
AS	wait a moment	GND	ground (earth)	SRI	sorry
B4	before	GUD	good	STN	station
BCNU	be seeing you	HI	laughter	SUM	some
BD	bad	HPE	hope	SWL	short-wave listener
BK	break, used to interrupt a transmission in progress	HR	here	TDA	today
		HRD	heard	TFC	traffic
BLV	believe	HV	have	TKS	thanks
BN	all between . . . and . . . (see AA)	HVY	heavy	TMW	tomorrow
BT	signal to mark the separation between different parts of the same transmission	HW	how	TNX	thanks
		INPT	input	TRX	transceiver
		K	invitation to transmit	TT	that
CFM	confirm (or I confirm)	KA	starting signal	TU	thank you
CK	check	KN	invitation to transmit (named station only)	TX	transmitter
CL	I am closing my station			U	you
CLD	called	LID	poor operator	UR	your
CNDX	conditions	LOC	locator	VY	very
CNT	cannot	LSN	listen	WA	word after . . . (see AA)
CPSE	counterpoise	MNI	many	WB	word before . . . (see AA)
CQ	general call to all stations	MSG	message	WID	with
CRD	card	ND	nothing doing	WKD	worked
CUAGN	see you again	NR	number	WKG	working
CUD	could	NW	now	WL	will
CUL	see you later	OK	we agree (or it is correct)	WUD	would
DE	"from . . ." (precedes the callsign of the station that is transmitting)	OM	old man	WX	weather (or weather report follows)
		OP	operator		
DR	dear	OT	old timer	XYL	wife
DX	long distance	PA	power amplifier	YDA	yesterday
ELBUG	electronic key	PP	push-pull	YF	wife
ENUF	enough	PSE	please	YL	young lady

Table 3: Abbreviations and procedure signals commonly used in CW and data modes contacts.

Readability
R1 Unreadable.
R2 Barely readable, occasional words distinguishable.
R3 Readable with considerable difficulty.
R4 Readable with practically no difficulty.
R5 Perfectly readable.

Signal strength
S1 Faint, signals barely perceptible.
S2 Very weak signals.
S3 Weak signals.
S4 Fair signals.
S5 Fairly good signals.
S6 Good signals.
S7 Moderately strong signals.
S8 Strong signals.
S9 Extremely strong signals.

Tone
T1 Extremely rough hissing note.
T2 Very rough AC note, no trace of musicality.
T3 Rough, low-pitched AC note, slightly musical.
T4 Rather rough AC note, moderately musical.
T5 Musically modulated note.
T6 Modulated note, slight trace of whistle.
T7 Near DC note, smooth ripple.
T8 Good DC note, just a trace of ripple.
T9 Purest DC note.

Table 4: The RST code.

Nowadays it is rare that a tone (T) report of anything other than '9' would be given, as modern transceivers should, unless something is badly wrong, generate a pure CW tone. The exception is under auroral conditions, when tones will sound raspy. In this situation, the number is usually replaced by the letter A to indicate auroral flutter (so a signal report might be 59A). It is rare to hear anyone give a readability (R) report of less than '3'. Anything less than that and you probably wouldn't be attempting to make the contact. An exception might be a pre-arranged 'sked' where the station is known to be there but is not readable.

As far as signal strength is concerned, this can be quite a controversial area, mainly because there doesn't seem to be any standard set of definitions, other than the rather qualitative ones that appear in the table. Although most transceivers have a signal strength meter, usually calibrated from S1 to S9, and then in decibels above S9, the reading is generally meaningless other than on a comparative basis. Even if you knew exactly what voltage you were measuring at the antenna terminals (which is, strictly, what signal strength is about), the reading probably tells you more about the gain (or otherwise) of your antenna system than it does about the absolute strength of the other station's signal. So what you are actually telling him is not how strong his signal is in absolute terms, but how loudly you are hearing him at your particular station, with the receiver settings in use at the time, and in the light of noise and interference on the frequency. There is also dispute about whether an 'S-unit' is 3dB or 6dB, to which there cannot really be an answer.

After the preceding discussion you might well be wondering why amateurs do continue exchanging signal reports. It isn't required by the licence or for awards and it's fairly meaningless most of the time! But, provided you aren't looking for scientific measurement, signal reports do give some idea of how well the other station is hearing you and therefore, for example, whether you should repeat information when you give it. As an example, a 59 signal report (599 on CW) would indicate that you are receiving at good strength and with good readability. A 579 report indicates that signals are moderately strong and perfectly readable (so there probably isn't much in the way of interference) whereas a 479 report would indicate that there is a problem, perhaps due to interference from adjacent channels, so the distant station should take this into account, perhaps slowing his sending speed on CW or using phonetics on phone.

Just to confuse things even further, most DXpeditions and contest operators nowadays pay only lip service to signal reports, always giving 59 or 599. It saves them having to slow down to record an alternative report, but is therefore meaningless, other than as a 'token' of information to give the contact a degree of validity. The main piece of information exchanged in such contacts is the callsign and, in the case of many contests, other data as required by the contest rules. More of this in the relevant chapters, though it is worth noting that some contest organisers have bowed to the inevitable and removed the need for exchanging signal reports altogether, instead replacing them with some alternative type of data, for example a serial number or QTH Locator.

Finally, it is worth noting that other signal reporting systems are used in specialised instances, the main examples being beacon-based datamodes, SSTV, QRSS, and specialist VHF / UHF modes (including meteor scatter). This is dealt with in the relevant sections.

Modes

Just a word here about operating modes, although they are covered more fully in Chapter 8. On SSB, the convention is to use USB (upper sideband) above 10MHz and LSB (lower sideband) below, except on the 5MHz channels, where USB should be used. This should quickly be obvious when listening on the bands, but can be slightly confusing at first.

On CW, most modern transceivers allow you to operate through either the USB or LSB filters in the transceiver. Normally you would always use the default setting, but sometimes switching to the alternative can help to minimise adjacent channel interference.

TELEPHONY OPERATION

On the HF bands, telephony operation is roughly equal with CW in terms of overall use, though many amateurs heavily favour one over the other. Most day-to-day operation on VHF is on telephony (especially FM), though CW is popular for DX working. Though telephony does not require knowledge of codes and abbreviations, correct operation is more difficult than it may appear at first sight, as is only too apparent after a listen to any amateur band. Part of the problem is that many operators will have acquired some bad habits in their pronunciation, intonation and phraseology even before entering amateur radio. To these are then added a whole new set of clichés and mannerisms derived from listening to bad operators. Some of these can be extremely difficult to remove once learnt, even if a conscious effort is made.

Microphone Technique

Unless there is very little external noise and room echo, it is best to hold the microphone fairly near the mouth, between 70 and 140mm away. Some microphones are unduly sensitive to letters like 'S' and 'P', and better audio quality may then be  obtained by speaking across the microphone, rather than directly into it.

Audio quality should be tested by running the transmitter into a dummy load and monitoring the output on a receiver with headphones. In this way the characteristics of the microphone and the optimum speaking distance will be apparent.

One of the popular Heil Pro Set series of headsets

If a separate receiver is not available, the opinion of a local amateur should be sought on the air.

Speech processing and / or compression can add to the 'punch' of an SSB (and, to a lesser extent, an FM) signal, and genuinely increase its readability, especially under marginal conditions. Be careful not to use too much compression, though, as the modulation quality can suffer greatly. Tests should be made to determine the maximum level which can effectively be used and this noted, or marked on the control. Be ready to turn it down if it is not really required during a contact. Many modern transceivers allow extensive tailoring of the audio via a series of menu options, so it may be worth experimenting while getting feedback from another amateur listening to your signals.

Conversation

It is important to speak clearly and not too quickly, not just when talking to someone who does not fully understand the language, but at all times as this is good practice. Plain language should be used when you are having a conversation with the other person and radio clichés should be kept to a minimum. Avoid the use of "we" when "I" is meant and "handle" when "name" is meant. Of course, use of phrases like "That's a roger" has to be a matter of personal taste, but don't feel you have to talk in slang like this to have an amateur radio contact. The use of CW abbreviations should normally be avoided and the Q code only used where it has become

Letter	Word	Pronounced
A	Alfa	AL FAH
B	Bravo	BRAH VOH
C	Charlie	CHAR LEE or SHAR LEE
D	Delta	DELL TAH
E	Echo	ECK OH
F	Foxtrot	FOKS TROT
G	Golf	GOLF
H	Hotel	HOH TELL
I	India	IN DEE AH
J	Juliet	JEW LEE ETT
K	Kilo	KEY LOH
L	Lima	LEE MAH
M	Mike	MIKE
N	November	NO VEM BER
O	Oscar	OSS CAH
P	Papa	PAH PAH
Q	Quebec	KEH BECK
R	Romeo	ROW ME OH
S	Sierra	SEE AIR RA
T	Tango	TANG GO
U	Uniform	YOU NEE FORM or OO NEE FORM
V	Victor	VIK TAH
W	Whiskey	WISS KEY
X	X-Ray	ECKS RAY
Y	Yankee	YANG KEY
Z	Zulu	ZOO LOO

Table 5: International phonetic alphabet.

accepted practice (eg "QRZ?" or "Please QSL via the bureau", "QRM", "QRN", etc) or when there is a language difficulty.

Phonetic alphabets should be employed when they are necessary to clarify the spelling of a word or callsign. If they are to be effective the listener should know them, and it therefore follows that the phonetic alphabet recommended in Appendix 14 of the ITU Radio Regulations and in Note (b) of the UK licence should normally be the one used. This phonetic alphabet is given here in **Table 5**. (As most of the words are taken from the English language, the official pronunciation guide given is presumably intended for users whose first language is not English. However, many would argue that if one is speaking in English 'Quebec' should be pronounced "KWUH BECK" and not as indicated, while a Scotsman would probably object to being told to pronounce 'Whiskey' as "WISS KEY"!)

In amateur radio usage, when struggling with weak signals under high levels of interference, the internationally recommended phonetic alphabet has been shown not to be perfect, with certain words (eg 'Golf' and 'Mike') sometimes being difficult to hear, some words sounding alike (eg 'Echo' can sound like 'X-Ray') and with certain combinations of words causing some difficulties. The recommended alphabet was selected to avoid ambiguity, and it can therefore be confusing to the listener if other phonetic alphabets are used. However, if it is found that a word is unheard or consistently being miscopied, use of other well-known words may well fix the problem, eg 'America' instead of 'Alpha'; 'Germany' instead of 'Golf'; 'Portugal' instead of 'Papa' etc. The best advice is to use the internationally-recommended alphabet in the first instance and only use other phonetics if conditions are such that you are not being copied correctly.

It can be easy to forget that the conversation is not taking place down a telephone line and so the listening station cannot interject a query if something is not understood and cannot give an answer until the transmitting station has finished. The result, especially on VHF / UHF, is often a long monologue in which the listening station has to take notes of all the points raised and questions asked if a useful reply is to be given. This should not be necessary if these points are dealt with one at a time.

Voice-operated changeover (VOX) operation can be used to enable a more normal two-way conversation to be carried on, and its use tends to avoid long monologues. However, it must be remembered that relays are supposed to be changing over frequently and prolonged "aaahs" spoken to prevent this happening are bad practice. Remember to give callsigns as often as required by the licensing authority in this type of contact. If VOX is not available, nimble use of the push-to-talk (PTT) switch is an acceptable substitute, although this requires more effort.

Procedure

As noted earlier, when calling a specific station on phone it is good practice to keep calls short, to use the callsign of the station called once only, followed by your own callsign pronounced carefully and clearly using the phonetic alphabet, for example:

"PJ4DX, this is Golf Three X-Ray Delta Victor calling."

Emphasis should be placed on the caller's own callsign and not on that of the station called. If there is no response, the caller's callsign may be repeated once more after a brief listen.

When calling a DX station, and especially a DXpedition, it is normal not to give the DX station's callsign at all (after all, he knows his own callsign!) and just to give your own callsign once, always using phonetics.

Some stations send very long calls because operators think that when everybody else has finished calling they will still be heard. This 'trick of the trade' rarely seems to work, it irritates others on the frequency and it causes interference to the station called if he has already replied to another station. 'Continuous calling' is to be avoided at all costs and under all circumstances!

CQ calls should also be kept short and repeated as often as required. An example would be:

"CQ, CQ, this is Golf Three X-ray Delta Victor calling, Golf Three X-ray Delta Victor calling CQ and standing by."

There is no need to say what band is being used (although it is very common to hear, for example, "CQ 20, CQ 20...") and there is certainly no need to add "listening for any possible calls, dah-di-dah" or "K someone please", as is sometimes heard. When replying to a call both callsigns should be given clearly, usually in the phonetic alphabet, so that the calling station can check his callsign has been received correctly. From then on it is not necessary to use the phonetic alphabet for callsigns until the final transmissions.

Once contact is established it is only necessary to give your own callsign at the intervals required by the licensing authority. A normal two-way conversation can thus be enjoyed, without the need for continual identification. If necessary the words 'break', 'over' or 'go ahead' may be added at the end of a transmission to signal a reply from the other station. In good conditions this will not normally be necessary. When FM is in use it is self-evident when the other station has stopped transmitting and is listening, because the carrier drops. There was a time when many amateurs adopted an end-of-transmission beep, perhaps

copying what they had heard from the NASA space programme. While it can be helpful under very weak signal conditions on the VHF / UHF bands, it is usually more irritating than helpful.

Operating procedures become more complex where three or more stations are involved, and it is a good idea to give your own callsign briefly before each transmission, for example:

"From G3XDV . . ."

At the end of the transmission the callsign should again be given together with an indication of whose turn to speak it is next, for example:

". . . PJ4DX to transmit, G3XDV and the group."

It is not necessary to run through a list of who is in the group, who has just signed off (and who may possibly be listening) after each transmission, although it may be useful for one person in the net to do this occasionally.

Signal reports on telephony are usually given using the RS(T) code (an indication of tone is not given on telephony of course). When the time comes to end the contact, end it. Thank the other operator (once) for the pleasure of the contact and say goodbye. This is all that is required. Unless the operator is a good friend there is no need to start sending best wishes to everyone in the household. Nor is this the time to start digging up extra comments on the contact which will require a 'final final' from the other station to answer - there may be other stations patiently waiting to call. It is recommended that both callsigns be given in the final transmission using the phonetic alphabet so that listening stations can check that they have them correct before calling, for example:

". . . This is Golf Three X-ray Delta Victor signing with Papa Juliet Four Delta X-Ray and Golf Three X-ray Delta Victor is now listening for any further calls."

Note that some indication to listening stations is useful to indicate what is planned next. Such an indication is also appropriate if an immediate change to another frequency is intended, for example:

When calling a DXpedition, such as this one, it is usual to give your callsign only once.

". . . This is Golf Three X-ray Delta Victor signing with Golf Two X-Ray Yankee Zulu Mobile. Golf Three X-ray Delta Victor is now monitoring V40 for a call."

Duplex Operation

Both PTT and VOX operation are simplex systems, ie communication can take place in only one direction at any given time. The capability of instant and spontaneous response typical of an ordinary telephone conversation is only possible if duplex operation is used, ie simultaneous communication in both directions. This requires two communication channels, which must be well spaced to avoid the transmitter desensitising the receiver. The two channels may be in the same band (in-band duplex) or in two separate bands (cross-band duplex).

Generally in-band duplex is not practical on the narrow HF phone bands due to receiver desensitisation and is not too popular even at VHF and UHF because separate transmitters and receivers for those frequencies are unusual items these days (and many amateurs cannot afford two transceivers for the same band!) Most duplex work therefore takes place cross-band (for example, 144 / 432MHz). If harmonically related bands are chosen, the receiver frequency needs to be well clear of any transmitter harmonics. Care should also be taken to comply with the relevant band plans which may be difficult with in-band duplex. It is best to avoid the usual simplex channels for what will appear to others as a one-sided conversation. In any case, it is wise to check that the transmit channel is clear at, say, five-minute intervals.

As with VOX operation, remember to give callsigns as frequently as required by the licensing authority, in this case also stating the other station's transmit frequency. Generally headphones should be used at least at one end of a duplex contact to avoid 'howl-round' but a carefully adjusted loudspeaker output does allow the other operator to hear how his transmissions sound and may even give a more natural quality to the contact; after all, this is what duplex operation is all about.

CW CONTACTS

All the codes and abbreviations discussed earlier may seem rather daunting to the newcomer - it is difficult enough to learn the Morse code without having a whole new set of codes superimposed. Yet after a few CW contacts have been heard and understood the usage begins to become clear and the value of the codes and abbreviations can be appreciated. To assist this learning process, an imaginary CW contact and its literal equivalent is reproduced below as an example.

CQ CQ CQ DE G3XDV G3XDV K
"General call to all stations from G3XDV. Over"

This is known as a 'three by two' CQ call, meaning that 'CQ' is sent three times and the callsign twice. A much longer call is not recommended, as noted earlier.

G3XDV DE NK1G NK1G KN
"G3XDV from NK1G. Over"

Note that the call is short, only 'one by two'. Quite often it is possible to hear a station still calling when the station called has replied to another station. Ending with KN shows that a reply is expected from the specific station indicated (as against K, which invites calls from anyone).

NK1G DE G3XDV GA OM ES MNI TNX FER CALL = UR RST 579 = NAME MIKE ES QTH NR LONDON = SO HW CPY? AR NK1G DE G3XTT KN
"NK1G from G3XDV. Good afternoon old man and many thanks for the call. Your signals are fully readable and moderately strong, with pure DC note. My name is Mike and my location is near London. So how do you copy me? NK1G from G3XDV. Over"

Each station has the other's callsign correct, so there is now no need to give callsigns more than once.

G3XDV DE NK1G R FB MIKE ES GM OM = UR RST 559 = QTH SR [error] SPRINGFIELD, ILL = NAME IS ED = SO HW? AR G3XDV DE NK1G KN
"G3XDV from NK1G. Roger. Fine business Mike and good morning old man. Your signals are fully readable, fairly good strength, and pure DC note. My location is Springfield, Illinois. My name is Ed. So how do you copy me? G3XDV from NK1G. Over."

'R' denotes all received correct and should not be sent if there was any part of the message which was not copied or understood. Some operators send it before the callsigns. Note the error made in giving the location and correction; '[error]' means the eight-dot error signal was sent.

NK1G DE G3XDV SRI OM QRM5 = PSE RPT UR NAME?? BK
"NK1G from G3XDV. Sorry old man, extreme interference here. Please repeat your name. Break."

BK NAME IS ED ED ED BK
"My name is Ed. Break."

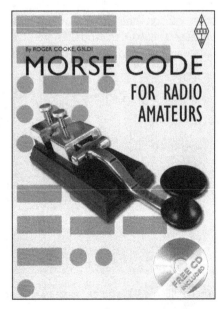

More on learning Morse code, improving your speed and much more can be found in this book from the RSGB.

Alphabet and numerals		Abbreviated numerals		Apostrophe (')	di-dah-dah-dah-dah-dit
A	di-dah	1	di-dah 6 dah-di-di-di-dit	Hyphen or dash (-)	dah-di-di-di-di-dah
B	dah-di-di-dit	2	di-di-dah 7 dah-di-di-dit	Fraction bar or	
C	dah-di-dah-dit	3	di-di-di-dah 8 dah-di-dit	solidus (/)	dah-di-di-dah-dit
D	dah-di-dit	4	di-di-di-di-dah 9 dah-dit	Brackets - open [(]	dah-di-dah-dah-dit
E	dit	5	di-di-di-di-dit 0 daaah (long dash)	- close [)]	dah-di-dah-dah-di-dah
F	di-di-dah-dit	S	di-di-dit	Double hyphen (=)	dah-di-di-di-dah
G	dah-dah-dit	T	dah	Quotation marks (")	di-dah-di-di-dah-dit
H	di-di-di-dit	U	di-di-dah	Error	di-di-di-di-di-di-dit
I	di-dit	V	di-di-di-dah	The @ in emails	di-dah-dah-di-dah-dit
J	di-dah-dah-dah	W	di-dah-dah		
K	dah-di-dah	X	dah-di-di-dah	**Spacing and length of signals**	
L	di-dah-di-dit	Y	dah-di-dah-dah	• A dash is equal to three dots.	
M	dah-dah	Z	dah-dah-di-dit	• The space between the signals which form the same letter is equal to one dot.	
N	dah-dit	1	di-dah-dah-dah-dah		
O	dah-dah-dah	2	di-di-dah-dah-dah	• The space between two letters is equal to three dots.	
P	di-dah-dah-dit	3	di-di-di-dah-dah		
Q	dah-dah-di-dah	4	di-di-di-di-dah	• The space between two words is equal to seven dots.	
R	di-dah-dit	5	di-di-di-di-di		
Accented letters		6	dah-di-di-di-dit		
à, á, â	di-dah-dah-di-dah	7	dah-dah-di-di-dit		
ä	di-dah-di-dah	8	dah-dah-dah-di-dit		
ç	dah-di-dah-di-dit	9	dah-dah-dah-dah-dit		
ch	dah-dah-dah-dah	0	dah-dah-dah-dah-dah		
è, é	di-di-dah-di-dit	**Punctuation**			
ê	dah-di-di-dah-dit	Full stop (.)	di-dah-di-dah-di-dah		
ñ	dah-dah-di-dah-dah	Comma (,)	dah-dah-di-di-dah-dah	**Table 6: The Morse Code and sound equivalents.**	
ö, ó, ô	dah-dah-dah-dit	Colon (:)	dah-dah-dah-di-di-dit		
ü, û	di-di-dah-dah	Question mark (?)	di-di-dah-dah-di-dit		

BK R R TNX ED = QRM GONE = RIG IS HOMEBREW WID 75W INPT = ANT IS DIPOLE = MNI TNX FER QSO ES CUAGN = 73 ES GB AR NK1G DE G3XDV SK

"Roger. Thanks (for the repeat) Ed. The interference has gone now. My rig is homebrew with an input power of 75W. My antenna is a dipole. Many thanks for the contact and I hope to see you again some time. Best wishes to you and goodbye now. NK1G from G3XDV. Over."

G3XDV DE NK1G R UR RIG T9X ES FB = RIG HR IS FT-897 = ANT IS 2EL QUAD = WL QSL VIA BURO = SO 73 ES GUD DX = GB G3XDV DE NK1G SK

"G3XDV from NK1G. Roger. Your rig sounds crystal controlled, and very nice. The rig here is an FT-897. The antenna is a two-element quad. I will send my QSL card via the bureau (and I hope to receive one in return). So best wishes and good DX. Goodbye. G3XDV from NK1G."

With both stations having sent 'SK', the contact is at an end and either station may be called by a third station for another contact.

It should be appreciated that this is a basic contact with only the essential details exchanged between the stations. Nevertheless this type of contact can still give much pleasure. There is of course nothing to prevent much more information being transmitted in such favourable circumstances, although the individual transmissions should be kept reasonably short. Strictly speaking, such details as name, location and signal report should be sent only once as shown here and if the other operator does not copy the details he or she should ask for a repeat. However, most amateurs find it easier to repeat these basic details the first time round, rather than risking time-wasting queries, especially if conditions are poor. The established CW operator may also like to bear this point in mind when contacting stations obviously new to CW operating.

This also brings us to the question of sending speeds. On the HF bands most day-to-day CW contacts take place at speeds in the 22 - 28WPM range, though you will certainly hear both slower and faster contacts taking place. CW contacts on the 136kHz band and at VHF and above tend to be made at slower speeds.

Experienced amateurs will normally be comfortable at these speeds, sending on an electronic key (keying with a hand key becomes uncomfortable above about 25WPM) and receiving by ear except to make a note of specific information for the log (name, location, signal report, for example). But don't feel intimidated. When answering a CQ call, answer at a speed you are comfortable with and a good operator will respond in kind, reducing his speed to match yours. When calling CQ, do so at the speed you would like others to respond but, again, if someone responds more slowly be courteous and slow down for them.

Contest operations often take place at higher speeds, usually around the 28 - 32WPM range. This need not be as intimidating as it sounds, as much of the contest exchange will be standard, so you do not have to copy as much information as during a 'rag-chew' type of contact.

For convenience, an extensive list of CW characters appears in **Table 6**, including accented characters used in other languages. You will rarely run across characters other than the standard ones, but may do so if you decide to try working foreign amateurs in their own language (see later section). This list had remained static for many years, but recently a new special character was added to denote the '@' symbol in email addresses.

Semi and Full Break-in Operation

One of the operating decisions you will make in respect of CW operation is whether to use manual, semi-automatic or full break-in operation. Manual operation is self-evident; you switch to transmit using the MOX button on your transceiver or maybe a foot switch. In practice, very few CW operators do so. Instead, the majority use semi-automatic break-in, whereby your transceiver goes to transmit when you first hit the key, and drops back to receive when there is a pause in sending. The length of the pause required before the transceiver returns to receive can be adjusted. In contest or slick day-to-day operating, for example, you may want to keep the break short, but if you are rag-chewing, perhaps at low speed, this could result in the transceiver reverting to receive between words or even characters, which can be distracting.

Full break-in operation, also known as 'QSK', is rather different. The transceiver will revert to receive between every dot and dash so that, to all intents and purposes, you are listening continuously. This allows very interactive contacts, and is invaluable if the other station needs to interject, for example to say that he is having trouble copying you, or maybe has to leave for a moment to take a phone call. Break-in operation takes a little time to get used to, but can be extremely satisfying. In contesting it is particularly valuable, because you can hear immediately if, for example, interference appears on the frequency.

Not all transceivers, however, are capable of full break-in operation and even some of those which claim to be are actually rather limited in their break-in capabilities. It's not too difficult to understand why. If break-in is to be possible without adversely affecting the CW (for example, shortening the dots and dashes), the switching between transmit and receive must be very fast indeed.

This is usually only possible with PIN diode switching; relays simply aren't fast enough. This capability must also apply to your linear amplifier, if you are using one. But very fast switching can lead to other problems, especially if you are operating split-frequency (for example when calling a DXpedition station), because the frequency synthesiser cannot always change frequencies fast enough, so your transmitted signal will be affected. It is really a case of experimenting, and getting to know the limitations of your equipment, perhaps by getting another station to listen while you try sending at different speeds, operating both co-channel and split-frequency.

FOREIGN LANGUAGE CONTACTS

CW

It is sometimes claimed that CW operation consists entirely of code groups and thus amateurs who do not possess a common language can communicate with each other. This is only partly true. A typical reply by a Russian amateur to a call would be:

"GM OM TNX FR QSO UR RST 589 QTH MOSCOW OP VLAD HW?"

Apart from the two Q code groups, every word is an English abbreviation. The Russian amateur does not necessarily see it like this - unless he is a linguist, he will probably have a list of phrases with the Russian equivalents and he will treat these phrases as code groups and not as abbreviations of English words, rather like we translate "73" as "best wishes".

Given a similar list of phrases in other languages, there is nothing to prevent a monoglot English speaker from having contacts in those languages. No knowledge of the language concerned is necessary, and on CW there is no problem of pronunciation or understanding the accent of the foreign amateur.

For generations, English speakers have expected everyone else to learn English in order to communicate with them but this attitude is not universally popular. Radio amateurs, with a minimum of effort, can make a real contribution to international goodwill by greeting fellow amateurs in their mother tongues.

Appendix B shows a list of 24 phrases which may be combined in various ways to cover the requirements of most simple contacts. No doubt, over time, you could collect other useful ones, too.

It is suggested that German should be the first language to be attempted, followed by French which it is used over the air quite extensively. Spanish is used throughout South America (except Brazil) and it is for that reason that it has been included in the list. British VHF/UHF and microwave operators, especially those located near coasts, will have their own preferred language to learn (perhaps French, Dutch, Danish or Norwegian) depending on where they are.

The effort involved in using a foreign language is well repaid by the thanks which will be expressed in almost every contact, and the final courtesy should be to include a few remarks in the language on the outgoing QSL card.

Most experienced CW operators will use a paddle similar to the one above together with an electronic keyer which is often incorporated into the transceiver.

Phone

The ability to conduct a straightforward contact in, say, French or Spanish is most useful for the DXer. Unlike the method of CW operation described above, this does require an elementary knowledge of the language, but it can still be broadly based on a few stock phrases committed to memory such as those given in Appendix B. The best way of learning them is to listen to contacts in the target language, recording them if possible. If the two speakers are fluent a good deal of the conversation will not be understood, but this is not important. The main thing is to discover how contacts are initiated, how details like name, QTH and signal report are exchanged, and how contacts are completed. If a few other useful phrases can be acquired at the same time so much the better, but be sure to learn the appropriate responses.

The process should be completed before any attempt is made to use this new-found knowledge, otherwise the results could be a little embarrassing. However, most foreign amateurs do appreciate the effort being made and assist where possible, so perfection is certainly not required. Many of the comments made in the foreign language CW section are just as relevant to phone operation and should be noted.

Contest operators often make a special effort to make contacts in another language. It isn't too difficult as the contest exchange will be quite specific, so you may only need to learn how to say numbers plus a few other words and phrases to help the contacts along. It can significantly increase your contest score and perhaps give you the confidence to take the whole matter further so that before long you are holding lengthy contacts in another language.

DATA MODES OPERATION

At one time, data modes meant RTTY, and that mode is still popular for two-way contacts on the HF bands. However, many other data modes are now available requiring little equipment other than a computer - which most shacks have as standard nowadays - and an interface between the computer and the radio.

It is difficult to generalise about operating procedures as the various modes differ considerably, but it is safe to say that there is much information and advice available for most modes and software packages, including web sites and special interest groups. A good starting point is an RSGB book *RTTY/PSK31 for Radio Amateurs* which contains much advice for beginners. It includes a CD containing freeware programs [3].

The most popular data modes are described in detail in Chapter 8.

SSTV OPERATION

Most Slow Scan Television (SSTV) operation congregates around well-known meeting frequencies (14230kHz on 20m, for example).

SSTV operation is very dependent on the actual software you are using. Read the manual and practice receiving images before you think about transmitting. The main issue

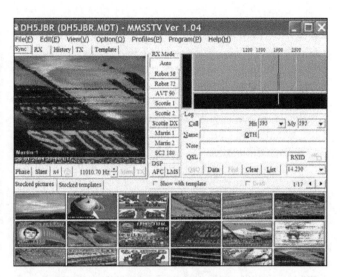

Using the *MMSTV* software to correct a sloping incoming SSTV picture

to overcome is the problem of sloping images, which are the result of not being properly synchronised (because all PC clocks tend to run at slightly different speeds).

Once you have everything set up to go, making two-way image contacts should be quite straightforward. But rather than exchange details of weather, antennas, etc, it is more normal to exchange pictures, maybe of your shack, your house or your local town. It is possible to send live pictures by grabbing each frame and holding it in a store while it is scanned and sent to the transmitter. More information can be obtained from the World Slow Scan Television Club [4].

ATV OPERATION

Amateur (fast-scan) Television (ATV) uses a combination of Audio, Video and RF engineering, sometimes also computer programming, to transmit television pictures locally and around the world.

The amateur bands from 28MHz to 28GHz may be used for ATV although most operation takes place on the 23cm, 13cm and 3cm bands. Modulation is either FM analogue or digital. Digital transmission uses much less bandwidth and provides a greater range and improved picture quality.

Picture content can vary between a typical shot of the operator in the shack and other local cameras, a series of captions or fully edited video recordings. The material shown must be copyright free or the copyright owned by the operator.

Fast-scan TV has changed significantly in recent years. Whereas much of the activity used to be on 70cm, most operation nowadays is on 23cm and above, largely through the chain of ATV repeaters (see Chapter 12). This simplifies matters considerably, as both sound and video are transmitted together and contacts can be established directly through the repeater. Of course, there is nothing to prevent direct contacts when signals strengths are sufficient, but it has to be remembered that TV requires much more bandwidth than, say, FM voice, and therefore requires much higher signal strengths for adequate signal-to-noise ratio (in a similar manner to voice transmission compared with CW).

Sometimes a separate voice channel will be opened on, say, 2m or 70cm to allow full-duplex contacts to take place, allowing both operators to stay in constant contact as they exchange video. It is worth remembering that ATV repeaters operate in 'beacon mode' when not otherwise in use, so they are always available as a set-up aid and a guide to propagation conditions. Video Streaming via the internet is also used to show the pictures to viewers who are out of range of the transmitter or repeater.

For the bands below 440MHz it is normal to use Reduced Bandwidth Digital Television or RB-tv. Although there is room in the 70cm band for a 2MHz wide channel.

ATV may be used in all the amateur microwave bands. The most popular are 23cm, 13cm, more recently 9cm and 3cm. Due to the ever growing restrictions in the 23cm and 13cm bands the 9cm, 3.4GHz band has recently be licensed for repeater outputs instead. One advantage of the 9cm and 3cm bands is that it is possible to receive these frequencies using an off the shelf regular C band or Ku band LNB. These are available at low cost from a variety of satellite receiving equipment suppliers.

Analogue FM transmission has traditionally been used on these bands but more recently amateurs are using digital transmission to improve picture quality and reduce the transmitted bandwidth. This is especially so for the 9cm band because it is only 10MHz wide and therefore not wide enough to fit in an analogue FM ATV transmission.

Signal reports on ATV are given using the P code - P0 representing no picture, to P5 representing a perfect, noise-free, broadcast-quality one.

EMERGENCY COMMUNICATIONS

UK amateurs, thankfully, are rarely involved in emergency communications. Raynet, the Radio Amateurs' Emergency Network, co-ordinates those UK amateurs who want to be involved in emergency preparedness. It runs training exercises, co-ordinates with potential user services (fire, police, ambulance, etc), and gives advice on operating matters specifically relating to emergency communications. Further information on Raynet, including how to join, can be found at [5]. The RSGB

A member of Essex Raynet assisting British Red Cross with checkpoints and safety communications for the Arleigh Hospice 'Cycle for Life' charity event.

Emergency Communications Committee [6] coordinates and checks group membership information held at RSGB headquarters to ensure members are correctly insured when taking part in Raynet activities.

Of course, there may be times when you are on the air and have to give assistance in some way, at short notice, for example an amateur on board a sailing vessel that is experiencing difficulties. Provided you are a competent operator, this shouldn't present any special problems. Perhaps the main concern is, unlike in your day-to-day operating, the necessity of keeping an accurate transcript of all communications, not only so that you can pass details to any parties you need to bring in (Coastguard, Police, etc), but also so that you can retrace the sequence of communications after the event, for any enquiry or investigation that might take place. The licence implications of handling emergency messages are covered in Chapter 2.

REFERENCES

[1]   ARRL DXCC list: www.arrl.org/country-lists-prefixes
[2]   *RSGB Prefix Guide*, 11th edition, Fred Handscombe, G4BWP; RSGB. Available from www.rsgbshop.org
[3]   *PSK31/RTTY for Radio Amateurs*, Roger Cooke, G3LDI, RSGB. Available from www.rsgbshop.org
[4]   World Slow Scan Television Club: http://wsstvc.org/
[5]   The Radio Amateurs Emergency Network (Raynet): www.raynet-uk.net
[6]   http://rsgb.org/main/about-us/committees/emergency-communications-committee/

THE EARLIEST AMATEUR RADIO transmissions were sent using Morse code as the mode of communication, keying a spark gap transmitter. It is perhaps astonishing that Morse remains so popular a century later, but the fact is that it still has many benefits. Nevertheless, amateurs were quick to adopt voice transmission as soon as it became feasible.

The earliest form of voice communication was Amplitude Modulation (AM), still used a little on the amateur bands, particularly by those who enjoy restoring and using earlier generations of equipment. AM sounds good on the bands when there is little interference and it remains in daily use on the long-wave and medium-wave bands, as well as on short-wave. However, many countries are now phasing out short-wave broadcasting which has mainly been on AM.

When single-sideband (SSB) first started to be heard on the amateur bands in the 1950s, there was huge resistance from many members of the amateur community. On most of the receivers of that time it was tricky to demodulate, and often sounded dreadful. But the benefits were too great to ignore. Half the bandwidth of AM, with all the power going into one sideband, rather than being shared between two sidebands and a carrier, so the signal-to-noise performance was substantially better than AM. Perhaps more importantly, as the amateur bands became more crowded, twice as many stations could be accommodated in the bandwidth available.

AM was still in fairly widespread use in the late 1960s and early '70s, but the increasing availability of affordable SSB transceivers meant that by the late '70s AM was all but dead, at least on the HF bands.

On the VHF bands, through to the early 1960s Amplitude Modulation (AM) was the mode of choice, gradually being replaced by Frequency Modulation (FM) which is in common use today. Even a narrowband FM signal is at least as wide as an AM signal. The usual channel spacing in the FM segments of the VHF and UHF bands nowadays is 12.5kHz (previously it was 25kHz). This is much narrower than the wideband FM used in VHF broadcasting, but still much wider than the 2.5kHz or thereabouts required for an SSB signal. On the VHF and UHF bands this is not a problem, and FM remains the mode of choice for mobile operation and day-to-day 'rag-chewing', particularly through repeaters.

For DXing on the VHF and UHF bands, SSB is preferred - while not having the fidelity of FM, it has better signal-to-noise benefits or more 'talk power', which is what you need when signals are weak or propagation is varying.

FM is also used in the top half of the 10m HF band, the only HF band wide enough to accommodate it. A number of recent DXpeditions have operated in the FM part of 10m and generated a lot of interest. Earlier HF transceivers did not cater for FM operation, but most modern ones do, not only for 10m use but also so that they can be used with transverters for VHF / UHF.

At the start of the 21st century, digital voice modes were first documented and have now become commonplace on the VHF and UHF bands (see box overleaf for full details).

Modes other than Morse and voice took a while to catch on, but by the 1960s Radio Teletype (RTTY) started to become popular with the release on to the surplus market of large numbers of mechanical teleprinters. Similarly, early Slow Scan Television (SSTV) systems used mechanical scanners to send and receive pictures. But the real explosion in the use of data modes, both text and picture, came about with the advent of the ubiquitous personal computer.

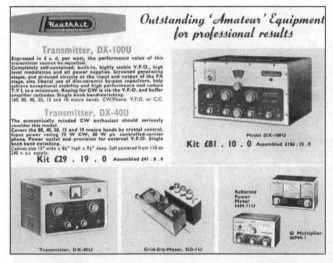

The Heathkit DX-100U was among the last of the stand-alone AM / CW transmitters before SSB gained supremacy. Most amateurs built them from kits, but they were also available ready-assembled. This extract from the Heathkit catalogue is from 1966. £81 10s is equivalent to about £1400 today!

The HAL3100, an early electronic RTTY terminal, from about 1980. Photo: Courtesy of Palatinatian, *Wikipedia*.

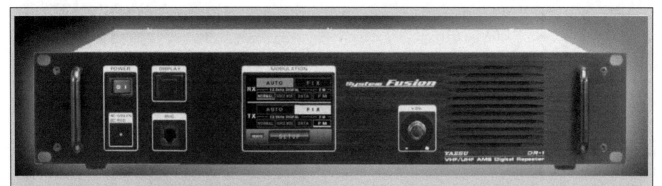

Yaesu launched their 'System Fusion' digital voice system in competition with the open source D-Star system favoured by Icom. This is the Yaesu DR-1 System Fusion VHF / UHF digital repeater.

Digital Voice (DV)

The use of digital voice is now quite common on VHF / UHF, thanks to several manufacturers offering transceivers and repeaters with digital voice as standard. The first to become available was the open source D-Star system promoted by Icom, which manufactures several amateur D-Star hand-held and mobile transceivers and a D-Star repeater system - more on D-Star can be found in Chapter 13. Since then, two more DV systems have become available: Yaesu's 'System Fusion' and DMR (Digital Mobile Radio). Unfortunately the three systems are completely incompatible with each other and although D-Star had a head start of several years it remains to be seen which (if any) eventually becomes the *de facto* standard for VHF / UHF amateur digital voice.

A number of amateurs around the world are now conducting experiments with DV also on HF, and the IARU Region 1 HF band plan lists DV centres of activity at 3630, 7070, 14130, 18150, 21180, 24960 and 28330kHz. In fact, HF DV has been around for longer than you might imagine: it was back in 1999 that Charles Brain, G4GUO, and Andy Talbot, G4JNT, first experimented with digital voice transmission. Using a home-made modem on 40m SSB they successfully communicated over a 70km path. An article was published in *RadCom* [1], a paper presented at the 18th ARRL / TAPR Digital Communications Conference, and another article in the May / June 2000 edition of the ARRL's technical journal *QEX*. The system used a digital vocoder and DQPSK modulation with 36 tone carriers spaced at 62.5Hz and an overall bandwidth of 312.5Hz to 2500Hz. This allowed the system to be used in a standard SSB bandwidth, as well as on other modes such as AM and FM.

The Japanese company AOR turned Charles's and Andy's ideas into a commercially-available piece of hardware, the ARD9800 'Fast Data Modem', which was released in 2004 and reviewed in *RadCom* in July of that year [2]. A 'Mk2' version followed. Both use G4GUO's open protocol and are stand-alone units which simply connect to the microphone input and speaker output connections of a transceiver and a suitable 12V DC supply.

Digital Voice is not a weak-signal (DX) mode, requiring about 25dB signal-to-noise ratio to work effectively but, when that is the case, it produces audio quality equivalent to NBFM using SSB as the mode of transmission and bandwidth. Whether for HF or VHF, digital voice is unlikely to replace SSB for weak signal (DX) voice communications. Like FM, digital voice tends to have a threshold above which the signal is 100% copy and below which it is more or less unusable. DXers require a mode in which copy deteriorates gradually so that contacts can still be made under marginal conditions, albeit requiring some perseverance on the part of the operators.

In 2015, AOR announced the AR-DV1, a 100kHz to 1300MHz general-coverage receiver that decodes virtually all the popular digital modes in addition to conventional analogue modes such as CW, SSB, AM and FM (both narrow-band and wide-band) [3].

In due course DV will probably become available as standard in transceivers too.

The AOR ARD9000Mk2 digital voice modem allows a standard analogue SSB (or FM) transceiver to be used to transmit and receive digital voice transmissions.

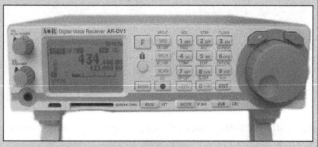

Released internationally in 2015, the AOR AR-DV1 is the first general-coverage digital voice (DV) receiver.

The first generation of systems required a terminal unit to interface between the computer and transceiver, taking signals from the computer's RS232 serial port, and converting them to tones which could modulate the transceiver. Most of the earliest terminal units were actually developed for VHF packet radio (AX.25), which took off in a big way in the late 1980s, especially when the licensing authority started licensing packet mailboxes. Use of packet radio is now declining as more data modes become available. Several terminal units, for example the popular AEA PK232, could generate and decode RTTY, FAX and other modes as well, and were pressed into service on these modes on the HF bands, not always with ideal results as the filters with which they were fitted were wide enough for VHF packet, so rather too broad for HF use. Later models put this right.

The revolution came when computers with sound cards became universal and somewhat more highly featured, so that separate terminal units were no longer required. Nowadays, the computer's sound card can generate the tones required, whether for RTTY, PSK31, SSTV or whatever new mode comes along, and these tones can then go directly to the transceiver's microphone input or, if it has one, auxiliary audio input. Received audio can be demodulated by the computer, with the software offering digital signal processing (DSP), to emulate the optimum filter(s) according to the mode in use.

The other major mode in use by amateurs is Fast Scan Amateur TV (ATV), equivalent to the day-to-day broadcast TV that we are all familiar with. These days many users of Amateur TV are moving from analogue techniques to Digital ATV.

New digital modes appear almost daily. Most significantly, perhaps, was a revolution in weak-signal communications. The *WSJT* suite of software, developed by Joe Taylor, K1JT, offers reliable communications via meteor scatter, EME and other extremely weak signal modes, such as extreme tropospheric propagation, to amateurs whose stations would previously have been considered totally inadequate for those paths. One result was a debate over whether contacts conducted by such means are 'valid' and in the 'spirit' of amateur radio, as the computer is doing most of the work. This isn't the place to debate such philosophical questions!

No-one is obliged to use those modes, but for many who do the *WSJT* software has brought new excitement to their hobby, which surely has been the story of amateur radio's progress over the decades.

VOICE MODES

There is little more to be said about the voice modes than what has been covered in the introduction. SSB and narrow-band FM (NBFM) are the two voice modes in widespread use in amateur radio, with a small amount of AM. Wideband FM has been used in the past on the microwave bands, though even on those bands it is more common nowadays to use the narrow-band modes because they are more effective for good communications, and the technology to generate them is now within reach of the home constructor.

What is important to note is that AM and FM are continuous transmissions, in that a carrier is always present even when no speaking is taking place. The result is that they have a much higher duty cycle than SSB (or CW). Most modern transceivers are rated for SSB operation, and should be de-rated accordingly for the other modes. For example, a 100W transceiver should probably not be operated at more than 50W carrier power on FM or AM but, to be safe, check the manufacturer's recommendations in the manual.

Some amateurs go to a great deal of trouble to improve the readability of their voice transmissions, and there are endless debates over microphone types and the need for tailoring of voice response. Many modern transceivers offer a range of audio tailoring. The Heil range of headsets has been available with two alternative microphone inserts, one designed for high-fidelity voice transmission and the other, with a +10dB rise at 2kHz, intended for DX working.

In practice, the only way to set up your transmitter to sound the way you want it is to listen to the transmitted output, or have a friend do so. There are two factors to take into account: the nature of your own voice and the effect you want to create. Everyone's voice is different, so there certainly can be benefits from making fine adjustments. And there really is a difference between the sort of 'armchair quality' audio that you might want for a rag-chew with a friend across town and the high-impact audio that you might prefer when trying to break a DX pile-up.

Joe Taylor, K1JT, developer of *WSJT*. Joe is a physicist who specialises in radio astronomy research. He won the Nobel Prize for physics in 1993 for discovering the first orbiting pulsar.

Bob Heil, K9EID, founder of Heil Sound and (left) the Heil Pro-Set+ headset which has both full-range and 'DX' inserts built in to the microphone boom, selectable by a small switch.

What is crucial is that you don't over-drive your transmitter by simply turning up the audio gain. The other common fault is to use too much speech processing. Although the meters on your transceiver will tell you a certain amount of the story, only by looking at your transmitted signal on an oscilloscope or monitor scope, or listening to it on the air, will you know whether your transmitted speech is distorted, or if you are over-driving the transmitter and generating spurious signals outside your immediate passband. But do remember that the microphone gain control is there to be used, and sometimes more gain is desirable. Many amateurs feel the need to shout loudly into the microphone, especially when they are chasing rare DX. Experienced contesters quickly learn that this is counter-productive - you will lose your voice long before the end of the contest! Instead, let the transceiver do the work for you. Speak at normal levels, and adjust the microphone gain and speech processor controls accordingly. For the cross-town rag-chew, you might not want to use the speech processor at all, as it reduces the fidelity of your signals.

When using speech processing do ensure that there aren't any extraneous noises in your shack which are being picked up by the microphone and transmitted on-air. Fans, in particular, can form a very irritating background noise when heard at the far end. And your voice may echo if your shack has many hard surfaces. Again, the best way is to get someone to listen to your transmissions.

And be aware if there are others talking in the background in your shack, as their voices can easily be picked up and transmitted.

If you choose to record various exchanges, for example CQ calls to save your voice in a contest, it is again important to check levels and ensure that the recorded audio drives your transmitter to the same level as your normal speech. It is not uncommon to hear some very distorted CQ calls in contests, where the transmitter is being overdriven by a pre-recorded message. It is also not uncommon to hear the CQ in a very different voice to the one that comes back when you answer! The better contesting programs allow each operator to record a personalised CQ call (and other messages) for use in a multi-operator contest environment.

When operating with any form of voice transmission, do bear in mind the person at the far end. If you are in contact with someone for whom English is not their first language, or if there is heavy interference, always speak slowly and clearly, using phonetics to pass any critical information.

Finally, some phone operators like to use VOX (voice-operated break-in), to come as close as possible to having a natural conversation, given that, unlike a telephone, amateur radio is inherently a one-way form of communication. All transceivers with VOX offer the ability to adjust several parameters such as the time it takes to activate and to trip out, and the level at which it activates and then drops out. These adjustments are quite critical to being able to use VOX successfully. Again, any background noise (from having a window open, for example) can cause the transmitter to activate even if you weren't actually saying anything. So by all means use VOX, but set it up with care.

MORSE CODE (CW)

There were those who thought that the removal of the mandatory Morse code test for access to the HF bands, as a result of a decision taken at the 2003 World Radiocommunication Conference, would spell an end to the use of Morse code on the amateur bands. Nothing could be further from the truth and the use of Morse has, if anything, increased in the years since most licensing administrations around the world started to issue 'code-free' HF licences. The fact of the matter is that Morse code stands on its own merits and it does not need amateurs to be compelled to learn it in order for it to remain a popular and useful operating mode.

Incidentally, the reason there was a Morse code test in the first place was because many of our HF bands were shared with other services which used Morse code. It was essential that, in the event of interference to their activities by an amateur station, they could call on Morse and ask the amateur to move. Since the discontinuation of Morse usage by those services, the requirement no longer applies. There are though still a few countries (eg Malaysia) which at the time of writing (August 2015) continue to insist on a Morse code test before an HF licence is issued.

Morse telegraphy continues to be, and almost certainly will continue to be, one of the most popular modes in use by radio amateurs. There is a certain satisfaction in being able to send and receive Morse competently, and Morse is still one of the most effective modes for working through heavy interference or with low signals (though, it has to be said, some of the data modes are even better than Morse in this respect). Morse abbreviations and Q codes make it a more suitable mode than telephony for overcoming language barriers. It is also much easier to build a simple telegraphy transmitter than a phone one.

Just a word of explanation here, as the previous paragraph mixed the terms Morse and telegraphy. We are talking here about using a method of transmission, in the case of CW, of keying the transmitter on and off or, in the case of MCW (Modulated Continuous Wave), keying a tone on and off which is then used to modulate the transmitter. In practice, when we use that method of transmission, we usually adopt

A straight Morse key and the best way to hold it.

the international Morse code for the purpose, as it is well established after well over a century of use.

Actually, the Morse code as we now know it is rather different to the code that Samuel Morse first proposed for those long-distance telegraph links across the USA, following the lines of the newly-created railways. There are many Morse characters that we in the UK don't come across too often, but which are used elsewhere because they represent alphabetical and grammatical characters that simply don't occur in English. In practice, they are rarely used on the air either, except perhaps by two stations of the same nationality. Much more on the history and practise of Morse code can be found in [4].

Sending and receiving Morse can be done in many ways. Most beginners start with a conventional straight key, with its up-down mechanism. Many are available, both new and old. A number of 'Straight Key' events are held each year to encourage amateurs to retain and practice their skills with straight keys. The very need for such events suggests that the world has moved on, just as it has from AM transmission.

After the straight key came the semi-automatic bug key, where dashes are created manually by holding the key to one side, but holding the key to the other side creates a series of dots, as a result of the vibration of a weighted arm. It takes a particular skill to send well with a semi-automatic key, but the advantage of moving from a straight key is that it makes it much easier to send at speeds more than about 25WPM than on a straight key, certainly for extended periods. The first semi-automatic key on the market was made by the American company Vibroplex in 1905 and their original design of 'bug' key is still made today.

Fully automatic keys, like semi-automatic ones, have a paddle which can be pressed to the left or the right. An electronic circuit generates dashes when the key is pressed one way and dots when it is pressed the other. Iambic keying goes one stage further - a twin-paddle which, when squeezed, will produce alternate dots and dashes.

Most modern transceivers have automatic keyers built in so it is only necessary to purchase the paddle. With automatic keys, the number of movements to send a sentence in Morse

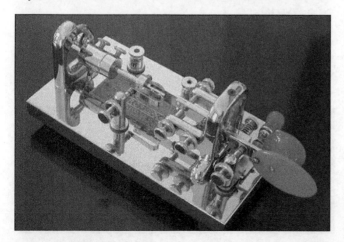

US company Vibroplex, one of the oldest names in amateur radio, still manufactures and sells their original design of 'bug' key.

A Bencher fully automatic iambic key.

is considerably less than with a straight or semi-automatic key, with the result that it is possible to send at very much higher speeds and with less fatigue. Competent CW operators, using an automatic key, tend to rag-chew or contest at speeds in the 30 - 35WPM range. Some can operate very much faster than this, but you then need someone else with an equal level of competence at the other end, or you are wasting your time!

Finally, Morse code can also be generated by a computer. Most logging programs allow the user to store CQ calls and regularly-sent messages (such as name, QTH and equipment details) and send them by pressing a function key. Free text can be keyed on the keyboard itself. Many choose to have a traditional keyer in parallel with the keyboard so that, in contests for example the standard contest exchanges are sent from the computer, but the operator can immediately resort to the keyer if there is a need to send anything other than the stored messages.

Most operators choose to receive Morse code by ear. Although there are programs for decoding CW, they tend not to work effectively in the presence of fading or heavy interference.

Many newly-licensed amateurs are unsure whether to copy everything down by hand, or to try to copy in their heads. It is very much a matter of experience. If you are engaging in a typical 'rubber stamp' contact with, perhaps, an overseas amateur with little English, the exchange is likely to be fairly predictable: RST, name, QTH, perhaps his equipment and / or the weather at his location. So you don't need to write everything down, just the salient details. When you hear "QTH" get ready to make a note of his location in your log. Generally it will be sent twice in any case. Experienced CW operators, engaging in a lengthy rag-chew on Morse, tend not to write down anything unless they specifically want to note something for later. Instead the whole exchange is copied by ear in exactly the same way as if the conversation were taking place using voice.

If you are new to CW, it can be daunting to call someone who is obviously an experienced CW operator, sending at high speeds. You may feel competent to copy a contest exchange (RST and a serial number, for example) at reasonably high speeds, but not to engage in a lengthy conversation. The trick is, quite simply, to ask the other station to slow down ("QRS pse"). Most will be only too happy to do so. If they don't, it is their loss. But every CW operator had to start somewhere, and probably enjoyed a similar courtesy from other amateurs at that time, so will almost certainly be prepared to do the same for you. Incidentally, don't assume that, just because you hear fast CW, you are listening to a competent operator. There are far too many operators on the bands who send somewhat faster than they really should, and end up spending much of their transmissions correcting errors!

Finally a word about your transmitted signal. Depending on the rise and fall time of your transmitted characters, it is possible for your transmitter to generate so-called key clicks, which can be heard some way from your carrier frequency. Some commercial transceivers are well-known for generating such key clicks though, in most cases, there are modifications readily available which go at least some way to cure the problem.

There can also be an issue when using break-in, either semi- or full-break-in. In the former you hit the key and your transmitter is activated which only goes back to receive after a pause of more than several dot's length, the length of the pause being adjustable; in the latter your transceiver goes back to receive quite literally at every gap in the CW, giving the effect that you are actually listening continuously to the band. Any transmitter will take a finite time to go into transmit, even longer if it is activating a linear amplifier, perhaps via a relay. So your first CW character can be foreshortened, leading to problems in copying at the far end. With full break-in, every character may be affected in this way. If you are operating split-frequency the synthesiser also needs to change frequency between every 'dit' or 'dah' and it may not be possible to do so above a certain speed. There will be a comfortable CW speed for break-in operation, above which your transceiver may start to struggle. The best way to check for this, and for key clicks, is to get a nearby amateur to listen to your transmission and maybe record it for you to hear.

High Speed CW

High Speed CW (HSCW) was used for many years for Meteor Scatter operation, though it has now been superseded by *WSJT* (see below). Messages would be sent at perhaps 1000 characters per minute, recorded at the far end on an old reel-to-reel recorder and replayed at lower speed. A random MS QSO could take several hours to complete, depending on the number of meteor 'pings'. High speed CW can also be used for conventional communications. The human brain has limits, however, and for general conversation on the air, speeds of more than 40WPM become very difficult.

Then there are those whose interest is to test their ability to the limit. There are annual speed contests in which proponents can show off their expertise. The world record is in *Guinness World Records*. There are several levels of achievement, measured according to the number of errors made. Andrei Bindasov, EU7KI is recorded as sending at 271 letters per minute and 230 figures per minute during the 2003 IARU World Championship in High Speed Telegraphy in Belarus,

Very Low Speed CW

At the other end of the scale, very low speed CW ('QRSS'), with each character taking tens of seconds, or even minutes, uses software to record and integrate the signals over a long period of time. It was first used on the LF bands but can also be heard on higher frequencies nowadays.

Using a very low speed means that very narrow bandwidths can be employed. As noise, which is usually the limiting factor in achieving a contact, is directly proportional to bandwidth, this approach enables weaker signals to be received, thereby increasing the distances that can be worked. Because the QSO takes a long time to complete, and because it is necessary to create a very narrow filter, the mode is carried out with suitable DSP software and your transmitter needs to be very stable.

The mode became known as 'QRSS' (QRS being the Q code for "Please send more slowly" in CW). It was originally implemented by a hardware DSP unit and software developed by Peter Martinez, G3PLX, but later purpose-designed software was developed which became popular with 136kHz operators.

The most commonly used receiving software is *Argo* [5] and *SpecLab* [6]. These are capable of displaying Morse with dot lengths from less than one second to over 100s. They work in conjunction with the PC's soundcard. In practice a dot length of three seconds (QRSS3) is the default mode on LF/MF. This allows a meaningful two-way contact to take place in less than an hour.

Because of the time taken to send QRSS signals, a simplified QSO format has been devised. The 'de' between callsigns is not used, and reports are in the form 'O' for perfectly readable, 'M' for readable with difficulty and 'T' for visible but not readable. Callsigns are rarely repeated and are abbreviated after the first full call.

However, in common with standard amateur radio practice, a contact comprises an exchange of full callsigns and reports, and the final 'rogers'. A typical contact, lasting about 40 minutes in QRSS3, is shown below (the locator is optional and would be omitted if it is already known or in marginal contacts):

CQ ON7YD K
ON7YD G3XDV K
XDV YD O O JO20IX K
YD XDV R M M IO91VT K
YD R TU SK

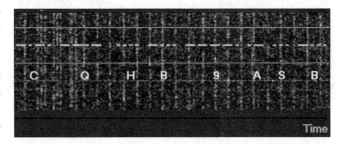

A received QRSS signal. The translated letters have been added to the picture; they are not present on the original display. The vertical lines are static crashes [pic: ON7YD].

DFCW uses different frequencies instead of dots and dashes. This says "G3AQC" [pic: ON7YD].

Because this is still rather time consuming a method has been devised to speed up the information transfer whilst still retaining the same bandwidth (and hence signal-to-noise ratio). DFCW (dual frequency CW) uses two closely-spaced frequencies, one for dots, the other for dashes, and can be received using exactly the same software and settings as QRSS. The time savings are made by making the 'dots' and 'dashes' the same length, and having only a very short gap between each dot or dash, resulting in up to 50% time improvement. In all other respects it is used in exactly the same way as QRSS, and cross-mode contacts are common.

Transmitting QRSS requires some software, such as ON7YD's QRS [7] or external hardware such as the 'Ultimate' multimode kit from QRP Labs [8].

QRSS can now be found on several HF bands, especially 10MHz. More on this mode can be found on ON7YD's web site at [7].

DATA MODES

Arguably, with the discussion of QRSS, the chapter has already moved on to data modes. QRSS is a good example of how previous distinctions between traditional modes (voice and CW), data modes and image modes, have become blurred.

The data modes which will be considered here fall into several distinct categories. There are data modes for sending text in routine situations on the VHF and HF bands, data modes specifically designed for specialist low-signal applications (meteor scatter, troposcatter, EME) and data modes specifically designed for image transmission. A recent development is the use of data modes that do not permit two-way contacts; instead they work as one-way 'beacons' that test propagation paths with the reports returning via an Internet connection.

The difference between radio communications and the Internet for data transmission is primarily that a radio circuit tends to much less reliable than a wired network. Usually it has less bandwidth, and it is also subject to propagation issues - some stations not hearing other stations on the same frequency, interference, fading and the like. It is to deal with these issues that so many new data modes have come into being in recent years.

Generally, what has happened to make each successive data mode possible, and better than its predecessors, is the increasing power of home computers. The early data modes used very little processing power, later ones may use quite substantial amounts. Given that most PCs now are very powerful indeed, the question might be asked as to why older modes like RTTY are still around. The reason is largely because it is a well-established standard, and many amateurs are equipped for it. RTTY allows others to 'listen in', to have quick 'one-line' overs and is especially suitable (and widely

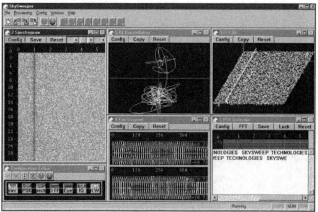

SkySweeper decoder and analyser software. The program is designed to decode a wide range of digital transmissions and provide comprehensive on-screen analysis for the signals. While the main use of the program is to receive, it can also transmit a dozen different common modulation formats including CW, RTTY, SSTV and PSK31.

used) in HF contests, yet it's based on technology invented many, many years ago for machines. Like Morse, its usefulness and simplicity have kept it going in the face of other more advanced data modes which, technically, are far superior in 'getting through when all else fails'. Meanwhile, some other data modes have come and gone, never having reached a high enough level of acceptance to survive when newer, more effective modes took their place.

Handshaking

In contrast to RTTY, some other modes like AmTOR, Packet, G-TOR, PacTOR etc, are 'handshaking modes'. Here, when in contact, the Information Sending Station (ISS) sends a small group of characters at a time, and the Information Receiving Station (IRS) receives these and performs a parity check to make sure the information 'adds up', ie "were the characters received correctly?" If so, the IRS sends a brief 'OK' and the ISS then sends the next group, and so on. When the time comes for the partner station to have its 'over', a 'changeover' occurs (your software handles all this for you) and the ISS and IRS change between the two stations. This is ideal if you are sending data to or receiving data from a remote computer, as there is no human operator at the far end to alert you if the message has been corrupted in any way. It can also work for some day-to-day two-way contacts but is less suited than 'old-fashioned' RTTY for quick, snappy operating.

Connecting PC and Transceiver

The first task in using any data mode, unless it is catered for directly in the transceiver (some allow you to connect a keyboard directly, and away you go), is to connect your computer to the transceiver. This has been covered in many publications (eg [9]) and on many websites (eg [10]). Some suitable interface circuits are also shown in **Fig 1 (a) and (b)**. To describe the process in the simplest terms, the received signal (taken, perhaps, from an auxiliary audio output on your transceiver, as you will probably want to listen to the incoming tones at the

A few transceivers can transmit and receive RTTY and PSK31 without the need of a computer. Left: The Icom IC-7600 which only requires a USB keyboard to send in these modes. Right: The IC-7600's comprehensive front panel screen showing an RTTY signal being received.

same time) goes to the microphone input on your PC sound card. Usually there is a facility within the data modes program you are using to enable you to adjust the levels. Alternatively, it is also possible to do so from within the *Windows* operating system.

The transmitted signal is taken from the sound card's output to an auxiliary (data) input on your transceiver or, if necessary, to the microphone input. In either case, ensure the microphone is disconnected when using data modes. The output from the sound card will almost certainly be too high for the microphone input of your transceiver and although some adjustment will be possible in the software, it is often advisable to use a simple resistive potential divider circuit to reduce the level by 10dB or so. Many of the commercial interfaces which you can buy for this purpose not only have a suitable potential divider, but also have an audio transformer or opto-coupler so there is no direct connection between sound card and transceiver. This minimises the risk of hum on the transmitted signal.

To check that all is well, load some suitable software for one of the more popular data modes (probably RTTY, as there are almost always RTTY signals to be heard on 40 or 20m) and see what you can copy. If you can copy RTTY signals correctly, you will almost certainly be able to copy other data modes without trouble once you have suitable software installed. Depending on whether your equipment and software is set for low tones or high tones (see next section) you may need to switch your transceiver to USB or LSB respectively. Similarly, once you are happy with the receive side, check the transmit side.

You are checking to ensure that you are not overdriving the transmitter (if, turning up the audio level from your sound card, transmit power stays the same, you already have the output set too high) and, ultimately, that other stations are able to copy your transmitted signal.

The most common mistake is to transmit inverted (the two RTTY tones reversed). Normally, if you are receiving correctly, you should also be transmitting correctly. It is assumed here that you are sending audio tones, rather than using the FSK input of your transceiver. The latter is fine for RTTY (check the wiring carefully and be aware that you may need

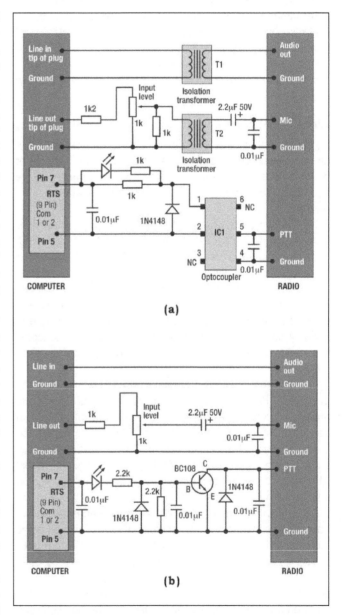

Fig 1 (a) and (b): Two typical sound card interface circuits. The circuit at (a) is to be preferred as it isolates the computer from the transceiver.

One of the popular RIGblaster series of interfaces.

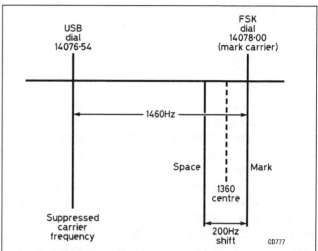

Fig 2: Relationship of the transceiver dial reading to the Mark frequency for USB and FSK operation.

to reverse the tones), but won't help you with getting going on other data modes.

A word of warning. Like FM and AM, most of the data modes described in the following paragraphs have a 100% duty cycle, so it is important to ensure that your transceiver is able to handle this, usually by turning down the power level to about 50% of the SSB / CW power rating.

RTTY

RTTY is the oldest and by far the most popular of the data modes. It is unsophisticated in modern terms, with no error detection or correction. It only handles upper case characters. But it is well suited to rapid-fire contacts such as in contest operation. And there are plenty of competent software packages available free of charge, which offer a wide range of RTTY facilities, probably the most popular software being *MMTTY* [11].

RTTY uses two tones, spaced 170Hz apart. It can be copied on most transceivers through a 500Hz and even a 250Hz filter, giving good receive performance. Alternatively, with suitable software, you can leave the filter open at full SSB bandwidth so that you can see a number of RTTY signals on the waterfall display on your PC screen, and then select the one you want to receive. *MMTTY* has its own internal

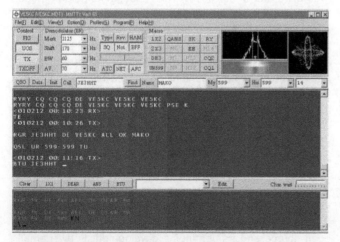

The *MMTTY* software in use.

audio-filtering capabilities (using the sound card) to extract the tones you are looking for and reject any interfering signals (provided they are not co-channel with either of those tones). This is a substantial improvement on many earlier systems.

Because RTTY uses two audio tones there can easily be confusion when RTTY frequencies are cited, as there are really two frequencies we might be interested in. One is the 'carrier' frequency, but this is almost irrelevant, as what matters is not the exact audio tone used for modulation but the separation between the two. In any case, in some parts of the world RTTY operators use so-called 'low' tones of 1275Hz and 1445Hz (a 170Hz difference), whereas most amateurs now favour 'high' tones of 2125Hz and 2295Hz (again a 170Hz difference). The advantage of high tones is that any harmonics are likely to be outside the audio pass-band. The other, more useful frequency to quote, therefore is the 'Mark' frequency, which is the one that is transmitted when no data is being sent, but even this will be designated differently according to whether high or low tones are being used, high-tone USB signals being 1.46kHz higher than LSB low-tone ones (**Fig 2** shows the relationships when using USB). In general tuning around there's no difference, but when arranging a 'sked' or chasing a spot from the Cluster system, it's important to define which you're using.

Much more about using RTTY can be found in [12].

PSK

PSK31 [13] was developed specifically as a replacement for traditional RTTY for real-time contacts. Its inventor Peter Martinez, G3PLX, argued that modes using error correction were inherently unsuited for real-time contacts because the users tended to be uncomfortable with the time delays inherent in hand-shaking between the two ends of the contact.

BPSK is an abbreviation for binary phase shift keying, and the 31 refers to the number of characters sent per second. The character set is based on a number of 'varicodes', ie variable-length codes, devised in a similar way to Morse code, whereby the more common letters can be sent more quickly than the less common ones. Without going into any more detail, the benefits to the user of BPSK31 (usually referred to as PSK31) compared with traditional RTTY are that it tends to work better in weak signal conditions and uses less bandwidth (a single carrier, as against the two of RTTY, with a theoretical bandwidth of 31Hz).

PSK31 requires a stable transmitter and receiver, but this is not a problem with modern transceivers. In any case, most of the software available for PSK31 uses a waterfall display and incorporates DSP filtering. Therefore operating the mode is simple. You can leave your transceiver's filters on a wide (SSB) setting and watch something like 2.5kHz of the band. This is room aplenty for many PSK31 signals. You can then click on an individual signal to decode it and start a contact. Unlike RTTY, it doesn't matter whether you transmit and receive in USB or LSB mode, as there is only one tone, so there are no issues about tones being reversed. And if you invoke automatic frequency control (AFC) it will stay locked to the signal, even if there is some subsequent drifting in frequency.

PSK63 [14] is a variant of PSK31 operating, as the name suggests, at a higher speed. It has been developed very much with contesting in mind, with the intention that contacts can be conducted that much more quickly. As you would expect, it takes up roughly twice the bandwidth of PSK31. Most of the popular software programs available for PSK31 also support PSK63. Programs include *Digipan*, *WinPSK*, *Winwarbler*, *Multipsk*, *PSK31 Deluxe*, *QuickPSK* and *RCKRTTY*. As well as text, PSK63 is capable of sending thumbnail pictures, with a transmission time around two minutes.

PSK08 is a low-speed variant of PSK 31, aimed primarily at 136kHz operators. Its narrow bandwidth requirement is ideally suited to low frequency operation, permitting the use of very narrow DSP filtering for receive, to enhance overall signal-to-noise performance.

Much more about using PSK31 can be found in [12].

SSTV / FAX

SSTV has been popular for many years with amateurs who have enjoyed the challenge of sending pictures over the HF bands. While Fast Scan TV (moving pictures) requires considerable bandwidth, SSTV is similar to FAX, whereby one image is sent at a time, over a normal voice channel. Originally, pictures were created by mechanically scanning a photograph and images were in black and white. Nowadays, colour pictures are sent as the norm, either generated from one of the popular graphics or paint programs, or captured from a digital camera.

As with all the data modes described so far, the best way to get set up on SSTV is to download one of the popular programs (for example, *MMSSTV* [15]), read the accompanying manual or help file, connect up to your transceiver via your sound card, and start decoding signals. The main difference between this and other data modes is that the signals will be images rather than text. Some useful hints and tips on getting started with SSTV appeared in a *RadCom* article [16].

Nowadays, most amateur interest in FAX operation is in receiving the various weather and news FAX services from around the world as well as images from dedicated weather

SSTV screen of JVComm32. The receive window can be any size up to full screen and many pictures can be open to select for transmitting. Note the CQ picture in large letters and response picture with a gap for callsign and report.

satellites. For amateur band service, images are exchanged using SSTV systems as described above.

MFSK

MFSK (multi-frequency shift keying) is supported by many of the popular data modes packages. It takes the two-tone concept of RTTY and extends this to several tones, which makes for a system that is more robust than PSK31 in the face of interference and when signals are weak. It is therefore more suited to DX working in a data modes environment. The tones are close-spaced and a stable transmitter and receiver are required.

Olivia

Olivia is a type of MFSK transmission designed to work well in low signal conditions in the presence of noise, fading, multipath propagation and auroral flutter. The signal can be copied when it is 10dB below the noise level.

It transmits seven-bit ASCII characters in blocks of five, with forward error correcting (FEC) code. In its default mode 32 tones each spaced by 31.25Hz are sent within a 1kHz bandwidth. Each block takes two seconds to transmit, so the effective data rate is 2.5 characters per second or approximately 30WPM. However, the bandwidth and baud rate can be changed depending on the prevailing conditions: there can be 2, 4, 8, 16, 32, 64, 128 or 256 tones and the bandwidth can be 125, 250, 500, 1000 or 2000Hz.

Early tests conducted between Europe and Australia on 20m showed that Olivia can perform well with power levels as low as 1W.

WSJT

WSJT was developed in 2000 / 2001 by Joe Taylor, K1JT (hence 'Weak Signal Communication, by K1JT'), but is now open source and its continuing development is by a small team. *WSJT* was originally written for weak-signal working, especially meteor scatter, on 2m and 6m [13]. It can decode signals propagated by fraction-of-a-second reflections from meteor trails, as well as steady signals more than 10dB weaker than those needed for conventional CW or SSB. The *WSJT* suite of programs comprises four main operating modes: FSK441, JT65, JT6M and JT4.

WSJT also offers *EME Echo* for measuring your own echoes from the Moon, A detailed description of the program is provided in the online *WSJT User's Guide*. The manual may be downloaded and printed from the website [18].

FSK441 - This was the first mode provided by *WSJT*, and was introduced in 2001. FSK441 effectively replaced high-speed CW as the preferred option for meteor scatter work. It employs multiple frequency-shift keying using four tones, at a data rate of 441 baud. FSK441 remains popular for MS work on 2m and 70cm.

JT6M - Also for meteor scatter working but optimised for 50MHz. JT6M employs multi-frequency shift keying with 44 tones. One of the tones is for synchronisation, leaving 43 carrying data. The data rate is 14.4 characters per second. It is no surprise that 6m is the focus for this mode, as it is by far the most reliable band for meteor scatter communications, open more or less around the clock, 365 days a year, and not only when major meteor showers occur. During major showers signals can be quite strong, but JT6M has opened up new horizons, allowing meteor scatter contacts to take place on a much more regular basis than previously.

JT65 - This really is a weak-signal mode, originally designed for EME and extreme troposcatter. JT65 can decode signals many dB below noise level, allowing contacts to be made without the signals being audible to the human ear. As with FSK441 and JT6M, JT65 employs MFSK, but with 65 tones and forward error correction (FEC). Due to the FEC, signals are either decoded correctly or not at all. Although originally intended for VHF / UHF working, many amateurs have discovered that it is also very effective for low power work on HF.

JT4 - Designed specifically for EME on the microwave bands, JT4 has an effective throughput of about 0.25 characters per second.

AmTOR

AmTOR, a derivation of the commercial mode SITOR, was developed for amateur radio use by Peter Martinez, G3PLX. Unlike RTTY, it allows direct linking between two stations with data acknowledgement and error checking. Because of the two-way to-ing and fro-ing which this requires, it is not ideal for contest QSOs, but is useful for ragchewing via the keyboard and has been used for mailboxes on the HF bands,

Communication with AmTOR makes use of a 'selcal', which is a four-letter combination. This is typically the first letter and the final three letters of your callsign, ie the selcal for 'G3XDV' would be 'GXDV', and when you're transmitting a 'CQ' you should also include your selcal in your CQ text as well as your callsign. Once in QSO, normal callsigns are exchanged as usual within the QSO text. For listening, all AmTOR terminal units and software also have a 'listen' mode where, providing signals levels are satisfactory, you can 'listen into' existing

contacts just like on RTTY, so you can call one of the stations at the end of a QSO if you wish.

Like traditional RTTY, one limitation of AmTOR is that is uses a 5-bit code, so cannot handle both upper and lower case character sets. Many terminal units were developed especially for AmTOR use, but the mode is waning, having largely been replaced by PacTOR for mailbox use (see below).

PacTOR

PacTOR and the later PacTOR II and PacTOR III were developed in Germany as an amalgam of the best in AmTOR and Packet, specifically to provide reliable file transfers to and from HF mailboxes. PacTOR operates at 100 or 200 baud depending on conditions, with net throughput of up to 18 characters per second. PacTOR-1 is an FSK mode, while PacTOR II (introduced in 1995) moved to PSK. It has the potential for higher throughput than PacTOR. PacTOR III is a software upgrade to PacTOR II, offering higher data rates still. PacTOR allows a 'listen' mode where, provided the path is of good quality, you can eavesdrop on PacTOR communications prior, for example, to calling one of the parties when their contact has ended.

Clover and Clover 2000

Clover was developed by HAL communications of the USA, specifically for HF data communications. It uses multiple-tone phase-shift encoding. Effective throughputs are similar to PacTOR-II. It serves a similar purpose to PacTOR, allowing error-free transmissions. It can be used for two-way contacts but is generally used for links with mailboxes.

G-TOR

G-TOR (Golay-TOR) is a proprietary FSK mode developed by Kantronics Inc of the USA. It is claimed to have better throughput than PacTOR, and better immunity to interference, multi-path and other effects encountered over radio links.

THROB

THROB, by G3PPT, develops MFSK still further, using a 9-tone signal. The throughput is slower that other text modes, but the system is reported to be more resilient in the face of low signals or propagation difficulties.

Hellschreiber

Strictly speaking, the various Hellschreiber [19] modes are not digital modes, but nevertheless are conveniently covered in this section. They are based on an old method for transmitting facsimile traffic over landlines that were invented by Dr Rudolf Hell in Germany in 1929, but have been adapted for use with modern software in the amateur radio environment. Text is not sent as discrete characters, but rather in the way of a facsimile transmission where a page builds up from a series of black and white dots to gradually form an image that could be text or even graphics of some sort.

The benefit over modes like PSK31 is that, in the face of interference or fading, the human eye may still be able to discern the transmitted characters whereas once they are lost with PSK31 or similar modes, they are lost forever. The overall bandwidth of Hellschreiber transmissions is about 75Hz, similar to PSK63, though there are several other versions including concurrent multi-tone Hell (C/MT Hell) and sequential multi-tone Hell (S/MT Hell).

WOLF

WOLF ('Weak-signal Operation on Low Frequency'), by Stewart Nelson, KK7KA [20], is a signal format and protocol designed specifically for the LF bands. It can be used for beacons and for two-way communications. Unlike existing formats, which are optimised for a particular S/N ratio (and corresponding speed), WOLF can operate over a wide range of signal levels. For example, a WOLF beacon transmits a 15-character message repeatedly. If the received signal would be adequate for conventional CW, copy will be displayed in 24 seconds. At a level barely enough for QRSS, copy will appear within two minutes. Even if the signal is another 10dB weaker, the message can still be received. It will take from 20 minutes to several hours, depending on the stability of the transmitter and receiver. It is also necessary that the propagation path remains open over the required interval.

Despite its obvious advantages, WOLF is rarely used as it complex to set up and requires a linear (or EER) transmitter which is the exception on the low frequencies.

Packet Radio

Packet radio arrived with a bang in the mid-1980s, mostly using a protocol known as AX.25, an amateur derivation of the X.25 protocol in use on commercial data networks. Although AX.25 can be used for real-time QSOs (and was, quite extensively, on 2m and 70cm in the early days), its main application was with unattended mailboxes for sending and receiving text around the country and, in due course, the world.

The use of amateur radio mailboxes has now been overtaken by the increased efficiency of always-on broadband Internet connections. However, some packet access points for the *Cluster* network (see Chapter 9) still exist. One popular use for packet radio is APRS (Automatic Position Reporting System) which is discussed in more detail in Chapter 13.

ROS

A keyboard-to-keyboard mode from José Ros, EA5HVK, ROS has two main modes, *ROS HF* and *ROS EME*. The HF version is based on the CDMA type modulation. It isn't actually spread spectrum because the 3kHz HF standard channel is maintained, but is described by the author as "rather the transmission of crisscrossed symbols along the full available bandwidth, crisscrossing the symbols along the time as well." *ROS HF* has three symbol baud rates: 16, 8 and 1 and can automatically detect the transmission rate allowing the sender to change symbol rate with propagation conditions. The software can be downloaded from [21].

WSPR

Unlike most of the modes described previously, *WSPR* is a personal beacon mode and is not used for two-way contacts in the conventional sense.

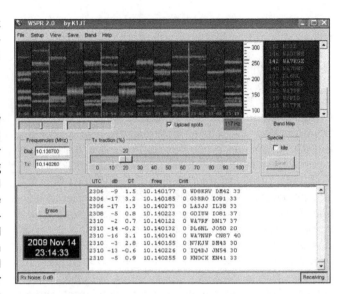

Typical *WSPR* screen showing multiple stations being received on the 200Hz wide waterfall display and a list of decoded stations below.

Weak Signal Propagation Reporter, pronounced "Whisper", was released in April 2008 by K1JT as a 'Manned Experimental Propagation Transmitter'. *WSPR* messages are structured to permit the efficient packing of callsigns, grid locators and other information The protocol includes forward error correction (FEC), so messages are almost always received exactly as transmitted, or not at all: false decodes are rare.

WSPR uses frequency shift keying (FSK) with a very small shift, occupying a bandwidth of about 6Hz. This means that many stations can be fitted into the 200Hz *WSPR* window. Stations running *WSPR* automatically send out a beacon signal on a given frequency. Each transmission lasts for just under two minutes.

When the system is not transmitting it is listening for other *WSPR* beacon signals. If it hears one it logs it and sends the details via the Internet to *WSPRnet* [22] which then logs your information and even displays it on a map, with a line showing the paths between the transmitting and receiving stations. It also logs the received signal-to-noise ratio, any drift, the grid locators of the transmitter and receiver and calcu-

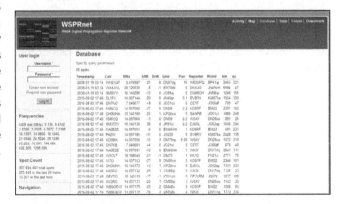

The *WSPRnet* database screen shows reception reports from all stations. Filters can be applied so reports for a single band or station can be selected.

Part of the display on the *PSK Reporter* web site showing successful paths between stations using *Opera* on the 10MHz band.

lates the bearing and distance between the two stations. The stations you decode are displayed on your own screen but because they, and everyone else's decodes, are uploaded to *WSPRnet* you can go to the web site [22] and see the reports of your own signal.

A slower-speed variant *WSPR-15*, developed especially for the low frequencies has a 15-minute transmission period.

OPERA

Like *WSPR*, *Opera* (created by EA5HVK) is a beacon-only, no-QSO, mode. However, it differs from it in several respects.

Only one frequency is used and, unusually, the data is sent by on-off keying making it ideal for simple home-made CW transmitters. Because *Opera* has a lower duty-cycle than PSK modes, transmitters can be operated at full power.

The keying speed varies depending on the band selected. For instance, on 136kHz a beacon transmission takes 32 minutes so the mode is described as Op32. On 1.8MHz, Op4 (four minute transmissions) is used. Other modes include Op2 on 3.5 - 18MHz, Op1 for 21 - 70MHz and OP05 (30 seconds) on 144 - 1296MHz.

Like *WSPR* there is a waterfall display and a list of received callsigns, but when connected to the Internet it also displays reports from the stations that hear you, so there's no need to access a web site for this information. That said, there is a web site where uploaded 'spots' can be seen on a map at *PSK Reporter* [23].

Opera can be downloaded from EA5HNK's web site [21].

AMATEUR TV

Fast-scan amateur television (ATV) is a special-interest activity, limited by its need for substantial amounts of bandwidth to 70cm and above. Nowadays, mainly due to the adoption of full-bandwidth colour transmission, and the increased use of 70cm for other activities, analogue ATV operation takes place on 23cm and above. New digital fast-scan ATV modes are being slowly adopted on 70cm and it remains the DX band of choice. Bandwidth-limited analogue transmissions still occur on 70cm, usually during contests, but usually without audio.

Voice comms usually take place on 144.750MHz FM, or 144.170MHz SSB for DX contacts. Narrow digital ATV modes

have been developed and are used on the newly extended 144MHz band above 146MHz.

There can be problems on 70cm with nearby voice repeater inputs: if someone opens a repeater it could be held open by the vision buzz from the analogue ATV transmission, so it is worth checking to see if the voice repeater is in use before going on the air. Repeater outputs within the video passband will cause patterning on the received signal. There is also AMSAT activity in the 70cm band and this too should be avoided. You are much more likely to find activity on 23cm.

ATV equipment tends to be home-constructed (from kits or published designs). There are also inexpensive transmit and receive modules available for 23 and 13cm. The growth of ATV also benefits from the establishment of a chain of ATV repeaters on 23, 13 and 3cm, covered in Chapter 13. Many of these include innovative features such as interlinking between repeaters, etc. They also normally operate continuously in beacon mode, sending out test cards and text pages, which is helpful for the newcomer to the mode who is setting up his equipment for the first time.

Those who want to watch what is going on without investing in equipment or antennas can watch the various streams on the British Amateur Television Club (BATC) streaming website [24]. A number of streams from repeaters and individuals can be seen there. The site is also used to stream live events, which may then be further relayed via ATV repeaters. The weekly RSGB *GB2RS* news from Roy, G8CKN, is recorded and available to watch.

Portable ATV

If portable operation appeals to you, try 10GHz ATV. Converting simple Doppler microwave burglar alarm unit and / or commercial satellite TV receivers can form the basis of a simple but very effective FM ATV station. On this band, even a small satellite TV-type dish can give very high gain, so you can achieve surprising DX contacts with the sort of power (a few tens of milliwatts) generated by microwave burglar alarm units.

Digital Amateur Television (D-ATV)

Most amateur TV operation, as described in the previous section, has been analogue, in that the image is modulated as a continuously varying voltage and frequency on to a carrier. The main drawback with analogue image systems is the bandwidth required to represent the image with full dynamic range, equating to the full spectrum of colour. An amateur FM ATV signal occupies 14MHz or more and so can only be used on 23cm and above.

Straightforward digitising of a colour signal initially provides a data stream that requires considerably more bandwidth than the comparable analogue signal. However, modern digital compression and reduction techniques pioneered for broadcast digital TV mean it is possible to reduce this data stream by such an amount that the required transmission bandwidth is far narrower than a comparable analogue one, while maintaining an acceptable level of quality.

Digital ATV is appearing on the 70, 23 and 13cm bands, and even 2m. There are a few ex-broadcast encoders and

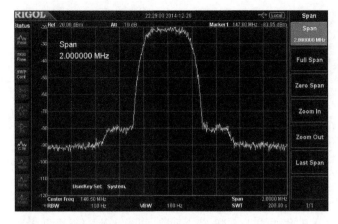

Spectrum of G4GUO's 2m D-ATV transmitter.

modulators that can be used with a transverter to transmit QPSK digital ATV on 70cm and above. These tend to be large and power-hungry but there are increasing numbers of amateur-designed D-ATV transmitters (some the size of a postcard) that will give direct RF output on 70, 23 or 13cm. QPSK transmissions can be received by an inexpensive commercial digital satellite TV receiver, although proprietary systems (eg the Sky Digibox) may not have the necessary flexibility to receive amateur standards.

Bandwidths of 2MHz or even less are adequate to support a full colour fast scan TV channel with two or four sound channels. In this instance the data rate would be about two megasymbols per second. This makes it eminently suitable for the 70cm band, which has better propagation characteristics than any of the higher frequencies. These systems have been developed by a number of amateurs to achieve bandwidths as low as 300kHz wide using a variety of digital compression modes from DVB-S MPGII to DVB-S2 H264 etc. In addition to this, very linear amplifiers have been developed to reduce the spectrum spread caused by distortion in the PA. Illustrated below is a spectrum plot from G4GUO. The shoulders caused by distortion in his PA is 60dB below the peak.

The narrower bandwidth also equates to an improved signal-to-noise ratio for a given signal strength. As with all kinds of digital transmission the signal is either there or it is not; there is no gradual degradation as the signal gets weaker as happens with analogue transmissions.

D-ATV is rapidly standardising on MPEG2 as used for terrestrial and satellite broadcast digital TV. The bit rate can be changed to suit the purpose so, for example, a high bit rate (and hence wide bandwidth) mode could be used to give very high quality pictures for local contacts, or for DX contacts the bit rate can be reduced, giving lower resolution pictures but, because of the smaller bandwidth, the range is increased.

There are several different types of modulation used for broadcast digital TV transmission, the two most popular being QPSK, as used on digital satellite TV, and COFDM, used for terrestrial digital TV. Both these schemes have been used for D-ATV and each has pros and cons. QPSK is relatively easy to implement and there is a large choice of satellite TV set-top boxes available that can be used as receivers, but it is very susceptible to multipath interference (it was, of course, designed for satellite TV where there is nothing to cause reflections). COFDM is much harder to implement and requires extremely linear power amplifiers in the transmitter but, being designed for terrestrial digital TV, it copes well with multipath distortion. Some ATV repeaters are now switchable remotely for inputs or outputs to be digital, and some are now outputting in digital only.

REFERENCES

[1]   'Digital Voice Communication', Andy Talbot, G4JNT, *RadCom*, October / November 1999.

[2]   'Digital Voice Transmission: the AOR ARD9800 Fast Data Modem', *RadCom*, July 2004, p18.

[3]   AOR digital voice products: www.aorusa.com

[4]   *Morse Code for Radio Amateurs*, Roger Cooke, G3LDI, RSGB. Available from www.rsgbshop.org/

[5]   *Argo*: www.weaksignals.com/

[6]   Spectrum Laboratory (*SpecLab*) is a sophisticated set of audio spectrum analysis tools that can be used for receiving QRSS: www.qsl.net/dl4yhf/spectra1.html

[7]   ON7YD on QRSS: www.qsl.net/on7yd/136narro.htm

[8]   Ultimate QRSS/WSPR transceiver: www.qrp-labs.com

[9]   *Radio Communication Handbook*, 12th edn, Mike Dennison, G3XDV, and Mike Browne, G3DIH, RSGB 2014. Available from www.rsgbshop.org/

[10] AA5AU RTTY pages: www.aa5au.com/rtty

[11] *MMTTY* download: http://hamsoft.ca/pages/mmtty.php

[12] *RTTY / PSK31 for Radio Amateurs*, Roger Cooke, G3LDI, RSGB.

[13] PSK31 homepage: http://bipt106.bi.ehu.es/psk31.html

[14] PSK63: www.qsl.net/kh6ty/psk63

[15] *MMSSTV* download: http://hamsoft.ca/pages/mmsstv.php

[16] 'An SSTV "how-to"', *RadCom*, May 2004, p24.

[17] 'WSJT: New Software for VHF Meteor-Scatter Communication', Joe Taylor, K1JT, *QST*, December 2001, p36.

[18] *WSJT*: www.physics.princeton.edu/pulsar/K1JT

[19] WM2U Hellschreiber page: http://www.w0btu.com/wm2u/hell.html

[20] WOLF: www.qsl.net/dl4yhf/wolf/index.html

[21] https://rosmodem.wordpress.com/

[22] http://wsprnet.org

[23] PSK Reporter: https://pskreporter.info/pskmap.html

[24] British Amateur Television Club: www.batc.tv

CHASING DX CONTINUES to hold great fascination for many amateurs. It appeals to our competitive instincts, and even in these days of the Internet and mobile phones there can be a real thrill from using your modest station to speak with someone on a remote Pacific atoll or the mountains of Bhutan. And there are many accepted ways of measuring your achievement and giving you goals to aim for.

But first, some definitions are required. Just what is DX, anyway? The term 'DX' has never been closely defined and attempting to define it can be difficult. On the bands below 1MHz and above 30MHz it is relatively easy: generally speaking 'DX' equates to distance. The further the contact, the greater the DX. To some extent the same is true on the lower-frequency HF bands such as 160m and 80m.

When a station puts out a "CQ DX" call on HF it is generally understood to mean that the station is looking for contacts outside their own continent. It would be considered legitimate for a US station to reply to a "CQ DX" call from someone in the UK, for example. Yet most amateurs would not really consider a contact with the Canary Islands (considered to be in Africa) or even New York to be 'DX', at least on the bands from 20m to 10m. On those bands, propagation is such that world-wide contacts are possible, if not on a daily basis then certainly with some regularity.

What then constitutes a 'DX' contact on these bands? Distance as such isn't really the issue, it is more to do with the 'rarity value' of the station. This can be illustrated by way of an example. From the UK, although any contact with North America is outside one's own continent, there are so many amateurs in the US, many of whom have high-power stations with high-gain antenna systems, that the east coast of the US is not considered to be 'DX' by most HF operators (unless they are running extremely low power). So a contact with Florida wouldn't be DX, yet contacts with the Bahamas (C6A), the Turks and Caicos Islands (VP5) or Cuba (CO) - none far from the coast of Florida - would be considered DX even though the distances involved are similar.

On 160 and 80m the definition can be extended somewhat. On 160m, for example, anything outside Europe can be quite tough to work from the UK, so might reasonably be considered DX. On 80m, although most would not consider a contact with New York DX, a contact with Los Angeles certainly would be. On the other hand, a QRP operator may well consider a contact with New York to be DX on any band. As may now be clear, the term 'DX' is something of a movable feast!

The DX Magazine [1] runs a survey in September - October each year to determine which are the 'Most Wanted' (and therefore 'rarest') DXCC entities. **Table 1** shows the 'top 20' rankings from the survey that took place in 2014. These are the overall world-wide results: further breakdowns were published in the January / February 2015 issue. Although this

2014 Ranking	Prefix	Entity name	2013 Ranking
1	P5	DPRK (North Korea)	1
2	KP1	Navassa Island	2
3	3Y/B	Bouvet Island	3
4	FT5W	Crozet Island	4
5	VK0	Heard Island	6
6	BS7	Scarborough Reef	7
7	VP8	South Sandwich Islands	9
8	FT5T	Tromelin Island	10
9	KH5K	Kingman Reef	12
10	KH5	Palmyra & Jarvis Islands	11
11	BV9P	Pratas Islands	14
12	E3	Eritrea	15
13	FT5J	Juan de Nova, Europa	13
14	CE0X	San Felix Island	19
15	KH3	Johnston Island	18
16	VP8	South Georgia	17
17	KH1	Baker and Howland Islands	25
18	KH7K	Kure Island	20
19	ZS8	Marion Island	8
20	VK0	Macquarie Island	22

Table 1: *The DX Magazine* survey of the 'most wanted' DXCC entities (in September / October 2014).

Rank	Prefix	Entity Name
1	P5	DPRK (North korea)
2	3Y/B	Bouvet Island
3	VP8S	South Sandwich Islands
4	FT5W	Crozet Island
5	VK0H	Heard Island
6	FT/J	Juan de Nova, Europa
7	KH5K	Kingman Reef
8	VP8G	South Georgia Island
9	KH5	Palmyra & Jarvis Islands
10	KH1	Baker & Howland Islands
11	BV9P	Pratas Islands
12	BS7H	Scarborough Reef
13	CE0X	San Felix Islands
14	KH3	Johnston Island
15	KH7K	Kure Island
16	VK0M	Macquarie Island
17	KP1	Navassa Island
18	FT5X	Kerguelen Island
19	SV/A	Mount Athos
20	3Y/P	Peter 1 Island

Table 2: 'Most Wanted' list generated August 2015 and derived from contacts uploaded to *Club Log* (using global logs, all modes, all bands).

QSLs from eight of *The DX Magazine's* Top Twenty Most Wanted DXCC entities - some new, some old: ZS8M Marion Island (2010), E30GA Eritrea (1998), VK0KEV Macquarie Is (2011), BQ9P Pratas Island (2002), AH3C/KH5J Jarvis Island (1990), FT5WO Crozet Island (2009), W6LAS/SVA Mt Athos (1983), & BS7H Scarborough Reef (2007).

will change from year to year (you can see how the same entities were ranked the previous year), some factors remain constant. DXCC entities are rare for one of two reasons. Bouvet Island and Heard Island (ranked 3rd and 5th respectively) are rare because they lie deep in the Southern Ocean, and any expedition is hugely expensive to mount. North Korea and Eritrea (ranked 1st and 12th) are relatively easy to reach and have international airports and hotels, but licensing is very difficult for political reasons.

For many years *The DX Magazine's* 'Most Wanted' survey provided the only available data, but the massive database of *Club Log* [2] allows any user to generate a 'Most Wanted' list from the 303 million log entries (as of August 2015) that have been uploaded. **Table 2** shows the result of an interrogation of the Club Log database in August 2015. It is also possible to determine which are the 'Most Wanted' entities in any particular continent or on any particular mode.

Looking at the VHF and UHF bands, the term 'DX' takes on a different meaning again. Because there is a limited number of countries workable on the VHF and UHF bands from any given location, VHF / UHF DXers seek other challenges, the most popular of which is chasing Locator squares. In this context, DX may be a rare square, even though its distance may not be especially great. Locator squares are explained in more detail later in this chapter.

Whatever the band you use, successful DXing comes down to the same set of elements. Firstly, a competitive station, both in terms of the equipment in the shack but also, and more importantly in most cases, the antenna system. You may choose to restrict yourself in some way to increase the challenge, for example by chasing DX with QRP (low power, usually 5W or less). Having a competitive station is not enough of itself, any more than it would be possible to take someone off the street, sit them in a Formula 1 racing car and expect them to be able to compete in races. More

important than the station is you, the operator. As in any competitive activity, DXing requires commitment and skill. In this case, the skill covers many areas, from a thorough technical understanding of your station in order to get the best out of it, through knowledge of propagation, to actual operating skills. It is also extremely helpful to have access to sources of information about what DX might be expected to be active on the bands, and when. All these aspects are covered in this chapter.

It is worth pausing to consider what drives DXing. In the early days of amateur radio, every contact was an achievement. Human beings are competitive creatures, though, and demand soon started to appear to be able to measure and recognise achievement. Various awards programmes were born, most notably the ARRL's DXCC awards and *CQ* magazine's Worked All Zones award. More on awards can be found in Chapter 10.

Amateurs started to chase countries and zones, but were happy to work each country or zone just once, regardless of band or mode. After all, building a high score was tough enough, without trying to repeat the exercise on additional bands and modes.

Over the years the situation started to change, especially as amateur radio activity started to develop again after WWII. With lots more activity on the bands, and the world returning to peace, high country scores became easier to achieve and amateurs started looking for new goals. New awards programmes came into being, and DXCC was extended to have a separate CW award.

The real explosion came with the introduction of the 5-band DXCC award in 1969 and the 5-band Worked All Zones award in 1979 (at this stage there were no 30, 17 or 12m bands, and 160m was excluded on the grounds that many countries had no 160m allocation and, as a consequence, few commercial transceivers included 160m capability). Amateurs who had high scores on, perhaps, 20 and 15m, started seriously to chase countries and zones on 80 and 40m.

This was actually a real boost to technical development, leading over the years to a much greater understanding of antenna designs (phased vertical arrays, low noise receiving antennas, etc) and improved receiver designs, able to cope with the wide range of signal strengths and high noise levels more common on the low bands than on the higher-frequency HF bands. DX stations and DXpeditions were also under pressure to ensure that they covered all bands during their operations, not just the backbone bands of 20, 15 and 10m.

In recent years DXers have found even more to chase. The ARRL has introduced individual DXCC awards for the nine regular HF bands as well as for 6m and 2m, and a DX Challenge programme which includes the 10 bands from 160 to 6m. Many DXers look for contacts with any given DXCC entity on all 10 of these bands, and on three modes (CW, SSB and RTTY), as the data modes have also ceased to be the preserve of a specialist few and have become accessible to anyone with a computer. The RSGB's Islands on the Air (IOTA) programme is also going from strength to strength. There's more information about awards in a later chapter.

One recent development is the trend of using specialist software such as the WSJT suite, originally designed for weak-signal working on VHF, on the HF bands. Programs such at JT6M and JT65, as well as other data modes such as MFSK16, Olivia, etc, are allowing HF operators - even those using low power or without the possibility of putting up large antenna systems - to work DX that previously would have been virtually impossible. During the sunspot minimum period from 2007 to 2010, which extended longer than any other solar minimum on record, the higher HF bands were effectively 'dead' most of the time, and yet DX contacts were still being made on those bands, thanks to the use of these specialist modes.

DXPEDITIONS

While the demand for DX contacts has increased, so has the supply. The availability of lightweight transceivers, the ubiquity and relatively low cost of international air travel, easing of amateur licensing between countries and other factors have made it much easier to mount modest DXpeditions, so that every day there is plenty of DX activity on the bands, with anything up to 280 or so entities from the DXCC list and hundreds of IOTA islands active in any given year.

Some HF DXpedition organisers have risen to the challenge by putting together mammoth operations, with large teams of operators and huge amounts of equipment in order to satisfy the demand for multiple band and mode contacts from around the world. Twenty expeditions in recent years have achieved over 100,000 contacts while just one (T32C from Eastern Kiribati in 2011) has broken the 200,000 contacts barrier. Jari Jussila, OH2BU, and Bernd Koch, DF3CB, compiled and maintain a database of statistics from the largest DXpeditions [3], a small extract of which appears in **Table 3**. It is interesting to note that all twenty of the biggest DXpeditions of all time, in terms of numbers of contacts, have taken place since the year 2000, and many of these were during the extended solar minimum period.

If you are a beginner to DXing, the thought of trying to contact each of the 340 DXCC entities on nine bands and three modes, which would require a minimum of 3042 contacts (not all DX, but many of them would be) might be enough to put you off before you even start! Or maybe you

Rank	Callsign(s)	DXCC entity	Year	Days	Ops	QSOs	Uniques
1	T32C	Eastern Kiribati	2011	32	41	213,090	49,495
2	HK0NA	Malpelo Island	2012	27	20	192,089	43,176
3	VP6DX	Ducie Island	2008	17	13	183,686	38,947
4	FT5ZM	St Paul and Amsterdam Islands	2014	18	14	170,010	36,302
5	D68C	Comoros	2001	21	26	168,722	45,315
6	7O6T	Yemen	2012	16	15	162,029	37,863
7	3B9C	Rodrigues	2004	25	32	153,016	37,466
8	ZL8X	Kermadec Islands	2010	18	14	148,571	31,219
9	K1N	Navassa Island	2015	15	15	140,004	35,649
10	3B7C	Agalega and St Brandon	2007	16	20	137,500	33,760
11	VK9DLX, VK9LM	Lord Howe Island	2014	16	16	128,269	30,818
12	ST0R	South Sudan	2011	20	13	121,286	27,994
13	N8S	Swains Island	2007	12	17	116,872	30,198
14	4O3T	Montenegro	2006	25	60	116,474	n/a
15	K5D	Desecheo Island	2009	15	22	115,589	32,362
16	TX5K	Clipperton Island	2013	8	24	113,601	24,480
17	5A7A	Libya	2006	14	29	112,219	31,212
18	VU7RG, VU7MY	Lakshadweep	2007	15	35	110,130	25,204
19	NH8S	Swains Island	2012	10	18	105,455	26,010
20	K9W	Wake Island	2013	14	12	100,031	22,989

Table 3: Extract from the 'Mega DXpeditions Honor Roll' (Ops = number of DXpedition operators, Uniques = number of individual callsigns contacted).

T32C, the 2011 DXpedition by the UK-based Five Star DXers Association, is the only DXpedition to date to have made over 200,000 contacts.

are embarking on chasing islands for IOTA, hoping to achieve that coveted award for 100 island groups, and then see the annual IOTA Honour Roll, with its leaders at over 1000 groups worked and confirmed. Perhaps you have looked at the countries and squares totals amassed by some of the more active VHF DXers. But the nice thing about DXing is that it is what you make it, and hopefully will maintain your interest for a lifetime.

If you worked them all in the first year, what would there be left to achieve? The trick is maybe to set specific goals. Perhaps focus on just one or two bands for a while, where you have a good capability, then when you feel you have achieved a reasonable score change your focus to a couple of other bands. Maybe set out to achieve RTTY DXCC. A good rule of thumb is to try to work 10% of missing band and mode slots in any given year although this is rather easier to achieve in high sunspot years than at the solar minimum!

When a DXpedition is expected on the bands, think about what you want to achieve. Is it a country you 'need' for an all-time new one ('ATNO')? In which case, think about which band is likely to be easiest to work it on. For example, 20m may offer the best chance of good propagation, but 30m might suit you better because fewer stations on 30m have high gain antennas, and therefore you may be able to compete on a more equal playing field. There again, it may be a country you already have on 20m, but you would like to catch it on at least a couple of other bands. If it is near the sunspot peak your best bet might be to focus the chase on 10m and 12m. At the end of the day, it comes down to your personal goals and practical factors such as location, station capability and personal restrictions.

If you work long hours and are frequently tied up at weekends, you may decide to focus on low-band DXing, as you can do most of that during those darkness hours when you are at home. On the other hand, if you work from home or are retired, it might well suit you to chase high-band DX, catching those tough ones when everyone else is at their office desk.

Islands On The Air (IOTA), managed by the RSGB, has grown hugely in popularity in the last 20 years or so, and

offers plenty to chase even during the years of sunspot minima when big DXpeditions may sometimes be few and far between. More details appear in Chapter 10. It is worth noting that the IOTA programme includes 6m, offering a great challenge to VHF DXers.

Having 'chased' and worked a few DXpeditions, you might want to try your hand at organising your own, either as part of a family holiday (the so-called 'holiday expedition') or with a group of like-minded amateurs. An IOTA DXpedition, possibly to one of the islands off the coast of the British Isles, is ideal for starters but, as has been mentioned, it has never been easier to mount DXpeditions to overseas destinations. Many of these are in demand, even if they do not appear in the 'Most Wanted' surveys. A lot of fun can be had by operating from DXCC entities such as Corsica, Madeira, Crete or Malta, not forgetting Jersey, Guernsey and the Isle of Man. This subject is covered under 'Operating as DX' below and also in more detail in Chapter 12.

DX ON VHF

On VHF, the fleeting nature of some of the propagation mechanisms such as Sporadic E is no respecter of office hours or weekends, but might happen at any time, so the most successful 6m DXers tend to be those who either work from home or can, at least, arrange to be at home at those times of the year when such propagation is most likely to occur.

Given that the VHF, UHF and microwave bands offer much smaller ranges than the HF bands, DXCC entities are less important as a measure of achievement. It is interesting to note that the ARRL held back from offering a 6m DXCC for quite some time as those concerned felt that it would be unachievable, and therefore frustrating to 6m DXers. How times have changed! Even 2m DXCC has now been achieved, though only by those with EME capability. But, again, the human psyche requires goals, and the most widely used on VHF is the Locator square. Thus the commonest measure of achievement, and the basis of most VHF operating awards, is the number of squares worked.

On the microwave bands even this is tough, so the most usual measure is distance, with awards available for achieving specified distances on each of the microwave bands. Whatever bands, modes or speciality you follow, there is no virtue in becoming so paranoid about DX chasing that it takes over your life. Those at the top of the tables are probably very old, never take holidays, or perhaps confined to their homes for domestic or health reasons. Don't expect to catch them up overnight! But set your own goals and enjoy making them happen. At the end of the day this is a hobby, not a matter of life and death.

Historically, most books of this kind would have dealt separately with HF and VHF DXing, but the approach taken in this chapter is slightly different. The distinction is drawn, instead, between what might be described as 'traditional' DXing and what VHF DXers tend to refer to as 'weak-signal' DXing. In some ways the latter term is a misnomer. All DXers wrestle with weak signals, whether through ionospheric absorption, the fact that the distant station is running QRP, or various other reasons.

It's true that HF DXing often involves chasing quite a strong DX station, the challenge being to get through in the face of competition from lots of other callers. But the same also happens on 6m, 2m and 70cm when the band is 'open' and perhaps a rare square is active. There are times, though, when HF DXers struggle to pull weak signals from the air waves, hence their interest in specialist receiving antennas, stacked Yagis (used from time to time on the higher HF bands) and other techniques to pull that weak one through. And 136kHz DXers revert to specialist software-based techniques to integrate signals over extended periods, a contact sometimes taking hours to complete.

When VHF DXers talk about 'weak-signal' DXing, they really have something a little different in mind. Because the VHF bands experience enhanced propagation only occasionally, VHF DXers have found ways of exploiting other opportunities to make long-distance contacts, for example by reflecting their signals off the Moon or off the ionised trails of meteors. The signals are indeed weak (most of the time - some meteor reflections can be quite strong during the big meteor showers), but there are other challenges too. The bigger

issue with meteor reflections, for example, is that the return signals are very brief, just short 'pings', with large gaps in between. A contact can take anything up to an hour or so to complete. So, specialist operating procedures have been adopted, and strict rules as to what constitutes a completed contact.

This chapter therefore talks about traditional DXing regardless of band. It then goes on to discuss 'specialist' techniques designed to allow contacts to take place at times when the traditional methods simply won't do the job.

DX INFORMATION SOURCES

Whether you are chasing DXCC entities, islands, US counties, or Japanese prefectures, just to give a few examples, the underlying principles of DX chasing are common to all. The aim is to secure a contact (essentially, a two-way exchange of callsigns and, usually, signal report) with the DX station, which requires that the DX station hears and answers your call or, less likely, he calls you.

The first task is to find the DX station you are interested in contacting. Many amateurs still enjoy doing so by tuning the bands, ready to be surprised at what they run across. Others will use every means at their disposal to find out about possible DX activity, through magazines, newsletters and the Internet. Nowadays any major DXpedition is likely to work very hard at publicity beforehand. After all, any individual or group making a big effort to set up from a rare location is going to be keen to ensure as many contacts as possible, to make the whole exercise worthwhile.

Sources of information are many and varied. Taking the long-term first, most of the monthly magazines carry information about forthcoming DX activity, provided it has been notified in time for their publishing deadlines. In the UK, the obvious examples are the monthly HF and VHF columns in *RadCom*.

There used to be several weekly DX newsletters available, but interest declined dramatically when the Internet became widely available, principally because the Internet delivers the information much more quickly. Not, as some have suggested, a case of the Internet taking over from amateur radio but,

Don Field, G3XTT, (who wrote some earlier editions of this book) with a Trident 5-element 6m Yagi.

DX World.net is one of the best DX information sources on the Internet.

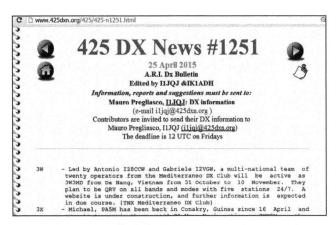

The *425 DX News* bulletin can be read on-line (as shown here), or it will be sent to you by e-mail each week if you take out a free subscription.

The *DX Summit* Internet Cluster allows users to filter the 'spots' so that only those of interest are shown. In this case all HF spots are included (therefore nothing on 6m and above is shown), except for 'DIGI' spots, which are excluded.

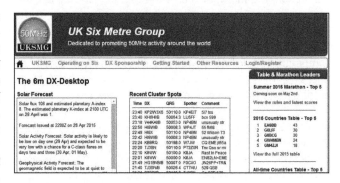

The UK Six Metre Group offers a DX Cluster screen for 6m DXers.

rather, taking over from the postal service. A good DX news website, which incidentally is also well illustrated with photographs of the DX locations mentioned, is *DX World* [4], run by Col McGowan, MM0NDX. *425 DX News* [5] and the *OPDX Bulletin* [6] are both published weekly and both are free to anyone who signs up for them. *QRZ DX* [7] and *The Weekly DX* [8] again are published weekly, but both are on subscription. *The Daily DX* [8] is, as it name suggests, published daily (on weekdays), again on subscription.

All these bulletins contain news of forthcoming and current DX activity, after-the-event information on many operations, QSL information and lots of other data of interest to DX operators. Unless you really do prefer to cut yourself off from outside information, it is well worth ensuring that you are in receipt of one or more of these electronic publications. Incidentally, all but *DX World* and *425 DX News* are US-based, but most of the information is of global interest. In addition, there are several Internet-based reflectors and news groups devoted to DX and DXing, which carry similar information as well as comments, controversies and speculation.

Real-time DX information is available from the global network of Cluster nodes linked by the Internet. The Cluster network carries real-time 'spots' of DX activity, announcements, solar data from WWV etc. Most end users view the Cluster on the Internet, although some do still access a local node via a VHF Packet radio link. You can also access it by using Telnet, a terminal emulation program available as part of your computer's operating system. Many modern logging programs also incorporate facilities for connection to the Cluster network, both via the Internet or a radio interface. Some logging programs allow you to filter the incoming information, for example only to display Cluster spots for bands or modes you are interested in, or for countries you still need to work.

The most popular web-based Cluster is *DX Summit* [9] run by the OH8X Radio Arcala group [10] in Finland. This collects Cluster spots from around the world and displays them in various ways according to which filters you select. You can also post your own spots and announcements to the Cluster network via *DX Summit*.

CLUSTER DOS AND DON'TS

- DON'T use ANNOUNCEMENTS unless the information is perishable (ie time-sensitive) and REALLY needs to go to ALL users immediately.

- DO try to keep ANNOUNCEMENTS to DX related matters. If you want to send out general mail, please use the BBS network instead.

- DO try QRZ.COM or the GOLIST QSL database before putting out a message to find a QSL manager.

- DON'T complain about VHF spots if you are an HF DXer, or HF spots if you are a VHF DXer. Use the filters to tailor what you get to your own tastes.

- DON'T rise to the bait if someone is obviously abusing the Cluster facilities.

There is more information on DX Cluster access in Chapter 4. However, if you don't need a direct connection to the Cluster network, several other popular websites also show Cluster spots. For example, the UK Six Metre Group's website [11], not surprisingly, takes only the 6m spots from the Cluster network, and makes them available to users (under '*DX-Desktop*'). At the end of the day, though, if you are a regular user of spots from the Cluster network, there is a moral duty to input information in return. This is very much a self-help network, relying on everyone to play a part by spotting interesting DX.

FINDING DX ON THE BANDS

It will be apparent from the foregoing that a budding DXer could simply sit in the shack, rig turned on, and wait for a DX station to be 'spotted' on the Cluster network. Then simply tune the radio to that frequency, turn the antenna to the correct beam heading (some logging programs will do both these things at the press of a function key) and, hey presto, one call and the DX station is in the log. A modicum of satisfaction, perhaps, but where is the skill? What have you learned about propagation?

In practice, it's rarely quite that simple. One of the disadvantages of the Cluster network is that, when a rare station is spotted all hell tends to break loose, with many stations calling at once. Unless you have full legal power and a huge antenna array, you might as well take time out for a cup of tea while the 'big guns' battle it out to make a contact. Better to use the Cluster and other information sources to learn about the DX station's operating patterns and, next time, be there before the masses.

This is where the real art of DX operating is developed, a skill which will be equally applicable if and when your interest turns to, for example, contest operating.

Let's start with the HF bands. You may know from a newsletter that a DXpedition is taking place to a Pacific island, maybe somewhere quite rare like Tokelau (ZK3). Or maybe you don't gather such information but, nevertheless, are interested in finding DX in the Pacific. The first aspect is to think about propagation. Which band or bands are likely to support propagation to that part of the world, and at what times? Propagation forecasts, such as those in *RadCom*, can be a good starting point, as can propagation prediction programs (see Chapter 6). Feed in the relevant solar data, and the location you are interested in, and see what comes out. By the time you have been active on the HF bands for several years you will have a pretty good idea, simply on the basis of past experience. Even if you have never heard or worked Tokelau, you will be aware that they are not too far from New Zealand. The path to New Zealand is actually quite reliable on several bands, especially 40, 30 and 20m, and Tokelau is rare from the UK not so much because of difficulties with propagation but simply because there is very little activity. Occasionally there will be a DXpedition, and usually just a one- or two-person effort.

When you've worked out what times propagation is likely to be favourable, it's not a bad idea to check what that means in terms of local time at the distant end. Let's suppose, depending on the time of year, that you feel there's a good chance of a contact around 0600UTC. The good news is that that's 2000 local in Tokelau. Not a bad time for someone to be on the bands. If it's a DXpedition you are after, they will probably be around on the main bands whenever propagation is likely. But if we are talking about a local amateur, remember that on weekdays he will probably be at work and at night (his time) he will probably be asleep! Remember also, by the way, that weekdays vary. In Muslim countries, weekends are Friday and Saturday and Friday can often be a good time to catch their local amateurs on the bands. French overseas territories observe French public holidays, so if you know it's

a French holiday, it might be a good time to look for amateur radio activity from Tahiti or Reunion. The moral of the story is to understand your quarry, whether local amateur or DXpedition. Try to put yourself in their shoes.

So you have some idea of when and on which bands you may find the station or country you are looking for. The next aspect is to think about what frequency the station will be on. Many DXpeditions publish their operating frequencies beforehand. Or you may already know, from the Cluster network, that the station you are looking for prefers a particular part of the band or a particular mode. He may be exclusively a CW operator, for example, or perhaps prefer RTTY. It is also worth checking whether there are any frequency restrictions that apply to the station or country concerned. Maybe the most regular operator has some sort of Intermediate licence class, which limits him to certain parts of the band or maybe the country concerned has country-specific band plans. As always, information is invaluable, and can be garnered from many sources, including those described earlier.

There are no hard and fast rules about where to find rare stations on the bands. From the UK, Pacific stations are often identifiable by having some 'flutter' on their signals, resulting from signals passing through the auroral zone. A local amateur, trying to avoid major pile-ups, might make a point of operating away from the more popular areas of the band, so may, for example, operate above 14050kHz on CW or above 14300kHz on SSB. He may also take refuge in one of the popular DX nets (dealt with later in this chapter). Accents are also important in alerting to you to a possible DX station. An Australian or Japanese accent is usually distinctive, while an American accent heard when the band is closed to the continental USA could be from somewhere like Hawaii.

DXpeditions, who very much do want to get noticed, tend to stick close to certain well-known frequencies. On CW, look 5kHz up from the bottom of the band or thereabouts on 80, 40, 30, 17 and 12m, and 25kHz up or thereabouts on 20, 15 and 10m. On SSB, 3795, 14180 - 14200, 21295 and 28495

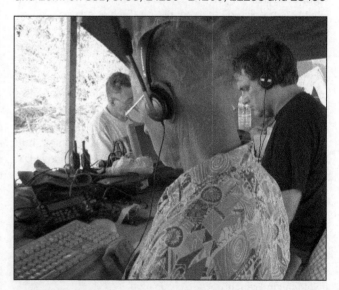

Three CW operators on an IOTA DXpedition: l to r: Mike, K9AJ; Derek, G3KHZ, and Steve, G4EDG, on Caroline (Millennium) Island. OC-281.

are perhaps the most popular DXpedition frequencies, although there has been a trend in the last five to 10 years for DXpeditions on SSB to move away from the 'traditional' frequencies. Since 2009, when 7100 - 7200kHz was released to the amateur service on a world-wide basis, the new IARU Region 1 band plan shows 7175 - 7200kHz as 'Priority for Intercontinental Operation', so it seems likely that many DXpeditions will now move to that part of 40m for SSB. On RTTY, around 070 on 20, 15 and 10m, but RTTY activity is increasing on the other bands too, for example around 10120kHz. Many expeditions will assume nowadays that most DXers have Cluster access and will therefore find them on the bands wherever they choose to operate.

If you are chasing some sort of specialist DX, then there may be relevant meeting frequencies. Those chasing US counties will want to check into the County Hunters Net on 20m. IOTA enthusiasts will look on 14260 and 21260kHz on SSB and on 14040 and 21040kHz on CW as a starting point. On VHF, an expedition to, say, a rare square, will probably call CQ on the recognised DX calling channel and then move elsewhere in the band as the pile-up starts to build.

So you've done your homework and thought about all the relevant factors necessary to maximise your chances of finding the DX station you are looking for. It's time to turn on your radio and turn the antenna in the right direction (remembering that, in some cases, you will be checking the long-path which is 180° different to the short-path bearing). It's time to start tuning the bands around those frequencies that you have determined are most likely. Careful tuning pays dividends. Make a note of stations you are hearing. Are they in the same part of the world as the one you are looking for? Check the beacons, for example the NCDXF beacon chain [12] on the HF bands or one of the very many beacons available on the VHF / UHF bands (a list of 2m and 70cm beacons, for example, can be found in the *RSGB Yearbook* [13] or on the 'Make More Miles on VHF' website [14]). How loud are they? What does this tell you about actual propagation, as against what was predicted? Incidentally, on CW it is a good idea to get used to tuning with a fairly wide filter setting, or it is easy to tune over a weak signal: only narrow the filters down when you want to home in on a specific station.

Often an immediate pointer to a rare station is the existence of a pile-up. This is bad news in a way, as it means you are going to be in a competitive situation. Better to be the first one to stumble across the DX station, when he calls CQ! There is an alternative, which is to call "CQ DX" yourself, but this tends not to be terribly productive. However, some DX stations will prefer to call others rather than call CQ themselves, so as to avoid getting into a pile-up situation, so it is always worth a try. And you may be able to give yourself a head start. Looking for Tahiti, for example, not only would you want to be aware that French-speaking stations tend to congregate around 14130kHz, but if you choose to call CQ, you will enhance your chances of that FO contact enormously if you call in French.

So you have found the DX station. You hear ZK3ZZ on what appears to be a clear frequency, but apparently working stations, although you can't hear them. What do you do

when he ends a contact? The temptation is to fire up on all cylinders and call him, "ZK3ZZ, this is G3XDV, Golf Three X-ray Delta Victor". Wrong, on several counts! The first thing is to determine what is going on. Spend a minute or two listening. It will pay dividends. The chances are that the reason you can't hear the people he is working is because he is operating split-frequency, in other words listening on a frequency different to the one he is transmitting on. Assuming he is a competent operator, he will announce his listening frequency from time to time or, at the least, indicate whether he is listening "up" or "down", ie above or below his transmitting frequency. If he is indeed operating split, this will dictate how and where you call him (see the section below, on split frequency operation). Whatever you do, never ever ask on his frequency "Where is he listening?", "What's his call?" or "QSL info?" or the like. This simply causes interference for everyone else.

Regardless of whether the DX station is listening split or co-channel, keep any call short. Normally give your callsign just once, phonetically if on SSB. If he is working quickly through a pile-up, don't give his callsign, he knows it already! By giving your callsign just once, you are helping everybody. If you are the first station the DX station hears, he will come back to you immediately and give you a signal report:

Him: "Golf Three X-ray Delta Victor 59".
Me: "QSL 59"
Him: "QSL. Zulu Kilo Three Zulu Zulu QRZ?"

. . . and away he goes with the next contact. If G3XDV had called twice his second call would just have slowed things down. Or if ZK3ZZ had responded to someone else's first call, G3XDV would just have been causing undue interference. If he had only heard part of G3XDV's callsign, no problem, the gaps can be filled on the next transmission:

Him: "The Golf Three with Victor, 59"
Me: "QSL, Golf Three X-ray Delta Victor, 59"
Him: "Golf Three X-ray Delta Victor, QSL, Zulu Kilo Three Zulu Zulu QRZ?"

. . . and so on.

Some amateurs advocate calling with only a partial call, "Delta Victor". This is bad operating and seems to have originated because DX stations often respond only with a partial call. That's not actually because they want partial calls, it's simply that that's all they have been able to hear through the pile-up! By coming back with at least a partial call, rather than calling "QRZ?" again, they can press on with the contact rather than wasting time, assuming there was only one station in the pile-up with "Delta Victor" in the call. Assuming, also, that everyone else takes the hint and stands by which, sadly, isn't always the case. But if you send only a partial callsign rather than your full call (quite apart from the licensing issues, whereby you are required to identify yourself when making "calls to establish contact with another amateur") you are wasting time. If you only send a partial call and the DX station only hears part of that, he may end up with just a single letter, which is more or less useless. Even if he hears you clearly, it will still require you to give your full callsign on the next transmission. And time really is of the essence. To use our ZK3 example, the opening to Europe may well be no more than an hour or so. If everyone is operating in a slick manner, the DX station can make maybe 150 contacts or more an hour on CW, 200 or more on SSB. That's a contact every 20 seconds or thereabouts. Waste 20 seconds and you have potentially deprived someone else of a contact. If the DX station wants to have a chat, or announce his QSL information, that's his prerogative. But don't slow things down with unnecessary requests or questions, unless things are quiet and he is repeatedly calling CQ with no response. If you need his QSL information, check on the Internet (for example on the *QRZ.com* site [15]) or wait for him to announce it. If you want to know when he will be on another band, wait for him to announce that, leave him on the loudspeaker while you do something else in the shack, and wait for him to close on that band and move to another, or go back to your propagation predictions and consider when, if you were in his shoes, you would think about moving to another band.

If you are used to exchanging pleasantries with other amateurs, these brief exchanges with DX stations can seem rather terse and impersonal, but DXing is immensely popular and most DXpeditions want to give as many people as possible the chance for a contact. You can chat with them to your heart's content when they get home to their regular locations. VHF operators in particular get frustrated if a DX station fails to give his Locator, but VHF openings, for example by Sporadic E on 6m or 2m, can be extremely fleeting and the DX operator will want to get as many callsigns into the log as possible. No doubt he will ensure that his Locator is prominently featured on his QSL card.

Perhaps the main piece of advice is always to take your cue from the DX station, even if he appears to be inexperienced and leaves you feeling frustrated. The better DX operators, though, will always give clear indications of what they are doing. For example, if the pile-up gets very large, a DX operator may listen by prefix or by numbers: "Only stations with Number One in the call". If he starts with One and you are an M0, it can be pretty frustrating to sit while he works his way through all the other numbers, but if the callers step out of line all it does is slow things down even more and, in the extreme, the DX operator will throw in the towel and switch off.

The above advice sounds all well and good, but life isn't always so simple. You may have only a modest station, and find that you are getting nowhere in calling the DX, despite doing all the right things. Well, you could try to be first on frequency the following day. If it's a big expedition, there for a week or two, you might just have to sit things out, hoping that, towards the end, the number of callers diminishes and you stand a better chance. But it's always worth hanging in there, as propagation may suddenly change and favour you, or the DX station himself might switch the odds to your favour: "Stand by Southern Europe, I'm looking for UK stations for the next five minutes" or whatever.

Some DX stations deliberately try to favour the more attentive callers, for example by suddenly announcing a spot listening frequency elsewhere in the band. If you're on

The Complete DX'er by Bob Locher, W9KNI, is full of useful hints and tips for all DXers, beginners and experts alike.

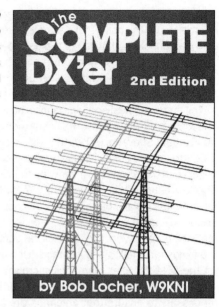

the ball you can move there, call and work him, while the masses are still calling on the original frequency. DXpedition operators from continental Europe will often make a brief announcement in their own language, which is often an invitation for their compatriots to call on a specific frequency. If you can understand enough of that language to work out what frequency the DX station is listening on, you may find yourself only competing with, say, Dutch or Norwegian stations and not the whole of Europe!

While the foregoing is generally applicable, there are plenty of variations which will be learned through regular operation on the bands. There are also some helpful books around, such as *The Complete DX'er* by Bob Locher, W9KNI [16], which, while coming mainly from a CW DXer's perspective, is absolutely full of useful hints and tips for all operators. The following few sections cover just a few of them here, in no particular order.

PREARRANGED SCHEDULES

Prearranging scheduled contacts on the HF bands in order to work a DX station tends to be frowned upon, although on bands below 1MHz and the higher VHF and microwave bands few DX contacts would take place without prior arrangement, other than when a contest or major band opening is in progress. But there are good arguments for making schedules on the more difficult bands, for example 160m.

Nowadays, with the Internet, this is very simple. Let's suppose you are trying to work a South American station who you know to be reasonably active and with a reasonable signal. There may be a good chance that several nights of listening at the time of optimum propagation would result in a contact. But the optimum time is likely to be around 0200 / 0300 local in the UK, which may not be conducive to domestic bliss if pursued several nights in a row. So it may well be worth contacting the distant station by e-mail and, at the least, checking which nights he is likely to be active, even if not making a schedule for a specific time and frequency.

Related to this is an arrangement made on another band. For example, you may work a DX station on 80m, and agree mutually to move to 160m, either immediately or fairly soon thereafter, on the basis that if signals were good on 80m there is a reasonable probability of the path being open on 160m, albeit with higher absorption. The same may apply at the other end of the spectrum, working a station on 12m, for example, and agreeing to move to 10m to see if the band is open.

For more specialised operation, such as 160m or the microwave bands, the ON4KST chat rooms [17] are the place to go. Alain Stievenart, ON4KST, set up his first chat room in 2001 to help 6m operators to make DX contacts. It was such a success he expanded the service to include chat rooms for the low bands (160 / 80m), 50 / 70MHz, 144 / 432MHz, and the microwave bands. There are now over 15,000 amateurs registered who use the service to chat about upcoming activity, propagation, etc, on their favourite band, and to set up skeds for 'challenging' contacts. One of the great benefits of the ON4KST chat rooms for microwave operators is that, because beamwidths are so narrow, prior arrangement is necessary to ensure that antennas are pointing in the right direction and at the right time. Use of the ON4KST chat rooms is free.

SPLIT FREQUENCY OPERATION

Nowadays, with the huge interest in DX chasing, most DXpeditions and many DX operators choose to operate split frequency. This is by no means confined to HF operation, being quite common on 6m or even 136kHz. The concept is simple. By transmitting on one frequency and listening on another, callers can hear the DX station clearly, rather than through a mass of other callers, and therefore know when to go ahead with their contact and, more importantly, when to remain silent while another contact is taking place. And rather than listening on a single frequency, the DX station may choose to listen over a range of frequencies, thereby making it easier for him to pick out callers.

If you hear an expedition making plenty of contacts, but you can't hear the callers, the chances are that you are listening to a split-frequency operation. Indeed, before calling any DX station on his own frequency, it's always worth waiting a moment to determine whether he is working split. Otherwise, if you call him co-channel, you risk the wrath of others who

Operating split: here transmitting on 14200kHz and listening to the DXpedition station on 14195kHz.

have been waiting and will almost certainly inform you of the error of your ways!

If a DX station is working split, what do you do? In the past many amateurs may have had a problem in that their transceiver was only capable of transmitting and receiving on the same frequency. In practice most transceivers came equipped with RIT and XIT (receiver and transmitter incremental tuning), allowing for a limited degree of split operation (typically up to 10kHz between transmit and receive frequencies). All modern transceivers go one step further and have two quite separate VFOs, giving total flexibility (though it's worth practising split operation in the peace and quiet of your own shack before you try it on the air and end up pressing the wrong buttons!) Almost all radios also allow you to check your transmit frequency, which is handy, because as well as listening to the DX station, half the trick can be finding the people he is working, and putting your transmitter on to that frequency. Higher-end radios go one step further still, with a second receiver. With that capability, you can listen to the DX station in one ear of your headphones (invariably DXers always use headphones and never a loudspeaker except for casual rag-chews) and the pile-up in the other ear. Then you know exactly what is going on.

Always listen to the DX station carefully. Often he will announce his receive frequency, and may also be giving other instructions (such as "UK stations only") which should always be followed carefully to avoid creating unnecessary interference and slowing things down. If no listening frequency is announced, the general rule is to call about 1 - 2kHz up on CW, or 5kHz up on SSB. But, again, a few moments listening should, in any case, quickly allow you to find the callers he is working. Listen for a little longer and you may also determine a pattern. For example, does the DX station always respond to callers on the same frequency or does he, for example, listen a little higher up the band after each contact, finally dropping back down the band and starting the whole process anew? Does he respond to stations only giving part of their callsign or does he (like many DX operators) only respond to callers sending their complete callsign? And so on. Some intelligent listening can pay dividends, compared with simply calling at random. This is how experienced operators running low power can often get through more quickly than less experienced operators running high power (No surprise there, I suppose: experience counts for more than brute force in most competitive sports and activities).

Unless the DX station is specifically taking 'tail enders', ie stations who call as the previous contact is coming to an end, never call over the top of a contact in progress but wait until the DX station signs and calls "QRZ?" or similar. Otherwise chaos ensues.

There is another form of split frequency operation which needs to be covered. This is split frequency when working less exotic DX, but where band plans and practical considerations demand it. On 80m SSB for example, UK stations along with the rest of IARU Region 1, are restricted to operation below 3800kHz, whereas General-class US licensees can only operate on SSB above 3800kHz. The answer is to operate split-frequency.

Provided you know how to operate your transceiver in split-frequency mode, there should be no fundamental problem, but some basic considerations need to be taken into account. If you are calling for US stations, you will need to find two clear frequencies, the first for your own CQ call and the second, in the US part of the band, to listen on. When calling CQ, announce your listening frequency clearly, and give potential US callers time to set up their VFOs for split operation and be ready to answer you. While conducting the ensuing contact, be sure to check your own frequency regularly to ensure that you are not causing interference to other European stations, or being interfered with by them. This is a case where having a transceiver with dual-receiver capability really comes into its own, as you can then monitor both frequencies simultaneously. The same is true when working certain other countries outside Region 1 which have allocations extending above 3800kHz. It also used to be common practice to operate split-frequency on 160m when working the US or Japan, in the latter case because Japanese stations used to have only a narrow allocation centred on 1910kHz. Nowadays most regular activity on 160m is co-channel, but occasionally split-operation may be appropriate for US contacts, given that the US allocation starts at 1800kHz whereas the UK allocation starts at 1810kHz. On the 136kHz band, QRSS transmissions aimed at intercontinental reception (beacons or two-way contacts) tend to operate split to avoid blocking local reception.

LISTS AND NETS

If you spend any time at all on the HF bands will quickly run across list and net operations. If you want to participate but are not familiar with the conventions relating to them you can end up getting yourself into hot water. There are many regular nets which exist purely for the purpose of 'rag-chewing' and keeping in touch with friends. Many are associated with a particular organisation, the Royal Signals Amateur Radio Society, for example. This section is more concerned with lists and nets specifically run for the purpose of enabling participants to work DX.

It is important to deal with one aspect right at the start. Many DXers consider lists and nets to be a form of cheating, in that you are enlisting the help of a third-party (the Master of Ceremonies, or MC) to run the operation and keep other stations at bay while you make your call to the DX station. Sometimes it gets even worse, when the MC or one of the other participants, perhaps getting restless, 'helps' things along by passing all or parts of callsigns or signal reports. A 'contact' made in this way is surely not a true two-way exchange. But a well-run list or net will avoid these pitfalls (see the sidebar with Guidelines for List and Net operations).

DX nets meet on (or near: a DX net has no more 'right' to the use of a particular frequency than any other amateur) frequencies that are usually well-publicised, and at regular times. 20m is a particular favourite for such nets, as propagation is reasonably consistent, but you will find them on other bands too. Usually, at the beginning of the net, the MC will ask for DX check-ins, at which point everyone hopes that one or more rare stations will turn up on frequency. Then

---

LISTS AND NETS: A CODE OF PRACTICE

1. The 'master of ceremonies' (MC), when taking the list, should endeavour to ensure a fair and even representation from all those countries calling to participate.

2. It is not desirable to take a list for use at some future date. In the case of poor propagation, however, a running list may be held over and continued when possible.

3. It is desirable to establish with the DX station beforehand how much time he or she has available, or how many stations can be worked in the time available.

4. A valid QSO requires some minimum two-way exchange of information. As stations are usually addressed by callsign this information has already been imparted to the DX station; nevertheless the MC should seek to avoid passing the whole callsign if possible. Convention has established that the exchange need only be a correctly received RS report by both parties. It is therefore the responsibility of the MC at all times to ensure that this is accomplished fairly, accurately and without assistance. While repeats are in order, if necessary, verification of partly received reports is not. Should a relay or a guess be suspected by the MC, the transmitting station should be instructed to make a second attempt with a changed report. The MC should not flinch from giving "negative QSO" when not satisfied with the exchange.

5. It is acceptable practice for the MC to nominate another station to monitor and assist with the procedure in difficult circumstances due to interference or linking for example.

6. If conditions fail the MC should terminate the operation rather than allow a 'free for all' under the guise of the list.

7. It is very important that the MC gives information out at regular intervals, relating to new lists, QSL managers, length of current list etc. This will be of great assistance to waiting stations not on the list, and minimise breaking and interference.

---

other check-ins will be called, sometimes by country or some other form of selection if things get hectic. This is your chance to call in, taking care to follow the MC's instructions carefully. The MC will then go round each of the participants in turn, asking them if they wish to call any of the DX stations. When your turn comes, make any calls you require, complete the contacts as quickly and efficiently as possible, and hand back to the MC. You will appreciate from this description there may well be lots of sitting around awaiting your turn, by which time the DX station you particularly wanted to call may have upped sticks and gone to work or whatever. But when things work well it means you don't have to compete with the howling pack of amateurs using linear amplifiers and stacked Yagis.

Lists are similar, but tend to happen spontaneously, often at the request of a DX station. Let's suppose a station appears from North Korea as P5/G3XDV, using just low power and a dipole. The demand for the North Korean station is such that, whenever he goes on the air, he is swamped by callers. He tries the obvious solution and operates split frequency (previous section), but his signal isn't strong enough in Europe to compete with those causing interference on his own frequency and his rate of making contacts falls almost to zero. What he could do then is to ask one of the stronger, better-equipped stations on frequency to act as MC, or "make a list". He will take maybe 20 callers at a time, and then indicate to each of them in turn as to when they should call. This way only one will be calling me at a time, so the frequency should remain clear and both callsigns and signal reports can be exchanged without problems from the screaming masses.

One major problem with such list operations is often that, due to propagation characteristics, the MC will pick up stations that have a strong signal with him but which have marginal or no propagation to the DX station they are trying to contact. At the same time, there may be many amateurs in a different part of the world that can copy the DX station well, but which are too weak with the MC to get on the list. Thus a lot of time is wasted by stations giving RS 33 reports to the DX station and struggling to receive the sent signal report (or sometimes even guessing it), while many stations who can copy the DX station well are not given an opportunity to make a contact at all.

It stands to reason that the MC should not pass complete callsigns or assist the contacts in any way (for example by relaying signal reports) - if P5/G3XDV cannot hear the station calling or vice versa, then no two-way contact has taken place.

QRP DXING

Relatively few amateurs are able to build highly competitive stations, with large Yagis and full legal power. Planning constraints and the proximity of neighbouring properties render this a dream for the majority. But having a modest station should not preclude you from chasing DX. Indeed, QRP DXing (generally, 5 watts or less) has been very much a growth activity in recent years. There are several reasons. Although organisations like the GQRP Club [18] have published some excellent designs for home-built QRP transceivers, there have been few commercial designs specifically developed for QRP operation (though most can have their power reduced to QRP levels if required). But, of late, all the major manufacturers have filled this gap and with equipment that is fully featured in every respect other than power output.

Most have add-on automatic antenna tuning units available, too, so they will work comfortably into almost any length of wire. The QRP DXer need not necessarily handicap himself further by using a non-optimum antenna, but local circumstances

may dictate this. Nevertheless, improvements in QRP transceivers, coupled with many more DX operations equipped to hear and work even the weakest of signals, has meant that QRP DXing can be a very satisfying pursuit. It is certainly harder than DXing with high power, requiring more subtlety and operating skill to make up for the lack of brute force, and therefore is perhaps more suited to experienced DXers who want a new challenge than to the newly-licensed amateur. But, equally, those with Foundation licences limited to 10 watts output should not be discouraged from chasing DX.

All the advice given up to this point is equally applicable to low power and QRP DXing, but you will usually be waiting in line behind those with higher effective radiated power (ERP). The phrase is used advisedly. It's not transmitter power, as such, that is relevant but the combination of that and antenna gain. So the low power or QRP DXer may need patience. That said, there is plenty you can do to use your DXing time in the most effective manner.

For example, there is a lot to be said for being active in the major DX contests, whether you consider yourself a contester or not. The benefits are two-fold. Firstly, the bands will be full of activity, including plenty of DX activity. So the chasers won't all be after just one DX station. They will be scattered throughout the bands, divided between lots of DX stations to chase. So you shouldn't have so much competition, especially if you wait until well into the contest, for example the second day of a 48-hour event. The other significant factor is that many groups go out and set up very big stations for the contest weekends (in fact, lots of these will usually be active up to two or three days ahead of time, while they check everything out; an even better chance to catch them). Places like the Caribbean islands, or islands off the African coast are especially favoured as they are good places to operate from to achieve a high score. But these groups know they will not achieve a high score simply by working the more competitive entrants. They need to make lots of contacts with casual participants, too, which means they need to be able to hear well. Some of the stations are set up on a permanent basis, for example the PJ2T contest station on

The American-made Elecraft KX3 is a QRP CW / SSB transceiver that, apart from its low power output, is a fully-featured rig that has quickly become a firm favourite among QRP DXers and DXpeditioners.

With antennas - and a location - like this, DX and contest stations will hear QRP signals. This is the station of PJ2T on the island of Curacao.

Curacao, with multiple towers and huge antennas. When such stations are active in a contest, you will hear them and be able to work them, especially towards the end of the event.

The same is true of an increasing number of major DXpeditions, which set out to ensure that they work not only the best-equipped DXers, but those with more modest stations, too. They recognise that many amateurs have restrictions on the sort of stations they can put together, but nevertheless want to participate in the DX game. The UK-led Five Star DXers Association expeditions to D68C (Comoros in 2001), 3B9C (Rodrigues in 2004), 3B7C (St Brandon in 2007) and T32C (East Kiribati in 2011) were good examples, with round-the-clock operation on all bands, good monoband antennas, on a waterfront site, and on site long enough to work their way through all the strongest callers and be left with more than enough time to ensure that the weaker stations find their way into the log. At least one UK amateur worked 3B9C using a Yaesu FT-817 transceiver and Miracle Whip antenna, while out for a walk!

One of the key pieces of advice to give to a QRP operator is to learn to listen. While someone with a huge signal can afford to be lazy and wait for Cluster spots, moving to the announced frequency and shouting over the top of other callers, the QRP operator doesn't have that luxury. You simply won't be able to compete when the hordes arrive on frequency. So it's a case of spending more time tuning the bands, with the hope of being the first to find a DX station before it is spotted on the Cluster network. The other key piece of advice is to use CW. It is far more effective than SSB in getting through when signals are weak. Some of the new data modes have an even greater advantage and can accurately decode signals 25 to 30dB below the noise level.

If your interest is in two-way QRP to QRP contacts, you will tend to confine much of your operation to the well-known QRP calling frequencies, where other QRP operators tend to congregate. But you cannot assume that DX stations will necessarily happen by these frequencies. The IARU Region 1 band plan lists the following as QRP 'centres of activity': 1836, 3560, 7030, 10116, 14060, 18086, 21060, 24906 and 28060kHz on CW and 3690, 7090, 14285, 18130, 21285 and 28360kHz on SSB.

Two final comments. Firstly, it is not considered legitimate to call with high power to attract the attention of the DX station and then to drop to QRP to conduct the exchange of signal reports. Secondly, do not append "/QRP" to your callsign when calling DX stations (or anyone else for that matter). Quite apart from the fact that, in the UK, it is against your licence conditions, as the only allowable appendages are /A, /P, /M and /MM, it is also counter-productive. Your time is better spent giving your callsign. Nothing is more frustrating to a DX station than to hear part of a call and then /QRP. He would rather hear the call repeated twice, which gives him twice the chance of copying it correctly. If you want to chase DX as a QRP enthusiast, then you simply have to be prepared to join in with everyone else and take your chances.

DXING ETHICS

Most manuals of this type steer clear of the ethics questions, either by choice or by default. But these questions are becoming increasingly relevant and it is worth spending some time thinking about where you stand on some of the issues which are explored in this section.

One of the questions that comes up with respect to working DX, is the extent to which it is 'ethical' to make duplicate contacts with the DX station. In days gone by, this might have been taken as making more than one contact with a DXpedition or DX station, full stop. Anything more might have been considered bad form, as it potentially deprived another station of a contact. But what has changed, as described earlier, is that there are now many more DXCC and similar awards, recognising achievement on every band and mode.

It is therefore considered fair game to work a DXpedition on every band / mode combination (though you may not wish to do so, or be able to do so). So a 'duplicate QSO' is considered to be a second contact on the same band and mode combination, for example 20m SSB or 30m RTTY.

Why would anyone want to do so? The most likely is that you were unhappy with your first contact. Perhaps the DX station got your callsign wrong to start with and, although you corrected it, he didn't acknowledge the fact. A duplicate contact in this situation is fair game, though often it is no longer necessary because many DXpeditions post their logs to the Internet even while the DXpedition is still in progress and you can check to ensure that your contact is in their log. If it isn't or your callsign has been copied incorrectly, don't ask the DXpedition operators to change their log. After all, it was your responsibility at the time of the contact to ensure that they had your call correctly. Instead, try to work them again.

Another valid reason for a duplicate contact might be that you worked the DXpedition on high power, and wish to do so again using QRP. Most DXpeditions will accept this.

A third reason might be that you hear the DXpedition calling CQ repeatedly but with no callers. This is most likely to happen on one of the 'edge' bands, for example 160m, 10m or 6m. In this situation, most DXpeditions would welcome your duplicate call, to assure them that they really are being heard and that it is worth continuing.

Duplicate contacts to ask for schedules on other bands, ask for QSL information because you haven't been able to find it elsewhere, to try out another antenna, and so on, are generally frowned upon unless the DXpedition really is running out of stations to work and the DXpedition operator is looking for any contacts to relieve his boredom. This rarely happens. Even those DXpeditions making more than 100,000 contacts still find that, even when they are coming to an end, there are still plenty of stations calling for their first contact on a particular band and mode. The demand nowadays really does seem to be almost never-ending and every unnecessary duplicate contact you make potentially deprives another station of a QSO he desperately wanted.

This leads on to ethics about working DX more generally. If you already have a particular DX entity worked and confirmed on a specific band / mode combination, should you work the next DXpedition to that location on the same band / mode, or should you refrain to allow more recently-licensed operators to have a contact? There is no easy answer to this. If your particular amateur radio interest is DXing, then you will want to contact every DXpedition that appears on the bands regardless of whether you have the entity in your log already or not.

But the next question might then be, if you already have a DX station (maybe a resident in a rare location) in your log, is it legitimate to work him again on the same band / mode each and every year, maybe for an annual table that you participate in, perhaps at your local club? Again, there is no simple answer. Some DX stations actually lay down their own rules, perhaps refusing to acknowledge your call if they already have you in the log from a previous year. If you hear them operating a contest, that's a different matter. They are then fair game, as they will want you in their log for points, regardless of whether you worked them recently outside the contest.

We now turn to look at other ethical questions. Firstly there are those things which are illegal, either because they contravene our licences or because they contravene the rules of specific awards or contests that we may be interested in pursuing. Examples might include operating with excess power, operating outside your allocated frequencies, or asking someone else to operate your station under your callsign in your absence (allowable in some countries but not in others). Do any of these things and it may increase your DX score, but would you gain any satisfaction from so doing?

Then there are actions which, while of no significance to the licensing bodies, are considered out of bounds within the amateur radio community. One example would be submitting forged QSL cards for awards. This is easily done - it is known that one person has quite openly obtained blank QSL cards from 200 different DXCC entities (samples from printers, cards on visitor boards at conventions, etc) and it wouldn't be

hard to complete these for hypothetical contacts. Only the most diligent awards manager would spot the fake if the details looked reasonably plausible. There are rumours that some high DXCC scores were boosted this way but one has to wonder whether the applicants concerned really get any satisfaction from such behaviour.

Also in this category there are many other forms of behaviour that are against the rules of the awards programme or contest concerned. A contest sponsor may, for example, prohibit the use of Internet-based support such as use of the Cluster, yet this is quite valid for awards. So you may decide to operate with such support in order not to miss any rare ones that appear during the contest, but not to send in a contest entry. That's absolutely fine. But as soon as you cross over the line, whether in terms of contest rules or award rules, then, again, there is surely no satisfaction to be gained because your score will not have been gained on the same playing field as other participants.

For most (hopefully all!) readers the previous couple of paragraphs received your immediate assent. But now we get on to much more grey areas, because many of them come down to personal choice. The classic example is the use of the WSJT suite of programs, which has caused a lot of controversy in recent years. Quite simply, the major awards (let's take DXCC as the prime example) allow contacts made by data modes to be counted towards your overall totals. So if you aspire to sit near the top of the tables you will need to include those modes in your armoury with all the tools at your disposal. But for many operators such software is anathema. They consider that it is nothing more than computer talking to computer and is no measure of true operating achievement. "How many squares has your computer worked recently?" is a typical put-down remark.

There is no right or wrong answer. If you have sweated for years to achieve a high score by what might be called 'traditional' means, you will probably be frustrated to see others catching you up at a rate of knots by using these recent advances. But if, for example, you are operating from a somewhat limited urban location, you will probably regard the digimodes as a lifesaver, allowing you to work stations that would be very difficult, if not impossible, using SSB or even CW.

A slightly different example is the situation, discussed in Chapter 4, where your station is remote from your home. Some operators would gain no satisfaction from having to resort to such means to work DX and would only be satisfied with contacts made from home. Others consider it the only way to be competitive if it is not possible to use high power or to put up large antennas at their home. There is no right or wrong answer, though in 2015 the ARRL changed the rules of their DXCC awards programme to permit the operator of a remote station to be located anywhere in the world: it is the location of the station (transmitter, receiver and antenna system), and not the operator, that is important.

At the end of the day most of these things are a matter of personal choice and you need to decide what matters to you and then, on the whole, stick with it so that you can measure your personal progress in a meaningful way even if you cannot

The DX Code of Conduct

- I will listen, and listen, and then listen again before calling.
- I will only call if I can copy the DX station properly.
- I will not trust the DX Cluster and will be sure of the DX station's callsign before calling.
- I will not interfere with the DX station nor anyone calling and will never tune up on the DX frequency or in the QSX slot.
- I will wait for the DX station to end a contact before I call.
- I will always send my full callsign.
- I will call and then listen for a reasonable interval. I will not call continuously.
- I will not transmit when the DX operator calls another callsign, not mine.
- I will not transmit when the DX operator queries a callsign not like mine.
- I will not transmit when the DX station requests geographic areas other than mine.
- When the DX operator calls me, I will not repeat my callsign unless I think he has copied it incorrectly.
- I will be thankful if and when I do make a contact.
- I will respect my fellow hams and conduct myself so as to earn their respect.

always compare your results with the published results of others.

Belgian DXers John Devoldere, ON4UN, and Mark Demeuleneere, ON4WW, have produced a 68-page PDF called *Ethics and Operating Procedures for the Radio Amateur*, which has been endorsed by the IARU. It is available for downloading from the ARRL website [19].

Allied to the topic of ethics and operating procedures is that of good on the air conduct. A DX 'Code of Conduct' has been published (see box above) which all DXers are encouraged to follow. By going to the DX Code of Conduct website [20] you can click on any of the topics to see a more detailed version.

OPERATING AS DX

There may be times when you find yourself as the DX station, rather than chasing DX. This can even happen from the UK if, for example, you are operating a sought-after special event station or undertaking an Islands on the Air operation off the British coast. There is a lot that could be said and the paragraphs below give some brief guidelines.

The first point to make is that, when you have a lot of callers because you are the perceived 'rare' station, it is up to you to take control of the situation or it may quickly get out of hand. There are several methods available to you and most are equally applicable whichever operating mode you are using. The first is to start operating split frequency, as described earlier in this chapter. This time, though, it is you who stays in one place and ask others to call you away from your transmit frequency. When it becomes clear that you will need to operate in this manner, ask the pile-up to stand by while you look for a suitable frequency to listen on. It should be close by, usually slightly high of the frequency you are operating on (by about 1kHz or so on CW or data modes, or perhaps 5 or 7kHz on SSB). But do find a clear frequency, rather than moving your pile-up on to the top of an existing contact. Now the callers will, at least, be able to hear you clearly, so that your instructions to the pile-up will (hopefully) be understood and followed.

That might be sufficient to bring things under control. What you want to achieve at this point is a clear pattern of operating. Try to pick a complete callsign out of the pile-up within the first few seconds or, if not a full call, then enough of a callsign that there is no doubt who you are answering. But do ensure you transmit regularly; if you are having trouble copying anything at all then say something like "the station with Alpha in the call". There probably is one and, more importantly, if you stay silent for long periods the callers will engage in longer and longer calls, just adding to the level of interference.

Whatever system you use to pick out calls, never work someone other than whoever you have tried to answer. For example, if you go back to "Delta Victor", then don't work Papa Juliet Four Delta X-Ray, however tempting it might be if he is still calling and very strong. Once you are heard to do this, the rest of the callers will take it as the green light for a total free-for-all. But if you stick to your guns, the message will eventually get through that they are only slowing things down.

If it is still too hectic, you can try to spread the callers over a range of frequencies, though keep it to no more than 2 - 3kHz on CW or 10kHz on SSB, or you will start to take over the band. Even these sort of splits are really only acceptable if you are on a major expedition to a very rare spot. The other alternative is to make directional calls, for example by taking stations with, progressively, number 1, 2, 3, etc in their calls, or perhaps by country (but this is very slow - there are lots of them - and callers will quickly get frustrated and start causing interference). Never take more than, say, 10 calls from one area before moving on, or the frustration factor will quickly increase. More common, and more importantly, it can be helpful to stand by for a particular continent. For example, if you are operating close to Europe, the European stations will be workable for many hours at a time, whereas band openings to North America or Asia may be fleeting. So make a point of asking European stations to stand by while you check for calls from other continents.

In contests, or with a less rare operation, split-frequency operation is neither desirable nor necessary, but you can still

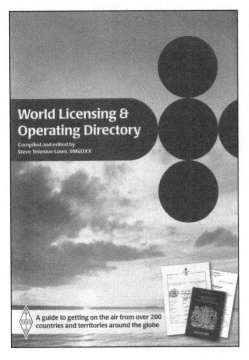

The *World Licensing and Operating Directory* tells you how to get licensed abroad and where to operate from when you get that licence.

use the other suggestions to thin the pile-up. In these situations, keep your operating crisp, avoiding unnecessary exchanges of information. Do give your callsign with every contact, or certainly every two or three contacts, but QSL information can be given less frequently, and there is usually no need to give out lots of information about name, weather, etc. You can indulge in longer chats when you are operating from home, but when you are sought after, then it is only polite to try to accommodate as many of the callers as possible, as presumably you will only be operating that rare station for a limited period of time (or it wouldn't be rare!)

Do try to avoid being drawn into list or net operations if at all possible, including taking your own lists. These only increase the overall number of exchanges that need to take place, and hence reduce the total number of contacts that can be made in the time available. One of the few times that it may be necessary is, as has happened with some IOTA operations, when you have limited battery power and therefore want to keep your transmit time to an absolute minimum, when it may be reasonable to ask for someone to maintain a list of callers for you. Ideally, in such an instance, the list taker should be in the same part of the world as you are. It simply doesn't work when, for example, a European station takes a list of other Europeans on behalf of a weak Pacific station. He will hear those other Europeans who are loud with him on short-skip (quite possibly because they have high-angle antennas) but who may have zero chance of working into the Pacific. On the other hand, he may well not hear the well-equipped European station in his dead zone who could easily have made the contact. In any case, when operating as the DX station in a list operation, the guidelines on List and Net Operation which have already been mentioned do very much apply.

Up Two - Adventures of a DXpeditioner, by Roger Western, G3SXW [21], is an excellent and entertaining account of what it's like to be at the DX end of the pile-ups. If you would like to give it a go yourself, take a look at the *World Licensing and Operating Directory* by Steve Telenius-Lowe, 9M6DXX (now PJ4DX) [22], which is full of advice on how to get licensed abroad and where to operate from when you get that licence.

VHF AND UHF DXING

Much of the foregoing applies to VHF and UHF DXing, except that, in many instances, the so-called DX station is not a DXpedition or rare station, but rather a perfectly ordinary station like yourself who happens to be a long way away (in VHF terms). Where, on HF, propagation is less of an issue, at least on the main bands, and DX is determined by the rarity of the station worked, the situation on VHF is different. Other than on 6m which can, at times, exhibit properties similar to any HF band, the issue on the VHF and UHF bands is very much one of distance, pure and simple. For UK stations, for most of the time, the DX they are working will be other European stations, not necessarily in rare locations, but rarely available simply because suitable propagation only occurs occasionally. Or, indeed, the path may only exist because strenuous efforts have been made to achieve it, maybe through setting up your equipment on top of a mountain or, perhaps, building a more effective station (high gain antenna, low loss feeder, masthead pre-amp, etc).

Let's take, as an example, a tropospheric opening on 2m or 70cm. Propagation may be quite stable for periods of several hours, or even days, at a time. And you won't necessarily be competing with many others for a particular contact, unless there is an identifiable 'rare' station on the band (perhaps an expedition to an otherwise inactive locator square, for example). So you should be able to call and work stations to your heart's content. However, given that propagation may change quite quickly and that others may be waiting in turn to work the station you are in contact with, it is usual to keep contacts relatively short. An exchange of signal report, QTH locator and, perhaps name. The same is especially true when using those even more ephemeral propagation mechanisms such as Sporadic E and Aurora, which could disappear at a moment's notice. Keep contacts slick and efficient. Unlike on HF, for the reasons outlined above, on VHF each participant in the QSO is likely to be DX. If he is DX to you, then you are probably DX to him, in respect of distance if nothing else.

Finding DX on the VHF bands is rather different to HF. It's not so much a case of researching newsletters or the Internet, but one of keeping a weather eye (quite literally in the case of some types of propagation!) out for band openings. The chapter on propagation talks about how to spot the signs of possible Sporadic E, tropospheric or other VHF band openings. When the band opens, much of what you hear will be (in VHF terms) DX. Take part, make contacts and enjoy.

One major difference between HF and VHF is that VHF antennas have much higher gain and narrower lobes than typical HF beams, so more care needs to be taken in changing beam direction a little at a time and tuning carefully for weak signals. To help the process along, there are recognised calling frequencies on most of the VHF bands for DX activity. When the band is dead but an opening is possible, the simple solution is to leave your receiver on the calling frequency and wait for something to happen. The other solution is to monitor the various beacon transmissions. Often you will hear a beacon before other amateur signals start to appear. The Cluster system is extremely effective nowadays in alerting the more casual DXers to VHF band openings, but more serious DXers will continue to make their own efforts to spot potential DX opportunities, monitoring constantly when enhanced conditions are expected.

The other modern tool which helps enormously is the spectrum scope which is incorporated into many current transceivers and software defined radios. It might also be a software 'scope such as *Spectran* with the receiver on a distant beacon, for example. This enables you to monitor not just one frequency, but a whole range, and can give an instant visual indication when signals start to appear. And as well as in-band signals, serious VHF DX operators are well aware of commercial and other stations operating close to the amateur bands and whose signals can often give an indication of enhanced propagation.

Moving up to the microwave region, DXing takes on rather a different flavour again. Many contacts are prearranged, for

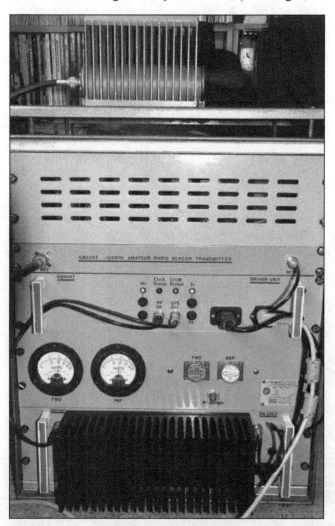

New 70cm beacon, GB3UHF, on test before installation.

example during an 'activity period' or contest, even to the extent of both parties heading out to separate hilltops to achieve a long-distance contact, perhaps to qualify for one of the various distance awards. This said, nowadays much of the current microwave DX happens from well equipped home stations; portable operation is no longer 'mandatory'.

Another popular technique is to set up a contact on one of the lower bands and, often, to maintain a link on that band until the higher band contact is completed. To take a simple example, two stations may establish contact on the 70cm band and agree to try a contact on 10GHz. Although they may have a line-of-sight path, their 10GHz antennas, probably dishes, will have very high gain and narrow beamwidth and have to be aligned with great accuracy before a contact becomes possible. However, with some contacts, especially by forward troposcatter, rain scatter or aircraft scatter, alignment accuracy is less critical. Not only will the alignment of their 70cm antennas give a good starting point for aligning the 10GHz antennas, but the 70cm link can be used for communications until the 10GHz link is working.

SPORADIC E OPERATING

Sporadic E operations on 50MHz and 70MHz are relatively common each summer and at some other times of the year, and propagation can exist for several hours at a time. Using Sporadic E to make QSOs is therefore no different to how you would conduct a QSO via any other day-to-day mode of communication. However, the probability of Sporadic E propagation declines rapidly with increasing frequency.

144MHz Es openings are infrequent and often very short-lived, so efficient operating is essential and an exchange of report and QTH locator is the most that should be attempted. It is possible for a station to appear, calling CQ, be worked and disappear totally in less than a minute. Avoid using the SSB calling channels; there is no hope of establishing an Es contact and then changing frequency as is normal practice with other propagation. All too often a station fades out during a contact and there is usually nothing to be gained by waiting in the hope it will reappear. It is best to 'cut your losses' and look for someone else.

The ionised reflecting layer, which may be relatively small in area, can move very rapidly and also tilt. For example, Maltese stations may be very strong one minute then fade out to be replaced by Sicilians which are in turn replaced by Sardinians, all in the space of a few minutes.

CQ calls should be brief, perhaps 10 seconds, and used with discretion: if an operator is in an area of high activity, any DX station is likely to have many UK stations calling him and be unlikely to reply to a call. Conversely, if an operator is isolated, he may have an opening all to himself and a pile-up of DX may call him. In this case one will want to work as many as possible, so just exchange reports with each station but give the locator on every third or fourth contact - the waiting pile-up will have heard it already. However, always remember that Sporadic E can be very localised and it is possible for a DX station which is S9 to one operator to be inaudible 10km away, and that a CQ call may well pay dividends, especially just as the band is opening.

AURORAL OPERATING

The beacon stations closest to the auroral zones are usually the first auroral signals to be heard in the south. The Swedish beacon SK4MPI (144.412MHz) is a good auroral indicator, as is the Faroe Islands beacon OY6SMC (50.035MHz) on 6m.

Auroral events are usually first noticed by amateurs in Norway, Sweden, Finland and northern Russia, who will be on the band making contacts before the auroral reflections extend to the south. Due to their northerly locations, they see far more visual auroras and participate in more radio events than stations in southern England.

Radio amateurs have noticed that the larger the change in geomagnetic activity, the farther south the area of auroral ionisation extends, and stations as far south as Italy can make auroral contacts in major events. If you hear someone calling "CQ aurora" and you have not operated in an auroral opening before, resist the temptation to call indiscriminately, and listen only. There are going to be many future auroras and this is your chance to learn the new operating techniques required for auroral contacts.

First select horizontal polarisation and beam between north and east at about 45°. Tune the beacon band between 144.412MHz and 144.445MHz; it will take some time to get used to the rough-sounding keying of the beacons which will be slightly off their usual frequencies due to Doppler shift. If you hear SK4MPI check whether DL0PR on 144.486MHz is readable. If these beacons are heard the aurora is extending at least as far as Germany, and is therefore a large-scale event which will probably last for a few hours and may repeat later in the evening. Turn the beam between north and east on each beacon heard and it will be noticed that different beam headings give peak signals for different countries. Generally the farthest DX is worked with the beam well to the east.

Next tune the SSB section between 144.160MHz and 144.400MHz and try listening to an experienced local station who is working auroral DX. Due to the distortion he will be speaking slowly, using correct phonetics and possibly end-of-transmission tones. Remember that you will hear the local station direct but the DX stations will be replying via the aurora and will be slightly off his frequency. A typical SSB auroral contact starts like this:

An aurora can benefit VHF radio signals well to the south of the spectacular visual display.

"CQ aurora, CQ Aurora, G3XDV, Golf Three X-Ray Delta Victor calling CQ aurora . . ." (repeated slowly several times) "and G3XDV listening." 'Pip' (end of transmission tone).

"G3XDV, G3XDV, G3XDV, LA1A calling. Lima Alpha One Alpha, LA1A calling G3XDV . . ."

End-of-transmission tones which give a low-frequency 'pip' are very helpful in auroral openings when signals are weak. The tone readily identifies the end of each station's transmissions and could be a 'K' tone or 'pip' tone.

RIT (receiver independent tuning) is a must for auroral reception as the amount of Doppler shift often changes in the middle of a contact. It will soon be seen that SSB contacts are difficult due to the distortion, and contacts tend to be limited to exchanging reports, names, and locators. Many amateurs also exchange and log the beam headings used at both ends of the contact as a study of these figures can reveal the particular area of ionised E layer being used.

During weak auroral events SSB operators in England, Northern Ireland, North Wales and Scotland can work each other and operators with better facilities can contact Norway and Sweden. During strong auroral events SSB stations all over the UK and north-west Europe can work each other.

A new operator listening in the CW section between 144.020 and 144.120MHz will hear a great many rough-sounding hissing CW signals during a strong event. Experienced operators are used to the strange sounding notes and contacts are completed quickly and efficiently. The letter 'A' is added when calling CQ and is also added after the readability and signal strength report, in place of the normal tone reports which are not sent during aurora openings as no signal sounds T9. The best auroral DX is worked on CW, just as on other propagation modes - CW is easier to copy in weak signal conditions and contacts are therefore completed faster. Some auroral operators use full break-in technique on CW, allowing them to listen for stations breaking in during the sending of a CQ.

Auroral openings can occur in three separate phases in a single 24-hour period. The first phase can start as early in the day as 1300UTC but usually takes place between 1500 and 1900UTC. The second phase can occur between 2100 and 2300UTC and a third phase can run from after midnight until 0600UTC. Very few auroral contacts take place around 2000UTC and there is often a fade-out between the evening phase and the after-midnight session. Some auroras have no afternoon phase and start in the evening, often continuing after midnight. Some auroras have no afternoon or evening phase, only starting after midnight. These are almost always weak events, sometimes heralding a larger occurrence the next day.

Due to the Doppler shift and distortion on signals, auroral contacts can only be made on CW and SSB. High power is not essential but helps greatly in weak events. During strong events almost anyone can participate. Signals reflected from the auroral curtain on 144MHz do not change polarity, and high-gain horizontal antennas give the best results. Operators

Shower name	Limits	Max	ZHR	N - S	NE - SW	E - W	SE - NW
Quadrantids	1-5 Jan	3-4 Jan	110	02-06 (W) 11-16 (E)	11-17 (SE)	23-03 (S) 15-17 (S)	00-05 (SW)
April Lyrids	19-25 Apr	22 Apr	15-25	22-02 (W) 06-10 (E)	23-03 (NW) 08-11 (SE)	03-06 (N)	22-01 (SW) 05-08 (NE)
Eta Aquarids	1-12 May	3 May	50	03-04 (W) 10-11 (E)	04-09 (NW)	05-11 (N)	08-12 (NE)
Arietids	30 May-18 Jun	7 Jun	60	04-08 (W) 11-15 (E)	05-09 (NW) 14-16 (SE)	08-12 (N)	04-06 (SW) 10-14 (NE)
Zeta Perseids	1-16 Jun	9 Jun	40	05-10 (W) 13-17 (E)	06-11 (NW) 15-17 (SE)	09-14 (N)	07-07 (SW) 11-15 (NE)
Perseids	20 Jul-18 Aug	12 Aug	95	23-04 (W) 09-13 (E)	08-17 (SE)	11-01 (S)	18-04 (SW)
Orionids	16-27 Oct	22 Oct	25	00-03 (W) 07-09 (E)	00-04 (NW)	03-06 (N)	05-08 (NE)
Taurids S	10 Oct-5 Dec	3 Nov	25	02-05 (E) 20-22 (W)	20-01 (NW)	22-03 (N)	00-05 (NE)
Geminids	7-15 Dec	13-14 Dec	110	04-09 (E) 20-01 (W)	22-02 (NW) 05-09 (SE)	01-04 (N) 03-07 (S)	03-07 (NE) 19-23 (SW)
Ursids	17-24 Dec	22 Dec	15	-	07-01 (SE)	00-24 (S)	16-09 (SW)

Table 4: Calendar of the principal meteor showers.

who are blocked to the south and south-east enjoy auroral openings as they can work stations, normally unheard due to the obstructions, by beaming well to the north of the direct path.

The amount of Doppler shift is proportional to the frequency band in use. For this reason auroral signals on the 50 and 70MHz bands are easier to read and have less distortion than on 144MHz. Inter-UK signals are generally stronger on 50 and 70MHz and the openings start a little earlier and finish a little later than on 144MHz. Auroral contacts have also been made on both CW and SSB on the 432MHz band, but signals are about 40dB weaker than on 144MHz, and the Doppler shift can be as much as 4kHz. Professional studies reveal that radar reflections have been received at over 3GHz.

METEOR SCATTER

Most amateur Meteor Scatter (MS) operation takes place on 144MHz and 50MHz, although 28 and 70MHz are also good bands. Operation on 432MHz is also marginally possible, but the path losses approach those experienced in EME operation.

Table 4 lists the major meteor showers, which occur on the same dates each year as the earth passes through those bands of particles on its passage round the Sun. Serious meteor scatter enthusiasts ensure they are ready for these events, with no distractions in their diaries! Nowadays, though, more casual operators may become aware of meteor scatter opportunities as they watch the Cluster and see stations exchanging sked information for MS QSOs. This is an example where VHF use of the Cluster system differs from HF use. While on HF it is deemed 'unsporting' to arrange skeds or self-spot via the Cluster system, on VHF the Cluster becomes a useful tool for setting up contacts on specialist modes. Skeds can also be arranged via the ON4KST chat rooms on the Internet [23].

The distances which may be covered by typical MS operation are similar to those possible via Sporadic E. Assuming most signals are reflected from a region at an altitude of 110km, the maximum range possible with an antenna exhibiting a main lobe at 0° elevation is about 2300km. Typical amateur antennas have a main lobe at 2 - 5° and thus the ranges to be expected are somewhat less.

Most MS contacts on 2m take place during the meteor showers. Rather fewer contacts are made via sporadic meteors during the intervals between, but 6m meteor scatter activity is possible on most days of the year using the specialist *JT6M* software (see below and Chapter 8 on modes).

MS QSO Procedure

Until the development of *JT6M* and *FSK441*, most meteor scatter work was on CW and SSB. The intermittent nature of MS propagation means that special operating procedures are necessary. Within IARU Region 1, a set of 'Operating Procedures for Meteor Scatter QSOs' was adopted at the IARU Region 1 Conference in 1978. The Operating Procedures were written specifically for CW and SSB MS working, although they were slightly reworded at a Region 1 interim meeting in Vienna in 2004 in order to take into account the use of machine-generated modes such as *FSK441*.

CW and SSB are still used for MS work, though less frequently than before. On CW, high speeds are employed. During skeds, speeds from 200 to over 2000LPM (letters per minute) are in use. In random MS work 800LPM is the recommended maximum speed. The IARU document 'Operating Procedures for Meteor Scatter QSOs' can be found on the web at [24]

JT6M and *FSK441* users should consult the *WSJT* software documentation [25] for the best way to set up their station to conduct MS contacts.

Equipment

Meteor Scatter contacts are possible with low power particularly on 50MHz, but on 144MHz higher ERP is necessary for consistent success. 100W RF at the feed point of a 10 - 14dBd gain antenna should be aimed for.

A genuine system noise figure of less than 2.5dB is highly desirable. Many commercial transceivers, especially the earlier models, have inadequate front-end performance but the new generation of DSP transceivers has helped somewhat. Masthead preamplifiers are used by serious operators but care should be taken to avoid too much gain which could degrade the performance of the transceiver.

Frequency setting is of paramount importance. A tolerance of ±500Hz is demanded on CW and 200Hz on SSB, with a stability of better than 100Hz/hr. Modern transceivers employ much more stringent frequency-derived systems than in the past. Stability is perhaps even more important when using software such as *WSJT*, using DSP techniques to integrate signals received in a very narrow bandwidth.

Most 2m MS signals will be quite weak so the antenna system should be as large as possible within environmental, structural and financial constraints. Long Yagis are popular, particularly the commercial 13 and 17-element models, although smaller antennas are also capable of good results. With a high-gain array, such as a box of four 17-element Yagis, received signals will of course be much stronger than those from a single 9-element antenna. However, many MS operators have found that a too 'sharp' array often misses signals coming into the broader capture angle of a smaller single Yagi. Experienced operators tend to favour two or more stacked Yagis since these give extra gain while retaining a broader E-plane lobe.

The timing requirements of MS technique are stringent but not too difficult to meet. A radio-controlled clock or watch is probably the most popular timepiece found in many shacks. The prices of these clocks / watches incorporating radio receivers phase-locked to radio transmitters such as MSF and Droitwich are now very reasonable. Your PC can easily be locked to one of the standard time sites available via the Internet, perhaps using software such as Dimension 4 [26]. Mains-driven clocks are to be avoided as they have poor short-term stability.

On CW, two other items of equipment are required; a means of sending repetitive messages at the speeds involved and a means of decoding the received CW. Nowadays this is usually by way of suitable PC software. The PC can generate CW, store incoming CW for replaying at lower speed and, if required, archive whole QSOs as .WAV files for future reference.

The majority of operators have now made the logical move to software such as *WSJT*. After all, if you are already using your PC for CW why not, instead, use a mode which has actually been designed for PC operation rather than one which was designed well over 150 years ago for manual operation? When using the *WSJT* modes, though, be aware that transmissions can be continuous for many seconds at a time, whereas many transceivers and especially amplifiers are designed for the low duty cycle of CW or SSB, so you may need to reduce your output power accordingly.

EME ('MOONBOUNCE')

Moonbounce, or Earth-Moon-Earth (EME) communication, presents some of the most significant technical and operating challenges in amateur radio. EME is special because it is only just possible to make contacts. In theory, stations who wish to communicate point their antennas at the Moon, which is then used as a passive reflector. If only it were that simple! Some of the difficulties that need to be overcome include:

- The Moon is a long way away, 360,000 - 405,000km, so the path loss is high (at best 252dB at 144MHz, 261dB at 432MHz and 271dB at 1296MHz)
- The Moon is a poor reflector so most of the signal is not returned - typically just 7%
- Relative motion of the Earth and Moon means the antennas must be 'tracked'
- The relative motion causes Doppler shift - it can be in excess of 20kHz at 10GHz
- The motion also causes a special type of rapid fading called libration fading.

All these difficulties make EME propagation different from any kind of terrestrial propagation so some specialised operating techniques are required. On the positive side, EME contacts can be relatively dependable and you do not need to wait for a tropospheric opening or Sporadic-E. The Moon will always appear on schedule!

In the early days amateur EME stations needed huge antenna systems, very high power transmitters and complex receiving set-ups. Today EME operation is within reach of most amateurs with a reasonable VHF station capability. Although SSB is sometimes possible, much EME operation is on CW and *JT65* digital modes.

In line with terrestrial activity the majority of EME operation is on the 144MHz band, closely followed by 432 and 1296MHz. Many hundreds of amateurs across the world are currently active on this mode, with a number having attained DXCC via EME.

EME operation does not necessarily mean sleepless nights, as the Moon is visible to radio signals as often during the day as it is at night. And EME operating sessions can be planned in advance, because we always know where the Moon is going to be.

Propagation and background noise effects are frequency sensitive and there is a complex interplay that gives each amateur band its own distinctive characteristics for EME. At the lower end of the VHF spectrum, local noise sources can be particularly troublesome and antennas with sufficient gain for EME are necessarily very large. This makes EME on 50 and 70MHz something of a rarity. The majority of newcomers to EME begin on 144MHz; less real estate is needed for the antennas, cable losses are still manageable and amplifiers are available off the shelf. Some of the necessary equipment may already be in the shack.

As one progresses into the UHF spectrum, generating sufficient power and getting it from the amplifier to the feed point become more of a challenge. At 1296MHz there is also a step change from Yagi arrays to dishes. High power amplifiers, low noise preamplifiers and accurate pointing of high gain narrow beamwidth dishes are just some of the issues faced by microwave EME enthusiasts. The USA, Europe and Japan have different 13cm allocations, meaning that EME QSOs take place with split frequency operation. The first 24GHz EME contacts were made in 2001, and in 2005, EME QSOs took place on 47GHz.

Early EME contacts were made using CW because it was the most effective mode available at the time, and this is where the basic QSO techniques were developed. Many QSOs are still made on CW. In a few instances, signals between larger stations are strong enough to permit QSOs using SSB. In 2001, Joe Taylor, K1JT, began to develop a suite of digital communication software programs, WSJT (Weak Signal Joe Taylor) [25]. In 2003, the first version of JT65 appeared for EME users.

It is no understatement to say that JT65 revolutionised EME by providing an effective increase in sensitivity. For the limited purpose of exchanging callsigns, signal reports and modest amounts of additional information, digital EME contacts can be made at signal levels some 10dB below those required for CW. For decoding callsigns, this level of advantage requires the use of 'Deep Search' mode within the WSJT software, which compares the decoded data with a callsign database. JT65 has undoubtedly given many smaller stations the confidence to attempt contacts via the Moon, and dozens of contacts take place every day using JT65. The original JT65 mode soon spawned a set of sub-modes known as JT65A, B and C. They have been 'tuned' in their tone spacing and decoding abilities to be suitable for the propagation vagaries of the different amateur bands. For example, JT65B is commonly in use on 2m.

Equipment for EME

Although QSOs have been made with relatively simple equipment, the basic requirement is for a transceiver or a separate receiver and transmitter with good frequency readout and excellent stability. For CW operation, the main receiver should have a narrow IF filter and calibrated receiver incremental tuning (RIT), and some operators find an internal or external audio peaking filter helpful too.

External transverters must have good frequency stability, as much as the transceiver. It can be really annoying if the station which you are listening to fades down in slow QSB and has drifted outside of your receiver passband when it reappears, which may be 15 or even 30 minutes later. You might not be able to complete a QSO if your own signal drifts by only a few hundred Hz. It should also be noted that the CW frequency is the carrier Tx frequency.

WSJT contacts are made in a conventional SSB bandwidth. Significant additional filtering takes place within the software

and it can be helpful to ensure that the bandwidth presented for WSJT reception is not restricted or 'coloured' by audio filters, shift or notch controls. It should be noted that the WSJT frequency is quoted as the SSB zero beat frequency (or SSB 'carrier') and that JT65 tones start at 1270Hz above this.

A low noise preamplifier mounted close to the antenna is essential for any successful EME operation. The most important pieces of coaxial cable in your system are those that run between the antenna feed points and the preamplifier. They impose a signal loss that can never be recovered, no matter how low the preamplifier noise figure is. These cables should be the best quality you can afford.

The very high path losses mandate high transmit power for all EME operation. Whenever possible you will need to run the maximum permitted power at the antenna. Although valve amplifiers used to be the norm for EME operation, an increasing number of amateurs are now using a solid state power amplifiers.

There are trade-offs that can be made between cable loss and transmitter power output, but lower loss feeder usually turns out to be the most economical answer.

Antennas for EME

Before considering large arrays and bespoke elevation systems, it is worth remembering that most amateurs on EME cut their teeth using their existing VHF antennas - one or possibly two Yagis, used without elevation. Twice a day, for an hour or so, moonrise and moonset allows stations without elevation control to make EME QSOs.

The antenna system is probably the most important part of an amateur EME station. A small improvement in the antenna affects both the transmit and receive performance and is therefore doubly useful. Antennas are often large and require significant effort in their construction.

Calculations based on the path loss, maximum legal power at the antenna and system noise figure arrive at the minimum antenna gain to detect CW echoes. These calculations result in a gain requirement of approximately 20dBd at 144MHz and 23dBd at 432MHz. On 144MHz four stacked and bayed long Yagis will yield the required gain whilst on 432MHz eight long Yagis will be needed. These antenna sizes are made on the assumption that the station is capable

'H frame' in use at G4ZTR supporting a four I0JXX Yagi array.

of a QSO with a station of similar size, but there are several amateurs that have systems up to eight times larger. As a result, even quite basic single-Yagi stations are capable of EME QSOs with such 'big guns'. Many stations have had good results with 3dB less antenna gain. The newcomer to EME will soon see the limitations of a single Yagi and graduate to two or even a 'box of four'. After this, probably the most common upgrade is to add vertical polarisation, as the first step to reducing the limitations caused by polarisation rotation.

For EME communications using *WSJT*, the antenna and power requirements are considerably reduced. Although a smaller antenna system will often receive greater background noise, there are many 144MHz stations who can detect their own echoes with a single three wavelength long Yagi antenna and 300W. Indeed there are many stations that now operate EME on 144MHz just a two wavelength long Yagi antenna and 100W. Sub-optimal antenna systems involve a steep learning curve but help to hone operating skills.

On 1296MHz and above the majority of EME stations use dish antennas ranging from 3m C band TVRO to 12m and larger ex-commercial systems.

The antenna support is very important. If possible, it is good to think ahead about your ultimate antenna system and engineer the support for that scenario, even if you are beginning with a more modest setup. Fortunately, especially if you are planning a large array, antennas for EME do not need to be high above the ground, but they do need a clear view of the Moon, preferably for all the likely trajectories from your QTH.

As for amateur satellite operation, EME antenna systems require elevation control in addition to azimuth rotation. Because of their size and weight, EME arrays usually require the largest heavy duty rotators.

EME Activity

As with many other aspects of amateur radio, the wise operator starting out EME will begin by listening - and then listening more. Such an apprenticeship will give you a good idea of the callsigns of the strongest active stations and the procedures in use on that particular band.

Activity peaks on EME contest weekends, on weekends when good conditions are anticipated, and when some choice DX pops up. On 144MHz many operators prefer specific weekends when the background noise temperature is at its lowest. These weekends are well publicised in the VHF community [27]. Monthly newsletters are available for EME operators, produced for 2m by DF2ZC and for 70cm and above by K2UYH and others al [28].

WSJT

The newcomer to EME will almost undoubtedly begin with *JT65B* from the *WSJT* software suite because of its superior sensitivity over CW and SSB. *WSJT* can be downloaded from K1JT's web pages [25]. In order to use *WSJT*, a computer with a sound card and a simple interface are connected to the audio output and the microphone input or 'line' input of a SSB radio transceiver.

For most UK stations, a check of *JT65* reception can be made without EME signals, because the GB3VHF and GB3NGI beacons transmit periods of *JT65B* [29]. Once you are happy with the setup of the *WSJT* software and your transceiver you are ready to listen for some EME signals. On 2m, most *JT65B* activity takes place between 144.100 and 144.150MHz.

The *WSJT* screen tells you where the Moon is, so no additional astronomical information is needed. Pointing at the Moon with a single three-wavelength Yagi plus mast-head amplifier, you should expect to see (but perhaps not hear) a number of the larger stations. With 100W or more of RF at that type of antenna you should be able to work most of the stations you can see on the *SpecJT* waterfall display.

The *WSJT* handbook contains all you need to know about operating procedures on *JT65B* and the software contains examples of recorded QSOs to practice decoding. Message protocol is quite straightforward.

CW

Because of the exceptionally low signal levels and frequent fading EME QSOs on CW normally consist of only the basic minimum necessary for a complete contact. For a QSO to be complete, both parties must have exchanged callsigns,

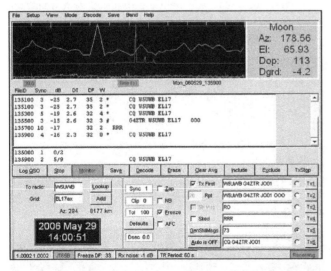

Typical JT65B EME QSO. W5UWB calling CQ and then working G4ZTR.

Live CQ EME reporting web site with 9 stations calling CQ.

reports and an acknowledgement that the report was received. For reports, 144MHz EME operators use a single letter, O, to signify that both callsigns have been received in full. On higher bands the reporting system takes more account of signal levels. For full details see [30], which applies to all of the higher bands.

Although a few stations still prefer to use a straight key, the majority of CW EME operation is made using some form of memory keyer. There is no doubt that precise, well-formed characters and regular rhythm can help improve readability at very low signal strengths. A steady 12 to 15WPM seems to suit most operators on 144MHz.

EME Information and Help

A question often asked is how you decide where to call CQ, or to listen for others. Fortunately, the Internet contains several useful sources of real-time information. *Live CQ* is a web page where automated EME receivers report their reception of CQ and QRZ calls [31]. The reception is based on SDR techniques and reported data includes the frequency, relative signal strength and received polarisation as well as the callsign. Once you have seen some activity on *Live CQ* you have a choice of replying to a CQ call, or finding a clear frequency in between.

Another excellent source of information is the NOUK web pages [32], a live chat room for EMEers to set up contact schedules, discuss equipment, or observe activity. While having a live chat, you must be careful to exchange the necessary information to complete a QSO exclusively on the radio, so it's best to keep quiet on the chat during a QSO;

For much more information, read the full article on which this short overview is based [33]. Also check the inspiring web pages of G4CCH [34], G4NNS [35], F1EHN [36] and W7GJ [37].

Moonbounce is one of amateur radio's ultimate challenges. If you have a good station for terrestrial VHF/UHF DX, then you are already half way there. As you can see from the foregoing, it won't be easy, but the reward is that every EME QSO will be something to remember.

LOCATORS

Locator squares (originally referred to as 'Maidenhead' squares, having been tabled at a meeting held in that town) formally came into use in 1985.

They are derived by dividing the Earth's surface into 324 'fields' (see Appendix A), each one being 20° of longitude by 10° of latitude, thus dividing the earth into an 18 x 18 grid. These 'fields' are given two-letter indices, 'AA' to 'RR', with the first letter specifying the longitude and the second the latitude, the origin being at the South Pole at 180°W. Thus the field AA runs from 180° to 160°W, 90° to 80°S. North of this is AB, east is BA and so on. The field covering most of the UK (50° to 60°N, 20° to 0°W) is then IO.

These fields are divided into 100 'squares' (they are not really square), each 2° wide and 1° high, labelled from '00' in the south-west corner to '99' in the north-east. The Europe map in Appendix A clearly shows these.

Each of these Locator squares can be further divided into 576 'sub-squares' each one being 5 minutes wide by 2.5

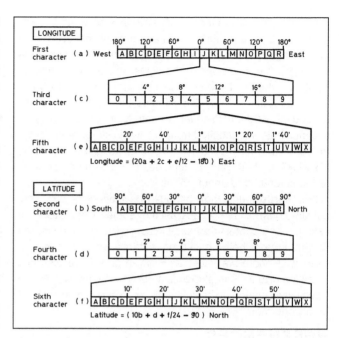

Fig 1: How the Locator system is built up into fields, 'squares' and 'sub-squares'.

minutes high. The sub-squares are labelled using two letters, again the first specifying the longitude and the second the latitude, starting from 'AA' in the south-west corner, and running to 'XX' in the north-east.

A full Locator thus consists of two letters, two numbers and two letters, with a typical reference being IO91IP.

Fig 1 shows how the Locator is built up from fields, squares and sub-squares. It may be noted that all of the longitude-defining characters - the first, third and fifth - run from west to east, while the latitude defining characters - the second, fourth and sixth - go from south to north. In addition, at all levels the east-west size, in degrees, is always twice the north-south size. In distance terms, each sub-square is about 4.6km from south to north. The east-west size varies with latitude, but in the middle of Britain (55°N) it is about 5.3km.

If you take the accuracy of the system as being the farthest you can get from the middle of a sub-square without actually leaving it, this gives a maximum error of about 3.5km (at 55° latitude), which is quite adequate for most normal operation. It is worth noting, though many operators are unaware of this, that the nearer one gets to the equator, the larger are the squares and, conversely, the closer one is to the poles, the smaller they become.

You can find out your Locator by consulting one of the Internet websites which will calculate your Locator from your latitude and longitude [38].

On the air the system should be called simply 'Locator'. For example, you might say "My Locator is IO83QP", or ask of another station, "What is your Locator?". On CW the recommended abbreviation is 'LOC', so that the CW equivalent of "What is your Locator?" is simply "LOC?" The various divisions of the Locator, fields, squares and sub-squares, have just those names. A VHF DX chaser might claim to have worked 300 'squares', or, for the real enthusiast, '20 fields'.

While the six-character Locator system is accurate enough for VHF / UHF use, more accuracy may be necessary for identifying locations and calculating distances and antenna bearings when operating in the higher microwave bands. In 1993 an extended Locator system was approved by the IARU. The 5 minutes wide by 2.5 minutes high sub-squares are divided into 100 'micro-squares' each 30 seconds wide by 15 seconds high and labelled from '00' in the south-west corner to '99' in the north-east. Thus a full micro-locator would be IO91IP37 and at 55° N latitude, the maximum error is reduced ten-fold to about 350m.

It is worth noting that, although developed for VHF use, Locator squares are now also used by some HF operators, for example as a contest exchange in specialist HF contests, the scoring system being based on distance worked. It is also used by LF operators where, as with VHF and above, distance is all-important. Some digital modes such as *WSPR* and *Opera* use Locators to calculate distance and to display them on a world map.

REFERENCES

[1] *The DX Magazine*: www.dxpub.com
[2] *Club Log*: www.clublog.org
[3] Mega DXpeditions: www.gdxf.de/megadxpeditions
[4] *DX World*: www.dx-world.net
[5] *425 DX News*: www.425dxn.org
[6] *OPDX Bulletin*: www.papays.com/opdx.html
[7] *QRZ DX*: www.dxpub.com
[8] *The Weekly DX* and *The Daily DX*: www.dailydx.com
[9] *DX Summit*: new.dxsummit.fi
[10] OH8X Radio Arcala group: www.radioarcala.com
[11] UK Six Metre Group: www.uksmg.org
[12] NCDXF beacons: www.ncdxf.org/beacon/beacon-schedule
[13] *RSGB Yearbook*, published annually, and available from rsgbshop.org
[14] 2m & 70cm beacons: www.mmmonvhf.de/bcn.php
[15] *QRZ*: www.qrz.com
[16] *The Complete DXer*, Bob Locher, W9KNI, Idiom Press 2003.
[17] ON4KST chat rooms: www.on4kst.com/chat/start.php
[18] GQRP Club: www.gqrp.com
[19] *Ethics and Operating Procedures for the Radio Amateur*, John Devoldere, ON4UN, and Mark Demeuleneere, ON4WW: www.arrl.org/files/file/DXCC/Eth-operating-EN-ARRL-CORR-JAN-2011.pdf
[20] *DX Code of Conduct*: www.dx-code.org/english.html
[21] *Up Two - Adventures of a DXpeditioner*, Roger Western, G3SXW, Idiom Press 2003.
[22] *World Licensing and Operating Directory*, Steve Telenius-Lowe, 9M6DXX (PJ4DX), available from www.rsgbshop.org
[23] ON4KST chat rooms: www.on4kst.com/chat/start.php
[24] *Meteor Scatter Operating Procedures*: www.vhfdx.de/ms_howto.pdf
[25] *WSJT*: www.physics.princeton.edu/pulsar/K1JT
[26] http://www.thinkman.com/dimension4/
[27] www.dxmaps.com/emecalendar.html
[28] Newsletters: www.df2zc.de/ and www.k2uyh.com/news.htm
[29] GB3VHF: www.gb3vhf.co.uk/GB3VHFReceiving.html
[30] 'EME operating Guide for 432MHz and Above': www.dl4eby.de/EME_Operating_Procedures.pdf
[31] *Live CQ*: www.livecq.eu/
[32] NOUK: www.chris.org/cgi-bin/jt65emeA
[33] 'An Introduction to Moonbounce', John Lemay, G4ZTR, and John Regnault, G4SWX, *RadCom* Feb-Mar 2014.
[34] www.g4cch.com/
[35] myweb.tiscali.co.uk/g4nns/
[36] www.f1ehn.org/
[37] www.bigskyspaces.com/w7gj/
[38] Grid square calculation: www.amsat.org/cgi-bin/gridconv

WHILE IT IS GREAT FUN to get on the bands and make interesting contacts, there has always been additional pleasure for most amateurs in sending and receiving QSL cards. This goes back to the very earliest days of the hobby and the concept is still very much as it was, though electronic QSLs have replaced conventional cards for an increasing number of operators.

A QSL card is simply a written or printed confirmation of a two-way contact (or of a heard contact in the case of listeners). It serves as a reminder and most amateurs take pleasure in displaying their cards on the shack wall, collating them into albums or, when the collection gets too large, into filing cabinets or boxes. Because QSL cards are a confirmation of a contact, they are also the common currency for claiming amateur radio awards and certificates (though some awards require only a certified extract from your logbook or electronic verification).

This chapter deals with QSLing in some depth, and then takes a quick look at some of the major awards programmes. It is not appropriate to try to mention all awards in these pages. Not only are there far too many of them, and application details change as voluntary awards managers come and go, but awards themselves also come and go, often focused around a specific event. The aim here is to point you to useful sources of information about awards and give you some hints and tips on how to gain awards.

WHAT IS A QSL?

A QSL is a confirmation that a contact has taken place. The name obviously derives from the more formal Q code, QSL "I am acknowledging receipt". For awards purposes or, indeed, for your own records, it can take several forms. It could be a handwritten letter or fax from the station you contacted, or maybe just a rubber stamp and signed confirmation returning a QSL card that you have sent to him. In practice, most amateurs use cards that are postcard sized.

The major requirements are pretty obvious. Firstly, the callsign used, plus name of the DXCC entity somewhere on the card (perhaps as part of the address). Then somewhere for the details of the contact being confirmed - callsign of station worked, date, time, band, mode, signal report. So far so good. If you're going to enter dates in the European format, it's worth the heading reading something like DATE (D-M-Y) or

(DD-MM-YY) or American recipients might misinterpret and be unable to cross check the contact in their log. Time should always be in UTC, but this should be made clear in the heading - TIME (UTC). Again, make the units clear for band, whether metres or MHz. Otherwise the entry "10" could mean 10 metres (28MHz) or 10MHz (30m). Mode should preferably indicate two-way, perhaps by using the heading MODE (2x). This is primarily because most mode-specific awards require both participants in a contact to use the same mode.

What else goes on your QSL? The full address is useful, and if this differs from the station location, then make that clear. Chasers of counties, for example, will get confused if your postal address is, say, Essex, whereas your physical location was, perhaps, in Suffolk. The island name (eg "Great Britain" or "Island of Ireland") is necessary for the IOTA awards and the IOTA reference can also be added. An e-mail address is always useful, though many people change e-mail addresses more often than they reprint QSL cards. WAB square, CQ Zone, Locator, etc are all helpful to at least some of the people who will receive your card.And, of course, any interesting additional material you choose to include about yourself, your station, your club memberships, your town, or whatever. And a "PSE / TNX QSL" tick box, or similar, to indicate to the recipient whether you are looking for his card in return, or that you have already received it (many contest stations these days send out QSL cards automatically, but specifically say they do not want your card in return).

Many amateurs still like to write out their cards by hand and sign them as well, in order to personalise them, but it is common to print the QSO data direct from the computerised log on to a sticky label, and simply allow space on the card to affix the label. Many QSL managers who use this method use a rubber stamp to overprint the label, to confirm authenticity. Many logging programs (see Chapter 4) offer sophisticated QSL management facilities, including printing of labels, ready sorted for the QSL bureau.

QSL cards have become more elaborate over the years as printing techniques have improved, bringing quality colour printing into the sort of price bracket many of us can afford. A decent photograph or some interesting graphics is always nice. Make sure, though, that the recipient's callsign can be read clearly by the sorters at the QSL bureaus, and also have

Two early QSLs. Far left: Bill Corsham, 2UV, sent this card in January 1922. It is now generally acknowledged as being the first card sent confirming a contact, and is thus the first QSL. Left: AC4YN, originally operated by Sir Evan Nepean, G5YN, during the British Political Mission to Lhasa, Tibet, in 1936. Later the same station and callsign was used by two other operators, Sidney Dagg and Reg Fox.

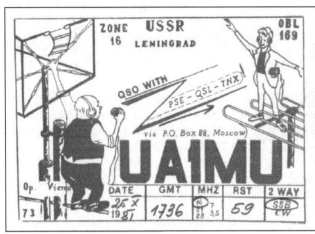

Then and now: a typical Soviet-era Russian QSL card, compared with its 21st century counterpart. The former a very basic design printed in one colour on one side of a poor quality card, and with no operator's address (PO Box 88, Moscow, was the address of the Soviet Union's QSL bureau system). The latter: full colour, printed on both sides of a glossy card and with a striking original design.

space to show, even more clearly, if the card is to be routed via a QSL manager in another country, as otherwise your card may end up at the wrong distant bureau entirely.

The size of QSL cards has become fairly standardised over the years, averaging around 90mm by 140mm, ie postcard size and able to fit into a C6 envelope or similar. Some amateurs, special event stations and DXpeditions are occasionally tempted to produce outsize cards which may look nice on the shack wall, but will almost certainly have to be folded for mailing in most return envelopes, and when sent by the bureau system really do cause problems. So please stick to standard sizes.

Finally, it is useful if any QSLs you have printed allow you to select "SWL Report" instead of "QSO", in order to be able to acknowledge properly any listener reports that come along.

THE QSL BUREAU SYSTEM

When the concept of QSLing first emerged in amateur radio, the usual practice was to mail the card to the station concerned. Undoubtedly this was why early QSL cards adopted the postcard format, as the mailing address could be written on the blank side and the card could be mailed for minimum postal rates. However, as the level of activity started to increase and more cards were being exchanged, national societies started setting up clearing houses for QSL cards: the QSL bureau system. The concept is simple enough. The sender sends cards to his national QSL bureau, where they are then sorted by destination country and bulk mailed to the national society in the country concerned. Similarly, the sender can lodge envelopes with his own national society to collect incoming cards from other amateurs.

The exact way in which the QSL bureau system works varies from society to society, though the IARU lays down guidelines as to how it expects national societies to conduct their part of the process. In the UK, RSGB members are automatically entitled to use the outgoing QSL bureau as part of their RSGB membership. Cards may be sent in bulk to the RSGB QSL bureau, but should be pre-sorted by country prefix to simplify the job of the sorters at the bureau. Incoming

cards are sent to volunteer sub-managers, each of whom handles incoming cards for specific blocks of UK callsigns. Any UK amateur, not only RSGB members, is entitled to lodge pre-paid envelopes with the appropriate sub-manager, in order to receive incoming cards. Normally these envelopes will be mailed when they contain enough cards to use up the postage on the envelope. Alternatively, the recipient can make specific requests, such as mailing an envelope when it contains 10 incoming cards, for example.

The international QSL bureau system handles many millions of cards each year, saving individual amateurs a fortune in postal costs. There are limitations, of course, and users need to be aware of these. First and foremost, from sending a card to receiving one in return can take years. Let's suppose, for example, that you work a station in Brazil and mail your card to the RSGB bureau the following day (though in practice you are likely to wait until you have enough cards to fill an envelope). It may be a matter of weeks before the RSGB has enough cards destined for Brazil to justify sending a package to the Brazilian society. That package will probably be mailed surface (it would be hard to justify the additional cost of airmail to save a few days, when the whole process includes so many inherent delays anyway), and will arrive in Brazil a few weeks later. But the Brazilian amateur himself may not receive it until several weeks after that, when enough incoming cards have arrived for him from around the world. Of course, you may have short-circuited the system by agreeing at the time of the QSO to send each other QSL cards. But, if not, when he receives your card he may write a reply card immediately, but probably won't mail it until he has enough outgoing cards to justify mailing a package. Or he may tackle his bureau QSLing chores once a month or perhaps only once a year. Then, of course, the whole process starts all over again, but in the reverse direction.

The QSL bureaus of many countries that have relatively few amateurs may only despatch cards to other bureaus once or perhaps twice a year, so the delay will be even longer in these cases.

A3	Tonga	S0	Western Sahara	ZA	Albania
A5	Bhutan	S7	Seychelles	ZD7	St Helena
A6	United Arab Emirates	S9	Sao Tome & Principe	ZD8	Ascension
C2	Nauru	ST	Sudan	ZD9	Tristan da Cunha
C5	Gambia	Su	Egypt	3B	Agalega, Mauritius, Rodrigues
C6	Bahamas	T2	Tuvalu		
CN	Morocco	T3	Kiribati	3C0	Pagalu Island
D2	Angola	T5	Somalia	3C0	Equatorial Guinea
D4	Cape Verde	T8	Palau	3DA	Swaziland
E3	Eritrea	TJ	Cameroon	3W	Vietnam
E5	North & South Cook Islands	TL	Central African Republic	3X	Guinea
HH	Haiti	TN	Congo	4J	Azerbaijan
HV	Vatican	TT	Chad	4W	Timor-Leste
J5	Guinea-Bissau	TU	Cote d'Ivoire	5A	Libya
J8	St. Vincent	TY	Benin	5R	Madagascar
KG4	Guantanamo Bay	V3	Belize	5T	Mauritania
KH0	Mariana Island	V4	St. Kitts & Nevis	5U	Niger
KH1	Baker & Howland Islands	V6	Micronesia	5V	Togo
KH4	Midway Island	V7	Marshall Islands	70	Yemen
KH5	Palmyra & Jarvis Islands	VP2E	Anguilla	7P	Lesotho
KH7K	Kure Island	VP2M	Montserrat	7Q	Malawi
KH9	Wake Island	XU	Cambodia	8Q	Maldives
KP1	Desecheo Island	XW	Laos	9L	Sierra Leone
P2	Papua New Guinea	XZ	Myanmar	9N	Nepal
P5	North Korea	YA	Afghanistan	9U	Burundi
PZ	Suriname	Z2	Zimbabwe	9X	Rwanda

Table 1: Countries with no national QSL bureau (source: ARRL). The list would appear to be incomplete, for example it is known that Ethiopia does not have a QSL bureau, yet it does not appear on this official list.

The other major limitation of the QSL bureau system is that many smaller national societies are unable to justify the cost or effort of running a QSL bureau at all. **Table 1** lists those countries believed at the time of writing not have national QSL bureaus (the list is taken from the ARRL website). For amateurs in those countries, the only recourse is to mail direct to them or via their QSL manager, if they have one. Where a station has a QSL manager in a country which has a QSL bureau, there is no problem. Simply make the QSL manager's callsign prominent on the QSL card, indicating that the card should be routed to the QSL manager rather than to the station worked.

Even if a country is not on the list in Table 1, it isn't always safe to assume that the bureau system will work effectively. The national society in a country with few radio amateurs may have neither the funds nor the volunteers to deal with large quantities of cards and, in any case, many of the operations are likely to have been by visitors to the country who have since left, often without a forwarding address and almost always without leaving any funds to cover postage. Most of the cards would eventually be consigned to the bin.

To summarise, other than for the major nations, it is safest to find a direct address or QSL manager if you want to be reasonably certain of getting a return card. Some countries' QSL bureaus restrict incoming cards to those amateurs who are members of the national society (though this goes against IARU guidelines). The countries include those listed in **Table 2.**

For those cards going to countries where the system works effectively, the question is, how do you go about using the QSL bureau? In the UK, RSGB members can bundle up their outgoing cards (sorted by prefix, please) and mail them to: RSGB QSL Bureau, P.O. Box 5, Halifax HX1 9JR, UK. There

are also deposit boxes for QSL cards on the RSGB stand at many of the major conventions and rallies. You are encouraged to write the destination callsign on both sides of the card, to reduce handling times. Full details of how to send cards to the RSGB QSL Bureau can be found on the RSGB web site at [1].

For incoming cards, identify your incoming QSL sub-manager - up-to-date lists appear in the RSGB Yearbook [2] and at [1] - and lodge self-addressed envelopes with sufficient postage, depending on how many incoming cards you are likely to expect. You can mark the envelopes with comments such as "mail after 10 cards" or, otherwise, the sub-manager will mail them when they have reached the weight limit for the postage on the envelope. An important point to note is that UK stamps marked "1st" or "2nd" class continue to be valid after postal rates have increased. You are therefore advised to use these stamps, rather than those with a precise monetary value on them, particularly so if you do not expect to receive cards from the bureau very frequently.

If you do use stamps with a fixed value, don't forget to send extra stamps to your sub-manager when postal rates

3A	Monaco	JA	Japan
9J	Zambia	LA	Norway
CT	Portugal	OZ	Denmark
DL	Germany	RA, UA	Russia
F	France	SM	Sweden
HA	Hungary	SP	Poland
I	Italy	ZS	South Africa

Table 2: Countries that currently deliver QSL cards only to members of that country's national radio society [source: ARRL].

Collage of cards received from QSL managers of DXpeditions and other operations that took place in 2014 and 2015.

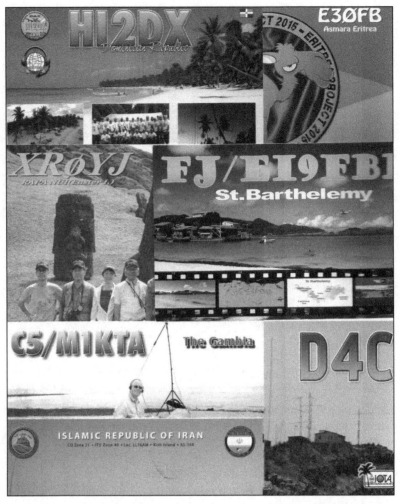

increase. And ensure that the envelopes you leave are large enough and strong enough to cope with the weight and bulk of cards that you are expecting each to carry. This advice may seem obvious, but it is surprising how many amateurs send flimsy or tiny envelopes, or forget, for example, that a postal rate increase has just been announced. The length, breadth and thickness of an item posted in the UK is important along with its weight, and this should be taken into account when buying stamps. Postal charges can be calculated online at [3].

One point often completely overlooked by most amateurs in countries with large amounts of amateur radio activity - such as the UK, Germany, Italy, Russia, the USA, Japan, and many others - is that their card is often not wanted by DX stations. This may come as a bit of a shock to someone who has spent a lot of time and effort having splendid colour QSLs printed at considerable expense, but it is a fact. You may want a card from Singapore, Fiji or Paraguay, but the chances are that the amateur there already has hundreds of QSLs from England and almost certainly will not want yet another one. Even if he is a keen DXer or IOTA chaser (and not all amateurs are), he will still only want one card from each DXCC entity or IOTA group, or perhaps one per band-mode combination. Often, in such countries, incoming bureau cards arrive once or maybe twice a year and if the amateur concerned has been fairly active there can be many hundreds of cards arriving from each country. It is perhaps not surprising if he fails to respond to your particular card or if it takes him several years to do so!

The answer is to use the QSL bureau only if you want a card from another country with a relatively large amateur population. If you desire a card from an amateur in a rare or even only semi-rare country, it is almost always better to QSL direct, rather than to use the bureau system.

DIRECT QSLING & QSL MANAGERS

If you are anxious to receive a QSL card for a particular contact or DXpedition, you will probably want to QSL direct. This may mean directly to the station concerned or, more likely, to a QSL manager: someone who handles the QSLing job for the DX station concerned. In the case of a DXpedition, the need for a QSL manager is obvious, as the DXpedition is a temporary operation from a remote location, but the QSL manager will be someone who is going to be available over a period of time, to deal with QSL requests.

Other DX stations quite often have QSL managers too. There are several reasons. The DX station concerned may be keen to spend as much time on the air as possible, and therefore want to pass the QSLing role to someone with more time available. Many countries also have problems with mail going astray, especially when it becomes known that mail to the person concerned quite often contains IRCs or dollar bills. So a QSL manager will be appointed in a country where this problem is less likely to arise. In some cases the DX station may feel that he simply cannot afford to print and mail QSL cards, and perhaps a well-disposed amateur in the US or Europe will volunteer to take on the responsibility.

Whatever the reason, for you as a DXer the approach to QSLing direct or via a manager is very much the same in every case. Obviously the first task is to determine the QSL manager, where appropriate, and his address. Often the DX station will announce this information at the time of the contact. If not, there are many sources on the Internet such as the well-known 'QRZ' site [4], as well as amateur radio newsletters and magazines. The source you use may include the actual address or you may need to find that elsewhere. There are several online callbooks nowadays, and the online FCC database [5] with the addresses of US amateurs is updated daily. Most DXpeditions have websites where you can find QSL information as well as all kinds of other interesting information. If all else fails, simply Google the callsign you are interested in: almost certainly, if that station has been at all active, you will get several useful hits.

When you send a QSL card direct or to a QSL manager, there are several considerations to bear in mind. Firstly, ensure that your card is correctly filled out. Don't omit the time, or enter it as local time rather than UTC. Ensure that everything can easily be read. Send it along with a self-addressed envelope (sensible size, C6 is suitable for most occasions) and most importantly some form of return postage.

There is endless debate about how to send return postage. Probably the least desirable solution is to send your SAE with local stamps for the country you are mailing to. You may think you know their international postal rates, but they may be about to change, or the QSL manager may actually be intending to mail your card from a different country. International Reply Coupons (IRCs) which are specifically for the purpose of covering return airmail postage from any-where in the world used to be popular but are unfortunately no longer sold at UK Post Offices, although they will still exchange any IRC you might receive for 76p worth of stamps.

The alternative is to include the ubiquitous "green stamps", ie US dollar bills. These are almost universally accepted nowadays, though some countries are very strict about currency of any sort being sent through their mail system, and a few are even more sensitive if that currency is American. Of course, throughout Western Europe and North America, you can expect 'green stamps' to be welcomed with open arms, especially as they are reusable in a way which IRCs aren't. The rising cost of international post in many countries means that one dollar is often now insufficient to cover the cost of a stamp. It is therefore now normal to send $2 with your SAE in order to have a QSL card returned by air mail. Indeed, many amateurs in countries where $1 is less than the cost of a stamp state that, if they only receive $1 with a direct QSL request, the return card will be sent via the bureau system.

Amateurs make many mistakes when sending direct QSL cards, making the QSL manager's job more difficult. For instance, odd-shaped and sized envelopes, QSL cards not completed with the correct details, address labels but no return envelope, putting the return envelope with the fold upwards, so that it gets sliced in half when the outward envelope is opened, asking for confirmations for large numbers of QSOs and enclosing just a couple of dollars for return postage, and so on. Always try to put yourself in the position of the QSL manager, and think about how you can make his task as easy as possible.

Of course, the other side of the coin is that many amateurs do the job very efficiently and also make a point of including an additional donation, knowing that the cost of mounting a DXpedition is always beyond any monies that will be received but that any donation, however modest, will go some way to offsetting those costs and be by way of a 'thank you'.

Beware when sending direct QSL cards to countries where the postal system may be suspect (some South American and African countries have particular problems in this regard). If there is any suggestion that the envelope may contain something of value, then there is a good chance that it will be opened and any currency removed, after which the envelope will probably be dumped. A callsign on the envelope is often the clue that a dishonest postal worker is looking for.

You may decide to send your card registered delivery to be on the safe side, but this can be even more of an invitation to open it up. Amateurs in these countries are usually well aware of any problems, and appoint a QSL manager in North America, Europe, Japan, etc.

ELECTRONIC QSLING

Unsurprisingly, as many activities are delegated to computers nowadays, there is increasing interest in electronic QSLing. Rather than wait months or years for a card to be returned via the QSL bureau, why not send one electronically and, therefore, instantly?

One argument against this is the potential for forgery. The eQSL website [6] sets out to overcome these objections, by requiring users to provide proof of their licence before uploading logs. eQSLs are now accepted for several (but not all) awards schemes.

A rather different form of electronic QSLing is the electronic request for a conventional QSL card. Many DXpeditions and increasingly these days also QSL managers offer the option of requesting conventional QSLs via e-mail or a web-based form. Your QSL cards will come back via the bureau, but you have avoided the delay of sending an outgoing card through the bureau system. A recent development is the possibility of requesting a direct card from a DXpedition or QSL manager via an online form, by making a small donation of, say, $5 using a secure payment service such as *PayPal*. Very few DXpeditions are interested in collecting your QSL card - it would probably only be consigned to the wastepaper basket once it had been dealt with - so the use of e-mail QSL requests and online forms for both bureau and direct QSLing of DXpeditions is likely to become prevalent in the future.

Logbook of The World

Logbook of The World (*LoTW*) [7], introduced in 2004 by the ARRL to support its DXCC Awards Program, addresses the sort of security issues described in the previous section. It does not, however, purport to be a replacement for QSL cards, as it incorporates no mechanism for generating printed cards. Such a mechanism would have the same limitations described in the foregoing; any printed card could just as easily have been printed from some other graphics program. Therefore *LoTW* limits its scope to providing QSO matching between electronic logs, for the purposes of applying for DXCC awards. As such, it complements rather than replaces paper QSLs. Many users may still wish to have traditional QSL cards from DX stations, as a memento of their contact, but may not wish to trust these valued cards to the postal service in order to apply for DXCC awards. Instead, the awards chaser can upload his log to *LoTW*, where any QSOs which match with others on their system, such as the log-

The ARRL's *Logbook of The World* uses electronic QSO 'matches' to confirm contacts for DXCC and certain other awards, in lieu of physical QSL cards.

book of a major expedition which may have been uploaded, will be available to be used in any DXCC submission.

The level of security comes from the way in which the logs are uploaded. Users must first provide proof of their licence. US amateurs can do so via the FCC database [5], but amateurs elsewhere need to provide a copy of their licence and some sort of identity document showing name and address, such as a copy of their passport or driver's licence. Once this proof has been presented to ARRL, the user will be sent a digital certificate, which can then be used to electronically sign all QSOs before they are uploaded to *LoTW*. This electronic signature, based on public key encryption techniques widely used in commerce, prevents the QSO records being tampered with and is the ongoing guarantee of authenticity.

To upload logs, you will need your log to be in Cabrillo (see Chapter 11) or ADIF format. It is then electronically encrypted, with each QSO record individually signed, as mentioned above, and e-mailed to ARRL. You will get an acknowledgement e-mail, confirming that all is in order.

When you apply for additional credits for your DXCC awards, you can mix and match traditional paper QSL cards and matching records on *LoTW*. Charges apply to both, but the charge for dealing with *LoTW* confirmations is lower than for paper QSLs, as less work is required by ARRL staff.

A useful feature of *LoTW* is that, once you are signed up and have your user ID and password, you will be able to see not only what matches you have through *LoTW*, but all your DXCC credits. This means that you no longer have to ask for a printout each year in order to be able to keep track of which new credits you should be applying for.

Notwithstanding the above, the ARRL has confirmed that it will continue to accept traditional QSLs towards DXCC for the indefinite future.

AMATEUR RADIO AWARDS

One of the reasons for collecting QSL cards is to be able to use them for gaining operating awards (though not all awards require QSL cards: some simply require an extract from your log, usually certified by two other amateurs or perhaps club officials). This is not the place to try to list all the operating awards which exist. They are covered in other publications, by K1BV on his excellent web pages [8] (you will need to subscribe), and on a wide range of other Internet sites.

It is, though, worth mentioning the principal RSGB and international awards, as they are often the motivation for becoming serious about HF and / or VHF bands operation, and may become the goal around which you design your station and focus your operating.

Types of Awards

Awards fall into several categories. The following paragraphs discuss some of the major international awards programmes that are well established and keenly fought after. The annual DXCC listing, for example, includes several thousand callsigns. The IOTA Annual Listings have now grown to around 1400 callsigns. To reach the pinnacle of these award programmes takes several sunspot cycles, though the entry levels are set such that even a beginner should be able to gain a certificate with-

in one DXing season (effectively a year). The joy of both these awards is that, having reached that entry level, you can continue to climb the ladder, and gain recognition as your score improves, with something to keep you going for much of your amateur radio lifetime.

Other awards tend to be more specific, geared to a particular event, to a club or to some specialism. Some have a specific time window during which contacts must be made, and then a deadline for applications to be submitted.

Where we move into something of a grey area are those awards sponsored by local radio clubs. Often they are introduced with the best intentions, but then the originator moves on and a committee member is left to deal with the awards who knows little or nothing about them, or does not have the time to process them. In some cases the award requirements are trivial and the charge is quite high and it is apparent that they have been introduced purely as a cynical effort to boost club funds. Fortunately these are in the minority, and many amateurs take great pleasure in collecting awards and displaying them proudly on the shack wall.

Chasing Awards

Obviously how you go about chasing an award will depend on what it is. The main DXCC awards are effectively what Chapter 9 (DX operating) is all about. Of course, you may chase DX without applying for DXCC, but your DXCC contacts will certainly amass you the band and mode counters that you will need for DXCC.

For more specialist awards, though, different considerations apply. While the Cluster has made life much easier than before where it comes to finding specific stations or types of station on the bands, many awards spawn meeting frequencies or regular nets for chasers. A good example is the *CQ US Counties* awards programme [9], very popular in North America but also chased by a number of European amateurs. With 3077 counties in the USA, many of them with few or no resident amateurs, working the lot is a huge undertaking (there are, it should be emphasised, lower awards for working 500 counties, upwards). If you participate in US contests (for example the ARRL International DX Contests) and QSL the stations you

This is to certify that amateur radio station 9M6DXX has made contact with 60 call areas in countries of the Commonwealth of Nations in Her Majesty the Queen's Diamond Jubilee year 2012

An example of a 'short-term' certificate: the RSGB Queen's Jubilee Diamond award, for working 60 Commonwealth call areas during the 60th year of the reign of Queen Elizabeth II (2012).

work, you may well have a few hundred counties confirmed. But the trick to building your score is to join in on the County Hunter nets that take place on 20m. County activators head off in their cars, check into these nets, and may operate from several 'rare' counties in one operating session. If you are checked into the net, you will get a chance to work them all. But otherwise you may never catch these counties in casual day-to-day operation on the bands. Special arrangements are also in place for collecting confirmations for counties, as it would be a huge undertaking to send and receive over 3000 QSL cards just for one award. Similarly, there are well-known gathering places on the bands for other popular awards programmes such as Worked All Britain (WAB) [10] or the RSGB's Islands on the Air (IOTA) [11].

Sometimes an award is for working just one station which may sound odd, but there can be a challenge in doing so in that, wherever that station is located, you will probably have good propagation on some of the bands but will find the chase much harder on other bands.

Awards chasing can actually be quite educational, as you start to learn about Swiss cantons or Japanese prefectures. Sometimes it can be the motivation you need to start holding QSOs in another language. Or an award may be just the incentive you need to try out a new band or mode. The 136kHz award described later in this section may not in itself be the motivation to become active on that band, but achieving it will be an indication that you have made substantial progress on what is a challenging band.

Finding out about Awards

How do you find out about the multitude of short- and long-term awards available? The RSGB awards are all described in the *RSGB Yearbook* [2]. No longer, though, are printed

awards handbooks produced as was once the case, because this is a moving feast, catered for much better by the Internet. There are several awards pages, such as that by AC6V [12], which point you to awards from around the world. K1BV, who used to produce an awards handbook now does the same via his awards page [8], for which there is an annual subscription. However, details of many of the short-term awards are available on his page to all-comers.

National magazines such as the RSGB's *RadCom* carry details of new awards from time to time and obviously those clubs who sponsor particular awards will make efforts to publicise them through the various online bulletins and elsewhere. The various DX bulletins mentioned in Chapter 9, are examples of publications which will carry awards information.

In addition to the foregoing, ON4CAS operates an Awards Reflector on the Internet [13] as a forum for awards chasers to exchange views, gather news and generally share with like-minded enthusiasts.

The main thing to ensure, before you start the time consuming (and costly, if you need to collect QSL cards) chasing of credits for an award, is that you have an up-to-date set of rules. There are tales of people spending long periods chasing an award, only to find that it is has been discontinued or that the requirements have changed. Often the rules can be downloaded from a website.

Applying for Awards

You will have the rules so you may well have an official application form, if there is one. Certainly, for the major awards like DXCC, there is a standard form available. As well as being able to request it by mail, you can also download it from the ARRL website [14]. Many other awards simply ask for a "log extract". Your application should be legible, and

```
                                              John Smith, G9ZZZ
                                              4 High Street
                                              Anytown
                                              England.


            Application for the XXX Award, Class 1


                 Endorsed all 14MHz, all 2 x SSB


   Date          GMT      Callsign    Band      Mode        His report    My report
   1 May 2010    1234     G9AAA       14MHz     2 x SSB     59            59
   2 May 2010    1345     G9ABC       14MHz     2 x SSB     58            57
     ..           ..        ..         ..         ..         ..            ..
     ..           ..        ..         ..         ..         ..            ..
   31 May 2010   1456     G9XYZ       14MHz     2 x SSB     55            55


   I certify that I have complied with my licence regulations.


   John Smith


                                         1 June 2010
     (Signed)                            (Date)
```

Fig 1: Suggested layout of application for an award that does not have its own standard application form.

contain the information appropriate to the award in question, usually date, time, callsign of station worked, band, mode, reports exchanged and the relevant award-specific data (County, Region, Club affiliation, or whatever). If you are applying for a specific class of award, or requiring it to be endorsed ("all CW" or "all 80m" for example), then make this clear in your application.

Quite often the rules will ask for your application to be countersigned by one, or even two, independent persons. Sometimes these can be any other amateurs, sometimes the rules ask for a club official to do so, sometimes it must the Awards Manager of your national society. The RSGB's Awards Manager can be e-mailed at the address at [15]. What they are certifying is that they have checked your application against your log or, if the rules require it, that they have seen the QSL cards relevant to the application. There are some awards which require you to send the QSL cards to the issuing body, but very few do, as most amateurs are reluctant to send their cards abroad, in case they are mislaid in the postal system.

A typical home-made application is shown in **Fig 1**. Always remember to show your own name, callsign and return address. Also an e-mail address if available, so that the awards manager can contact you if anything in your application is unclear.

There is a charge for most awards, usually quite modest and intended primarily to cover printing and mailing costs. Note how this should be paid. Usually there are several options, nowadays most likely to include dollars and euros. Take care if sending cash through the mail: electronic means of funds transfer such as *PayPal* are now becoming more commonplace.

Now your application is ready to mail. Again, check that the mailing address hasn't changed. Most awards managers are volunteers and the position is likely to change hands from time to time. Ideally, send an e-mail prior to mailing your application, to do a final check. When all is well, put your application in the mail and wait for that nice certificate to arrive.

DXCC AWARDS PROGRAMME

The ARRL's 'DX Century Club' (DXCC) awards programme is one of the oldest and most respected in the world. The basic DXCC certificate is awarded to those who can show confirmations - either QSL cards or matches on the *Logbook of The World (LoTW)* system - from a minimum of 100 'entities' on the DXCC List. The DXCC List is based on Clinton B DeSoto's, W1CBD, 1935 *QST* article 'How to Count Countries Worked, A New DX Scoring System'. DeSoto's article discussed problems DXers had in determining how to count the DX, or entities, they had worked. He presented the solution that has worked successfully for succeeding generations of DXers. In DeSoto's words: "The basic rule is simple and direct: Each discrete geographical or political entity is considered to be a country." This rule has stood the test of time - from the original list published in 1937, to the ARRL DXCC List of today. DeSoto never intended that all DXCC "countries" would be countries in the traditional sense of the word. Rather, they

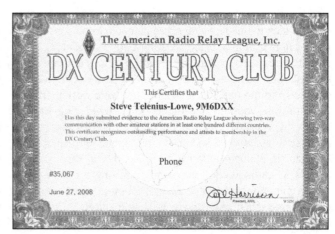

The basic DX Century Club - DXCC - certificate for working and confirming 100 entities on the DXCC List (in this case for Phone contacts only).

are the distinct geographic and political entities which DXers seek to contact. Individual achievement is measured by working and confirming the various entities comprising the DXCC List.

The DXCC List has been the standard for DXers around the world for more than 75 years, although the criteria for inclusion on the DXCC List have been changed over time. The List remains unchanged until an entity no longer satisfies the criteria under which it was originally added, at which time it is moved to the 'Deleted List'. Many entities have come and gone over the years. For example, the former East Germany ceased to be a separate entity upon reunification and was moved to the Deleted List, whereas the former Yugoslavia now consists of the DXCC entities of Serbia (YU), Croatia (9A), Slovenia (S5), Macedonia (Z3), Bosnia & Herzegovina (E7) and Montenegro (4O).

The DXCC awards programme has grown from a single award to a whole family of awards, by mode and band (see sidebar).

All stations must be contacted from within the same DXCC entity and must be made using callsigns issued to the same licensee. Therefore you can 'feed' a single DXCC award from several different callsigns: for example if you start DXCC as a Foundation licensee, progress through the Intermediate licence and eventually upgrade to an Full licence all the contacts made with the M6 and 2E0 callsigns can be counted towards your M0 DXCC award. However, if you start your DXCC in England, but then move to Scotland, you must start DXCC all over again.

Contacts made with legally licensed, remotely controlled stations are allowed to be used for DXCC credit. DXing ethics, and the use of remote stations, were dealt with in Chapter 9, but the ARRL has made the following comments on this matter:

"Issues concerning remotely controlled operating and DXCC are best dealt with by each individual carefully considering the ethical limits that he / she will accept for his / her DXCC and other operating awards. As the premier operating award in amateur radio, DXCC draws intense scrutiny from its participants. As DX chasers climb up the standings there will be increased attention given to these achievements and the

The different types of DXCC awards available

Except where otherwise stated, all are available for contacts made from 15 November 1945 onwards.

a) **Mixed**

b) **Phone** (confirmations for cross-mode contacts for this award must be dated September 30, 1981, or earlier.)

c) **CW** (contacts must be made using CW since 1 January 1975. Confirmations for cross-mode contacts for this award must be dated 30 September 1981, or earlier. CW contacts dated 31 December 1974 or before are credited as Mixed mode.)

d) **Digital** (contacts can include QSOs using any / all digital modes, in any combination (except CW). Digital modes include RTTY, PSK-31, JT65, etc and any modes that are only machine-readable, and any that use computer sound card technology, with the exception of digital voice, which counts for Phone.)

e) **160m**

f) **80m**

g) **40m**

h) **30m**

i) **20m**

j) **17m**

k) **15m**

l) **12m**

m) **10m**

n) **6m**

o) **2m**

p) **70cm**

q) **Satellite** (contacts must be made using satellites since 1 March 1965. Confirmations must indicate satellite QSO. Satellite contacts do not count towards any awards noted in a) to p) above.)

r) **Five-Band DXCC** (5BDXCC): The 5BDXCC certificate is available for working and confirming 100 current DXCC entities (deleted entities don't count for this award) on each of the following five bands: 80, 40, 20, 15 and 10m. The 5BDXCC is endorsable for these additional bands: 160, 30, 17, 12, 6 and 2m. 5BDXCC qualifiers are eligible for an individually engraved plaque.

s) **The DXCC Challenge Award** is available for working and confirming at least 1000 band-entities on any amateur bands, 160 to 6m (except 60m). Plaques can be endorsed in increments of 500 entities. Deleted entities do not count for this award. QSOs for the 160, 80, 40, 30, 20, 17, 15, 12, 10 and 6m bands qualify for this award. Confirmations on bands with less than 100 entities are acceptable for credit for this award. Certificates are not available for this award.

t) **The DeSoto Cup** is presented to the DXCC Challenge leader as of 31 December each year. Only one cup will be awarded to any single individual. A medal will be presented to a repeat winner in subsequent years. Medals will also be awarded to the second and third place winners each year.

u) **Honor Roll**: To qualify, you must have a total confirmed entity count that places you among the numerical top ten DXCC entities total on the current DXCC List (eg if there are 340 current DXCC entities, you must have at least 331 entities confirmed). Deleted entities do not count towards the DXCC Honor Roll. Available for Mixed, Phone, CW and Digital scores.

v) **Number 1 Honor Roll**: To qualify for a Mixed, Phone, CW or Digital, you must have worked and confirmed every entity on the current DXCC List.

owner of these achievements needs to be comfortable standing behind his / her award and numbers. Peer attention has always been a part of awards chasing, of course, but in these times with so many awards and so many players it is more important than ever to 'play the game' ethically.

"Technological advances, while welcome, also add to the difficulty in defining rules for DXCC, but the intent of the rules is what is important. It is never OK to remotely use a station outside of the 'home DXCC entity' to add to the home-entity DXCC totals - just as it is never OK for you to ask someone else at another station in another place to make QSOs for you. Remotely controlled stations must be properly licensed if they are to count for DXCC. It will continue to be up to the operator to decide what types of legal remote control operating he / she will use (if any) to contribute to an operating award."

It used to be considered impossible to work all of the DXCC entities, because in the past some countries such as China and Albania did not allow amateur radio under any circumstances. The last such country was North Korea, which has permitted a small number of acceptable operations, most notably that by P5/4L4FN in 2001 - 2002. The result is that many DXers who have been on the air for long enough now have all current DXCC entities worked and confirmed but, of course, they can continue the chase by repeating the process on other bands and modes. The 2m DXCC must be the toughest of them all, only possible if you exploit every available mode including moonbounce.

Full details of the DXCC awards programme and how to apply for the awards can be found on the ARRL website [14]. If you are applying from the UK, note that you do not need to send your QSL cards to the ARRL in the USA as there are UK 'DXCC Field Representatives' who will check the cards for you (and don't forget you can also gain credits for matches via *Logbook of The World*). The UK DXCC Field Representatives are (if you live in England):

• Ian Capon, G0KRL, Northview, Barway Road, Barway, Soham, Cambs CB7 5UB; (e-mail: g0krl@arrl.net)

or, for the rest of the United Kingdom:

• Rob Ferguson, GM3YTS, 19 Leighton Avenue, Dunblane FK15 0EB; (e-mail: gm3yts@btinternet.com).

Requests for information, application forms, queries etc should be sent to: Fred Handscombe, G4BWP, by e-mail [16].

Often, one or more of these volunteers will be available at major conventions and rallies, so that you can have your cards checked on the spot.

ISLANDS ON THE AIR (IOTA)

Among awards that stimulate daily activity on the HF bands, two stand out head and shoulders above all others - DXCC for working country entities, and IOTA for contacting island groups. The programmes are similar in character - both are international in coverage, both have a strong rule structure and neither is open-ended. Moreover, in practical terms they complement and strengthen each other because activity to promote one often provides valid contacts for the other.

IOTA, or the Islands On The Air Programme to give it its full title, was created in 1964. It was taken over by the RSGB in

The RSGB Islands On The Air Programme is second only to DXCC in terms of the numbers of participants world-wide.

100 Islands of the world	Asia
200 Islands of the world	Europe
300 Islands of the world	North America
400 Islands of the world	Oceania
500 Islands of the world	South America
600 Islands of the world	Arctic Islands
700 Islands of the world	British Isles
800 Islands of the world	West Indies
900 Islands of the world	World Diploma
1000 Islands of the world	
1100 Islands of the world	750 Islands Plaque of
Africa	Excellence
Antarctica	1000 Islands Trophy

Table 3: The many categories of IOTA awards will suit all levels of activity and any location. Full details can be found at [11] and in the *IOTA Directory*.

1985, at the request of its founder, the late Geoff Watts, a leading British short wave listener. It was already a favourite for many DXers and its popularity has grown each year, not only among ever-increasing numbers of island chasers but also among a rapidly expanding band of amateurs attracted by the possibilities for operating portable from islands. For both it is a fun pastime adding much enjoyment to on-the-air activity.

The basic building block for IOTA is the IOTA Group. The oceans' islands have been corralled into some 1200 IOTA groups with, for reasons of geography, varying numbers of 'counters', ie qualifying islands, in each. Only in very few cases do the rules of IOTA allow single islands to count separately, DXCC island entities (such as Barbados) being one. The number of groups is now capped and further changes are expected to be minimal.

Each group activated has been issued with an IOTA reference number, for example EU-005 for Great Britain, OC-001 for Australia. Part of the fun of IOTA is that it is an evolving programme with new groups being activated for the first time. Currently just over 1100 have so far been activated.

The objective, for the island chaser, is to make radio contact with at least one counter in as many of these groups as possible and, for the DXpeditioner, to provide island contacts. A wide range of separate certificates, graded in difficulty, is currently available for island chasers as well as two prestigious awards for high achievement (see **Table 3**). Applicants may be any licensed radio amateur (or SWL on a 'heard' basis) who has had confirmed contacts with the required number of IOTA Groups. All of the categories are for all bands, however some are also open to those operating on 50MHz and above but with different requirements.

The *IOTA Directory* [17], details all of the rules and gives a full listing of IOTA groups, together with the names of 15,000 qualifying islands.

Applicants for the award should prepare and submit their

applications electronically on the Internet. Full details of the procedure and a list of checkpoints can be found on the IOTA website. After signing off your application on-line for processing by your checkpoint, you should immediately send him your cards by post and the appropriate checking fee.

Island Chasing

1000 or more IOTA Groups may seem an enormous target. If you are a long-time DXer who has worked it all and are looking for something new, you will already have amassed a very respectable IOTA score from among your DXCC contacts. If, however, you are new to the bands or one of the many amateurs who adopt a more relaxed approach to their operating, you can take full advantage of a very high level of IOTA activity, comprising easy and semi-rare groups, to launch you on your way. Well over 600 IOTA groups are usually activated over a three-year period with, during a typical summer weekend, some 20 - 25 groups being heard around the IOTA meeting frequencies. An enthusiast should be able to gain the IOTA Plaque of Excellence for working 750 groups in about six years, operating mainly at weekends.

IOTA is one of the few award programmes that has an annual Honour Roll and other performance listings. These create a great deal of interest when they are published. Many IOTA enthusiasts are more interested in participating in these listings than in collecting the certificates. All you need to enable you to participate is the basic IOTA 100 certificate.

Operating from an Island

Many amateurs are fortunate enough to live on an island and to be able to give out an IOTA every time they make a contact. Others are not so lucky. For both there is the lure of operating portable from a rare or rarer group - the fun of being at the other end of a pile-up for a few days. Many islands lie within a few hours' reach and, subject to the availability of suitable equipment, could be put on the air relatively easily.

Those amateurs lucky enough to be able to activate a rare or semi-rare IOTA group can expect to generate huge pile-ups with thousands of contacts during even a short two to three day period. Rare groups are not all remote and difficult to

The basic IOTA '100 Islands of the World' certificate.

The *RSGB IOTA Directory*, published in 2014 to mark the 50th anniversary of the founding of the IOTA programme.

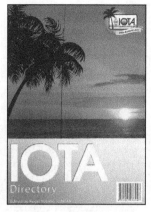

access. Even in Europe and North America there are many that are needed by the chasers. For those interested, a list of most-wanted IOTA groups in each continent, ranked by rarity, appears in the *IOTA Directory* [17] or can be viewed on the IOTA website [11].

Finding IOTA Stations

Nobody and no group in amateur radio is entitled to reserved frequencies, but the IOTA community has adopted a number of 'meeting frequencies' which island stations are encouraged to use when they are free - and to operate close to, without causing interference, if they are occupied. The frequencies are 3755, 7055, 14260, 18128, 21260, 24950, 28460 and 28560kHz on SSB and 3530, 10115, 14040, 18098, 21040, 24920 and 28040kHz on CW. No specific frequency has been nominated for 7MHz CW, but it is recommended that operations should include a frequency above 7025kHz when the band is open to North America.

Additionally, the RSGB IOTA Contest now attracts more than 2000 entries so it provides an opportunity annually, during the last weekend of July, to work large numbers of rare and semi-rare IOTA Groups. The IOTA Contest rules and results are available from the RSGB Contest Committee website [18].

Sources of IOTA Information

RSGB IOTA's website [11] and the linked IOTA Manager's website [19], between them, provide a host of useful information including up to date news of IOTA activity. The RSGB IOTA website allows you to search the island listings by IOTA group number or island name - and returns the relevant listing together with details of rarity and past and future operations.

SOME OTHER MAJOR AWARDS

Worked All States

Another popular ARRL awards programme is Worked All States. The name is self-explanatory. There are nine distinct awards in the programme, covering the various HF bands, 160, SSTV, RTTY, digital modes and satellite. For UK amateurs, the toughest aspect is often finding those elusive contacts with Alaska (KL7) and Hawaii (KH6) especially, say, on 160m, but some of the mid-Western states can be tough, too, with relatively little amateur radio activity compared with, say, the states of the eastern seaboard [14].

VUCC

The ARRL's VUCC awards are available to amateurs worldwide for working grid squares on the VHF, UHF and microwave bands. On 50MHz, 144MHz, and satellite the minimum requirement is 100 squares, but the requirement reduces on the higher bands. As with DXCC and WAS, full rules are available from the ARRL web site [14].

Worked All Continents

The IARU's Worked All Continents (WAC) award is available in the UK via the RSGB. It is available to any RSGB member who can produce evidence of two-way contacts with amateur stations located in each of the six continents: Europe, Africa, Asia, North America, South America and Oceania. Full details are in the *RSGB Yearbook* [2].

Worked All Zones

The Worked all Zones Award, and 5-Band Worked All Zones, are run by the US magazine *CQ*. For the purposes of the award, the world is divided into 40 zones (not to be confused with the 75 ITU zones) which are roughly of similar size. A rule of thumb is that working all 40 zones is of a similar degree of difficulty to working 200 countries, and it is not unknown for contest stations to work all zones in a weekend, even on a single band. But the award remains a worthwhile challenge and the 5-Band WAZ award is a very tough one indeed. Managing contacts with all 40 zones on 80m is a major exercise, and a huge achievement when completed. Rules are available from the *CQ* magazine website [9].

OTHER RSGB AWARDS

In addition to the Islands on the Air Programme, the RSGB issues a wide range of operating awards for both HF and VHF / UHF / Microwave operation. The rules in full, together with up to date information on all of the RSGB's awards can be found in the *RSGB Yearbook* [2] and on the RSGB web site at [15].

RSGB LF - HF Awards

RSGB 136kHz Award: This recognises achievements in both transmission and reception on the 136kHz band. It is available to those making two-way contacts with five countries, to SWLs and to those making cross-band contacts involving 136kHz.

The IARU Region 1 Award: For contacts with countries that are members of IARU Region 1. This award is available in 3 classes for contacts with 40, 60 and all member countries, with endorsements for single band or mode contacts available

The Commonwealth Century Club (CCC): A series of awards for contacts with call areas of the Commonwealth of Nations. The basic award is for 100 call areas, with a Supreme Award for contacting all call areas. There is also a 5-band (80, 40, 20, 15, 10m) award in five classes with endorsements for WARC and 160m bands

Worked ITU Zones (W ITU Z): Requires contacts with stations located in ITU Zones. The basic award is for working 70 of the 75 ITU Zones, with a Supreme Award for contacting all 75 Zones. There is also a 5-band (80, 40, 20, 15, 10 m) award

70MHz	20/4	144MHz	40/10	432MHz	30/6
70MHz	25/6	144MHz	60/15	432MHz	40/10
70MHz	30/8	144MHz	80/18	432MHz	50/13
70MHz	35/8	144MHz	100/20	432MHz	60/15
70MHz	35/10	144MHz	125/20	432MHz	70/15
70MHz	40/8	144MHz	150/20	432MHz	80/15
70MHz	40/10	144MHz	175/20	432MHz	90/15
70MHz	45/8	144MHz	200/30	432MHz	100/15
70MHz	45/10	144MHz	225/30	432MHz	110/15
70MHz	50/8	144MHz	250/35	432MHz	120/18
70MHz	50/10	144MHz	275/35	432MHz	130/18
70MHz	55/8	144MHz	300/40	432MHz	140/20
70MHz	55/10	144MHz	325/40	432MHz	150/20
		144MHz	350/45	432MHz	160/20
		144MHz	375/45	432MHz	170/23
		144MHz	400/50	432MHz	180/25
		144MHz	425/50		
		144MHz	450/50		
		144MHz	475/50		

Table 4: The RSGB Squares and Counties Awards. To qualify, applicants need contacts with the specified number of Locator squares (first figure) and countries (second figure).

in five classes with additional endorsements for WARC and 160m bands.

RSGB VHF - UHF - Microwave Awards

50MHz awards: Three awards are available for this band: Two-way Countries (minimum 10 countries), DX Countries (minimum 25 countries, cross-band permitted) and 50MHz Squares (minimum 25 Locator squares).

Squares and Countries Awards: These are intended to mark successful VHF / UHF achievement. The title of each award gives the number of locator squares and countries needed to qualify for the basic award (see **Table 4**). Stickers are available for larger number of squares and countries.

Foundation Award: Available for contacts made by Foundation licensees in the first year of their licence on the 50, 70, 144 and 432MHz bands.

Intermediate Award: This award is for holders of 'Intermediate' callsigns only and is designed to encourage activity in the CW, SSB and FM simplex sections of the 50, 144, 432 and 1296MHz bands.

RSGB Awards for Listeners

All RSGB Awards are open to short wave listeners but the **DX Listeners Century Award (DXLCA)** is especially for SWLs. The basic award is for obtaining QSL cards from amateur stations in 100 countries, with subsequent endorsements for additional countries.

VHF AWARDS

It is worth mentioning, before closing this chapter, that most awards and certificates for HF operating can also be gained for work on the higher frequencies, though this is usually much more difficult. For example, a Worked All Continents award is easy for the average 14 or 21MHz operator to acquire, but a 432MHz WAC is another thing altogether, implying the use of

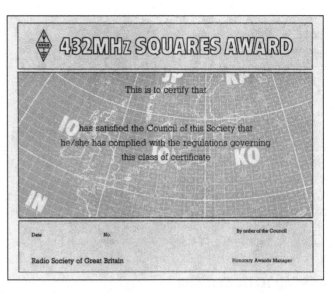

One of the series of RSGB VHF / UHF / microwave awards.

moonbounce techniques, and possibly years of technical refinement. Of course, 6m is a different matter and, at least at times of peak solar activity, it is realistic for an active operator to be able to achieve the 6m DXCC award, or to collect enough islands to qualify for one of the IOTA awards.

As far as VHF-specific awards are concerned, in addition to the RSGB awards and the ARRL's VUCC mentioned above, many other organisations issue awards aimed at VHF / UHF and microwave operators, and many of these will be achievable by UK-based amateurs.

REFERENCES

[1] RSGB QSL Bureau: http://rsgb.org/main/operating/qsl-bureau/

[2] *RSGB Yearbook*, RSGB, published annually. Available from www.rsgbshop.org

[3] UK postage prices: www.royalmail.com/price-finder

[4] QRZ website (online callbook): www.qrz.com

[5] FCC database: http://wireless2.fcc.gov/UlsApp/UlsSearch/searchLicense.jsp

[6] eQSL: www.eqsl.cc

[7] *Logbook of The World*: www.arrl.org/lotw

[8] K1BV awards information: www.dxawards.com

[9] CQ magazine awards: http://www.cq-amateur-radio.com/cq_awards/index_cq_awards.html

[10] Worked All Britain: http://wab.intermip.net/default.php

[11] IOTA website: www.rsgbiota.org

[12] AC6V awards site: www.ac6v.com/hamawards.htm

[13] ON4CAS reflector: https://groups.yahoo.com/neo/groups/HAM_awards/info

[14] Awards on ARRL website: www.arrl.org/awards

[15] RSGB awards pages: http://rsgb.org/main/operating/amateur-radio-awards/

[16] Fred Handscombe, G4BWP, e-mail fredch@homeshack.freeserve.co.uk

[17] *IOTA Directory*, ed Roger Balister, G3KMA, 2014 edition, RSGB. Available from www.rsgbshop.org

[18] RSGB IOTA Contest: www.rsgbcc.org/hf/iota.shtml

[19] RSGB IOTA Manager: www.g3kma.dsl.pipex.com

L IKE DXING, CONTEST OPERATION appeals to our competitive instincts. Contests are sporting competitions between amateur stations on specific bands and modes according to published rules. In some countries, particularly in Eastern Europe, the activity is referred to as 'radiosport', and this term has now caught on in the West. In some countries radiosport enjoys the same sort of recognition as other sports activities; indeed the Chinese national amateur radio society is even called the China Radio Sports Association. The main difference from other sports is that it is generally undertaken from the privacy of our own homes and radio stations, although the World Radiosport Team Championship [1], held approximately every four years, is an attempt to bring the world's top contesters together to compete on the closest possible radio equivalent to a level playing field.

The nice thing about radio contests is that, like public marathon races, although there will also be serious competitors, there is room for everyone, competitor or casual participant, to take part and enjoy the fun. In practice, the casual participants invariably outnumber the serious entrants by a large margin. But there is a lot to be said for building up your contesting skills as the years go by. Serious contesters spend countless hours improving their stations, practising their operating skills and even undertaking physical exercise in order to be able to maintain high levels of concentration for many hours at a time.

BENEFITS OF CONTESTING

Contests attract flak from some sections of the amateur radio population, usually because they have a habit of filling up the bands at weekends, at just the time that many amateurs want to get on the bands and chat with their friends. But the very fact that the major contests tend to fill up the bands is evidence that contesting is a very popular activity. It is also one of the growth areas of amateur radio. The *CQ* World Wide DX contests ('*CQ WW*') [2] are undoubtedly the biggest events each year. A bulletin issued by the *CQ WW* Contest Committee on 20 August 2009 stated, "In spite of the Sun's reluctance to produce new sunspots, contest activity continues to grow at an unparalleled rate. The 2008 *CQ* WW contests occurred with the solar flux about as low as it can get. In spite of challenging conditions, over 10,000 contesters submitted logs. The *CQ* WW is a fantastic competition which brings out the best in amateur radio: team work, station construction, antenna design, propagation knowledge and

You don't have to be a 'big gun' for contesting, but it helps as VY2GQ's Commonwealth Contest station (VY2TT) shows.

operating skills. Just turn on your radio during the . . . CQ WW and you can join in the fun. Once you listen to the bands during the CQ WW, you will be hooked and guaranteed to have a good time."

There may be arguments that there are too many contests on our bands, but the truth is that most are short, geographically-limited, events which have little impact on other band activity. And if you really want to avoid contests, the 30, 17 and 12m bands are kept contest-free at all times. On the VHF bands, contests are often very welcome, bringing activity to what might otherwise be a dead band.

And this is, at the basic level, why contests appeal. They bring about a level of activity which guarantees that there will be stations about for you to work. That may be general activity, or it may be specific to a particular band, mode or country. For example, if you are chasing US states for the Worked All States award, the ARRL International DX Contests are an ideal opportunity. Not only will there be lots of US activity, looking for contacts outside the US, but US stations include their state as part of the contest exchange, so you know immediately which state you have worked. When the PSK31 mode started to become popular with datamodes enthusiasts, activity was low and you could call CQ for hours without finding another station equipped for the mode. So some short contests were introduced, with the result that PSK31 operators could go on the bands, knowing that other like-minded enthusiasts would be on at the same time. This helped to build interest in the mode to the critical level needed to ensure its ongoing success.

So contests help to create activity on the bands, which is great if you are chasing countries, islands, Swiss cantons, or whatever. There will undoubtedly be one or more contests each year which bring on to the bands the very stations you are looking for.

For those of a competitive disposition, contests are obviously a way of enjoying competition in the context of amateur radio. This is no different to most other hobbies. Angling competitions, photographic competitions; every group of enthusiasts tends to find ways in which individuals can compare themselves with fellow enthusiasts and measure their progress as the years go by. Of course, DXing is also a competitive activity, but one which is much longer-term. It will take many years to build up a serious squares total on 2m, or achieve DXCC Honor Roll on the HF bands. But a contest is a defined activity, with a clear start and finish time, so that even the busiest people can plan their diaries to be available for the duration.

Surprising as it may seem to anyone who hasn't actually participated in a contest, contests are also social occasions. Admittedly, in a major HF contest, where the winners are likely to be averaging 100 - 200 contacts an hour for the whole of the event, there isn't much time for an exchange of pleasantries, though if you know the amateur who calls you, there is usually time for a quick "Hello Steve" or whatever. In the less frenetic events, which includes most VHF contests and quite a few of the HF ones, there is more than enough time to exchange greetings without adversely prejudicing your final score. To this extent, contesting is more sociable than

DXing, where everyone sits in the same pile-up calling the DX stations, so the chasers never get to speak to one another. When you contest regularly, you will soon get to know the regular participants, and there is a level of recognition, even if you aren't always aware of their name. And, of course, there is always the opportunity to be part of a multi-operator team, which involves a great deal of camaraderie, as well as being ideal for picking up operating and technical skills from more experienced contesters.

Contests are also an ideal focus for developing our stations and our operating skills. If a DXpedition is active for a couple of weeks, then provided you follow the sort of advice offered in Chapter 9, and have a half-decent station, you should eventually be able to work them, even if you have to spend an hour or two in the pile-ups. But a contester doesn't have that sort of time to spare in an event which may be only 12 or 24 hours long in total. He wants to be able to call stations and work them on the first or second call, if at all possible. So he will squeeze every decibel out of his station, focusing on the antenna system, feeder cables, and everywhere that improvements are possible. And on the operating side, while at first sight it may seem that contesters simply sit at the radio saying "5914" or whatever, there's a whole lot more to both the strategy and the tactical side to consider, as well as the actual operating itself, as this chapter will try to show.

The time and effort put in by contesters to improve their stations and operating skills have a spin off into other aspects of the hobby. In emergency situations, contesters have on several occasions come to the fore. Their stations are usually able to put out a stronger signal and hear a weaker signal than those of day-to-day 'ragchewers' and DXers. Their operating skills are more honed to short, concise, accurate exchanges of information. And they are physically able to maintain a high level of operating skill over long hours in front of the radio.

If ever there was a clear focus to the self-training, which is one of the major justifications for our hobby, then contesting is it.

THE CHALLENGE OF CONTESTING

Listening to a contest in progress, it is easy to assume that it is simply a matter of calling CQ and exchanging reports, or tuning the bands and calling stations to do the same. But like most competitive activities in life, there is much more to it than this. Every contest has a unique set of rules, and radio propagation is a constantly changing phenomenon, affected by the sunspot cycle, time of day, solar disturbances, etc. So every contest requires a particular strategy, determined by its scoring and multiplier structure, but entrants also need to be flexible, ready to respond to band conditions and activity on the day. This is what makes contests fun; the mix of skill and chance.

For example, in the RSGB National Field Day (NFD), 10m and 160m contacts count double points, so savvy entrants will be sure to check these bands at every opportunity, because even a handful of extra contacts on them could make a big difference to the final placing. Missing a short Sporadic E opening on 10m could cost your group several places in the final listing. So before the contest you will have made sure you have a radio and antenna system which can change bands very quickly to check and, if necessary, start to operate on 10m. When the contest is in progress you will translate that into practice, remembering to check 10m even when you appear to have a reasonable QSO rate on, say, 15m. Similarly, preparing for a summer 6m contest, you will be hoping for some Sporadic E openings, but preparing for the eventuality that you have to make every contact the hard way. Who knows, the day may come when propagation favours your particular location, your equipment performs faultlessly for once, and everything falls into place for a great contest score that brings a certificate or plaque for the shack wall.

HOW TO TAKE PART

Contests are organised by national societies, clubs, magazines, even individuals. Some are designed to appeal on a local level, or perhaps are aimed at beginners as a means of improving their operating skills. Others are truly global in scope, running for up to 48 hours, demanding the most of both station and operator. So the first question you need to ask yourself is what sort of event appeals? Many amateurs who are members of a local radio club have their first experience of contesting during a Field Day event. In the UK there are HF Field Days, both CW and SSB, and the annual multimode VHF Field Day. All are geared round the idea of being able to set up and operate in emergency conditions, so you are only allowed to move on to the site 24 hours or less before the contest, and may not use mains power. Some clubs take Field Days very seriously indeed. Others use them as a social occasion, an occasion for club members and friends to get together for a barbecue and some operating. For your first Field Day, you may be asked just to help out, and do some of the heavy lifting involved in setting up the station and antennas. Or you may get to do some operating. But whatever your level of participation, you will undoubtedly find it a valuable learning experience.

Alternatively, you may be pressed into, for example, taking part in one of the RSGB Club Championship events, short (90-minute) single-band contests where even the most modest score contributes to your local club's total in the final listings. Most countries have similar events. Hopefully, one of the other club members will walk you through what is required,

and probably one of the committee members will be designated to collate and submit the logs.

It is important to note that you do not have to preregister in any way to take part in a contest: this is perhaps one of the commonest misconceptions. If you tune around the bands and hear a contest in progress, then by all means start to make a few contacts. It's a great way of getting your feet wet. Call one of the participants who doesn't appear to be too busy at the time. When he answers you, with a contest report and exchange, be prepared to ask him what he needs from you in return by way of a contest report. Once you have an idea of what's going on, make some more contacts. You don't need to worry about how to send in an entry at this stage, just log the contacts in the way you would any other day-to-day contact.

Incidentally, one of the joys of contest operating for some amateurs is that, because they are for short periods only, it is sometimes possible to put up temporary antennas that far exceed anything you could leave up on a permanent basis. A US amateur living in the UK some years ago was in a rented house on a housing estate where no external antennas were permitted, but on contest weekends he put up a 30ft mast, topped by an HF tribander and enjoyed great success. There were no planning issues as this was a very temporary installation, similar to putting up a marquee for the weekend.

TYPES OF CONTEST

Once you are ready to think about participating a little more seriously, you will want to prepare yourself before the event. Every contest is different, quite deliberately so, to make for interest and variety. They differ in who can contact whom, they differ in the scoring system, they differ in length, in the modes and power levels, even antennas, you can employ, and they are at different times of the year which makes for a variety of different propagation experiences. Most are at weekends, obviously to avoid clashes with work and other commitments, but some short events take place on weekday evenings to encourage band activity. Some are specifically aimed at, for example, portable operation (Field Days are one example, but the popular VHF Backpackers events are another).

Contests also range from domestic events, where you will mainly be working other stations in your own country, to fully-fledged international events. The former are usually organised by national radio societies, or by other local and national clubs and bodies. The major international contests have a much higher profile, though again are organised by national societies or, in some cases, by magazines (the *CQ* contests being the best-known example). The smaller domestic events are usually the best place to cut your teeth, as they are less intimidating than the big international events. Neophyte contesters sometimes complain, for example, at the CW speeds being used by most contesters in the *CQ* WW DX CW Contest. But several of the RSGB's domestic CW contests have a 'QRS corral', where participants are encouraged to slow their speed and look for contacts with less-experienced operators. If you were interested in motor

Tony Collett, G4NBS operating in VHF NFD [Photo: G0LCM].

racing you wouldn't expect to start at the Formula 1 level, and it's a little bit the same.

Whatever your particular interest, by band, mode, etc, and whatever your level of proficiency, there will almost certainly be contests suited to you. So do take the plunge.

WHERE TO START?

The first step is to locate the contest rules. Many appear in national society magazines, but nowadays they will almost certainly appear on the Internet and this should be your first port of call. A number of specialist sites such as those of SM3CER [3] and WA7BNM [4] list most contests, with links to the relevant rules and results pages. Once you have the rules, you can start planning your strategy for the contest. If you can't track down the rules, or come across a contest already in full flow on the bands, you may well be able to determine at least the basics (for example, the contest exchange) just by listening to a few contacts being made.

Some contests are limited in their participation, perhaps to a certain club or country. The RSGB's Commonwealth Contest is a good example; only amateurs in Commonwealth countries can be worked for points. But the majority of contests allow all comers. The serious participants will welcome the points they make from contacting you. Other participants will simply enjoy the activity, to which you and they are contributing.

Equally, just because you take part in a contest, there is no obligation to send in a log. However, most contest organisers welcome every log received, if only because it enables them to be more thorough in checking the logs of the leading participants (where life can get very competitive, with small margins between the leading players). Some organisers will offer incentives to get your log, for example a certificate for everyone making more than a certain number of contacts. In any case, there are usually many separate sections in which you can compete, so although you may not be competitive at the highest levels, you may be able to enter a section alongside entrants similar to yourself – for example, Low Power (100W or less) or QRP (5W or less) - and perhaps even win a trophy of some sort.

Rules for RSGB contests appear in the *RSGB Yearbook* [5], and also on the RSGB's Contests Committee website [6]. In any case, always check the latter as any late changes to the rules will be found on the relevant website. The ARRL website [7] covers not only ARRL events, but the popular IARU HF World Championship event too. The rules for most major contests stay the same, apart from minor changes, over long periods, partly because it is hard to ensure that rule changes are propagated to all possible participants (the Internet has made this easier) and partly because it allows scores to be compared year on year. Most major contests have dates which are entirely predictable year on year. A list later in this chapter shows the weekends on which a number of major contests take place.

PLANNING FOR A CONTEST

Most serious contesters plan their contest calendar months in advance, blocking out the key dates and warning friends and family of their unavailability. Of course, you can participate in a contest on a casual basis, with relatively little planning, just taking part for a portion of the time, and enjoying the fun of making a few contacts. However, whatever your level of participation, there are things you can do beforehand to enhance the experience.

The first thing is to ensure you have a copy of the rules. Once you have the rules to hand, you then need to determine a number of key things. What is the contest exchange? Typically this is RS(T) – invariably 59(9) – and maybe a serial number plus, in many cases, one other item of information such as your Locator or Club name. You may be able to deduce this by listening to other participants, but it isn't always possible. For example, you might hear an entrant send 59927. Is the 27 a serial number, the ITU zone, his age, or maybe the number of years he has been licensed? Then there is the major question of what the scoring system is. This is less important if you are intending to operate casually. But if you are proposing a serious entry, it is essential to know the scoring system beforehand to determine your plan of attack. More about this later.

What else do you need to know? Obviously the start and finish times are vital, translated into local time (most rules specify contest times in UTC). Not only start and finish times, but also operating times. Some contests, for example, allow single-operators to take time out for resting, eating or whatever. You will need to understand what the rules are regarding these 'time outs', and plan to use them in the most effective way so as to have least impact on your final score.

It is also very important to know who you can work in a contest. Some contests are of the 'everyone works everyone' variety. Others are along the lines of 'everyone works Francophone stations – France and its overseas territories' or whatever. Such contests can be excellent opportunities to collect counters towards specific awards (in the example given, maybe French *départements*).

The rules will also tell you about the contest categories in terms of power, bands, etc. A look at previous years' results may suggest that you have a better chance of winning one particular category rather than others, maybe because you have a more effective antenna on one particular band, for example. You may also be swayed by the trophies and certificates on offer, which may encourage you to enter a particular category.

YOUR CONTEST CALLSIGN

In recent years, special short calls have been available for use by UK clubs in certain RSGB and international contests. These callsigns have just a single-letter suffix, the idea being that they save time in a contest, when you may have to send your call several thousand times. A number of other countries have adopted a similar system, too. If your or your club has requested one of these callsigns, you may decide to use it instead of your regular callsign. The rules for requesting and using these special callsigns, including a list of contests in which they may be used, appear in the *RSGB Yearbook* [5] and on the RSGB Contest Committee web site [8].

In practice, some amateurs take great pride in using their own callsign regularly in contests, to the point where it

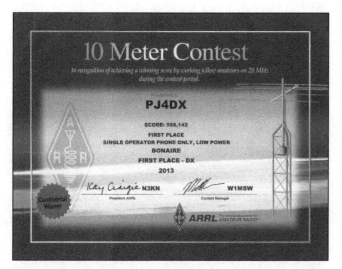

Certificates are usually awarded to the highest placed entrants in each category.

becomes well known on the air. Others value special callsigns, especially if the callsign concerned has an unusual prefix, as this may attract additional callers who you might not otherwise work. It is very much a matter of personal preference.

CONTEST SCORING

Whatever the sport, the way you approach it from a competitive point of view will depend on the rules and, especially, the system of determining the final result. In the case of amateur radio contesting, although each event has its own distinct flavour, the basic system is that every qualifying contact will generate points while, in many cases, there is scope for increasing the score through bonuses or multipliers.

To take QSO points first. In the popular *CQ World Wide DX* contests, contacts with your own country count zero points, with other countries in your continent one point and contacts with other continents three points (there is one exception to this, but it is not necessary for the present discussion). Clearly there is an advantage in trying to make contacts outside your continent, which is very much the thrust of the event which is billed as a 'DX' contest. So if, as a UK station, you can be making 25 QSOs an hour on 15m, most of which are with the USA, that is better than, for example, staying on 40m to work European stations at 60 an hour (75 points an hour versus 60). In many VHF contests the scoring system is based on distance, computed from the Locator of the station worked (fortunately, modern computer logging software makes this computation trivial). Again, depending upon band conditions, there may be a strategic decision to take as to whether to beam to a nearby population centre and make lots of low-scoring QSOs, or whether to try and seek out those higher scoring distant contacts, even if they are few and far between.

Bonuses and Multipliers

A bonus is an additional score added each time a specific goal is reached. It might be a new county, country or zone, or even based on working a specific station on additional bands. A multiplier is similar except that, instead of being

added to the QSO points, it is used to multiply them. It may well be based on the same goals – counties, countries, zones, etc. So the final score could be made up of QSO points + bonuses, or QSO points x multipliers. Again, the scoring system will help to determine your strategy. If a QSO is worth 3 points and a new country adds a bonus of 15 points, then it's worth missing five other QSOs while chasing that new country. But if the new country is a multiplier, it could be worth very much more than five QSOs, and it may well be worth making a much greater effort to put it in the log.

All in all, a close study of the rules is well worthwhile. A couple of examples may help to put flesh on the foregoing discussion:

CQ WPX contest: Each year the *CQ* WPX contests are popular events in the calendar. There are three events, SSB, CW and RTTY.

Let's consider the *CQ* WPX CW Contest, held annually on the last full weekend of May. The contest exchange is RST plus serial number. Scoring is based on points per QSO, multiplied by the total number of prefixes worked, regardless of band. QSO points are 1 for contacts with your own continent and 3 for contacts with other continents. However, these points are doubled on the low bands (40, 80 and 160). So, for example, working US stations at a rate of 40 an hour on 20m (generating 120 points an hour) is equivalent to working European stations at 60 an hour on 40m. But in May, in the northern hemisphere, the nights are quite short. What's more, single operators are only allowed to operate 36 out of the 48 hours of the contest (which starts at 0000UTC, or 0100 local in the UK). Where are the QSO points going to come from? Mainly, perhaps, assuming you are operating from the UK (and depending on where we are in the 11-year sunspot cycle), from working Europeans at 2 points each on the low bands, and North Americans at 3 points each on the high bands. This tends to suggest operating throughout the hours of darkness on the low bands, and during the afternoon and early evening on the HF bands (when they are most likely to be open to North America). This suggests that sleeping and eating should be done during the mornings. A similar thought process should be followed wherever in the world you are, though the conclusions may be different.

As for multipliers, there are so many prefixes around and you only need to work each one once, so it probably isn't worth spending a lot of time searching for new ones. If you have a good enough signal, call CQ and they will come to you. To that extent, *CQ* WPX is what is generally considered to be a 'rate' contest, where the aim is to get as many contacts into the log as possible and the multipliers will largely take care of themselves.

6m contest: Let's take a completely different example. Suppose you intend to operate a 6m contest in June (many are scheduled for this time of the year, as there is a high likelihood of Sporadic E propagation). The rules may require you to exchange RS(T) and Locator, and the score may be based on the distance for each QSO. Let's also suppose this is a mixed-mode contest, but you are only allowed to work each station once, regardless of mode. And the contest is for 24 hours.

How to maximise your score? Clearly it isn't simply a matter of getting lots of contacts in the log. A large number of local contacts won't score anywhere near as highly as a handful of distant contacts. So you need to focus on making those long-distance contacts. Some will come, hopefully, from Sporadic E openings. When Sporadic E comes along, you should be able to make contacts with even a modest station, but it is essential that you are alert to the band opening up. Don't stray from the radio just because the band has been quiet for a while. A Sporadic E opening may be short. And it can happen at any time during quite a wide time window. For example, from the UK in June, it is not uncommon to have double-hop Sporadic E to North America around 0100 to 0200 local time.

For the times when the band isn't wide open, though, you will want to maximise your score by working the best distances you can during flat conditions. If you live on a hilltop you may be well-placed to do so. Otherwise, you may consider operating the contest from a portable site, selecting the site with consideration to where the main populations of activity are likely to be (major cities, for example). The nature of VHF propagation and antennas also means that you can easily miss stations who are at the limit of propagation. A QSO may only be marginally possible when you are beaming directly at the distant station and he at you. With high-gain antennas with narrow beamwidth, the probability of this can be quite small, but you need to maximise it. There are several things you can do, for example by ensuring that you keep moving your own beam heading and calling CQ regularly to all parts of the compass (a voice keyer may be a good idea for this!) You should also spend time tuning the band each time you change beam heading, to catch stations you haven't already worked – there may not be another opportunity. And you probably need to be comfortable with CW operating, for those contacts where conditions are so marginal that CW may be the only way of completing.

These two examples show why it is important to think ahead. Once you have decided what category to enter, and what sort of strategy will be required to be effective, then you can start planning in earnest. What antenna system will you need? Does this require changes to what you already have, perhaps by supplementing it with some additional hardware for the contest weekend? If you plan to go out portable, then you need to locate and arrange a site, maybe organise a generator and camping equipment, and so on. And then there's your station itself. It may be fine for day-to-day ragchewing or DXing, but will it be suitable for the contest?

There are several aspects. Is the equipment itself optimised for the contest, or do you need to add more filters or borrow a second receiver for finding multipliers, for example? Is your PC fully integrated for logging (and *Cluster* access if you intend to enter an Assisted category)? The more automated your station, the better. While you may be happy to change bands manually on the PC for day-to-day logging, for example, 40 hours into a 48-hour contest and you may be too tired to remember to do so.

Station ergonomics are important, too: your operating chair, the position of the tuning dial and the keyboard. Again, what works well for casual operating may lead to backache over an extended period of contest operation. And what about arrangements for eating and other requirements during the contest? Really serious contesters arrange to have food prepared beforehand or have someone to bring it during the contest, so that they don't have to leave the operating chair. Some even go to the extent of having an empty container in the shack to avoid breaking off the pile-ups to go to the bathroom!

Do you have logging software tailored for the particular contest, so that you can track your progress as you go along? This makes a big difference. But take time to be familiar with the software before the contest; there will be too much happening during the contest itself to be in a learning situation.

Obviously there is plenty of other pre-contest preparation you could be doing. For instance, station maintenance, analysing logs from previous years, running propagation predictions in order to have some idea of which bands to be on at any given time, and which directions you should be targeting as the contest progresses. Maybe you will take part in some smaller contests in order to improve your operating skills, or use one of the various contest simulators for the same purpose. You can check the Internet and other sources to see what expeditions may be active during the contest, or try to identify where your major competition is likely to be coming from. Then there is planning your sleep patterns before the contest, so that you start the event alert and ready to be awake for long periods. And so on. For many contesters, this period of preparation and anticipation is almost as rewarding as the contest itself. This is especially true when planning a multi-operator event, maybe a Field Day entry with a local club. Planning such an activity can be a great social experience, bringing club members closer together.

YOUR CONTEST STATION

The previous section made some references to the particular requirements of a contest station. Most of the things you can do to improve a contest station, such as thinking about equipment positions on the operating table, or improving your antennas, will help your day-today operating as well, but any limitations in your station are much more likely to become a real nuisance in the hothouse atmosphere of a contest. Some have likened DXing to a form of much extended contest. For example, if a rare station appears on the band and it takes you a couple of hours to make a contact, this is all part of the fun. But in a contest, if a new multiplier appears, it may only be 'worth', say, five ordinary QSOs, so if you don't manage to work that multiplier in the space of a few calls you are wasting time. This is why contesters are the ones who seem to build the biggest and best stations.

But this doesn't mean that you need to have something which emulates the BBC to be a successful contester. You might, for example, focus on a particular band, and set up highly effective antennas for that one band. And if you are plagued by EMC problems, you could set your sights on entering the Low Power or QRP categories which most contests have nowadays. But there is no excuse for settling for second best. Just because you focus on QRP, for example, doesn't mean you have to use an elderly direct-conversion transceiver and a compromise wire antenna. Aim to do the best you can within the rules. Stick within the limits for transmit power, but ensure you have an excellent receiver, and the best antenna you can put up at your location. Install low-loss coaxial cable. Automate your station to a high degree so that during the contest you can focus your energies on the actual operating. In other words, set your sights high, and try to improve with every contest you enter.

Most of the relevant equipment considerations have already been considered in Chapter 3. The major additional concern for contest operations is if you want to be able to listen on one band (for multipliers, for example) while transmitting on another (by sending an automated CQ call from a voice or CW keyer). On the HF bands you may well find that you suffer breakthrough between bands. There are several solutions in terms of bandpass filters and tuned coaxial stubs, and a number of suitable commercial products are available if you don't feel able to build something yourself. The problem is multiplied many times in a multi-operator multi-band contest station, and great care needs to be taken not only with filtering but with the orientation of antennas and feeder cables, earthing, and so on. Usually these multi-operator stations will have one or two team members who are well versed in tackling such problems.

On the VHF bands, it is not unusual to hear very wide signals during contests. This may be because the other station is over-driving his amplifier or it may be because your own receiver really isn't up to handling the very strong signals often encountered in the contest environment.

Many of the earlier VHF-only transceivers were designed for casual day-to-day operating, and struggle in contest situations. One solution is to use a modern HF transceiver with transverter for the VHF bands. And to pull out those very weak signals, you may well need to think in terms of a masthead preamplifier. Of course, you may also take the opportunity,

especially if you go out portable, to put up a bigger antenna system than your usual one, perhaps a stacked array of some sort.

Because contests are repetitive in the sense of needing to make repeated CQ calls, and of sending certain parts of the contest exchange during every QSO, voice and CW keyers are absolutely invaluable in taking some of the load off the operator. Modern logging software is designed to integrate closely with these. It saves your voice (or keying hand) and also frees you to be doing other tasks, such as tuning another band or checking propagation predictions with a view to changing antenna direction, for example.

There is also a strong case for recording contests, something which has always been possible with tape recorders but which is now so much easier using the sound card and hard disc of your PC. You then have a permanent record if there are later queries, or for analysis when preparing for the next contest.

OPERATING THE CONTEST

The joy of operating an amateur radio contest is that you never know exactly what to expect. Radio propagation, like the weather, doesn't lend itself to accurate predictions, and there will always be surprises. A successful contester learns how to play these to his advantage, rather than being thrown by, say, a solar storm or an unexpected band opening.

The trick is to be continually aware of what is happening in the contest environment. If you are entering a multi-band contest, you will need to be forever evaluating whether you are on the right band. Is there likely to be an opening on another band that you need to take advantage of? Propagation predictions, a display showing sunrise and sunset times such as *Geoclock*, and previous years' logs can help here. So can having a second receiver, so that you can check the other bands at regular intervals. Those transceivers and receivers that have spectrum displays, in particular SDRs, can be invaluable too; when a band opens the spectrum display will suddenly start showing lots of signals.

One of the key tactical decisions in any contest is when to call CQ ('run') and when to tune the bands ('search and pounce'). There is no simple answer to this; it depends on the contest rules. If there is a finite number of multipliers, it may be worth spending substantial amounts of time tuning the bands to find new ones. It will also depend on how 'loud' you are. Weaker stations will almost certainly spend more time tuning and calling, because their CQ calls are less likely to be heard. Louder stations will almost certainly spend more time calling CQ. But there is no hard and fast rule. Even a QRP station can sometimes call CQ successfully, when a band is wide open to a major area of population. It depends on the contest, too. In the biggest international contests (*CQ* WW, for example) the number of participants runs to many thousands, and the HF bands simply cannot accommodate everyone calling CQ at once, and it can be hard if not impossible to find a clear frequency on which to call CQ. In contrast, on the VHF bands there is usually plenty of room for everyone to call CQ, should they wish to do so, though clearly if everyone only called CQ, no QSOs would result at all.

Showing that you don't need a big station to achieve competition success is Roy, G3MPB, recipient of a medal in the 77th RSGB Commonwealth Contest. He operates from a 'postage stamp' suburban garden garden and uses 100W from a multi-band vertical with a single 1.2m ground rod.

The actual operating is very much the same as during day-to-day ragchewing and DXing, except that it needs to be very 'tight', with no wasted words or transmissions. Serious contesters don't indulge in pleasantries, and have recognised that in a contest where they might make, say, 4000 QSOs (an average of 43 seconds a contact over a 48-hour contest), a second saved on every contact is 4000 seconds saved, or time for an additional 93 contacts over the course of the contest. This might be all the difference between a first and second place. Of course, this is less of an issue in, say, a VHF contest, where time is less likely to be a crucial factor.

There are many ways to save time in a contest. The most obvious is to keep the transmission to only the essential data:

"CQ contest from Mike Zero Charlie."
"Golf Three X-ray Delta Victor" – *no need to give his call, he knows it already.*
"Golf Three X-ray Delta Victor 591013" – *he gives my report just once. If I miss it, I can always ask for a repeat.*
"QSL, 59784" - *All he needs is his report from me.*
"Thanks, Mike Zero Charlie, contest" – *And away he goes, looking for the next contact.*

The same principles apply on other modes. Some RTTY contesters are notorious for including unnecessary information in their transmissions, presumably because it is easy to program other data into the buffers, but it wastes time. It's no different to runners in a race. They might be the best of friends, but during the race they don't chat with each, they are focused on being first at the winning post. There is no group of amateurs more animated than contesters when they get together at social events. They are always anxious to swap contesting stories and share hints and tips. But during the contest itself they are totally focused on maximising their scores.

When calling CQ, keep your calls relatively short, but remember that stations tuning the bands will not only hear you, but need time to check whether they have already worked you. So allow a moment or two after your CQ call for them to respond. On VHF, longer calls are generally more appropriate, as distant stations may need to adjust their beam heading to maximise their reception of you.

When everything is going well, there may be times when you have two or three stations calling you at once. The trick, which comes with experience, is not to get flustered but to try and keep up a steady rhythm, going back to one station at a time. If you didn't get his full call, then make it clear, and acknowledge later in the QSO that you have it correct:

CQ contest, CQ contest, Golf Three X-ray Delta Victor.
Mike Zero Alpha India Mike.
Mike Zero Alpha Station, 59123.
Mike Zero Alpha India Mike, 59005.
Mike Zero Alpha India Mike, thank you, Golf Three X-ray Delta Victor, contest.

Many contest logging programs take care of this automatically, when you are using them to key your transceiver in a

G3ZVW (alias AF6SU) and N6RC operating WC6H in the *CQ WPX SSB* Contest.

CW or RTTY contest. In other words, if you amend the callsign on the screen during the course of the contact, they will send the corrected call with the final exchange, so that the other station knows you have his callsign correct in your log.

By the way, before calling CQ in a contest, as at any other time, always check that the frequency isn't already in use. It isn't always obvious.

When you are in 'search and pounce' mode, tuning the band, you need to be alert to every station you hear. Some contesters have a routine, for example always tuning from the bottom end of the band upwards. If you hear a station you haven't worked, assess whether you should call immediately. Is he loud and unoccupied? Is he a multiplier, or a high scoring contact? If he is busy, you may decide to put the frequency into one of the memories on your transceiver, to come back later. One of the joys of computerised contest logging programs is known as 'Check Partial': you can key in any part of a callsign, and the program will immediately show you which stations you have already worked with that particular combination of letters in the call.

On the HF bands in a major contest, a good 'search and pounce operator' should be able to maintain QSO rates of 60 an hour or better. This may be slower than you could achieve by calling CQ but if, by tuning the band, you are also collecting multipliers, then your score may be going up faster than if you stayed in one place, letting others call you.

There are plenty of other tricks for maximising your contest score, of course. For example, and depending on the scoring system, it may be worth moving callers from one band to another, for additional points. With modern transceivers this is quite feasible. You can move bands, work the station concerned, and be back on your original frequency before anyone realises you had gone.

Contesting with *Cluster* assistance is a rather different matter again. Every time a 'spot' appears for a station you haven't worked, especially if it is a multiplier, you have to make a conscious decision whether to move from what you are doing to chase that spotted station (knowing that many others are probably about to do the same). Not for nothing is the Single-Operator Assisted category sometimes referred to as 'Single-Operator Distracted'! To use the *Cluster* to advantage is an art that can only be developed over time.

AFTER THE CONTEST

The serious contester finds plenty to do after the contest. Fortunately, in these days of PCs, the actual log submission has got immeasurably easier than it used to be when logs were written on paper. Nowadays, most contest logging programs generate the required log (usually in the widely-accepted Cabrillo format, where both log and summary data are in one electronic file – see 'A Cabrillo Primer' (overleaf), which can then be e-mailed instantaneously to the organisers.

In theory, it should be possible to submit your log within minutes of the contest ending. In practice, it is rarely a good idea to do this. There are mixed opinions about the extent to which it is legitimate to edit a log after the contest has finished. For example, you logged G3XDV but, after the contest, you read that he had actually been operating from Wales as GW3XDV. Should you change your log? The answer is "no", in that you clearly made an operating error, and once the contest is finished the log is effectively closed. But suppose you logged E15DI, knowing perfectly well that this was EI5DI but simply hitting the wrong key on your PC. Most contesters would accept that it is legitimate to correct this before sending in your log (especially if you made a note at the time to go back and fix it). Most importantly, though, check the Summary information in the log. Are all the details (name, address, e-mail address, category entered, etc) correct? If you belong to a club and need your score to count towards the club score, are the details in there?

The trend towards electronic submission of logs is very well advanced and is encouraged. It helps both you and the adjudicators. It helps you because you don't have to do all that manual work any more, especially if you were using a computer to log during the contest itself. All you need to do is enter the relevant details (name, address, section entered, etc) into the header of the log and e-mail it to the published address. Several contest organisers including the RSGB have a webpage for contest log submissions as an alternative to e-mailing the log. The RSGB now requires web submission for most of its contests. With Cabrillo submissions, there is no need to identify duplicate QSOs, or even to score the logs, as all this will be done anyway during the adjudication process.

For the organisers, electronic log submission removes the days of wading through heaps of paper logs, and it allows computers to do what they do best and human beings do badly, which is to plough through perhaps millions of QSO records, identifying those which tie up, and those where there are errors (for example, a miscopied callsign). Once this checking is complete, the computer can calculate the final scores. This helps to speed up the whole process of adjudication and, to help matters along even more, results are usually posted on the web, saving the inevitable delays in publishing on paper (magazine, results booklet, etc).

Incidentally, the adjudicators are the unsung heroes of contesting. Despite the impact of computers, there is still a huge amount of work to be done in adjudicating a major contest, right through from ensuring the rules are published correctly, to checking the logs and tabulating the results, maybe writing some sort of commentary to go with the results, organising the distribution of trophies and certificates, and reviewing the rules in readiness for the following year.

Given this level of effort, adjudicators tend not to take kindly to those who have made the minimum of effort in sending in their entry – most adjudicators can tell tales of logs without key information such as section entered, logs in formats which bear no relation to that detailed in the rules, even logs for a different contest entirely!

Even if you do only enter casually, contest organisers are keen to have your log as it helps them to check the logs of the serious entrants, so do take a few moments to submit it after the event.

But even when you have sent off the log, there is plenty you could be doing. The main thing is to make notes of anything you need to be aware of. Problems with your station that need to be addressed. Unexpected band openings that you need to plan for in advance of next year's contest. Strategic and tactical errors which you need to be aware of when planning for the next one. This is the time to capture all this data, while it is still fresh in your mind. It is this sort of attention to detail which separates the good contesters from the great contesters, just as in any other competitive area of life.

CONTEST ADJUDICATION

It's worth spending a little time describing contest adjudication. It is the part that you, the entrant, don't see, but it helps to understand something of what goes on behind the scenes.

Contest adjudication is not there to penalise you (unless there are very good reasons to do so!), but to ensure that the final scores accurately reflect the relative standings of all the entrants. For example, it isn't uncommon for some entrants to use the wrong scoring system, so their claimed score is in error. Even if you think your log is scored correctly, the adjudicators may have additional information. A good example would be the Shetland Islands in the CQ WW contests, where they count as a separate multiplier to the rest of Scotland. Many participants who work Shetland may not even realise they have done so, but the adjudicators will have a database of who is where, and will rescore those logs accordingly.

While it is possible for an experienced log checker to cast his eye down a paper log and see any obvious incorrectly-copied callsigns, there is a limit to the amount of cross-checking that can be done. To take the RSGB IOTA contest as an example, in the 2009 contest there were over 2000 logs received, accounting for a total of more than 580,000 contacts. Some of these cannot be cross-checked, as the station worked has not sent in a log. But a high proportion of them can be. With the best will in the world, cross-checking over 400,000 contacts for callsign, band, mode, report, serial number and IOTA reference is going to take an awful lot of time. But by ensuring that all logs are in a single database (paper logs have to be retyped to achieve this), the cross-

A Cabrillo Primer

by Don Field, G3XTT

The RSGB HF Contests Committee has adopted the Cabrillo format for RSGB contest entries.

Why Cabrillo?

The first thing to say is that it makes the Adjudicator's job a lot easier if logs are in a common format.

The ARRL faced exactly the same issues as the RSGB in dealing with many log formats, and asked Trey, N5KO, to work on a standard which would meet their requirements for something which was simple to implement, but would give them what they wanted. The thinking behind Cabrillo is essentially:

1. Text based, with no html or other tags, both for simplicity of implementation and with the added benefit that a log can easily be viewed as a text file to determine whether it contains the required information.
2. All information in a single flat file, rather than having separate log and summary files, which would need to be sent as attachments. As a result, the log can usually be sent within the body of an e-mail if necessary, or uploaded to a web site.
3. Header information (name, mode, power, etc) is, as far as possible, generic, rather than contest-specific. This simplifies the job of the software authors, but when correctly implemented the contest sponsors should easily be able to determine which category has been entered.
4. Each QSO record contains all data relevant to that QSO (callsign of both stations, band, mode, etc), allowing the log to be sorted in various ways for checking, but easily recreated as required.
5. The data format, while specifying desired character position and format for each item of QSO data (time, call, band, sent and received exchanges, etc) is actually very undemanding. Essentially, provided there is white space (tab or space is fine, no slashes, commas or full stops please!) between each element, the Adjudicator should be able to make sense of the log.

Cabrillo deliberately doesn't ask for data which can perfectly well be determined by the Adjudicator. So, for example, it doesn't ask you to indicate multipliers, QSO points, duplicate contacts, off periods, etc. Too many entrants get

these things wrong, or handle them in disparate ways. All can be figured out as and when required by the checking software.

What does a log consist of?

Let's have a look at a typical Cabrillo log:

```
START-OF-LOG: 2.0
CONTEST: CQ-WW-RTTY
CALLSIGN: G3XTT
CATEGORY: SINGLE-OP ALL-BAND HIGH-POWER
CLAIMED-SCORE: 484750
OPERATORS: G3XTT
CLUB: Chiltern DX Club
NAME: Don Field
ADDRESS: 105 Shiplake Bottom, Peppard Common,
ADDRESS: Henley-on-Thames, RG9 5HJ
ADDRESS: England
QSO: 21000 RY 2002-09-28 1146 G3XTT 599 14 DX
RV3WU 599 16 DX
QSO: 21000 RY 2002-09-28 1146 G3XTT 599 14 DX
SP9LJD 599 15 DX
END-OF-LOG:
```

Much of this will be common to all contests, but obviously the actual QSO data varies (typically the contest exchange). So the early part of the QSO line will remain the same (Band, Mode, Date, Time, MyCall) while the rest will vary by contest. To deal with this, preferred formats are specified on N5KO's Web page, and for RSGB contests there will also be links from the rules pages on the Web. Software authors support the preferred format for the various RSGB events. In the IOTA contest, the majority of logs are generated from just a handful of popular contest logging programs, which all create the correct format.

That's it!

And that's about all you need to know. For many contests which have already adopted Cabrillo, the server runs a little routine to check for key fields in the log, and will generate an error message back to the sender if data is missing or suspect (for example if the dates and times don't correspond to the contest which is being entered). Entrants are then able to resubmit their log, when the problem has been fixed. This saves the Adjudicators a lot of time which might otherwise have been spent in correspondence.

checking can be done in a matter of hours with a suitable computer program.

The key thing that you, the entrant, need to know is what happens when there is an error in your log. Perhaps you have miscopied a callsign or a serial number, or mislogged the band. In the case of most RSGB contests you will probably lose all points for the contact and, if it is a multiplier, you will lose that as well (but you may, of course, have worked another

station which would also count for that multiplier). Some contest organisers apply additional penalties, to encourage participants to ensure logging accuracy. In the case of the CQ WW contests, the penalty is three times the value of the QSO, so if it's a one point QSO, you lose three points, and if it's a three point QSO you lose nine points. Knowing this helps you to decide what to do if, at the time of the contact, you are unhappy about whether you have logged it correctly.

The adjudication of a contest, therefore, takes on several distinct stages. The first is to record all incoming logs and ensure they are assigned to the right category (high power / low power, single band / multi-band, CW / SSB / Mixed mode or whatever is applicable). If the entrant hasn't included this information in his log, the adjudicator will either try to contact the entrant and find out or simply default the entrant to the lowest common denominator (so a Low Power entrant who has failed to mention this might end up consigned to the High Power category).

The next step is to get all the logs into a single database. This is where it is much easier if entrants use the recommended log format. The RSGB Contest Committee tries to be flexible, but some logs are extremely difficult to convert if they are in an odd format - and some paper logs can be pretty much unreadable!

Once the database is complete, the cross-checking can take place. Comprehensive cross-checking relies on a good proportion of the participants (or the more active participants, at least) sending in their logs, either as an entry or as a checklog (where it will be used in adjudication but not listed in the final results). The computer software will then identify errors. At this point it may rescore the logs immediately or, in most cases, require human intervention to decide what penalties, if any, should be applied. The final scores are then drawn up.

It then remains to publish the scores and a writeup of the event. Nowadays, many contest results are published on the Internet well before their publication on paper. The RSGB produces an annual 'sports radio' results book which will be sent to all contest entrants, and be available to others on request. The ARRL has adopted a system for its contests whereby extended write-ups are available on its members-only web pages.

One of the great benefits of computerised log checking is that many contest organisers now offer feedback on your log. The best known are the 'UBN' (UBN standing for 'Unique', 'Broken' and 'Not in log') reports which are available after *CQ* WW log checking. The title makes it clear that the feedback is essentially on how well you copied the other station's callsign. Unique calls are ones which do not appear in anyone else's log. Normally they are not penalised. You may really have worked someone who came on and made just one

contact, though it is also possible that you miscopied his callsign. Broken calls are those where the other party to the contact has sent in a log and it is clear who you actually worked. Not in log is where you think you worked someone, but he hasn't logged you. For the RSGB IOTA contest a report equivalent to *CQ* WW's UBN is provided automatically to entrants. For contests other than *CQ* WW and IOTA the type and level of feedback varies.

Of course, the adjudicators will have other work to do, dealing with correspondence and queries from entrants, organising certificates and trophies for the winners, and reviewing the rules for the next year's event. When you need to contact them, do remember that, for most contests (and all RSGB contests) these are unpaid volunteers, with jobs and families and who like to get on the air occasionally and take part in contests themselves!

RSGB HF CONTESTS

The RSGB organises several HF contests throughout the year. Some are for RSGB members only, or clubs affiliated to the Society, whilst others such as the IOTA Contest are for all-comers. **Table 1** shows when the events are held. Note that the months given are from the 2015 calendar and may vary. See the *RSGB Yearbook* or the RSGB Contest Committee web site [E] for the dates and full rules.

AFS Contests

These are for RSGB Affiliated societies and are held on one of more of the 1.8, 3.5 and 7MHz bands on either CW or SSB. Newcomers to contesting are encouraged and a 'QRS Coral' is set aside for inexperienced Morse operators.

80m Club Championship

A series of short weekday evening contests on 3.5MHz, promoting competition between Affiliated Societies. Individual scores in every event count towards a Society's overall score, so it is important for contest organisers to get members to come on in as many sessions and as many modes as possible.

1.8MHz Contests

The top-band contests are some of the oldest organised by the RSGB. The first one of the year is a CW and SSB event whilst the second is CW-only. The contests are of the "everyone works everyone" type.

Commonwealth Contest

The Commonwealth Contest promotes contacts between stations in the British Commonwealth of Nations. A more relaxed contest environment gives everyone the opportunity to work some choice DX.

RoPoCo Contests

RoPoCo stands for ROtating POst COdes, so called because the contest exchange depends on that received in the previous QSO, and the exchanges consists of entrants' postcodes. There are two of these short contests per year: SSB in April, and CW in August. These contests are a real test of your operating skills.

G3TBK/P operated by G3TBK in the 2014 RSGB National Field Day event.

National Field Day

This popular portable CW contest (abbreviated to 'NFD') is an excellent club activity with varied areas of expertise required, such as antenna design, construction and erection, generator maintenance and computer literacy. Therefore all club members can give their CW operators some much-needed support! The QRP Section is limited to 12 hours of operation which should assist groups who have difficulty in finding operators to cover the full 24 hours.

Low Power Contest

This a serious event for QRP CW operators on the 3.5 and 7MHz bands. It provides a choice of fixed station operation or outdoor fun.

RSGB HF Contests Calendar

Month	Contest Name
January	AFS Contest CW
	AFS Contest PHONE
	February 80m CC SSB
	80m CC DATA
	1st 1.8MHz Contest
	80m CC CW
	80m CC DATA
March	80m CC CW
	Commonwealth Contest
	80m CC SSB
April	RoPoCo SSB
	80m CC CW
	80m CC SSB
	80m CC DATA
May	80m CC SSB
	80m CC DATA
	80m CC CW
June	80m CC DATA
	NFD
	80m CC CW
	80m CC SSB
July	80m CC CW
	80m CC SSB
	Low Power Contest
	80m CC DATA
	IOTA Contest
August	RoPoCo CW
	80m Club Sprint CW
	80m Club Sprint SSB
September	SSB Field Day
	80m Club Sprint SSB
	80m Club Sprint CW
October	21/28MHz Contest
	80m Club Sprint CW
	80m Club Sprint SSB
November	80m Club Sprint SSB
	Club Calls (1.8MHz AFS)
	2nd 1.8MHz Contest
	80m Club Sprint CW

Table 1: The HF contests organised by the RSGB.

IOTA Contest

Part of the Islands on the Air (IOTA) scheme - see the chapter on Awards - the aim of the large international contest is to promote contacts between stations in IOTA island groups and the rest of the world, and to encourage expeditions to IOTA islands. It takes place on the 3.5, 7, 14, 21 and 28MHz bands, and on both CW and SSB.

RSGB SSB Field Day

A popular multi-operator club activity. Finding the best ratio of contact rate to country multipliers provides a challenging backdrop to a weekend outdoors. Separate Open and Restricted sections allow less well-equipped stations to compete.

21-28MHz Contest

Designed to encourage activity on these bands, this event is on both CW and SSB with either single- or mixed-mode entries allowed. Power categories include legal max, 100W and 10W.

NON-RSGB HF CONTESTS

This section gives a brief summary of the rules of those non-RSGB contests that are the most popular with UK amateurs. Many more are shown in **Table 2**.

CQ World Wide DX (CQ WW); CQ Worked Prefix (WPX) Contests

CQ magazine runs these major events annually on CW, SSB and RTTY. Each is a full weekend (48 hours) long on each mode and literally thousands of amateurs enter. CQ WW usually provides great opportunities to work rare countries, often activated by DXpeditions who go there specifically to operate in the contests.

In CQ WW the contest exchange is signal report and CQ zone, which for the UK is 14 (see Appendix A of this book for the CQ zone of other countries). DXCC entities and CQ zones worked on each band (160 - 10m) count as multipliers. In the WPX contests, scoring is by multipliers for each prefix, rather than entity. This contest is unusual in that multipliers may be counted only once, regardless of band. The full rules are published in CQ magazine, and on the websites for CQ WW [2] and CQ WPX [9].

ARRL DX contests

The American Radio Relay League (ARRL) organises major international DX contests on SSB and CW. These events, where the rest of the world works the 48 contiguous US states plus Canadian provinces on all six bands 160 to 10m, are almost as popular as CQ WW. US / Canadian stations send report and state / province while all other stations send report and power output. The multiplier is the number of states / provinces contacted on all bands. The ARRL also runs single-band contests on 160m and 10m.

IARU HF World Championship

The International Amateur Radio Union runs this major multi-mode (SSB and CW) event on all the HF bands in mid July

HF CONTEST CALENDAR

Only major international events are shown, not national contests. Contests take place on Saturday and Sunday unless other-wise specified: note that most events take place on the nominated full weekend, ie if the 1st day of the month is a Sunday, the 1st full weekend is the 7th and 8th (you are advised to confirm the precise dates in the official rules). All contests listed as 'SSB / CW' allow a singlemode entry on either SSB or CW, or a Mixed-mode entry using both modes.

Weekend	Contest	Mode(s)	Official rules
JANUARY			
1st	ARRL RTTY Round-up (but never on 1 January)	RTTY	www.arrl.org/contest-calendar
Last	CQ World Wide 160-Meter Contest (2200UTC Friday for 48 hours)	CW	www.cq160.com
FEBRUARY			
2nd	CQ World Wide WPX RTTY Contest	RTTY	www.cqwpxrtty.com
3rd	ARRL International DX Contest	CW	www.arrl.org/contest-calendar
Last	CQ World Wide 160-Meter Contest (2200UTC Friday for 48 hours)	SSB	www.cq160.com
MARCH			
1st	ARRL International DX Contest	Phone	www.arrl.org/contest-calendar
2nd	RSGB Commonwealth Contest	CW	www.rsgbcc.org/hf (click on 'Calendar')
Last	CQ WPX Contest	SSB	www.cqwpx.com
APRIL			
2nd	Japan International DX Contest	CW	http://jidx.org
MAY			
2nd	CQ-M International DX Contest	SSB / CW	www.cq-m.andys.ru/rules_eng.html
Last	CQ WPX Contes	CW	www.cqwpx.com
JUNE			
1st	RSGB NFD / IARU Region 1 Field Day	CW	www.rsgbcc.org/hf
3rd	All Asian DX Contest	CW	www.jarl.org/English
JULY			
2nd	IARU HF World Championship	Phone / CW	www.arrl.org/contest-calendar
Last	RSGB IOTA Contest	SSB / CW	www.rsgbcc.org/hf/iota.shtml
AUGUST			
2nd	Worked All Europe DX Contest	CW	www.darc.de/referate/dx/contest/waedc/en/
SEPTEMBER			
1st	RSGB / IARU Region 1 SSB Field Day	SSB	www.rsgbcc.org/hf
1st	All Asian DX Contest	Phone	www.jarl.org/English
2nd	Worked All Europe DX Contest	SSB	www.darc.de/referate/dx/contest/waedc/en/
3rd	Scandinavian Activity Contest	CW	http://www.sactest.net/blog/
4th	Scandinavian Activity Contest	SSB	http://www.sactest.net/blog/
Last	CQ WW RTTY Contest	RTTY	www.cqwwrtty.com
OCTOBER			
1st	Oceania DX Contest	Phone	www.oceaniadxcontest.com
1st (Sunday)	RSGB 21 / 28MHz Contest	SSB / CW	www.rsgbcc.org/hf
2nd	Oceania DX Contest	CW	www.oceaniadxcontest.com
Last	CQ World Wide DX Contest	Phone	www.cqww.com
NOVEMBER			
2nd	Worked All Europe DX Contest	RTTY	www.darc.de/referate/dx/contest/waedc/en/
2nd	Japan International DX Contest	SSB	http://jidx.org
Last	CQ World Wide DX Contest	CW	www.cqww.com
DECEMBER			
2nd	ARRL 10m Contest	Phone / CW	www.arrl.org/contest-calendar

Table 2: HF international contest calendar.

David Millard, M0GHZ's portable station for 432MHz AFS.

[10]. The RSGB Headquarters station is one of many stations around the world representing a country's national society. All such stations count as additional multipliers.

WAE DX Contests

In the 'Worked All Europe' contest Europe works the rest of the world. Extra points can be earned by DX stations sending back to European stations details of their previous QSOs (called 'QTCs'). The rules are quite complex and anyone intending to enter should first read the rules carefully [11]. This contest is organised by the German national society DARC.

RSGB VHF/UHF/MICROWAVE CONTESTS

RSGB organised contests on all bands above 30MHz are responsible to increased activity in Western Europe. Some are one-off events whilst many others occur several times a year, sometimes offering the opportunity to combine scores from several sessions. Most involve a contest exchange of serial number and Locator and almost all are multimode. Scoring is usually based on distance, sometimes enhanced by a multiplier.

Table 3 shows when the events are held. Note that the months given are from the 2015 calendar and may vary. See the *RSGB Yearbook* or the RSGB Contest Committee web site [E] for the dates and full rules.

Activity Contests

These are held every month throughout the year (except the Christmas period) with different bands on different weeks. All bands from 50MHz to 10GHz are included.

AFS Contests

These are for RSGB-affiliated societies. Entrants can compete in the Open (portable stations and multi-operator fixed stations) or Single Operator Fixed categories. There are events for 50, 144 and 432MHz.

RSGB VHF/UHF Contests Calendar

Activity contests are scheduled regularly during the year as follows:

Every 1st Tuesday of each month	144MHz
Every 2nd Tuesday of each month	432MHz
Every 3rd Tuesday of each month	1.3GHz
Every 4th Tuesday of each month (Jan-Nov Only)	2-3 - 10GHz
Every 4th Tuesday of each month (Jan-Nov Only)	50MHz
Every 5th Tuesday of each month	70MHz

In addition the following events are held each year. Contests may run concurrently or overlapping with others:

Month	Contest Name
February	432MHz AFS
	70MHz Cumulatives
March	144 432MHz
	70MHz Cumulatives
April	First 70MHz
	First 50MHz
May	432MHz-248GHz
	432MHz Trophy
	10GHz Trophy
	70MHz CW
	144MHz
	1st 144MHz Backpackers
	70MHz Cumulatives
June	2nd 144MHz Backpackers
	50MHz Trophy
	50MHz CW
	70MHz Cumulatives
July	VHF NFD
	3rd 144MHz Backpackers
	70MHz Trophy
August	144MHz Low Power
	4th 144MHz Backpackers
	432MHz Low Power
	70MHz Cumulatives
September	144MHz Trophy
	5th 144MHz Backpackers
	Second 70MHz Contest
October	1.2GHz Trophy / 2.3GHz Trophy
	432MHz-248GHz
	50MHz AFS
November	144MHz CW Marconi
December	144MHz AFS
	50/70/144/432MHz Christmas Cumulatives

Table 3: The VHF/UHF/SHF contests organised by the RSGB.

Cumulative Contests

These differ from most contests in that the Adjudicators will 'normailise' the score for each session (that is compare your points to the score of the leading station) and then pick your best sessions from your entries during the year. This should even up scores distorted by good conditions in one event.

CODE OF PRACTICE FOR VHF / UHF / SHF CONTESTS

1. Obtain permission from the landowner or agent before using the site and check that this permission includes right of access. Portable stations should observe the Country Code.

2. Take all possible steps to ensure that the site is not going to be used by some other group or club. Check with the club and last year's results table to see if any group used the site last year. If it is going to be used by another group, come to an amicable agreement before the event. Groups are advised to select possible alternative sites.

3. All transmitters generate unwanted signals; it is the level of these signals that matters. In operation from a good site, levels of spurious radiation, which may be acceptable from a home station, may well be found to be excessive to nearby stations (25 miles away or more).

4. Similarly, all receivers are prone to have spurious responses or to generate spurious signals in the presence of one or more strong signals, even if the incoming signals are of good quality. Such spurious responses may mislead an operator into believing that the incoming signal is at fault, when in fact the fault lies in the receiver.

5. If at all possible, critically test both receiver and transmitter for these undesirable characteristics, preferably by air test with a near neighbour before the contest. In the case of transmitters, aim to keep all in-amateur band spurious radiation, including noise modulation, to the lowest possible level. Levels expected of big stations are of the order of -60dBc at 10kHz spacing, rising to -100dBc at 50kHz spacing. Similarly, every effort should be made to ensure that the receiver has adequate dynamic range.

6. Remember that contesters cannot claim exclusive use of any part of any band. Please respect other operators at all times by avoiding using, or causing interference to, frequencies set aside for other legitimate users. This applies whether the other use is prescribed by an official bandplan (e.g. the 144.300MHz SSB calling frequency on 2m), by recognised code of practice (e.g. the 50.100-50.130MHz DX window on 6m), or by common convention (eg the GB2RS news broadcasts on 144.250MHz). If asked to QSY because of interference to any such use, please do so quickly and courteously.

7. Above all, be friendly and polite at all times. Be helpful and inform stations apparently radiating unwanted signals at troublesome levels, having first checked your own receiver. Try the effect of turning the antenna or inserting attenuators in the feedline; if the level of spurious signal changes relative to the wanted signal, then non-linear effects are occurring in the receiver. Some synthesised equipment has excessive local oscillator phase-noise, which will manifest itself as an apparent splatter on strong signals, even if there is no overloading of the receiver front-end. Pre-amplifiers should always be switched out to avoid overload problems when checking transmissions. If you receive a complaint, perform tests to check for receiver overload and try reducing drive levels and switching out linear amplifiers to determine a cure. Monitor your own signal off-air if possible. Remember that many linear amplifiers may not be linear at high power levels under field conditions with poorly regulated power supplies. The effects of over-driving will be more severe if speech processing is used, so pay particular attention to drive level adjustment. If asked to close down by a Government Official or the site owner, do so at once and without objectionable behaviour.

Stations may move location between cumulative activity periods.

144-432MHz March and 144MHz May Contests

In these 24-hour contests the categories of entrant, include Open, single operator fixed and 6-hours. The latter allows one or two operating periods totalling six hours.

50MHz and 70MHz Contests

Four short morning events that boost activity on these low VHF bands. There are two contests on each band, one for all modes and the other CW only.

432MHz-248GHz Contest

With one in the Spring and the other in the Autumn, these 24-hour contests cover no fewer than twelve bands, so they represent a particularly interesting challenge. The contests operate in conjunction with the three Trophy events described in the following paragraph.

432MHz, 1.3/2.3GHz and 10GHz Trophy

Arranged to coincide with the first few hours of one of the two 432MHz-248GHz events, these three 8-hour contests increase activity for the 24-hour contest whilst not requiring entrants to have the same level of commitment in time or equipment. The 432MHz and 10GHz events are in the Spring, whilst the 1.3/2,3GHz one is in the Autumn.

144MHz Backpackers

There are five of these 4-hour, all-mode portable events from May to September. The first of two categories of entrant caters for those using 3W or less and not housed in, or powered by, a vehicle. The other permits up to 10W and the station may be run from a vehicle, but must the engine must not be running (ie charging the battery). Most of the events coincide with another contest on the band. Unusually, the contest exchange includes the first two letters of the postcode. 50MHz CW Contest

50 and 70MHz Trophy Contests

Held in mid-Summer, these two events include multipliers in the scoring system. On 50MHz the score is multiplied by the number of countries and Locator squares worked, whilst on 70MHz it is postcodes and Locator squares.

VHF National Field Day (VHF NFD)

The biggest portable contest in the calendar is mainly for clubs and groups to enter. It coincides with similar events elsewhere in Europe, so lots of activity is guaranteed. All bands from 50MHz to 1.3GHz are included and the various categories of entrant ensure that even the smallest club can compete. There's even a category for fixed stations, but with certain restrictions.

The Code of Practice for VHF/UHF/SHF Contests (shown above) is particularly relevant to those taking part in this event.

144MHz and 432MHz Low Power Contests

Catering for both portable and fixed stations, the maximum power allowed is 25W. The single-band contests are held on consecutive days over a single weekend. The 144MHz event coincides with the 144MHz Backpackers contest.

50/70/144/432MHz Christmas Cumulatives

Held over four consecutive days starting on Boxing Day, This covers four bands, 50, 70, 144 and 432MHz, Unusually, scoring is one point be contact regardless of distance, multiplied by the number of countries and Locator squares.

THE INTERNET AND COMPUTING

Because the process of adjudication described above inevitably takes many weeks or months for a major contest, several informal means have evolved for contesters to compare notes and their claimed scores shortly after a contest has taken place. The '3830 Scores' [12] has become a focal point for posting claimed scores for many of the more popular international contests. There are also similar systems on the Internet specifically set up for contesters to share news and views, of which the US-based CQ-Contest reflector is the best known. In the UK, there are Yahoo groups for HF contesting [13] and VHF/UHF contesting [14] as well as one for the IOTA contest [15].

If it seems that contesting is heavily software and Internet-based, that is no surprise. Contesters are, by their very nature, a competitive sub-group within our hobby, and use every new development that comes along if it helps them achieve higher scores, reduces their overall workload, or generally improves their lot (like getting contest results out quicker).

The Cluster system was introduced in the first instance by one of the US east coast contest groups, to enable their members to exchange data about contest multipliers. Only later did it come into use as a tool for the wider DXing community.

Just a few of the magnificent trophies awarded each year to winners of RSGB contests.

Nowadays there are those who argue that the *Cluster* system should be turned off during major contests, obviously unaware of the network's genesis!

Cluster

Which takes us nicely to the use of the Cluster system in contests. The use of 'spotting' during contests goes back to when multi-operator contest categories were first introduced. Major contest clubs would have several operators at the contest site, but would encourage other club member to tune the bands and pass information about contest multipliers to the main station. Once *Cluster* nodes had grown up around the world and been linked, single-operator contesters saw its potential for helping them to achieve higher scores. But clearly that would put contesters without the facility at a disadvantage. Contest organisers responded in various ways. The most common is that entrants are welcome to use the *Cluster* to aid their contest efforts, but are put into a separate 'Assisted' category where they compete with others who have done the same, or are classified along with multi-operator entrants (the latter is the case with most RSGB contests).

Skimmer

CW Skimmer is a very clever piece of software which is described in detail in Chapter 4. Briefly, Skimmer takes signals from a receiver, processes them using the computer's sound card and produces a waterfall display of the part of the spectrum being received, decoding and identifying all CW signals it finds within that spectrum. The amount of spectrum received and decoded is dependent on the IF bandwidth of the receiver: this could be, say, 500Hz if a CW filter is used, 2.4kHz if an SSB filter is used, or even up to 192kHz if *Skimmer* is used in conjunction with a software defined radio (SDR). *Skimmer* can thus be used to record all the CW activity on the band, and later to play back the entire range of signals heard. This could well become a powerful adjudication tool for contest organisers.

The ability of *CW Skimmer* to decode and simultaneously identify all the stations operating within the CW part of a band clearly has serious implications for CW contesting, and its release caused some controversy among contesters. The

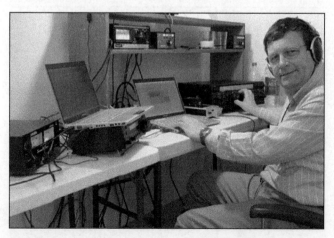

G4CWH operating as a guest operator at VP9GE's station.

argument goes that the use of *Skimmer* debases one of the most important skills a CW contester has: the ability to tune across the band in 'search and pounce' mode, locating and identifying new multipliers or simply stations that have not been worked before. With *Skimmer*, this is all done for you: you know the callsign, you know the frequency, all you have to do is go to that frequency and work the station. In a way, this is similar to the *DX Cluster*, but a major difference is that with a *Cluster* spot you are never sure that you will be able to receive the station being spotted until you move your receiver to that frequency. With *Skimmer*, your receiver is already actually receiving the station concerned. Of course, the technology also exists to allow *Skimmer* to be used with remote receivers located anywhere in the world.

The competitive advantage of *Skimmer* is that it can identify a new station calling "CQ contest" on the band within seconds of that station appearing, allowing a contest operator to click on a spot, work the station and claim points without having done the hard work of searching out the signal manually.

Contest organisers have responded in various ways. Some have decided that *Skimmer* puts its users at an unfair advantage and have prohibited its use in their contests. Others, including the organisers of the *CQ* World Wide DX CW contest, take a more pragmatic view and, realising that there will always be technological developments that challenge existing notions of what is 'right' or fair, allow the use of *Skimmer*, but put Single Operator users in the 'Assisted' category, the same as those who use the *Cluster* network.

PORTABLE & GUEST CONTESTING

Everything that has been said so far applies as much to VHF contests as to HF contests. Perhaps the major difference with VHF contests is that, for many entrants, it makes sense to operate away from home if you want to achieve a good score. Long-distance VHF propagation is much more reliant on a high, or at least a clear, takeoff, which isn't possible from many suburban locations.

Rather than deal with portable operating here, it is covered in Chapter 12, as it is also applicable to special event and DXpedition operations. Of course, some HF contests will require portable operation, too, especially the Field Day events.

Another way to achieve a higher score in a contest than you might from home is to become a guest operator at another amateur's station. This can be an informal arrangement, but some amateurs offer their stations for rental for the major contests, especially if those stations are on exotic islands and ready-equipped with antennas, transceiver and amplifier. *The World Licensing and Operating Directory* [16] lists many stations available for rent.

AMATEUR RADIO DIRECTION FINDING

Amateur radio direction finding (ARDF) in the UK goes back to the mid 20th century when competitions were run using the 1.8MHz band. This tradition is continued to the present day with competitions organised by the British Top-Band DF Association [17]. These competitions generally involve locating two hidden transmitters and take place across most of an Ordnance Survey 1:50,000 map sheet. There are eight qualifying rounds each year prior to a three transmitter National Final in September. The 1950 RSGB Council Cup is awarded to the winner although the competitions are no longer promoted by or run directly by the RSGB. The British Top-Band DF Association organise other smaller events, some of which take place after dark.

The arrival of the commercial VHF hand-held radio in the 1970s spawned a different kind of direction finding competition generally using the 144MHz band. These events are organised by local clubs. Usually a club member parks up in the countryside and makes a series of transmissions using a mobile 144MHz radio. The other club members attempt to locate him and the event often concludes by comparing notes in a local hostelry.

In continental Europe, things developed along a different track. At the time, only in Great Britain, Ireland and Czechoslovakia were amateurs allowed to operate on 1.8MHz, so countries wishing to introduce surface wave direction finding simply used the lowest frequency band available to them, which was 3.5MHz.

Today, this choice is embodied in the set of rules supported by the IARU and also in thousands of DF receivers for this band across the world. Region 1 of the IARU has an ARDF Working Group responsible for the formulation of rules and since by far the greatest interest is in Europe, it is usual for Regions 2 and 3 to adopt the rules originating in Region 1.

Now there are many competitions, including World championships, Region 1 championships, youth championships and various national events. Competitions are organised using both the 3.5MHz band, where propagation is predictable and good bearings are generally obtained, and the 144MHz band, which exhibits significant multi-path propagation, sometimes leading to misleading bearings being obtained. The competitions take place entirely on foot and no motor vehicles are involved.

This international style of ARDF made rather a late start in the UK, with the first event being held in 2002. Many European countries have 50 years of experience, especially in the old Eastern Bloc countries and that has made them dominant at world level.

Direction finding competitions involving motor vehicles may well be regarded as illegal in the UK nowadays. Therefore, the RSGB now promotes and directly supports ARDF competitions using the IARU rules and which take place solely on foot. In this way the provisions of the 1988 Road Traffic Act are not contravened in any way.

Introduction to the IARU Rules

Five low-power transmitters are deployed in the area to be used. If 3.5MHz is being used the output power is 3W and on 144MHz it is 800mW. All the transmitters operate on the same frequency but not all at the same time. They transmit in sequence and send an identifier in Morse code for one minute each. It is not necessary to know the Morse code: the identifier is simply a matter of dot counting.

The first transmitter sends the letters MOE in Morse. The first two letters involve all dashes and serve to keep the transmitter on the air for a while to allow the competitor to swing the aerial carried and assess the direction of the transmitter. The last letter is a single dot, so one dot denotes transmitter 1. This transmitter sends for one minute before shutting down.

The second transmitter then radiates the Morse sequence MOI. The last letter (I) is two dots to denote transmitter number 2. Transmitters 3, 4 and 5 transmit MOS, MOH and MO5 respectively. (see **Fig 1**).

In the UK it is now a licence condition that the callsign of the supervising licensed amateur is radiated at the end of each transmission, so the one minute transmission terminates with a burst of higher speed Morse code which is this callsign.

In addition to the five hidden transmitters, there is a beacon transmitter operating on a different frequency, which radiates the letters MO repeatedly in Morse and is interrupted at intervals with the callsign of the supervising licensed amateur. This transmission is continuous and enables competitors who get hopelessly lost to simply DF the beacon to find their way to the finish.

All the transmitters use some form of omni-directional antenna. For 3.5MHz an 8m vertical wire with an 8m counterpoise is frequently deployed and 144MHz a pair of crossed horizontal dipoles or turnstile antenna at a height of about three metres is commonplace.

Clearly it is necessary for the competitor to demonstrate that each assigned transmitter has been visited and this can be done in one of two ways:

a) The competitor carries a control card with a space for each of the five hidden transmitters plus one for the beacon if the latter is to be registered. At each transmitter there is a needle punch, which is used to mark a unique pattern of needle holes in the card. In international competition the beacon will be 'punched' but practice varies in domestic races.

b. Electronic timing equipment may be used. Each competitor carries a microchip, which is inserted into a unit at each transmitter. The transmitter writes its identity plus the time of the visit to the microchip. At the completion of the

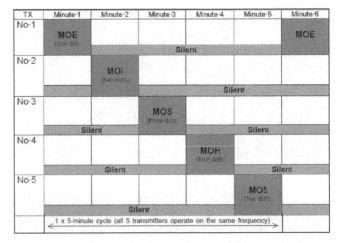

Fig 1: The timing of the five hidden transmitters.

course, the competitor downloads all the data to a computer, which is able to print the time taken, the transmitters visited and all the split times.

ARDF is organised into a series of age categories (**Table 4**). To explain how the system works, consider the age group M21. The M denotes a male age group. A man enters the M21 class on 1 January of the year in which he becomes 21 and leaves it on 1 January of the year in which he becomes 40 (M40 being the next age group). The older age groups hunt fewer transmitters over shorter distances than the younger age groups.The result of this is that competition is against one's peers and this broadens the appeal of this radio sport considerably.

Men	Women
M19	W19
M21	W21
M40	W35
M50	W50
M60	W60
M70	-

Table 4: ARDF competition adult age categories.

There are three further rules, which can be of great significance depending on the shape and size of the area used for the competition. No transmitters can be placed within 750 metres of the start. In domestic competition, this distance is frequently reduced to 400m to avoid 'sterilising' a large part of a small wood as far as transmitter placement is concerned. The second restriction is that there can be no transmitter within 400m of the finish. Finally, transmitters must be placed at least 400m apart.

A time limit is rigorously enforced for competitions with the rule that any competitor over time is placed below a competitor who has found at least one transmitter and is within the time limit. It can be rather galling to find all five transmitters and come in one minute outside the time to be beaten by someone who took nearly two hours to find just one transmitter. The time limit is decided by the course planner, but two hours is a frequent choice with ninety minutes for easier areas. The object of this rule is to constrain those competitors who are determined to find all the transmitters at any cost, even if this sees them still hunting as darkness falls.

Equipment Required

Competitors will require a receiver for the frequency band being used and a directional antenna for that band. These two items are normally combined into one unit and at UK events there is usually equipment available on loan, although it is sensible to confirm this with the organiser beforehand. The receiver should be an AM/SSB receiver, since the direction to the hidden transmitters will be determined by swinging the antenna from side to side and noting changes in signal amplitude. The amplitude limiter in an FM receiver makes it less suitable for this task, although it can still work in this application.

There is a need to plot bearings on the map provided at the start. Beginners should plot more bearings than experienced competitors. To do this, the map should be taped to a lightweight board of some kind and either a spirit pen or a chinagraph (wax) pencil can then be used to mark the map. Lines can drawn by both of these markers on any clear plastic covering used to protect the map. Neither of them will run if they later become wet but only the chinagraph will make a satisfactory mark if the plastic is already wet.

A compass will be required to measure the bearings and the type with a rectangular base plate also doubles as a protractor. The compass is best looped round the wrist with the cord normally provided. Proving the visit made to each transmitter involves carrying either a control card or an electronic 'chip' (colloquially known as a 'dibber'). The dibber is a plastic encased microchip used for electronic 'punching'. It is on a small elastic strap which allows it to be attached to the index finger. The control card is best pinned with safety pins to the front of the clothing.

A whistle should be carried and in some competitions is mandatory. The emergency signal is six blasts of the whistle at one-minute intervals. Also desirable is a circle stencil to mark the circles around the start and the finish in which no controls can be placed. Obviously a different stencil is required for a map at 1:10,000 scale to one at 1:15,000 scale. A check list is given in **Table 5**.

Competition hints

Pre-start: There is normally five minutes after being given the map and before getting the signal to start, in which the competitor is able to:

Item carried	Notes
Receive	Usually fixed to the antenna.
Antenna	Usually fixed to the receiver.
Map	Normally issued at the start line, 5 or 10 minutes before starting.
Lightweight rigid board for the map	To deal with wet weather conditions, the competitor will need waterproofing (a plastic folder or sticky backed plastic film) to cover the map and possibly tape to fix the map to the board.
Compass	The type with a rectangular back-plate doubles as a protractor.
Spirit pens and / or wax pencils	Will not run if it rains but note that only wax pencils will write satisfactorily on plastic film that is already wet.
Circle stencil	750 and 400 m circles at the map scale in use
Control Card or SI 'dibber'	To register that the competitor has visited each assigned transmitter.
Whistle	Emergency signal is 6 blasts at 1-minute intervals.

Table 5: Check list of equipment to be carried for an ARDF competition.

- waterproof and protect the map as deemed appropriate for the weather conditions,
- on the map, draw a 750m circle around the start and a 400m circle around the finish (in domestic competition the 750m start circle is often reduced to 400m),
- study the map to identify height features in particular.

Start + 5 minutes: After being given the start signal, the rules oblige the competitor to keep moving to the end of the start funnel. Once at the end the aim should be to listen to each transmitter in turn, assess the strength of the signal and plot the bearing – all within the 60 seconds that it is on the air. Prior practice at this procedure will pay big dividends for the beginner. If the 144MHz band is being used, bearings taken from high spots are more accurate than those taken from valleys. It may pay to sacrifice a complete transmitter cycle and climb to the top of a nearby hill or spur from which more accurate bearings can be obtained.

Decision time: Based on the information gained by listening just once to each of the transmitters, the most important decision of the day must be made. This is the choice of the first transmitter to be visited. In the case of a co-located start / finish, the penalties for getting it wrong are not as severe compared to a split start / finish. With a co-located start and finish, a poor choice can often be rectified on the route back from the furthest transmitters to the finish. When the start and finish are at separate locations, a bad decision may mean a lot of 'back tracking' and hence wasted time.

Bearing quality: The surface wave propagation on 3.5MHz during daytime leads to bearings which are generally pretty accurate. While it is wise to avoid wire fences and overhead power lines when taking bearings, the accuracy of the plotted bearing is determined by the equipment and skill of the competitor. This results in fast runners being able to get to the transmitters first, assuming that they also have reasonable direction finding skills.

On 144MHz, there is a lot of multi-path propagation with the signal being reflected or scattered from steep hillsides, rock outcrops and even the edges of wooded areas. The bearings obtained vary greatly in 'quality'. A sharp, clear peak in the signal as the antenna is swung from side to side, is indicative of a single path signal and this is often the direct path from the transmitter. Multi-path propagation most often reveals itself as a rather diffuse bearing as the antenna is swung. Sometimes there may be more than one distinct peak to the signal and this is where an antenna with very low side and back responses comes into its own to differentiate between the direct and the multi-path signals. All this interpretation of bearings coupled with the need to view the bearings against the background of any high ground in the vicinity; leads to the winner needing to process all this information quickly and accurately. Hence, being able to run fast is no longer such a key quality to gain victory.

On the course: Here are some 'top tips' for use during the competition itself:
- As mentioned earlier, it can pay big dividends to be located high up when taking bearings on 144MHz. Bearings thus taken should get a better accuracy 'rating' than those obtained in valleys.

- When trying to decide the direction of the incoming signal on 144MHz, it is wise to move about by some tens of metres at right angles to the perceived direction of arrival of the signal and to observe any changes to the direction and the sharpness of the bearing. Some places will give a much sharper and clearer bearing than others and this is often a more accurate result. On 3.5MHz bearings are much more reliable although wire fences and power lines should be avoided, as mentioned above.
- Try to locate yourself at a track / path / forest road crossing as the wanted transmitter is about to come on the air. This gives a choice of four (or more) directions in which it is possible to move freely in response to the direction of the incoming signal.
- When some distance from the transmitter (as indicated by the signal strength still being at the low or medium level), use the path network to move roughly in the direction of the transmitter without necessarily heading through the forest down the exact bearing obtained.
- As you hunt down the first transmitters try to build up some sort of mental picture about the location of the remaining transmitters. This might be relatively vague, eg 'numbers 3 and 4 are the other side of the road and I will hunt them when I have found all the transmitters on this side'.
- The transmitters all radiate similar power and use near identical antennas. Signal strength is a guide to the distance to the transmitter, especially on 3.5MHz. On 144MHz this needs to be looked at with the topography of the area in mind. Range estimation is only ever going to be approximate but even this level of accuracy can pay big dividends. It is a skill well worth acquiring but it only comes with experience.
- When the signal strength is getting distinctly loud, position yourself in any relatively runnable terrain so that you can manoeuvre freely when the transmitter next fires up.
- Keep turning down the gain of the receiver as you get close to the transmitter. The human ear is relatively insensitive to changes in volume when the audio is set at a high level. The direction of arrival will be determined more accurately at modest audio levels.
- If you are trying to run down the transmitter in the 60 seconds that it is sending and it goes off the air, transfer the direction to the compass and carefully continue to run down the same bearing looking for the flag.
- If the transmitter is sending as you move quickly along a straight path and the bearing appears to alter, then you are close to the transmitter and are moving past it.
- Finally, whenever a transmitter comes on the air, always re-check the sense on 3.5MHz and on 144MHz check the signal strength from behind you. You would not be the first competitor to run past a transmitter and then be oblivious to the fact that it now lies to the rear.

Your First ARDF Event

Finding out about competitions is clearly the first step and there are currently around 15 – 20 held in the UK each year. There is usually a break around Christmas and January and the 'season' generally commences in February with the last event in November or December. The ARDF page on the

RSGB President, John Gould, G3WKL, presents the 144MHz salver to Andrew, G4KWQ as he becomes 2014 British Champion on this band.

RSGB website [18] is the gateway to information about ARDF events.

As far as clothing is concerned, for a first outing, stout shoes and outdoor attire is sufficient. As you become more committed, studded orienteering shoes, gaiters to protect the lower leg against brambles and nettles and an orienteering suit are more appropriate. On occasions when the weather is particularly inclement, a cagoule or other waterproof garment will be needed.

Events that are run in conjunction with an orienteering event will benefit from the direction signs to that event. ARDF events that are freestanding are not likely to be extensively signed so the competitor should ensure that a copy of the Grid Reference and of the map extract that is frequently given with the event details, are carried on the journey to the venue. Once there, it is necessary to register and pay the event fee (usually of the order of £5 - £6). This provides for entry for all the competitions taking place on the day. There is usually a full scale event in the morning followed by a lower key competition after lunch. All of this provides an excellent day of radio sport and makes it well worth while to travel a fair distance for a full day of radio in the open air.

At registration you may have to make a choice regarding the number of transmitters you wish to hunt. Details of the frequencies of the transmitters (hidden transmitters on one frequency and the homing beacon on a second frequency), the radius of the zone around the start in which transmitters may not be placed and your individual start time will be given to you. Finally, the time limit for the event should be noted.

If electronic timing is being used, it will probably be necessary for you to hire a dibber. If pin punching is in use, you will be given a control card. Fill this out with your details, if it is made of plain paper or thin card protect and strengthen it with Sellotape, and pin it to the front of your clothing with safety pins.

An orienteering style map will be in use and the most common scale in domestic competition is 1:10,000. These maps show much more ground detail than an Ordnance Survey map. The first thing to note is that the white bits are trees – quite the opposite to an Ordnance Survey map. The white parts of the map denote runnable forest and various shades of green show less runnable areas with dark green being really impenetrable and well worth avoiding. Fortunately it is very unlikely to have transmitters located in these latter areas. Open and semi-open areas are shown in a yellow ochre colour. Only the start (a triangle) and the finish (a double circle with a smaller circle inside a larger one) will be marked on the map.

The previous section covering 'competition hints' should give a guide about how to proceed. In simple terms, listen to all of the transmitters to get a bearing and an idea of signal strength of each one, decide which transmitter you wish to visit first and then head for the one selected. Finding your very first hidden transmitter is a great moment and one to be remembered for a long time. Keep an eye on the clock, so that you get back to the finish inside the time, and see if more transmitters can be located.

Newcomers are usually a bit erratic in their first events, as is to be expected. For some a brilliant performance at the first outing can be followed by poor and disappointing results at subsequent events. Experience tells us that it takes about six outings for the majority of competitors to settle in and be able to locate all the assigned transmitters inside the time on a reliable basis. In other words don't get discouraged by a few poor results; it will all come together for you with a bit of experience.

After finishing there is the opportunity to compare notes with other competitors and to get some tips on how to avoid any mistakes at future events.

OTHER VARIETIES OF ARDF

There are two variants of the IARU direction finding format, one covered by the IARU rules and the other not.

FoxOring

This format is quite popular in Western Europe and in the UK it is often used to add a lower key second competition on a day of ARDF, or alternatively to introduce ARDF to Orienteers. It is a combination of Orienteering and ARDF. The competitor is given a map with a number of control circles marked. The organiser guarantees that the hidden transmitter associated with each control circle will be audible on a receiver of reasonable sensitivity if the competitor stands inside the circle. However, there is no guarantee that the hidden transmitter will itself be located inside the circle and often it is not. The output amplifier of the transmitter is usually a pair of CMOS 4001 gates in parallel, so it is seriously low power! The range of the transmitter depends on the sensitivity of the receiver but ranges of 100 – 200 metres can be expected. Sometimes organisers will use bigger antennas to give ranges up to about 400m.

The competitor has to navigate using map and compass, to the location of the circle. Once there, the transmitter will become audible. In the UK the transmitters are modulated with the Morse letter corresponding to its identifying letter printed alongside the circle on the map. A knowledge of Morse code is not needed because the competitor can just focus on the characteristic sound from each transmitter, although a key for Morse code is normally provided anyway. In some cases the transmitters radiate continuously but at other times they can be set up to radiate for a part of each minute. Radiating times of 30 seconds, 20 seconds and 10 seconds in each minute can be selected by the organiser.

Once the signal has been picked up as the control circle is approached, the competitor now uses direction finding skills to locate the transmitter. Signal strength plays a more important part than is the case for the normal competitions. This is because the competitor is quite close to the transmitter and any movement on his or her part can be a significant fraction of the distance to the transmitter, which results in a noticeable change in signal strength.

A typical FoxOring competition would see between seven and 10 transmitters deployed. The format is a lot of fun since the transmitters can be hunted down quickly and there is far less standing around waiting for the 'target' transmitter to come on the air, compared to the full rules. Competitions often take place in a much smaller area than the ones with five full power (3W on 3.5MHz and 800mW on 144MHz) transmitters operating.

Sprint ARDF

The rules of ARDF that came into force on 1 January 2010 provide for a sprint format as an optional component of a World or IARU Regional Championship. This is designed to raise the profile of ARDF to a wider audience of the general public and the media, by making this radio sport more of a spectator event. It is designed to be staged in parks or areas with easy public access, adjacent to towns and cities.

These events use the 3.5MHz band and have a total of 10 hidden transmitters deployed. These are in two groups of five using two different frequencies with one group having fast keying and the other slow keying. The transmitters use lower power than normal (0.3 – 1.0W) and are also spaced much closer than usual with at least 100 metres between transmitters and no transmitters located within 100 metres of the start and finish. Each group of five transmitters operate in a one minute cycle with each transmitter sending for 12 seconds. In addition to the 10 hidden transmitters, there is one transmitter on a third frequency at the spectator control and finally a finish beacon on a fourth frequency. It is possible to combine the spectator control and the finish beacon into a single transmitter which would then be 'punched' twice.

Each competitor runs through the start corridor, which leads to the area with transmitters No 1 to No 5 (slow keying). After finding all the required transmitters from this loop,

he / she runs to a spectator control and through the spectator corridor to the area with transmitters No 1F to No 5F (fast keying). After finding all the required transmitters from this loop, the competitor runs to the finish beacon and through the finishing corridor to the finish line. The expected winning time should be approximately 15 minutes. The map scale used is typically 1:5,000.

Further Information

This description of competitive direction finding cannot be exhaustive in the space available in this book. The RSGB book *Radio Orienteering – The ARDF Handbook* [19] goes into much fuller detail and is essential reading for the beginner. Event information is available on the RSGB website [20] with results of competitions, details of the big international events and sources of suitable equipment. An article 'Getting Started in ARDF' appeared in *RadCom* in 2014 [21].

REFERENCES

[1] World Radiosport Team Championship: http://wrtc.info
[2] CQ WW DX Contest: www.cqww.com
[3] SM3CER contest pages: www.sk3bg.se/contest
[4] WA7BNM contest pages: www.hornucopia.com/contestcal
[5] *RSGB Yearbook*, RSGB, published annually. Available from the RSGB Book Shop at www.rsgbshop.org
[6] RSGB HF contests: www.rsgbcc.org
[7] ARRL contests page: www.arrl.org/contests
[8] http://www.rsgbcc.org/hf/information/scc.shtml
[9] CQ WPX Contest: www.cqwpx.com
[10] IARU HF Championship: www.arrl.org/iaru-hf-championship
[11] WAE DX Contest rules: www.darc.de/referate/dx/contest/waedc/en/
[12] www.3830scores.com
[13] http://groups.yahoo.com/group/uk-hf-contesting
[14] http://groups.yahoo.com/group/uk-vhf-contesting
[15] https://groups.yahoo.com/group/iota-contest
[16] *World Licensing and Operating Directory*, Steve Telenius-Lowe, 9M6DXX, RSGB 2008. Available from the RSGB Book Shop at www.rsgbshop.org
[17] British Top-Band DF Assoc: www.topbanddf.org.uk
[18] RSGB ARDF page: www.nationalradiocentre.co.uk/ardf/
[19] *Radio Orienteering – The ARDF Handbook*, Bob Titterington, G3ORY; David Williams, M3WDD, and David Deane, G3ZOI, RSGB 2007. Available from the RSGB Book Shop at http://www.rsgbshop.org
[20] http://rsgb.org/events/rsgb-events-site/radio-sport/ardf-events/
[21] 'Getting started in ARDF', *RadCom*, Feb 2014.

12 Mobile and Portable Operating, Special Event Stations

W HILE THERE IS a huge amount of fun to be gained from operating our home stations, one of the joys of the hobby is that, because radio waves travel happily through the ether, we can conduct our operations from almost anywhere. This includes mobile and portable operation, special event stations set up at local and national events and venues, and DXpedition operating in every sense, from activating a hilltop for the Summits on the Air [1] programme to participating in a major DXpedition to a remote tropical or Antarctic island. And with the advent of cheap air fares, ever more compact transceivers, and international licensing agreements, especially through the CEPT Licence, there are few barriers to taking your hobby with you around the world. This chapter addresses these matters, giving some pointers for successful operations away from home.

MOBILE OPERATING

Mobile operating has been popular almost since the dawn of amateur radio, but is so much more accessible nowadays with compact, yet highly-featured transceivers, and a huge network of repeaters developed primarily to enable mobile operators to extend their range. Internet-linked digital repeaters have increased the possibilities.

Although the approach in this book overall has been to try to minimise the historical distinction between HF and VHF operation, it remains quite relevant to mobile operation. Mobile operators fall very much into two categories.

Firstly, there are those who enjoy the ability to chat with other local amateurs, perhaps during the commute to the office, using one of the VHF / UHF bands, usually through a repeater. This allows reliable communications over a relatively wide area, provided that the mobile station is effectively line-of-site to the repeater. In some parts of the world, where repeaters can be set up high on mountains, mobile to mobile range can extend to well over 100 miles. The use of channelised operation and repeaters with a wide coverage area allows the mobile operator to communicate safely, as there is little or no necessity to adjust the transceiver once a contact has been established. With Internet linking (Chapter 12), even VHF operators can enjoy world-wide contacts from their mobile stations.

The other category of mobile operators is those who operate on the HF bands. Often this is done as an alternative to struggling from an unsuitable home location. Although a mobile operator is constrained by way of antennas (even on 10m, a full-size quarter-wave vertical is about 8ft long), there are compensations. The mobile operator can find an unrestricted hilltop or seaside location, taking advantage of the propagation benefits of such sites, and perhaps avoiding EMC problems that might occur from home. In many cases, the actual operation will take place while the car is stationary, to allow attention to be focused on tuning the transceiver,

perhaps setting up for split-frequency operation, making adjustments for interference and changing signal strengths, and all the other aspects that are part and parcel of HF operating. The more successful HF mobile operators have country totals which would be the envy of many fixed-station operators, and there are some fascinating success stories even on the low bands, for example New Zealand to Europe on 80m, with the mobile station at the New Zealand end located right on the coast for best signal take-off.

Equipment

Mobile transceivers have to contend with relatively inefficient antennas, high electrical noise levels and rapidly fluctuating signals. A high-sensitivity receiver is required, with efficient AGC and a noise blanker (SSB) or with excellent limiting characteristics and a correctly adjusted squelch (FM). The acoustic noise level will be high and a reasonable audio output of about 2W will be found necessary.

Adequate protection of the RF power amplifier against high VSWR is essential. Many mobile antennas exhibit high VSWR when wet, and if a loaded whip is used this may well have a narrow bandwidth, giving a high VSWR when operated away from their resonant frequency. Many modern HF and VHF / UHF transceivers feature automatic ATUs which can be very useful in allowing the matching of a mobile whip which is slightly off-resonance. However, such radios are larger than those without ATUs and space considerations may necessitate the use of one of the separate remote-controlled ATUs which can be mounted elsewhere in the vehicle.

Mobile safety is paramount, and this demands a minimum of easy-to-operate controls with clear and unambiguous dials and meters, preferably illuminated at night.

The 12V power requirements should not exceed the spare capacity of the vehicle generation system. In practice this

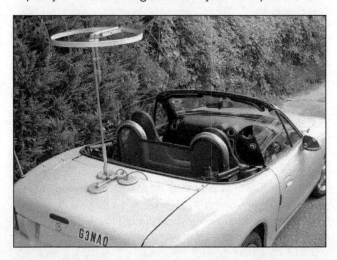

G3NAQ designed and built this antenna for 2m SSB operation from his car. Note the substantial magnetic mount.

may, for example, confine the use of a 100W HF transceiver to daylight hours when the vehicle lights are not required. The average vehicle voltages fluctuate considerably and are 'spiky'; therefore internal transceiver voltage regulation and over-voltage protection are very desirable. Vehicle interference may be a problem and require suppression.

A mobile transceiver should be small enough to fit in or under the dashboard - such transceivers are available in HF as well as VHF / UHF models from all the major manufacturers Some transceivers are available with a remote head for the dashboard, allowing the rest of the rig to be tucked away out of sight. Security is increasingly a problem for equipment mounted in vehicles and such head units can be easily stowed out of sight in a glove box or even taken away from the vehicle. No matter what the attractions of larger equipments are, they will demand special mountings which will spoil the car interior and may lack operating convenience.

Rugged mechanical construction is essential, because a great deal of vibration will be encountered. Extremes of temperature and humidity are common in vehicles.

When planning a mobile installation, consideration should be given to the possibility of using the transceiver in other modes of operation, particularly as a portable station, where the requirements are in many ways similar. For example, if a hand-portable SSB or FM transceiver is available, all that needs to be done is to obtain an add-on RF amplifier and antenna, and leave these permanently in the vehicle.

Expensive radio equipment left permanently attached to the vehicle should always be insured against theft [2] as the driver's ordinary insurance may not cover this eventuality. A burglar alarm should always be fitted and, if possible, the transceiver disguised or removed completely when not in use.

Last but not least, it is important to ensure that the radio equipment will not affect the vehicle's electronics. This is increasingly an issue with the complex electronic engine management systems in many cars, and some models have proven to be particularly susceptible to RF, especially at the power levels typically used on the HF bands.

Mobile Antennas

The best positions for HF mobile whip antennas are the rear wings or the rear bumper bar. Commercially-made bumper mounts are available and can considerably lessen the risk of unsatisfactory mounting.

Many modern vehicles have plastic bumpers and therefore care needs to be taken to ensure that an effective earth connection to the bodywork of the car can be obtained so that the performance is not compromised. If the car is fitted with a towing hitch, this can also serve as a very effective mounting point for a HF antenna. The ideal position for VHF or UHF mobile antennas is the centre of the roof, but this is not always possible or desirable for other reasons. Various types of mounting are available for those who do not wish to drill the car metalwork. These include gutter mounts, window-clip mounts, magnetic mounts and boot-lip mounts. An alternative method of mounting HF antennas is the triple magnetic mount which is quite an effective way of mounting an HF whip, although difficulties may be experienced when travelling at

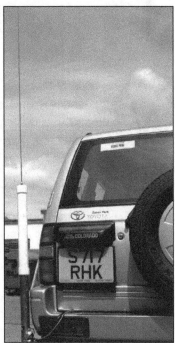

Rear bumper mounting of an HF mobile whip antenna [Photo Peter Dodd, G3LDO].

high speed, especially if there are gusty cross winds.

Whatever antenna is chosen, the fixing must be mechanically strong enough not to be damaged when the vehicle is travelling at high speed, or succumb to a blow caused by a low-hanging branch or other obstruction. Care should also be taken that the antenna does not project horizontally from the vehicle, even at speed, in such a way that it becomes a danger to other vehicles or pedestrians.

A good place to mount a large HF antenna on a four-wheel drive or similar vehicle is the front bullbar, because the support is very rugged. You can also see the antenna and so be confident that it can clear overhanging obstructions. The only downside is that the antenna feed has to be routed through the engine compartment, which can lead to interference problems.

On the HF bands, the antenna system is the most critical component in any mobile installation, even more so than with fixed stations. The whip antenna with loading coil normally used has a low feedpoint impedance and a narrow bandwidth, and this involves careful tuning and matching for optimum results. There are several types of commercial HF mobile antenna available, including base and centre loaded designs using loading coils (eg the Hustler range), helically wound (such as the Australian 'Outbacker' type) and the 'Screwdriver' design (eg High Sierra and Little Tarheel), which are popular. The latter design has a motor-driven loading coil which can be remotely adjusted from inside the car, allowing the operator to change frequency and even bands without having to stop the vehicle.

Most VHF FM operators use a 5/8-wave whip mounted on the rear wings, although in some cases this may have only marginal advantages over a 1/4-wave whip mounted on the roof. The most popular UHF antenna is the collinear, usually roof mounted. However, dual or even triple-band antennas are growing in popularity as they can cover two or three bands with only one mounting. All popular VHF and UHF mobile antennas are a good match to 50-ohm coaxial cable, and no special matching circuit is necessary.

Mobile Safety

In the UK, The Highway Code [3] warns against the dangers of operating equipment while mobile. The current edition states (rule 149): "You MUST exercise proper control of your vehicle at all times. You MUST NOT use a hand-held mobile phone, or similar device, when driving or when supervising a learner driver, except to call 999 or 112 in a genuine emergency when it is unsafe or impractical to stop. Never use a hand-held microphone when driving. Using hands-free equipment is also likely to distract your attention from the road. It is far safer not to use any telephone while you are driving or riding - find a safe place to stop first or use the voicemail facility and listen to messages later."

The Department of Transport, in a letter to the RSGB, adds: "*The Highway Code* is an advisory code of practice in that a failure to observe any of its provisions is not in itself an offence. Such failure, however, may be used in any court proceedings which may arise. Current legislation already places the responsibility on drivers to have proper control of their vehicles at all times. A motorist who fails to do so as a result of distraction or lack of concentration is liable to prosecution".

Well-known mobile operator Peter Dodd, G3LDO, commented: "These days there are a lot of very nice lightweight boom microphones available, with or without the single earpiece (don't use a double earpiece headset), which are much more convenient than the fist microphone. I found the combination of boom microphone and VOX a pleasant operating experience - rather like talking to a passenger in the car. I have learned to suppress the unguarded 'remark' when someone cuts you up or pulls out in front of you!"

A wireless unit offers a neat way of providing hands-free mobile operation. The basic necessity is to leave both hands free for driving and to allow the driver's head unrestricted movement, while keeping the mouth-microphone distance roughly constant. A lightweight microphone similar to those used for hands-free mobile phones is ideal. Whichever alternative is chosen, operators should bear in mind the recommendations of the *Highway Code* and the need to maintain good audio quality. This can only be achieved by making sure that the microphone is reasonably close to the operator's mouth and that the audio gain is not excessive. It may be that if the vehicle is excessively noisy the audio gain must be kept low and the operator must speak more loudly to compensate. It must be borne in mind when making adjustments in the relative quietness of a stationary vehicle that we all tend to speak more loudly when the vehicle is moving. There is a need to ask for reports over the air and to take action to improve the quality if unfavourable ones are received. It may not be possible to operate in a noisy vehicle travelling at 70MPH with all the windows wide open as the readability of the signal can become R3!

Operation

Mobile operation on the HF bands (and in the DX portion of the VHF and UHF bands) is little different to normal SSB fixed station operation in that there are no specific mobile calling frequencies or sub-bands allocated. The HF SSB mobile operator is usually more interested in working DX stations in fixed locations rather than other mobile stations, and mobile to mobile contacts are fairly rare, except perhaps on 1.8MHz SSB and 29MHz FM.

RSGB MOBILE SAFETY RECOMMENDATIONS

1) All equipment should be so constructed and installed that in the event of accident or sudden braking it cannot injure the occupants of the car.
2) Mobile antennas should be soundly constructed, taking into account flexing at speed and possible danger to other vehicles or pedestrians. The maximum height must not exceed 14ft (4.3m) above ground.
3) Wiring should not constitute a hazard, either electrical or mechanical, to driver or passengers.
4) All equipment should be adequately fused and a battery isolation switch is desirable.
5) The transmit / receive switch should be within easy access of the operator and one changeover switch should perform all functions.
6) The microphone must not impair the vision or the movement of the driver.
7) A driver / operator should not use a hand microphone or double headphone.
8) All major adjustments, eg band change by a driver / operator, should be carried out whilst the vehicle is stationary.
9) Essential equipment controls should be adequately illuminated during the hours of darkness.
10) Logging or note-taking must not be attempted by the driver whilst the vehicle is in motion.
11) All equipment must be switched off when (i) fuelling, (ii) in close proximity to petrol tanks and (iii) near quarries where charges are detonated electrically.
12) A suitable fire extinguisher should be carried and be readily accessible.

As the frequency is raised, the effects of the terrain through which the vehicle is passing become more pronounced. On the HF bands this is usually confined to a relatively slow variation in signal strength but on VHF, and especially UHF, individual buildings and trees will markedly affect the radio path, giving rise to a rapid and characteristic signal 'flutter' when the vehicle is on the move.

Sometimes a poor VHF signal may be obtained when the car is parked in an apparently good position on the side of a hill. This may be caused by the vehicle being in a 'null', and the solution may be to move the car forward a few metres and try again.

A number of HF DXers confine their operations to when the car is stationary, but enjoy excellent results through careful choice of operating site, for example a hilltop or a location close to saltwater. For those with limited antenna facilities at their homes, this sort of operation can be especially pleasurable.

Most mobile-to-mobile working takes place on the FM sections of the 144 and 432MHz bands. 50 and 70MHz are also becoming increasing popular, especially as there are several 50MHz repeaters and it is also possible to work into the Continent during the Sporadic E season on the DX portion of the band. There are 10m FM repeaters licensed in the UK and elsewhere in Europe, and this band offers the possibility of working DX relatively easily during the Sporadic E season and appropriate parts of the sunspot cycle.

Using the standard 10 - 50W transceiver and a 5/8-wave whip on 2m it will usually be found that the range for mobile to mobile simplex work is very unpredictable in low-lying urban areas, and that mobile 'flutter' is a problem, particularly when both stations are on the move. Of course, one solution is to fit an add-on RF amplifier to boost the transmitter power, and perhaps a preamplifier to improve the receiver sensitivity. Although these measures can give a useful increase in range, the extra expense, spectrum pollution and power consumption involved have led to a different and much more sophisticated technique being preferred - the use of repeaters. Repeater operation, along with Internet-linking, is covered in much more detail in Chapter 13.

Operating in the FM sections of the bands is channelised, which has considerable safety and convenience advantages for the mobile operator. Instead of fine tuning a VFO dial, the operator can click a rotary switch round to change frequency and, with practice, this can be done without taking the eyes off the road. Most HF and VHF / UHF transceivers feature memories and these are extremely useful for mobile operators in that they allow fast, accurate frequency changes while on the move.

The use of FM is convenient because one of its character-istics is that strong signals will obliterate weak ones in the receiver (the so-called capture effect). Therefore operation on the same channel is often possible with two pairs of stations only 20km apart, without the level of interference that would be experienced if using SSB.

The channels are spaced 12.5kHz apart in IARU Region 1 and, to avoid the necessity of giving long strings of digits when specifying frequencies on the air, they have been given an identification code. Lists of repeaters and their channels are given in the RSGB Yearbook [4].

The normal way to set up a simplex contact while operating VHF / UHF mobile is to make (or answer) a CQ on the calling channel and to change frequency as soon as contact is made to one of the 'working' channels. For example, the FM calling channel on the 145MHz band is V40 (145.500MHz) and the working channels are V16 (145.200MHz) to V46 (145.575MHz), although some of these channels are desig-nated for particular priority uses such as emergency commu-nications and RTTY. It is important to be aware of the band plans at all times. This procedure does have its difficulties: one or more of the working channels may be occupied, but sometimes this is not apparent to both stations.

PORTABLE OPERATING

Portable operating can cover a multitude of situations. The best known is the typical Field Day situation, mainly because this has been a feature of amateur radio operating since almost the very beginning. Field Day events have been encouraged as a form of emergency preparedness, promoting self-training in setting up and operating an amateur radio station under some sort of pseudo-emergency conditions. For example, some Field Day contest rules restrict access to site until 24 hours before the contest, and most insist on

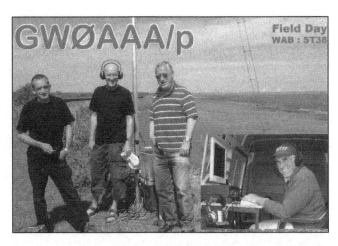

National Field Day (CW) and SSB Field Day are popular ways of preparing for emergency situations, encouraging self-training in setting up and operating an amateur radio station under emergency conditions.

battery or generator powered operation. In the days of high-voltage valve transceivers, setting up and operating a Field Day station over a weekend could be quite a challenge. Nowadays many Field Day stations are highly sophisticated, with motor caravans ready-equipped with operating positions and even pneumatic masts, so that the whole station can be driven on to site and set up in a matter of an hour or two and operations can take place in relative comfort.

The International Lighthouse and Lightship Weekend [5] held annually in August, the National Mills Weekend in May [6] (which is now actually an international event) and the International Museums Weekend in June [7] provide other great opportunities for individuals and radio clubs to mount portable operations.

Kites have been used to support HF wire antennas since Marconi's day and are particularly suited to portable operation, where a large open area such as a farmer's field, or perhaps an uncrowded beach, is available. **Fig 1** shows two methods of supporting a wire antenna from a kite.

The International Lighthouse and Lightship Weekend in August provides a great opportunity for individuals and radio clubs to mount a portable operation.

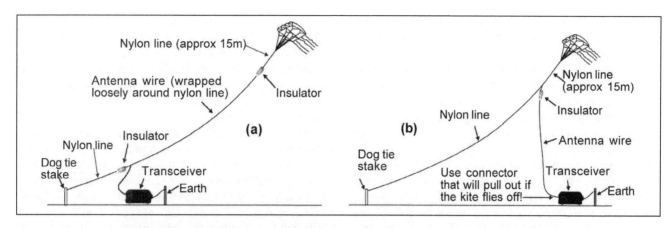

Fig 1: Two ways of supporting a wire antenna from a kite (a) a long sloping wire, (b) a shorter vertical wire.

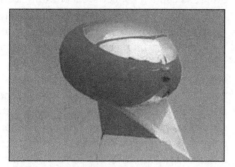

The Helikite, a helium balloon-assisted kite.

A modern take on the kite is the 'Helikite', a combination of kite and helium balloon. The helium provides just enough lift to raise the line - or in our case wire antenna - into the sky. Once up, the higher-level winds take over and the kite then keeps the whole structure aloft. The Helikite is ideal for use on calm days when it would be difficult to launch a kite without the initial assistance of the helium. When the weather is calm, the Helikite can also be used in a relatively confined space, as the wire will be raised almost vertically (note though that even a light breeze can turn your vertical into a sloper!)

As transceivers have become smaller and more power-efficient, other forms of portable operation have evolved, particularly what might be described as 'backpacker' style operations. SOTA, the Summits On The Air programme (see below) is growing rapidly in popularity, combining as it does the joys of hill walking with the specific goal of making contacts from the summit. Often, these operations will take place with a hand-held transceiver, but it is quite possible to carry enough materials in a backpack for a more ambitious operation. For example, a lightweight fishing pole can make

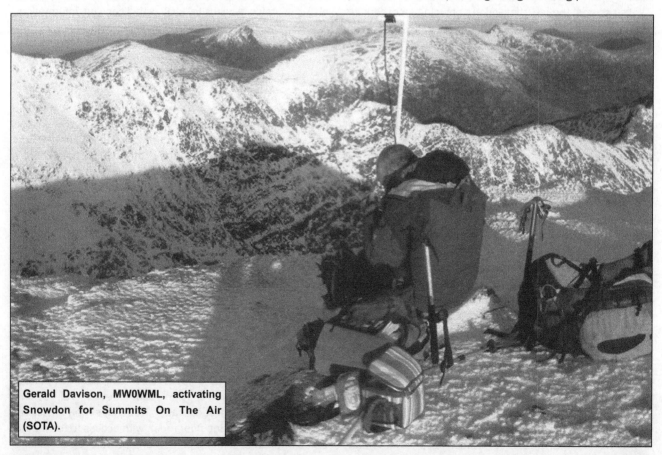

Gerald Davison, MW0WML, activating Snowdon for Summits On The Air (SOTA).

an extremely effective antenna support for a wire dipole or vertical on HF, or can even support a lightweight VHF beam of some sort.

The *RSGB Radio Communication Handbook* [8] includes a chapter entitled 'The Great Outdoors' written by backpacking expert Richard Marshall, G4ERP. This gives much useful, practical information on how to get the most out of portable operations, particularly those embarked upon by an individual on foot.

For all types of portable operation, one issue to consider is access and permits. It is essential to have the landowner's permission to operate if the hobby is to avoid getting a bad name. Many Field Day groups have long and fruitful relationships with landowners and return to the same site year after year. Of course, this is unlikely to happen if there are problems, for example by leaving litter behind after the operation or leaving guy pegs in the ground which may harm animals. Common sense obviously applies here.

DXPEDITIONS

The term DXpedition suggests something more than a portable or Field Day type of operation. It is more likely to be from some sort of fixed location such as an hotel, where mains power is available (though not in the case of DXpeditions to uninhabited islands, of course). There may be facilities for reasonably ambitious antennas. There are even holiday homes available to rent in exotic locations which come ready equipped with antennas and / or equipment; these are listed in the *World Licensing and Operating Directory* [9]. All you have to do is turn up and operate.

Let's assume, though, that you are planning an expedition where you need to take everything with you. Whether a small, holiday expedition or a major multi-person effort the same approach applies, which is to plan every aspect before you go. The tick list is essentially the same, though the actual inventory will be much greater for the bigger expedition. The main headings will be licence, accommodation, equipment and antennas (including transportation) and participants. If the expedition is to a remote location, it may also be necessary to consider power and living essentials (shelter, food, drink, sanitation).

Licensing

In the UK, licensing is not a problem, and it is necessary only to change your prefix as appropriate if operating from a different part of the United Kingdom (eg GW3XDV or GW3XDV/P if G3XDV were operating portable from Wales). Many UK operators, looking for a suitably rare or semi-rare location for a DXpedition overseas, overlook the fact that there are three more-or-less on their doorstep: the Isle of Man (GD / MD), Jersey (GJ / MJ), and Guernsey and the other Channel Islands (GU / MU). UK amateurs may consider these almost commonplace, but they are considered to be rare DX entities in places like the West Coast of North America, the Far East and in Australia and New Zealand.

Nowadays licensing in many other countries is extremely straightforward, too. The European common licence (usually known as the 'CEPT Licence'), which also covers many countries outside Europe, enables licence holders from any of the qualifying countries to operate from any of the other applicable countries without any prior authorisation. All that is required is to prefix your home callsign with the relevant prefix of the country visited, LX/G3XDV, for example, for Luxembourg. The CEPT licensing arrangements were discussed in more detail in Chapter 2.

Many other countries have so-called 'reciprocal' licensing arrangements. In this case, it is necessary to apply for a visitor's licence when you want to operate from the country concerned, but (provided reciprocal licensing arrangements are already in place) that permission will readily be forthcoming, based on the class of your home licence. Incidentally, you must follow the licence conditions of the overseas country concerned. For example, most countries do not have an allocation on 4m so you may not use that band even though your UK licence permits you to do so.

Where no reciprocal licensing arrangements exist, the situation can vary enormously from country to country. Many countries have what might be termed a 'unilateral' licensing arrangement and are happy to issue licences to visitors with a UK, US, or other CEPT Licence, even if there is no official reciprocal arrangement in place. A number of countries will only issue a licence if you apply in person at the local licensing office when you arrive in country. In some of the emerging nations the process can take several days, requiring repeat visits to the licensing authority. A huge amount of information on licensing in virtually every country in the world can be found in [9], or a search on the Internet may turn up the information you require to obtain a visitor's licence. OH2MCN also maintains a website [10] with licensing information. Alternatively, track down someone else who has operated from the same location in the past, and they will almost certainly be willing to help.

It is important to point out that licensing alone is not enough in some locations. For example, although the CEPT Licence covers the French overseas territories, operation from several of its Indian Ocean islands, for example, requires additional permits from the specific jurisdiction relating to those islands. Without this additional authority, any operation is likely to be closed down by the authorities and, in any case, will not be accepted by any of the major award schemes such as ARRL's DXCC.

Accommodation and Sites

Finding somewhere to operate from away from home can be difficult. Unlike most tourists, radio amateurs have very specific requirements. Even to do some casual holiday operating, you will need to be able to erect an antenna of some sort. And it doesn't make sense to try to sneak an antenna out of your hotel room without first discussing this with the hotel management, as there may well be difficulties if the management later discovers what you are doing.

Usually, by far the best way is to contact your hotel beforehand, explaining your specific requirements, and seeking their help. For a modest operation, you may simply be asking for something like a top floor room, with access to the roof to be able to string a wire dipole or erect a vertical. Surprising as it may seem, given that most hotels in Europe or North America would probably look askance at such a request, in many parts of the world such a request will be readily accommodated. Often one of the hotel employees will be made available to help with your project, climbing palm trees, running cables, or whatever is required. All that is asked in return is a modest tip.

For more ambitious operations, other options need to be considered. You may want to seek out a location with specific attributes, such as space for several antennas, or a seafront location in order to take advantage of the enhanced propagation which is characteristic of a take-off over salt water. Renting a villa or caravan may be preferable to hotel accommodation. There are now many 'rental stations' around the world owned by radio amateurs and available for rent by visiting radio amateurs. Some are simple locations offering basic accommodation but with a transceiver and perhaps a triband beam on a tower available for use, whereas others may offer luxurious accommodation and some of the most advanced automated contest stations around. Note, however, that many such stations will be booked for the major contest weekends well in advance.

In the case of expeditions to uninhabited islands, for example for IOTA purposes, different considerations will apply of course, and it may be necessary to take tents, along with a generator for power, and the necessary prerequisites for cooking and general outdoor living.

On HF, the best sites for expedition or Field Day operations are usually somewhere wet, ideally close to the sea but other-

W6JKV recommends a sea-front location, even for VHF DXpeditions. Here, his 6m beam on Anguilla is right over the sea.

wise with a high water table. However, it is worth bearing in mind that additional antenna gain can also be achieved from a high site where the ground slopes towards the direction(s) of most interest.

At VHF there is something of a myth that height above sea level is everything, but this is far from being the complete story. What is more important than plain elevation is whether the site has a clear unobstructed take-off in the important directions. This can mean that even a small rise of a few tens of metres can be a very good location if the surrounding land for a good number of miles is essentially flat. The alternative view, propounded for example by W6JKV, with numerous suc-

A DXpedition to an uninhabited island, with tents for accommodation, generators for power and verticals right on the ocean.

cessful 6m DXpeditions to his credit, is that a low take-off angle and maximum signal are best achieved from a sea-front location, benefiting from 'ground enhancement' and low signal absorption over salt water.

If you happen to live near to the coast a site on or very close to the water can be excellent. On 70cm and above you will be able to take advantage of the fragile marine ducts which some-times form over water and break up very quickly when they hit land. This said, nothing is ever hard and fast, and these sorts of conditions are not present much of the time, so under nor-mal circumstances you could well be better off on a site which is further inland but higher. If, like many people, you are plan-ning to use a site which is some way inland, then height cer-tainly seems to become more important and you ideally want to be a good few hundred feet above the surrounding terrain. However, even away from the coastal plains of the country there are many flattish parts of the country where sitting on top of a relatively small dimple will pay big dividends. The final decision depends on what sort of operation you envisage, and the various constraints you may be facing.

Suppose, for example, you were looking for a site for a VHF contest. Since there is no 5000ft mountain in the UK which has a clear shot for 360°, and which is only 10km from the coast in all directions - and even if there was it would already be well and truly booked by a major contest group - it is very important to try to decide what directions are important to you, and these may vary from contest to contest. For a major Europe-wide contest, the bulk of activity is likely to be in Central and Southern England and of course in the rest of Europe - for this sort of event you will want to pick a site with a good take-off in those directions. However, a UK-only contest with postcode multipliers will lead you to wanting a different site, with a good take-off to most of the UK, and you may be prepared to sacrifice some performance into Europe. If you are planning to travel any distance, you will probably make your initial choice of site from looking at the Ordnance Survey maps; however, you cannot rely on this alone - you really need to go and take a look at your proposed site before the contest to check out how to get access etc. At this point a good hint is to take a small station with you - perhaps even just a mobile - and make sure that the beacons or even repeaters are as loud or louder at your proposed site than in the rest of the surrounding area. If you do not have any amateur station with you, you can get a fair idea from just using ordinary broadcast VHF stations on the car radio.

As a quite different scenario, you may be planning an HF expedition to a Pacific island, with the hope of making plenty of European contacts. It probably won't be feasible to make a reconnaissance trip, but you may be able to contact others who have operated from there and ask their advice on locations. Perhaps a particular hotel is well sited or has been especially helpful to DXpeditioners in the past. But you will also want to check out the topography of the island to ensure that, for example, there isn't a mountain between you and the path to Europe. Note that because the great majority of the active amateurs in the world are in the Northern Hemisphere - Europe, North America and East Asia - from most DX locations (and all locations in the tropics or the

Southern Hemisphere) the great circle path to all these parts of the world will be towards the north direction. An ideal loca-tion, therefore, is on the north-facing coast of an island, with a clear sea-path take-off towards Europe, USA and Japan. The only exception might be if you expect to make a large number of contacts via long-path, in which case obviously a south-facing coast would be preferable.

Even when you locate a suitable hotel, there may be a need to negotiate for a particular room, for example one that is separated from other parts of the hotel and with access to land on which you can site your antennas, or perhaps roof access for the same reason. Some DXpeditioners, when undertaking such operations, actually leave the final decision on location until they arrive, building a day or two into their itinerary to seek out the most suitable location.

Whatever your portable site, whether a field for a 24-hour contest or a hotel location for a three-week DXpedition, it is usually a bad idea simply to turn up on the day and hope for the best. Good Field Day sites are usually already known to, and used by, active contest groups. DXpedition rental locations also tend to be booked well ahead, especially for major contests. So, unless you choose the approach described at the end of the previous paragraph, do make contact with the owners well in advance, discuss your requirements and, if possible, make a site visit or, at the very least, try to find another amateur or group of amateurs who have operated from that location, and seek their advice. It is especially useful to make contact with local amateurs if they exist. If you do so, then you stand a good chance of building up a relationship which could prove extremely valuable. If you fail to do so, you risk alienating them, with the complaint that you are somehow invading their 'turf'. This is true also of local radio clubs.

When setting up temporary antennas and stations, whether in a field or in hotel grounds, both in the UK and overseas, do be sensible - don't obstruct gateways and paths, don't damage any of the surroundings, don't leave litter (many of the items we use such as tape and cable can be harmful to animals) - basically, observe The Countryside Code [11] (The Countryside Code applies in England and Wales; Scotland has a separate Outdoor Access Code [12]).

Equipment and Antennas

The choice of equipment and antennas for expedition opera-tions will, of course, be determined largely by the goals of the operation. For Field Day and other UK-based contest and temporary operations, there may be little to limit you. Some groups have been known to tow several trailer-mounted towers to a site and set up multiple antennas, along with quite sophisticated stations, perhaps in a caravan or other similar vehicle. Some groups have even managed to transport a station of this magnitude overland (and by ferry) to Morocco, to set multi-operator records in the CQWW contests which will probably stand for many years. Of course, if you are planning, say, a Restricted entry in Field Day, the rules will limit what you can use, but it does make sense to take back-up equipment, as Murphy invariably joins the team on such occasions too!

DXpedition antennas: a combination of Hexbeam and verticals (4W6A, Timor-Leste, 2011).

For many overseas contest and expedition operations, there may well be limitations imposed by airline or other baggage restrictions. Airline baggage restrictions vary according to ticket type, by airline and by geography. A limit of 20kg for hold luggage plus 5kg for hand luggage is not atypical. Given that a portable transceiver probably weighs around 7kg, a suitable switched-mode power supply a further 2kg, and a laptop maybe 3kg, the allowance will usually preclude heavy antennas or a linear amplifier, especially if you need to take along some clothes and other essentials, too! If there are several people in the group, it may be possible to take advantage of part of their baggage allowance in addition to your own. If weight restrictions are critical, the easiest antenna to pack is a pre-cut length of wire, with lightweight coaxial feeder, which can then be suspended from a suitable support on site. For example, a sloping dipole can be tied to a hotel room balcony at the high end and to a suitable tree at the lower end. If you need to take your own support, a 10m fibreglass mast, suitable for both verticals and lightweight dipoles or loops, will weigh only about 2kg. Of course, you can always pay for an additional baggage allowance, if you so wish, but be aware that most airlines charge on the basis of 1% of the first class fare per kg of baggage above the agreed limit. An alternative is to ship some of your equipment ahead through one of the many freight companies such as DHL or FedEx, but beware that it may well sit in customs at the far end until you arrive, along with local licence and the necessary duty, to arrange for its release. This subject is well covered in *DXpeditioning Behind the Scenes* [13].

Depending on your destination, it is always advisable to take along a basic tool kit for sorting out the kind of problems which inevitably arise. A screwdriver, wire cutters and insulating tape are probably the bare minimum, but a small multimeter, soldering iron and solder and an antenna analyser such as the MFJ-259B or RigExpert AA-54 may also prove invaluable. In many places, of course, you will be able to buy basic tools at a local hardware store if necessary. Conversely, if you are heading for a remote island, it will be necessary to prepare

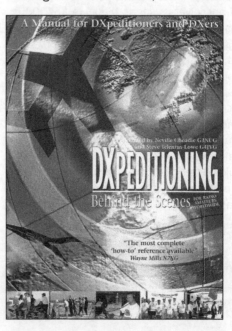

Shipping of equipment overseas is covered well in the book *DXpeditioning Behind the Scenes*.

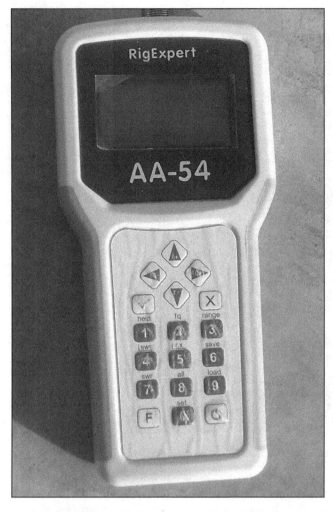

An antenna analyser is almost a necessity for DXpeditioning in the 21st century.

for a wide range of eventualities and to anticipate what tools and spares might be needed.

In this day and age, it is particularly necessary to be aware of restrictions placed by airlines on the sort of items which can be carried. Transceivers such as the Icom IC-7000 or IC-7100, the Yaesu FT-857D, the Kenwood TS-480SAT/HX or the Elecraft K3S are of a size and weight which make it feasible to carry them as hand luggage on to the aircraft. For the most part, though, amateur radio equipment is best sent as checked-in baggage, as many of the tools we use are prohibited from carriage in your hand luggage. Of course, this then runs the risk of your baggage being delayed or misrouted. Unfortunately, these are inevitable consequences of the world in which we live.

Much more could be said about planning for, and successfully undertaking portable and expedition operations: see [9, 13] for further reading.

BICYCLE AND PEDESTRIAN MOBILE

With the advent of tiny, lightweight multi-band and multi-mode transceivers, bicycle and even pedestrian mobile is perfectly feasible, and both options are being practised by a small but growing number of amateurs in the UK and overseas.

In its simplest form, bicycle mobile consists of strapping a VHF or UHF hand-held to the handlebars of a bike and using it with a headset and boom microphone. In this section, however, we look at the possibility of operating on HF using equipment carried on a bicycle and in a backpack or on a hand trolley.

Probably the best-known and most successful advocate of both bicycle and pedestrian mobile in the UK is Dave Starkie, G4AKC. Dave regularly works stations all over the world at power levels of up to 250W while on his mountain bike. He uses a handlebar-mounted Alinco DX-70TH in a zipped waterproof cover, powered by pairs of 7Ah 12V gel batteries. The radio provides continually variable power from 10mW up to a maximum of 50W output. The batteries give a total of about four hours use at the maximum output power. Two of the batteries are mounted on the rear pannier and the other two under the cross bar.

G4AKC also uses a small trailer towed behind the bicycle and which allows for high-power operation. The trailer contains two 12V / 40Ah gel cells in parallel powering a solid-state linear amplifier that can run up to 250W output, although to conserve battery power it is usually run at about 150W.

He also operates pedestrian mobile using a small two-wheel lightweight easy-to-pull trolley to transport the equipment to the operating site, which can then be transferred to a backpack. He emphasises the importance of 'location, location, location' when operating at low power and with simple antennas, and often operates from the beach at Blackpool, where the sea provides a perfect ground plane. The antenna is a lightweight home-made top-loaded vertical about 3.5m long tuned against the frame of the backpack or trolley using a ground tuning system.

G4AKC's qrz.com page [14] has many more photographs, videos and links to bicycle and pedestrian mobile websites.

Another practitioner of both bicycle and pedestrian mobile is Carl Gorse, 2E0HPI, who uses a Yaesu FT-817ND at power levels of between 2.5 and 5W PEP to a Super Antenna MP1B vertical mounted on the back of his bike. When operating pedestrian mobile the Super Antenna MP1B is attached to a

Dave Starkie, G4AKC, seen here with his car, bicycle and pedestrian mobile set-ups.

The Amateur Radio Operating Manual

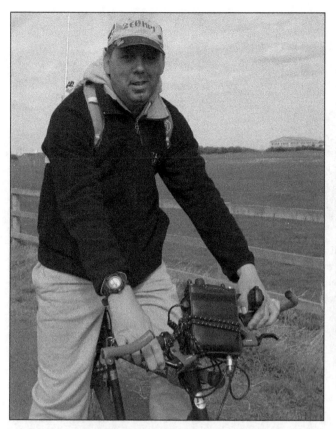

Carl Gorse, 2E0HPI/M, with his FT-817ND on the handlebars and Super Antennas MP1B vertical on the rear of the bike.

2m decorating pole fixed to a camping rucksack and Carl then uses a 20m-long counterpoise. Like G4AKC, 2E0HPI emphasises the importance of finding a good location right on the coast, and he often operates from the sea front at Hartlepool, from Teesmouth Nature Reserve or St Mary's Lighthouse in North Tyneside. Carl worked 73 DXCC entities in the first eight months of 2015 whilst operating QRP bicycle or pedestrian mobile.

SUMMITS ON THE AIR

SOTA - Summits on the Air - was founded in March 2002 by John Linford, G3WGV, with the assistance of Richard Newstead, G3CWI. The purpose of SOTA is to encourage amateur radio activity from the summits of hills and mountains in countries around the world and to provide an award system for radio amateurs in all DXCC Entities. The programme identifies distinct summits in a DXCC Entity and scores them based on height bands. Each summit is given a unique reference number. Activators climb a summit and make a minimum of four contacts to qualify for the points. Chasers can be anywhere, including on another summit, and get the points for one QSO with a given summit in any 24-hour period. There is also an SWL section which works on the same general principles.

Certificates are issued for 100, 250 and 500 points in each section (Activator, Chaser and SWL). At 1000 points the 'Mountain Goat' or 'Shack Sloth' award is made. The programme has several Activators who have achieved Mountain Goat status and a number of Chasers hold the Shack Sloth award.

Co-founder of SOTA Richard Newstead, G3CWI, often uses a mountain bike to reach the SOTA summits.

A requirement of SOTA is that Activators must use their own physical effort to get to the top of the hill. Operation from cars, motor bikes, etc is prohibited, as is the use of generators or permanently installed power sources. The programme deliberately includes lesser summits as well as the highest mountains so that practically anyone can participate. The minimum height for a valid summit is usually 150m ASL. On some of these lower summits, one need only walk a little distance away from the car, whilst many of the larger mountains will require several hours of hiking.

Crowborough Hill in East Sussex is a SOTA summit. This gentle hill sports a road and a residential estate! A valid expedition to this summit, reference G/SE-007, would involve no more than parking your car, walking a few yards and making four or more QSOs. At the other end of the scale activating England's highest mountain, Scafell Pike, G/LD-001, will require several hours of walking and a reasonable level of fitness.

SOTA was designed from the outset to be an international programme. Each DXCC entity (or sometimes a part of an entity) forms a SOTA Association that determines which hills and mountains will count in the SOTA programme. As of 2015 there are over 100 active SOTA Associations. Each Association publishes an *Association Reference Manual* listing all the summits and setting out important navigational and safety information.

The Internet is used extensively to bring all the SOTA threads together. This is an excellent example of the Internet supporting and enriching amateur radio. The General Rules and all the *Association Reference Manuals* are available for download from the web [1]. There is also an on-line Honour

Roll for both Activators and Chasers and an activation notification system. Finally, there is a reflector that is used for general discussion about the programme and for notification of activations.

SOTA permits and encourages operation on all bands and there is no doubt that it has increased VHF and UHF activity in the UK, especially in the more mountainous regions. While a large proportion of activity is on 2m and 70cm FM, several SOTA Activators are regularly QRV on 40m CW or SSB, and 30m is also popular because of its reliable propagation and the ease of putting up antennas for the band.

SPECIAL EVENT STATIONS

Setting up a special event station, perhaps as part of a local show or celebration, is physically much the same as setting up a portable Field Day style station. What is different about a special event station is that there will be members of the public around the station. Indeed, its very purpose is to showcase our hobby to the public at large. This has a number of implications for those organising the station. Firstly, safety aspects must be paramount. See the sections on safety later in this chapter and in Chapter 3. It applies to all portable and expedition operations, but is particularly important when members of the public are in the vicinity, as they will not be familiar with the hazards of antenna systems (guy wires, trailing cables, winches, etc) and equipment (high voltages, interference if they accidentally touch a key or microphone, etc). Secondly, attention must be given to ensure that the public understands what the amateur radio station is about, or the effort will be wasted. Thirdly, there may be issues of interaction with other activities at the event (radio controlled aircraft, PA systems, etc).

There is nothing worse as a member of the public than arriving at an amateur radio demonstration, only to see the backs of the operators, perhaps busy on CW, with no information about what is going on. Unfortunately, this scenario is all too common. Of course, it's not easy to ensure that a nice 59 phone contact is in progress at all times for visitors to listen to. Most will not be able to read Morse code and many will have trouble with the sound of SSB. Even when signals are crystal clear to the amateur radio operators, if the operators are using amateur radio jargon, the conversation may well be impenetrable.

As far as possible, EMC issues with other aspects of the event requires proper pre-planning and tests. At a local show, for example, it is important to check before the show opens to the public that there is no interference to the PA system or other key installations. Be ready with clip-on ferrite rings and other anti-interference measures.

PUBLICITY AND PR

This is not the place to go into a great deal of detail about publicity and public relations. However, suffice to say that at the planning stage of any expedition, contest operation or special event it is worth thinking about what sort of publicity is required and how best to achieve it. Many operations will

Two Mill Hill School students passing greetings messages at the 2SZ special event station set up to commemorate the 90th anniversary of radio communications between the UK and New Zealand (Photo: John MacDonald, *Fulton/Edgware and Mill Hill Times*).

benefit from some sort of pre-announcement in the various amateur radio bulletins and magazines, though this is less appropriate for contest operations unless they are from somewhere rare and exotic. Special event operations, to be successful, also need wider publicity, perhaps in the local press. Have material ready, and be prepared to ghost write any articles, to avoid a reporter who knows little or nothing about the hobby putting the wrong slant on what you are trying to do. The RSGB, either directly from headquarters or via its various regional representatives, can usually help with background material, but you will also want to put together a story that links this to the particular event that you are attending. When the operation is under way, take plenty of photographs and video for later use.

The Internet is also a great way to promote what you are doing. Most DXpeditions, many contest operations, and quite a few special event stations have excellent websites which help to generate interest throughout the amateur radio

It is important to have a knowledgeable person to explain amateur radio to visitors, as you never know who will drop in! Here 2002 RSGB President Bob Whelan, G3PJT, talks about the GB50 special event station to HRH Prince Philip, Duke of Edinburgh, KG, KT.

community and beyond. A couple of examples are given at [15, 16].

SPONSORSHIP

A word, too, about sponsorship, as this often comes up in the context of DXpeditions and special event operations. It is rather less appropriate to contesting, which amateurs do very much for their own gratification, so that it is unreasonable to expect others to cover the costs (though it can be argued that this happens in many sports!) Sponsorship can range from having a local company help with the production of QSL cards in return for some publicity, to the loan of the latest transceivers and antennas.

When seeking sponsorship, always put the case not only for why you believe it is appropriate (for example, by explaining the nature of the special event and its significance to radio amateurs and / or the public), but also what the sponsor can expect to gain from it. Unfortunately some amateurs, having successfully obtained sponsorship for an event or expedition, rapidly forget about their sponsors after the event, neither mentioning them in articles or talks, or even doing the courtesy of a thank you letter with some words about how well the event went. Sponsors remember this next time! The importance of keeping your side of the bargain with sponsors is well covered in [13].

SAFETY

Portable operating generally means that antennas should be erected as high as practicable, usually supported by means of a tubular mast. Select the antennas you intend to use carefully - the German-made Spiderbeam [17] and UK-made Hexbeam [18] are lightweight multi-band beams that give good performance.

Now for the mast itself, the erection of which may well be the most dangerous activity contemplated in setting up for the contest, special event or expedition - so do have sufficient help and plan carefully exactly what you are going to do and make sure everyone helping understands what is expected of them.

If you have not erected a mast before or have a limited amount of help, do not be too ambitious. Choose thick-wall scaffolding poles, not the thin-wall TV antenna masts which tend to buckle very easily. The tubular section should be joined with external sleeve clamps, not the interior expanding type of connector. When using a sleeve with a bolted flange arrange the flanges to oppose the bending during lifting, or better still weld two more ribs at 90° to the bolt flange to provide additional rigidity. The person in charge of the group erecting the antennas should check personally that all of the bolts have been tightened. It is worthwhile using shake-proof washers.

A falling derrick (usually called a gin-pole in the UK) is practically essential, and if properly constructed will simultaneously ease erection of the mast and increase the overall safety of the operation (**see Fig 2**). As a rule of thumb, the gin-pole should be a third of the length of the mast. If a base plate is being used it should be securely fixed to prevent slipping when lifting the mast. There should be a ring of four guys for

This is what can happen if you use thin-wall TV antenna masts to support too heavy an antenna!

each section of the mast. Calculate the length of guys beforehand and have them already prepared and clearly marked - allow a reasonable amount of spare for handling and tying off. The guy stakes should be placed on a circle with a radius not less half than the height of the mast. Use substantial lengths of angle iron driven into the ground at an angle away from the mast. The depth required will depend on the soil composition but usually if they are driven in about 60 - 90cm they should be adequate for most installations. Strips of reflective material to mark the low end of guys and stakes may prevent one of the helpers driving or walking into them in the dark. Be especially careful in placing guys and stakes if you are on public property and near to public footpaths.

If there is a wind blowing always raise and lower the antenna into the wind. The force that can be applied to a beam at 15m by a strong breeze may take the guys right out of everyone's hands. Be prepared to accept reduced height rather than risk the loss of the entire installation to a powerful gust of wind.

Use gloves to handle rope, and everyone working close to the mast should wear some form of protective head gear. As shown in the plan view in Fig 2 the side guys should be securely tied to the stakes though they will probably need adjustment once the mast is up. The back guys should be tied to the back stakes rather than risk the mast going 'over the top'. The gin pole must always have side guys and these should be tied to the side guy stakes. It is best to allow some slack when side-guying the gin pole.

If the mast does get out of control and starts to fall, call to everyone on site to stand clear and if possible, let it fall gradually. Heroics could mean a trip to the hospital - antennas are easier to mend than bones!

Generally, with a knowledgeable and experienced team, it is realistic to think in terms of heights of up to 60ft for a gin-pole erected mast which will support only wire antennas, and up to 40ft for a mast supporting some sort of HF Yagi or VHF array.

A safer alternative to the scaffold pole and gin-pole arrangement is the use of a push-up mast. Several lightweight and heavy duty aluminium push-up masts at heights from 10m to 18m are now available on the amateur market, eg from [17]. The bottom section is guyed securely, the antenna and feeder connected, and then each section is pushed up in turn and held in place by heavy-duty compression

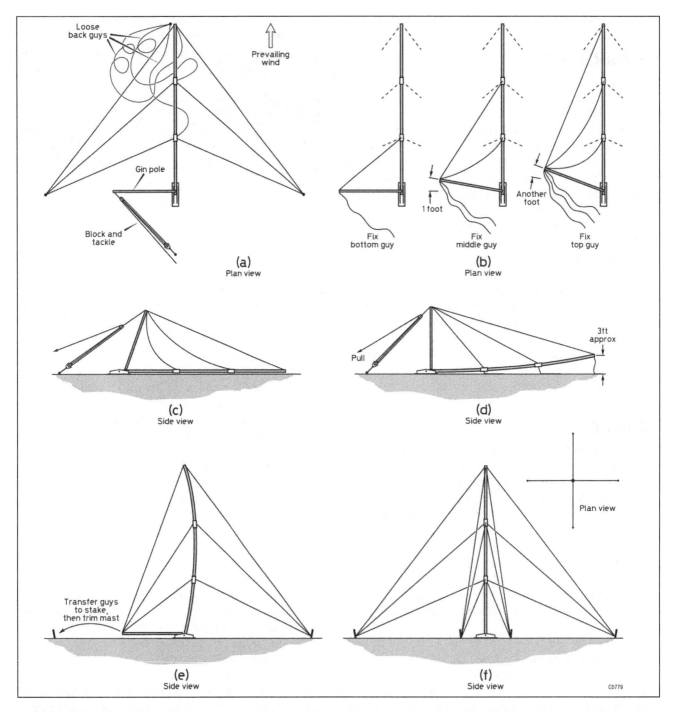

Fig 2: The falling derrick (gin-pole) method of erecting a scaffold-pole mast. (a) Overhead view showing the mast and gin-pole laid out on the ground prior to erection. (b) Setting the pre-bend; the amount varies depending on the top load. (c) Side view showing the gin-pole being raised using the block and tackle. (d) As the guys take the strain, the mast should be slightly bent as shown. The antenna can now be fitted to the top of the mast. (e) With the mast in position, the gin-pole guys are transferred to stakes and adjusted to remove the bend (the other two sets of guys are not shown for clarity). (f) The mast in final position. Note the procedure should be reversed to lower the mast, ideally lowering away from the wind.

clamps. Guy rings allow the whole mast to be rotated if necessary, either by hand (the so-called 'Armstrong' method of rotation) or by a ground-mounted rotator.

Alternatively, ex-army push-up and hydraulic pump-up masts are sometimes available on the surplus market.

Electrical safety is also very important when using mains-powered equipment literally 'in the field'. Check the earth continuity of all earth leads on distribution boards and cables that are likely to be used. Do not rely on the generator frame sitting on the wet grass as the safety earth return - use a proper earth spike and bond it to the generator - this can also help to reduce interference. All gear should be fully enclosed against misplaced fingers.

Never erect masts near overhead power lines. Finally, remember that weather can play strange tricks on high exposed locations. Go prepared with plenty of warm clothing

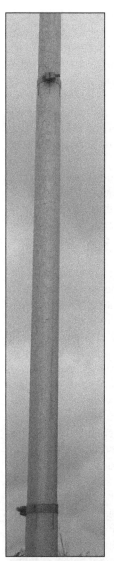

Left: A Spiderbeam 14.5m heavy-duty aluminium push-up mast is capable of supporting HF beam antennas such as a Spiderbeam, Hexbeam or similar. Above: Guy-rings allow the whole mast to be rotated.

Below: Antennas on a push-up mast can be rotated by using a ground-mounted rotator if suitable guy rings (see above) are attached to allow the whole mast to rotate.

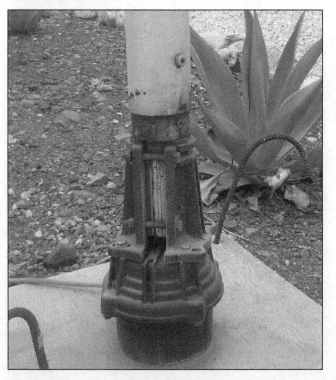

as well as some in reserve, sleeping bags and the means of obtaining some hot food under extreme conditions.

There are many other aspects of safety which you should think about before undertaking any sort of operation away from home. In the UK, from a site not too far from a major town, it may be sufficient to have a First Aid kit and mobile phone available on site, preferably with at least one member of the team knowledgeable in First Aid. At a more remote location, you might need to let others know where you will be and when you are expected back. Expeditions to remote overseas location may be faced with a wide range of other hazards. The UK-based Five Star DXers Association, for example, in planning its DXpeditions to Indian and Pacific Ocean islands, has had to plan for the dangers of malaria, tropical cyclones, and the need for medical evacuation off the island for anyone likely to need a blood transfusion or anything more than basic treatment. The group has also tried to ensure that at least one team member is a qualified doctor. In addition, one section of their DXpedition Manual, which all participants are expected to be familiar with, deals specifically with Health and Safety matters. DXpeditions to the more remote Antarctic islands often have to go to the extreme of having a ship with helicopter standing off, in case a rapid evacuation is required.

It is also worthwhile, if you are going to be in a remote location, to be aware of any medical concerns relating to team members. For example, there may be a diabetic on the team who needs to ensure that he has sufficient supplies of insulin, and the team doctor or first aider needs to be aware of where these are kept.

Whatever safety considerations are appropriate for the type and location of operation you are undertaking, do ensure that all team members are aware of them and know what to do in the event of an emergency.

Has all this sounded rather negative? It is difficult to treat a subject such as safety in anything but a serious manner. Above all, safety on site is the application of common sense. Being aware of the potential dangers and doing something about them can help to ensure an enjoyable and successful operation.

GENERATORS

Finding a source of power at any portable site is a major consideration for many portable operations. If you are just running a few tens of watts you may well be able to get away with battery power (many Islands on the Air and Summits on the Air operations do, for example), but more substantial stations require an inordinate amount of effort to ensure a ready supply of battery power - particularly if you are at the top of a mountain! The obvious alternative is a generator, and these can be extremely reliable and behave just as you expect. However, equally, they can be an immense source of frustration and the cause of hours of lost operating.

The basic choice is between diesel and petrol (although gas power is also feasible) but nevertheless all the options are expensive to buy or hire. Most sets produce 220VAC or 240VAC, although battery charging 12 or 24VDC sets produce an attractive alternative solution for modestly-powered

The Honda 3000 series is a popular choice for Field Day and DXpedition operations.

stations. Petrol or gas engines can both stop in driving rain, and have been known to lose regulation upwards, which is potentially dangerous. Putting a box in line between the generator and equipment which will cut the load if voltage outside the limits 200 - 270V is detected is an excellent insurance policy. Some groups opt to use a UPS (Uninterruptible Power Supply) between generator and station. This has several benefits, ensuring constant voltage and an uninterrupted supply should the generator fail or need to be stopped for refuelling.

You should bring the generator up to its governed speed before connecting the load, and also isolate the load before stopping the generator. Sometimes it is necessary to have a steady load such as an electric fire constantly connected to ensure steady operation of the generator, as the requirements of an SSB or CW station are very variable and can be more than the generator's governor can cater for.

Both petrol and gas engines use spark-ignition which can cause potential EMC problems, and the storage and transport of upwards of 20 gallons of petrol needs to be considered. 'Hot' filling of petrol generators can be very hazardous, especially in windy weather.

Diesel sets can be difficult or impossible to start after long periods of storage unless they are 100% healthy, and summer grade fuel can freeze in March. Diesel is very prone to develop bacteriological contamination during storage, particularly in the summer, and especially when stored in clear or white vessels / pipework. Diesel sets are bigger and heavier than similarly-rated petrol sets, but are far more economical and, as an extra bonus, fuel can be tax-exempt 'red' diesel, available from boatyards etc. Anything bigger than 5kVA is best trailer-mounted in order to reduce the manhandling hazards in rain or snow.

Generators of all types need to be sited away from the main antenna lobe, downwind, and where cables do not cross footpaths. One big issue is how big a generator do you need? In general, a much bigger one than you might at first expect! This is because most transmitters have capacitor-input power supplies which draw current only on waveform peaks, causing high copper losses in the alternator. As a 'sizing' guide, aim for a generator with a VA rating four-fold greater than the required transmitter output PEP. Even with a generator significantly bigger than this, with most valve amplifiers you should not expect to see the same power output on the generator as you do at home, mainly because the HT will be down. As an example, on a 240V mains supply a typical amplifier using a pair of 4CX250s has the EHT supply sitting at 2.6kV off load, and the amplifier will deliver about 600W - on a 9kVA 230V generator it is down to 2.3kV, and will only deliver 450W, and on a 2.5kVA petrol generator you are down to 300W out. The only real solution to this problem is either to have much bigger amplifiers than you need, or to use those with choke-input supplies which take current over the whole mains cycle. Some forms of switched-mode supplies can also be a good option.

Cable size may be less significant than expected, because of the high source impedance of the generator as compared with domestic mains. Ex-building-site alternators are often 220VAC brush-less types and produce a square-wave EMF. Better types with proper sine wave output exist, but these have brushes, and may therefore be less reliable and present possible EMC problems. Beware of heavy oil consumption - smoky generators could run out of oil and seize if run continuously for 24 hours. Also beware of vibration: avoid the temptation to get 240VAC out of a 220VAC mechanically-governed set by raising the governed speed by 10%. The engine mountings may have a high Q and be ineffective (or worse) at anything other than the intended mechanical frequency.

Many alternators have the neutral connected to the frame, but others have the L-N output fully insulated. Chalk hilltops in summer present earth conductivity problems, even assuming it is possible to drive in an earth stake, and in all cases it is necessary to think carefully about safety in terms of fusing and RCCB / ELCB performance, especially if using multiple generators as part of a single installation. If you don't fully understand this side of the system, get good advice from someone who does!

One final point is that of physical safety - when using a crank handle, fingers and thumb must go on the same side to avoid risk of injury in event of kickback, and all belts, chains and shafts must have guards.

MARITIME MOBILE OPERATION

Maritime mobile operation is an excellent way of combining an interest in the sea with one in amateur radio. The two go well together, amateur radio acting as a way of keeping in touch with friends and, if the worst should happen, a means for securing assistance. VHF operators will also welcome the activation of 'wet' squares, those Locator squares consisting purely of sea.

Chapter 2 dealt with the licensing issues related to using your UK licence from a seagoing vessel, including just what is regarded as Maritime Moble (/MM) and what is simply Mobile (/M). However, if you operate from a vessel of foreign registry, as well as obtaining permission from the ship's Master, you must obtain a reciprocal operating authorisation from the country of registry. This may be relevant if, for example, you wish to operate from a cruise ship. This is analogous to obtaining licensing authority from the country concerned, and discussions elsewhere in this manual regarding CEPT Licensing, reciprocal licensing, etc are equally valid.

Complications can arise when you leave international waters and enter the territorial waters of another country, when you must also have a licence from the country concerned. You are advised to check carefully if you anticipate operating maritime mobile under these circumstances. You should also be aware of the ITU region of the world in which you are operating, as amateur radio frequency allocations vary between regions.

Equipment

Favoured equipment, both by yachtsmen and ships' radio officers, is the smaller portable transceiver which will operate on 12VDC. While not a problem in a large ship's wireless room, the climatic conditions encountered on board a small yacht, especially in the tropics, were certainly not envisaged by the manufacturers of rigs, who thought their equipment was destined to be tucked, warm and dry, beneath the dashboard of a car. Initially many yachtsmen make the mistake of locating the rig among their other radio gear around the chart table. Such a position is almost inevitably going to expose the equipment to a splash of sea water sooner or later. Better to put it inside a locker next to the chart table, and run a multi-way cable to a remote alternative operating position in the cockpit.

Spares

If a yachtsman is going to set off across the Atlantic working regular skeds with friends back home it is irresponsible to do so without both spares and some knowledge of the potential weaknesses of the particular 'black box' that will be aboard. While retailers and manufacturers may maintain that the gear they are selling just never goes wrong, they will usually become

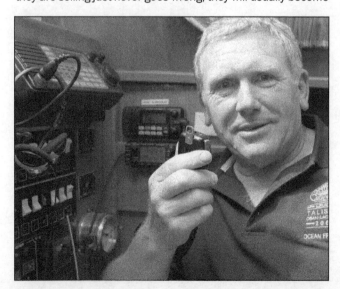

Hilton Willott, MW0OPS/MM, operating from on board his yacht *Ocean Freedom*.

a lot more helpful if approached with a full explanation of just why the enquiry is being made! If a /MM station goes off the air suddenly with equipment failure in mid-ocean, great concern is likely to be caused to friends who have been keeping skeds. Certainly, they know that the most likely cause is radio equipment failure, but when it actually happens they can hardly be blamed for fearing worse.

Power Supplies

Even a modern 100W PEP transceiver will represent quite a considerable drain on a yacht's batteries and at sea it is easy to become involved in quite long operating periods without thinking. Ideally a separate battery should be carried specifically for the rig, with suitable means to isolate it from the ship's main batteries. Here again, not a 'big ship' problem for in that case the ship's 110V or 220V AC supply will be available.

Antennas and Earths

Due to its ability to operate with a perfect earth system a boat will put out a remarkably good signal with quite modest power. For instance, when working the UK from the West Indies, a yacht running 150 watts to a vertical dipole may well be given the same report as a shore station on an adjacent island which is running 500 watts to a two-element cubical quad. The problem is more that of the antenna being non-directional, and with the pile-up of callers who may be anxious for a contact there is no way to notch out any of the interference.

Shipboard antennas are normally vertically polarised and radiate an excellent low-angle signal. The favourite seagoing antenna is normally a vertical half-wave dipole although if the boat is of steel construction a quarter-wave ground plane driven against the ship's hull may be better.

Seagoing RF

On a merchant ship the antenna is usually well elevated and the operating position is adequately screened, but on a yacht the reverse is true and everything can easily become 'live' with RF. The stray resonant circuits provided by the stays, rigging and wiring on a yacht can be positively dangerous when excited by a strong RF field. It is therefore far better to keep the power level down and make a really serious effort to get maximum radiation and minimum reflected power. If part of a boat's rigging is used as a radiator, remember that rigging usually comes in symmetrical pairs. For example, if one of the mast stays is a convenient 15m long, its opposite number must be detuned. The favourite technique is to bridge across about 500mm with 1.2mm (18SWG) copper wire with a 500pF mica capacitor in the middle.

Even with low power, other electronic equipment on board may seriously misbehave when subjected to RF fields - remember, the makers of equipment used in small yachts never had it in mind that their gear would have to tolerate a 14MHz SSB signal in close proximity. Electronic speed/distance logs and quartz crystal clocks should be carefully checked out for RF tolerance before setting out on any major voyage.

Operating Frequencies

Throughout the world, most /MM operation is carried out on the 14MHz band, irrespective of the stage in the sunspot cycle. Each region has its own net frequencies and sked times. Several websites carry details of Maritime Mobile nets around the world, for instance the one at [19], and it is worth carrying an up-to-date list for the areas in which you will be travelling.

Net operations should be allowed to proceed, without interruption, to their natural conclusion before an attempt to contact them is made. Most /MM operators are always prepared to chat and reciprocate with a QSL card provided they are not interrupted when talking to their /MM friends - after all, exchange of information about harbours, fishing and RF in the rigging is to the /MM operator what life is all about.

REFERENCES

[1]   Summits on the Air: www.sota.org.uk
[2]   'RSGB Insurance Clinic', *RadCom*, May 2104.
[3]   *Highway Code*: www.direct.gov.uk/highwaycode
[4]   *RSGB Yearbook*, RSGB, published annually.
[5]   International Lighthouse / Lightship Weekend: http://illw.net
[6]   National Mills Weekend: www.mills-on-the-air.net
[7]   International Museums Weekend: www.radio-amateur-events.org/IMW
[8]   *Radio Communication Handbook*, 12th edn, Mike Dennison, G3XDV, and Mike Browne, G3DIH, RSGB, available from www.rsgbshop.org
[9]   *World Licensing and Operating Directory*, Steve Telenius-Lowe, 9M6DXX (PJ4DX), RSGB, available from www.rsgbshop.org
[10] OH2MCN overseas licensing: www.qsl.net/oh2mcn/license.htm
[11] *The Countryside Code* (England and Wales): http://www.gov.uk/government/publications/the-countryside-code
[12] *Outdoor Access Code* (Scotland): www.outdooraccess-scotland.com
[13] *DXpeditioning Behind the Scenes*, eds Neville Cheadle, G3NUG, and Steve Telenius-Lowe, G4JVG, available from www.t32c.com/DXpedition_Book
[14] G4AKC/M qrz.com page: www.qrz.com/db/g4akc
[15] FT4TA Tromelin Island DXpedition: www.tromelin2014.com/en
[16] EP6T Iran DXpedition: www.rockall.be
[17] Spiderbeam: www.spiderbeam.com
[18] G3TXQ Broadband Hexbeam made by MW0JZE: www.g3txq-hexbeam.com
[19] http://www.mayaparaiso.com/maritime_mobile_frequencies.php

MUCH OF THIS BOOK relates to real-time, point-to-point communications, where you are in direct contact with another amateur station, either line-of-sight, or taking advantage of various propagation modes to send your signals beyond the horizon. This has its limitations. The station you are in communication with must be on the air at the same time as you are, and propagation must be such as to make the contact possible.

Not surprisingly, amateurs have sought means to overcome both these limitations (time and distance). The chapter discusses those means, and how to take advantage of them.

Voice repeaters have now been in use in amateur radio for over 40 years and exist in order to permit VHF / UHF communications over distances well beyond the horizon, even when band conditions are 'flat', in other words when signals really are limited to line-of-sight (**Fig 1**). They operate mainly on the VHF, UHF and microwave bands, though there are also some repeaters on 10m. The solution, quite obviously, is to site repeater stations at a high point such as a hilltop and/or on top of a very high mast, so that it can receive signals from a wide area and retransmit them over a similar area. Depending on the location of the repeater station, contacts can be made reliably over quite large distances.

There are also ATV (fast-scan Amateur TV) repeaters which, because of the huge bandwidth required, remain independent of the other systems discussed here.

With the advent of data communications, especially Packet Radio, the way was opened up for dealing not only with distance but time. The Packet Radio network which evolved in the 1980s allowed global distances to be covered, by passing data from node to node, using an addressing and routing system which ensured that the messages got to the correct place. But it also removed the need for both parties to be in their radio shacks at the same time, as messages could be left at mailboxes, from which they could be collected later. This network is now in decline as always-on broadband Internet connections make land-line data communication more efficient.

More recent developments, also springing from Internet technology, take both voice and data networks a step further. The linking of voice repeaters and other nodes to the Internet has removed any distance restrictions so that it is now possible to use a handheld VHF radio to talk to someone on the other side of the world, very much as you might do with a mobile phone.

The Internet, not so much because of its technology but because of the commercial structure under which it operates, is essentially distance-independent, so that there is no more cost or difficulty in linking voice repeaters in Australia and the UK as there would be in linking similar repeaters in London and Birmingham. And unlike the telephone system which is based on point-to-point communications, the Internet allows anyone to connect from anywhere, so that many parties can participate simultaneously in such communications.

At the same time, the Internet has become the backbone for linking national Packet Radio networks, so that it is no longer necessary to use limited HF or amateur satellite facilities to carry packet traffic around the world.

The Automatic Positioning Reporting System (APRS) described in this chapter takes full advantage of Internet linking, although it can certainly be used independently of the Internet for specific applications.

In recent years VoIP (Voice over Internet Protocol) technology has allowed digital voice modes to link analogue repeaters. Now, by using digital transceivers and digital repeaters it is possible to have a station to station link using digital modes only, and to send various types of data at the same time. Your handheld or mobile transceiver can be the means of communicating with voice, image and data to other amateurs throughout the world, marrying fixed network (Internet) and radio technology for total flexibility.

Coordination of the UK repeater system is by the RSGB Emerging Technology Co-ordination Committee (ETCC) [1].

VOICE REPEATER OPERATION

Voice repeaters were introduced initially to facilitate mobile operation. As you travel round in your car, perhaps talking to another mobile operator, the distance between the two of you can change rapidly, and you may easily lose contact. Repeaters were installed to help avoid that. However, they also facilitate operation with small handheld transceivers. There is nothing to stop them being used by fixed stations either, though the normal code of conduct is that mobile and portable stations take priority.

The repeaters on the 10m HF band allow extended range operation at times when the MUF is low (eg at times of sunspot minimum), allowing the band to be useful for more

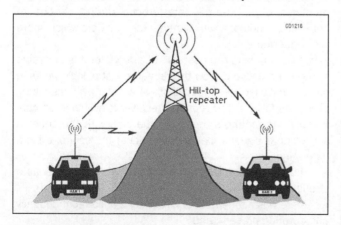

CD1216

Hill-top repeater

Fig 1: A repeater in operation.

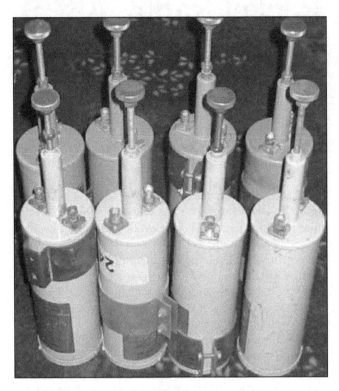

Most repeaters use cavity filters like these at GB3OH to ensure that the receiver is not blocked by the transmitter.

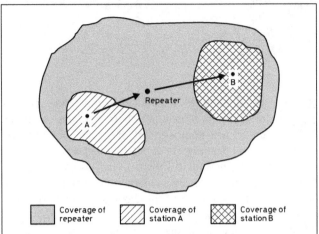

Fig 2: The improved range of communications available between mobile stations when using a repeater. The simplex coverage areas of mobile stations A and B shown are constantly changing shape as the two vehicles pass through different terrain. The two stations would need to be quite close before reliable communications were possible without using the repeater.

than just ground-wave communications when ionospheric propagation is impossible.

A repeater is a device which will receive a signal on one frequency and simultaneously transmit it on another frequency. Thus a low-power transmitter, for example in a vehicle, can transmit on the repeater's input channel and the signal will be faithfully reproduced on the repeater's output channel. Careful design and filtering has meant that repeaters can receive and transmit in the same band which means that one antenna can be used for both reception and transmission.

In effect the receiving and transmitting coverage of a mobile station becomes that of the repeater and, since the latter is favourably sited on top of a hill or high mast, the range is usually greatly improved over that of unassisted or simplex operation (see **Fig 2**). Typically the effective range is increased from the order of 10–25km from the mobile station to something like 50km in any direction from the repeater, depending upon terrain and band used. Another advantage is that contact with other stations becomes more predictable. The coverage of stations A and B in Fig 2 continually change shape as the two stations pass through different terrain. Thus it is never easy for the mobile operator to estimate his or her simplex range. In contrast, the repeater service area is a known and much less variable factor. One further advantage is that mobile 'flutter' on FM transmissions is usually diminished due to the superior antenna location at the repeater site.

How an FM Repeater Works

A repeater is an unmanned relay station and therefore requires an automatic system to control its operation. This logic system must ensure as far as possible that the repeater only relays signals intended for that repeater, and that those signals it does relay come up to an acceptable standard in respect of frequency, strength and deviation. For example, there is little point in the repeater relaying a signal which is so weak that it is unintelligible.

It would be very wasteful of power to have an FM repeater transmitter left on continuously if there were no signals being relayed, and so it is arranged that it is only switched on when a signal for relaying is present on the input channel. To ensure that signals which are not intended for relaying cannot accidentally switch on the repeater transmitter, UK repeaters on 2m, 70cm and 23cm require a short 1750Hz audio tone ('toneburst') to be sent by a user at the start of a transmission or alternatively, in most cases, a particular sub-audible CTCSS tone (see over). Either the 1750Hz toneburst or the CTCSS tone tells the repeater to switch on its transmitter. Once this has been done other stations may carrier re-access the repeater indefinitely until it is no longer required. It will then automatically switch its transmitter off and another toneburst will be required if further use is to be made of it.

50MHz repeaters require a CTCSS tone to be transmitted continuously in order to access them. This is to avoid the problems of co-channel interference during periods of enhanced conditions with Continental repeaters which share the same frequency.

In order to make the best use of a repeater it is desirable to have knowledge of how the repeater control logic works in outline, and a typical sequence of events during a transmitting over is as follows. The repeater receiver is switched on continually and monitors the input channel, with the squelch set. When a signal appears on the input the control system determines if:

• the signal has tripped the squelch (ie it is of adequate strength);
• there was a toneburst or CTCSS tone of correct frequency and duration present; and
• the received signal is correctly deviated.

If these initial conditions are satisfied (known as a valid access) the control system will switch the repeater transmitter on and allow the receiver audio output to modulate it. During the transmission, the control logic continuously monitors the incoming signal level, and if it falls at any time below the standard required for valid access, may switch off the transmitter or disconnect the receiver audio from the modulator. When the transmission is finished and the incoming signal disappears from the input channel, the repeater squelch will close and indicate to the control logic that it must ready itself for the next over. After a short delay the repeater will signal it is ready by transmitting a 'K' or 'T' in Morse code.

The short delay between the end of an over and the 'K' (or 'T') is quite important. During this interval the repeater will still relay any new signals on the input channel. Consequently this interval may be used by a third station to announce its presence by giving its callsign. The use of "Break" is unnecessary as the repeater users will already be listening for such a call. This practice is termed 'tail-ending' and is a good way of inserting urgent or emergency messages between overs. If the repeater has relayed a signal for more than a certain period of time (typically 2min on 144MHz and 5min on 432MHz) the control system may go into a time-out mode, close the talk-gate, and possibly transmit some form of busy signal until the incoming signal disappears off the input channel. This is done primarily to prevent overs from being too long, but is also a useful anti-jamming measure. It should be noted that some repeaters do not incorporate time-out devices. It is good operating practice to keep repeater overs to less than a minute whether or not time-out is fitted.

CTCSS Repeater Tones

The Continuous Tone-Coded Squelch System (CTCSS) is available on almost all UK repeaters (see **Fig 3**). It is an additional means of access on 145MHz and 433MHz repeaters but in the case of 29 and 50MHz repeaters it is the sole means of access. On 145 and 433MHz the system operates in parallel with the 1750Hz access tone – either can be used to access a repeater.

The principle of CTCSS is that a sub-audible tone is continuously transmitted in addition to the usual signal. Being below the normal speech frequencies, it does not affect the received signal.

The UK has been divided into 23 different CTCSS regions using ten different tones, as shown in Fig 3. A repeater user who is on the border of two or more repeaters' coverage areas can now be selective. By transmitting the appropriate CTCSS tone, only one repeater will be activated rather than the others on the same channel.

Repeaters with the CTCSS facility available transmit the appropriate letter in Morse code after the callsign. A repeater only transmits its CTCSS tone when relaying speech, but not with its periodic identifications. A suitably-equipped station can screen out the annoying identifications, so making it more convenient to monitor the repeater.

The CTCSS tones for accessing all of the UK's repeater network can be found on the ETCC's web site [1] and the *RSGB Yearbook* [2].

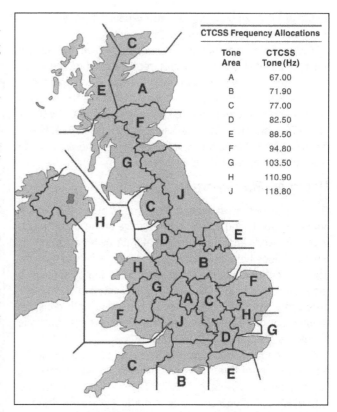

CTCSS Frequency Allocations	
Tone Area	CTCSS Tone (Hz)
A	67.00
B	71.90
C	77.00
D	82.50
E	88.50
F	94.80
G	103.50
H	110.90
J	118.80

Fig 3: CTCSS tone areas and frequencies. (Most stations adhere to this plan although there are a few exceptions.)

Repeater Frequencies

Repeaters on the 10m band using frequencies between 29.620 and 29.690MHz, designated 'RH1' to 'RH8'. and spaced at 10kHz intervals. This standard world-wide system has input channels 100kHz lower. Your transmitter's FM deviation should be set at around 3kHz and certainly should not exceed 4.5kHz. In the UK, access is by means of a CTCSS tone.

There is a similar system on the 50MHz band, with 10kHz channels (R50-1 to R50-15) and CTCSS access. Repeater inputs are 500kHz above the output.

All 144MHz repeaters, whether analogue (FM) or digital, have their inputs 600kHz lower than the outputs, in accordance with IARU Region 1 recommendations. The channels are designated 'RV'.

On the 432MHz band, FM repeaters have their inputs 1.6MHz higher than the outputs in the UK which is different from most others in Europe. The channels are designated 'RB'. Digital repeaters on this band may use the 'RU' channels, or have inputs 7.6MHz higher ('RU') or 9MHz lower ('DVU') than the output frequencies.

FM channels on both bands are 12.5kHz-spaced and if you are using old equipment (originally designed for 25kHz spacing) it is important to ensure that your FM deviation is set correctly. Too wide a deviation risks causing interference to the repeaters both 12.5kHz lower and higher in frequency than the channel you are operating on.

UK FM repeaters on 1.3GHz are on 25kHz-spaced channels from 1.297.000 to 1297.375MHz, designated 'RM').

Inputs are 6MHz below outputs. ATV repeater frequencies on this band are dealt with later in this chapter.

Most modern commercial transceivers have the useful ability of being able to reverse this frequency shift at the touch of a button. For example, assuming the transceiver was set to channel RV62 (145.175MHz transmit, 145.775MHz receive) the frequencies would be reversed as soon as the REVERSE-REPEATER switch was depressed, becoming 145.175MHz receive, 145.775MHz transmit. It thus allows the operator to listen on the repeater input channel.

Using an FM Repeater

The proper use of a repeater requires a high standard of operating ability and courtesy. Knowledge of the way in which repeaters work and confidence that your own equipment is 'spot on' does help, but also required is an ability to express yourself concisely; this being especially important on a repeater with a high level of activity. It must also be remembered that the primary purpose of repeaters is to facilitate mobile communications, and therefore mobile stations should be given priority at all times.

If it is required to test access into a repeater, the callsign and purpose of the transmission should be stated, eg "G3XDV testing access to GB3ZZ". The repeater will respond with a 'K' or 'T' if access has been made. Do ensure that the transmitter, receiver and toneburst are operating correctly before you try using a repeater – do not align equipment through a repeater.

CQ calls are not normally made through repeaters; instead stations usually announce they are "listening through" the repeater, eg "G3XDV listening through GB3ZZ". One such announcement is sufficient.

If it is apparent after setting up a contact that the stations are likely to be within simplex range of each other, the input channel should be checked. If signals are reasonable, the repeater should be vacated and the contact completed on one of the simplex channels. This is especially important if both are fixed stations. Sometimes stations outside the repeater's service area will access the repeater successfully, but their signals will be very noisy and they may only open the repeater squelch intermittently. If this is the case, the contact should be terminated and another attempt made when a better signal into the repeater can be obtained.

If you wish to join an existing contact on the repeater, you should send your callsign in the gap immediately after one of the participating stations drops carrier but before the 'K' or 'T'. The repeater will inhibit the 'K' or 'T' as soon as it senses another transmission is taking place. To insert emergency or urgent messages, use the time before the 'K' or 'T' to announce your callsign and the problem, eg "G3XDV/M emergency, road traffic accident A46 / A606 junction".

Because many UK repeaters will time-out after a few minutes, lengthy repetition of callsigns wastes the time available for each transmission. For example, "From G3XDV" is quite sufficient at the beginning and end of each over. A spell of listening will soon show that two common operating errors are timing-out and forgetting to wait for the 'K'. As a result, the repeater may eventually interrupt communications and

---

Code of Practice for Voice Repeater Operation

1 Avoid using a repeater from your base station; it is really for the benefit of the local mobiles. If you really must use it, use the lowest possible power and a directional antenna to avoid interfering with other repeaters on the same channel which you may not be able to hear. To be sure, use a CTCSS tone to access only the repeater you want.

2 Listen to the repeater before you transmit to make sure it is not in use. If you hear a local station you wish to call, listen on the input frequency to check whether the station is within simplex range before calling.

3 Unless you are specifically calling another station, simply announce that you are "listening through", eg "G3XDV listening through GB3ZZ". One announcement is sufficient. If you are calling another station, give its callsign followed by your own callsign, eg "G2XYZ from G3XDV".

4 Once contact is established:

(a) at the beginning and end of each over you need give only your own callsign, eg "From G3XDV";

(b) change frequency to a simplex channel at the first opportunity (especially if you are operating a fixed station);

(c) keep your overs short and to the point or they may time-out, and do not forget to wait for the 'K' or 'T' (if used);

(d) do not monopolise the repeater as others may be waiting to use it;

(e) if your signal is very noisy into the repeater, or if you are only opening the repeater squelch intermittently, finish the contact and try later when you are putting a better signal into the repeater.

5 If the repeater is busy, emergency calls may be made by tail-ending before the 'K', and announcing (a) that you have emergency traffic, and (b) which facilities you wish a station to provide. This will normally in most 'risk-to-life' situations be a telephone so that the other station can alert the emergency services. Do not reply to an emergency call if you cannot provide the services requested.

---

the user, quite unaware of this, may spend up to a minute or so blocking the repeater to no avail. A simple time-out warning device may therefore prove useful.

There are two selfish attitudes which should be discouraged. The first is the practice of "taking another 'K'", ie dropping carrier for a short time within the middle of a transmission in order for the repeater's timer to reset itself: this defeats the idea of sharing out the available air time to all users. The second bad practice is to use the gap before the 'K' to make a comment about the previous over. A good operator waits for his / her over before commenting because they realise that otherwise they are preventing the proper use of the gap to allow others to join in by inserting their callsign.

Certain repeaters, especially those outside the UK, may have different requirements, but if the rule 'listen before transmitting' is followed this should present no particular problem.

Digital Repeaters and Linking

There is now a huge global network of repeaters which provide end-to-end digital service. In other words, the connection is digital from your own transceiver, via the repeater network, to the transceiver of the station with whom you are contact. Over 150 digital repeaters are licensed in the UK.

Because the voice signal is already digital when it is transmitted, it can be shared or relayed over digital networks (radio and Internet) easily (**Fig 4**). There are many advantages in this, for instance the repeaters can easily be interlinked to give potentially world-wide coverage. One major disadvantage at present is that there are several systems, each of which is incompatible with the others and there is limited connectivity with the existing FM repeater network.

Whatever system you use you will need a suitable radio to transmit or receive digital voice (see Chapter 8 for more on digital voice). Some transceivers can be configured to transmit and receive either FM and digital as appropriate.

Digital voice (DV) is digitally-encoded voice and / or data sent by means of complex audio tones over a narrow-band analogue FM channel. DV mode sends error-corrected voice in a transmitted bandwidth of only 6.25kHz. Since callsigns are sent as part of the transmission, the receiving radio is able to display who is originating the transmission. Short messages showing status, etc are also supported as part of this information.

The repeaters tend to use off-the-shelf hardware and software. Some can operate as conventional FM repeaters as well as digital, automatically selecting their mode according to the input signal.

Interlinking becomes easy with digital technology. A single repeater may well have inputs on more than one band and be able to route each input to any output. Similarly, they can be linked to other repeaters via the Internet. A digital repeater can be used locally in exactly the same manner as an FM unit, but they can also be linked to others in order to cover a large area or even the entire world.

Voice transmissions are error-corrected which gives rise to an all-or-nothing effect whereby the signal is either 100% clear and readable, or not there at all. The absence of fading noise can be a little disconcerting to those who are used to conventional FM.

The IC-5100 Deluxe is a VHF / UHF digital (D-Star) mobile transceiver featuring integrated GPS.

Depending on the system, data can be transmitted and received alongside the speech channel or instead of it. This may lead to the further decline of the packet radio network.

It is possible to access some digital networks without a radio, using just a computer with a microphone/headset and an Internet connection. This gives rise to potential security issues and measures are in place to ensure that only licensed amateurs can produce an output that will appear on a radio link.

Three systems dominate: D-Star, DMR and Fusion. They are dealt with separately below. It remains to be seen whether just one will come to the fore or whether there will be a way to increase compatibility, at least from the perspective of the end user.

D-Star (Digital Smart Technology for Amateur Radio) is a communications protocol developed by the Japan Amateur Radio League (JARL) in conjunction with universities and amateur radio companies. As it is an open standard, anyone can make D-Star compatible equipment without paying a royalty. The first range of D-Star compatible mobiles and handhelds were produced by Icom but others are likely to join them. Because D-Star had a head start on the other systems its worldwide network is the largest. The main D-Star mode is digital voice. This uses a 4800-bit data channel divided into 2400 bits per second for voice, 1200bps for forward error correction (FEC) and 1200bps for user data. Header data includes information such as the user's callsign, destination callsign and repeater information (where applicable) which is sent alongside the main data. These settings are programmed into the radio by the user. Registration is required - normally via the local repeater group. A central server on the network holds a database of callsigns and the repeater they last used. This allows contacts to be set up with specified stations regardless of where they are in the world. Amongst the numerous features of D-Star radios is a selective squelch that opens the squelch only when a call to your own callsign is being received.

DMR (Digital Mobile Radio) is an open standard devised by Motorola engineers who were also radio amateurs. It can be used for both voice and data. Equipment is produced by a number of manufacturers. The DMR-MARC network comprises hundreds of interlinked repeaters in over 18 countries. DMR networks uniquely use time division multiplex (TDMA) providing two separate voice channels within a single

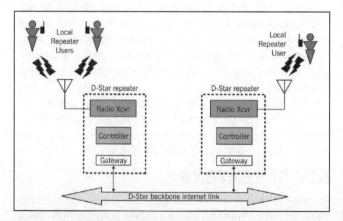

Fig 4: A digital network (in this case D-Star) showing repeaters linked by an Internet connection.

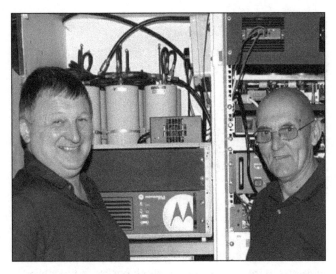

Michael, G1XCC and Mick, M0LEV with the GB7TD DMR repeater.

12.5kHz channel, therefore enabling two completely separate contacts to take place at the same time. A typical use of this facility would be to have one channel for world-wide interlinking and the other for more conventional local use. In order to access the system, users first need to register online with DMR-MARC, who will provide a seven figure ID that should be programmed into the transceiver. The ID includes a country specific identifier, which is used by the system to route a contact to the desired talk-group, produce a 'Last Heard' log of on-air users and to compile system data.

Some users have found that DMR is easier to use - especially in a mobile situation - than D-Star. It is also argued that DMR is more user friendly for those who may be less technically minded, even being especially suited to the visually impaired. The downside is that the network is currently much smaller than the D-Star network. For more on DMR repeaters see [3].

Fusion, Yaesu's digital radio network uses System Fusion. Its repeaters, and digital radios, have the facility to detect whether FM or digital (C4FM) is being used and automatically change mode. A repeater can be configured in two ways. It can replace an existing FM repeater and FM users are dealt with as normal. Digital transmissions are converted to FM for the repeater's output. Thus digital users can communicate with FM users.

A disadvantage is that this arrangement removes the data normally sent with a digital transmission. In the alternative configuration, the repeater can detect whether the input is conventional FM or digital and then relay the signals unchanged. However, in this arrangement the two types of user cannot communicate with each other. It is possible to transmit pictures over a Fusion repeater using an optional camera microphone. Some radios have built-in GPS to take advantage of System Fusion's navigation functions.

The Yaesu FT1-D digital (Fusion) handheld.

The UK Repeater Network

Over 450 UK repeaters are operational in the 29, 50, 144, 432MHz 1.3GHz, 2.3GHz and 10GHz bands, giving coverage of most of the country. Some 150 are digital and more than 30 are for ATV. The number of repeaters offering digital voice is increasing rapidly.

All repeater systems in the UK are designed, built and maintained by groups of enthusiasts under the overall management of the RSGB Emerging Technology Co-ordination Committee (ETCC) [1]. The ETCC has full responsibility to the licensing authority for all aspects of repeater operation, including technical standards and frequency allocation.

There are no 'closed' or private repeaters in the UK – all are available for general use. The annual cost of a repeater is considerable and every regular user should join the local repeater group to support it and contribute to its funds.

At one time the lowest frequency band used for repeaters in the UK was 145MHz, but in recent years three have been licensed for 29MHz FM and 24 for 50MHz.

On the 145MHz band, 144 repeaters are licensed. Many are either digital or dual mode. There are twice the number of 432MHz repeaters than on 144MHz in the UK. UHF repeaters have more of a local and community character than those on VHF. Several inband 1.3GHz repeaters are currently licensed, and this is also the main band for ATV repeaters.

The frequencies used by UK repeaters are described earlier in this chapter. The *RSGB Yearbook* [2] includes a full list of UK repeaters, including some useful coverage maps. You can also find a full, sortable list on the RSGB ETCC website [1].

Repeater Abuse

From time to time in urban areas there is abuse or jamming (mostly on 2m repeaters). The best advice is:

• Do not respond in any way at all on the air to unlicensed transmissions or abusers.

• Do not approach suspected offenders as this can encourage further abuse and may prejudice investigations already underway.

• Help to gather as much information about the problem as possible. For example, write down dates, times, and frequencies when the interference took place. Note any pattern of operation, suspected location of offenders, details of any bearings obtained with DF equipment etc. Tape recordings of the interference can be useful. Also details of other callsigns, names and addresses of those who have heard the interference as well. A copy of this information should be sent to the repeater keeper (see [1]).

If problems persist, copies of all correspondence and information should be sent to the ETCC Chairman, c/o RSGB HQ. Further information on procedures to be followed can be obtained by contacting the AROS Co-ordinator c/o RSGB HQ.

ATV REPEATERS

Amateur Television (ATV) operation is covered in earlier chapters. ATV repeaters differ in their purpose from voice repeaters in that they are designed for use by fixed stations. ATV repeaters are needed because path losses at

23cm and above, along with the very high signal strengths needed for good reception of high bandwidth signals, mean that direct contacts are much more difficult to achieve than on CW or SSB. ATV users are not usually chasing DX, but wanting to exchange good quality pictures, and the repeaters facilitate this. ATV users can leave their antenna pointing towards the repeater and monitor the repeater output, and see immediately if any other ATV-equipped station is active. The *RSGB Yearbook* [2] shows the callsigns, locations, coverage areas and operating channels of operational ATV repeaters in the UK. The BATC [4] and RSGB ETCC [1] websites also carry this information, as well as links to repeater group websites.

The average area covered by an ATV repeater is of the order of a 30km radius. All currently operate on 23cm, 13cm or 3cm (a few cross-band). As with voice repeaters, Morse code identification is given at regular intervals on the audio channel.

Essentially, ATV repeaters are much the same as their voice counterparts. However, there are four very important differences, from a user standpoint:

• To access an ATV repeater, all you need is a fast-scan TV signal with the video conforming to the repeater specification;
• ATV repeaters do not require a toneburst or CTSS for access, but switch out of beacon mode to repeat mode whenever they receive a valid ATV signal on their input;
• Most ATV repeaters have no timeout; and
• Perhaps most importantly for the constructor, when a repeater is not repeating a received picture it broadcasts its own pictures, from test cards, colour test screens, textual information screens, outside masthead cameras shots, etc all scrolling round in an endless loop.

When in repeat mode many ATV repeaters have large selections of options available, eg relaying weather pictures, giving signal and picture reports, or being able to select which of several antennas you are being received on. In other words, ATV repeaters are operational 24 hours a day, either radiating on-board generated pictures or repeating incoming received pictures.

With an ATV repeater, as with a voice repeater, there is no reason why multi-way contacts cannot occur, each station taking it in turns to transmit video. As with any other form of operation, you will need to identify your station frequently, in this case both in vision and sound.

INTERNET 'RADIO'

Digital repeaters are now interlinked using the Internet to provide global networking, so that 'DX' contacts can be had whilst using a VHF / UHF mobile or handheld. It is also possible to use VoIP (Voice over Internet Protocol) on your computer to access repeater networks or to talk to individual amateurs without using a radio.

Why would anyone want to use the Internet - since that is most certainly not amateur radio - to link two amateur stations together? Well, what if you live in a block of flats and you are unable to put up any external antenna whatsoever? Or you may have antenna restrictions, and find it difficult or impossible to make anything other than local or semi-local

The locations of 23cm ATV repeaters licensed in the UK (note that not all may be operational). This is from the RSGB ETCC web site [1] which also shows the approximate service area of each repeater.

contacts. Even those lucky enough to be able to put up a large HF beam sometimes find themselves frustrated by the lack of reliable 'ragchew' contacts with stations on the other side of the world.

The Internet provides a solution for these scenarios: it is possible to have 59+ FM-quality conversations with other amateurs while using simple equipment such as a 2m or 70cm handheld, or even your home computer.

Several different systems have been developed to make Internet gateways possible, given that there needs to be some way of identifying yourself to the gateway and routing your call to a particular distant gateway, controlling the QSO while it takes place, and then logging off when you are finished. Two gateway systems are currently in use: *EchoLink* [5], and *IRLP* [6].

World-wide, there are now many thousand amateur radio Internet gateways, many available 24 hours a day. K1RFD developed *EchoLink* in 2002 and in its first two years 110,000 amateurs in 147 countries had registered copies. Its rapid recent further development has undoubtedly been due to the huge increases in Internet speed and the availability of broadband connections at affordable rates.

Security Issues

This ability to connect to a VoIP network directly from the Internet raises some security issues, as the system can only be used by radio amateurs. Even if the connection at your end is via your PC, at some point on the network your voice will be carried over an amateur radio frequency. The different systems handle this in different ways, but all require that you provide some sort of proof of identity (eg a copy of your licence) and then issue you with a username and password or security key to enable you to access the network. For further details, see the RSGB ETCC's UK Repeater website [1].

PACKET RADIO

Packet radio is a form of data communications mainly used on VHF / UHF. There are two protocols in use, AX.25 (which is an amateur radio derivation of X.25, a packet protocol used in professional communications) and TCP/IP, the same protocol used for routing data over the Internet. Without going into too much detail, each packet of data contains routing information (based on your amateur callsign) and data. The data can be text, a program, an image, or indeed pretty much any information at all. Messages, like e-mails, can be posted to or taken from a local packet bulletin board (BBS). The network of stations can also provide other facilities such as conference (even world-wide) and DX information nets.

In cases where the distance between stations is too great for normal point-to-point working, a network of stations, called nodes, exists for the purposes of relaying these messages to their destination. In this respect, they are akin to the voice repeaters discussed above. One of the benefits of packet radio is that, because it uses a protocol which can handle 'collisions' between packets (where two stations transmit at once), several stations can share a common frequency. So a number of users can be accessing a mailbox or DX Cluster node at the same time, without necessarily being aware of each other (though data throughput starts to slow down when the channel becomes congested).

A typical VHF / UHF packet station comprises an FM radio, a home computer, some suitable software and an interface similar to that used with other data modes.

Packet radio was very popular a couple of decades ago, particular for its network of bulletin boards, but interest has declined with the advent of always-on broadband Internet connections.

APRS

The Automatic Packet (or 'Position') Reporting System, APRS came about as a means of automatically exchanging information such as positional data, messages, bulletins, announcements and alerts by packet radio.

This information is relayed by a number of 'digipeaters' (a station that relays APRS packets) and 'Igates' that not only relay the packet over RF but upload it to the APRS network on the Internet [7]. If you look at [7] you can see how active

APRS is in your area (see picture). The UK APRS frequency is 144.800MHz.

APRS builds on the capability of packet radio to send 'beacon' messages without being connected to a specific station. Those beacon packets contain data such as location and type of station, which can then be used to generate maps, reports and other summary data as required. Position information can be fed into the system from a GPS unit, or manually. For example, a weather station could feed in data about the location of a severe weather event, and this could then be tracked over time.

Getting started with APRS is relatively simple, especially if you already have packet radio capability. All you will need to do is download suitable APRS software. A popular package is UI-View32 [8]. If you want to add real-time positioning data, you will also need a GPS unit.

Some transceivers now come APRS-capable out of the box with a facility to connect a compatible GPS unit. For home use you can plug in certain weather stations and send weather data over APRS.

APRS has established itself rapidly in recent years, mainly due to the links which have developed between it and the Internet (APRS-IS, the APRS Internet System) [9]. Amateurs operating mobile are able to use APRS to transmit their location on a continual basis to other connected stations (not just licensed amateurs) anywhere in the world. Indeed, anyone, With an APRS terminal in your car, your family can connect to the Internet and watch your progress as you drive around the country or farther afield.

Some amateur satellites (see Chapter 14) have incorporated a facility specifically to support APRS. This is known as ASTARS (APRS Satellite Tracking and Reporting System) [10] and is simply a general term for any satellite that allows end-user to end-user real-time digital data exchange, typically between mobiles and handhelds. The PCSat download page on the Internet [11] is a good place to get an idea of what is available. It shows, both on a map and in a table, the callsigns and positions of last 50 amateur stations copied by PCSat, as well as the positions of several other ASTARS-equipped satellites. The intention is that the system can be used by ground stations using simple equipment with APRS capability.

REFERENCES

[1]   RSGB ETCC UK Repeaters site: www.ukrepeater.net
[2]   *RSGB Yearbook*, RSGB, published annually.
[3]   'GB7TD - A digital repeater', John Barraclough, G0SJB, *RadCom* November 2013, RSGB.
[4]   British Amateur Television Club: www.batc.org.uk
[5]   *EchoLink*: www.echolink.org
[6]   *IRLP*: www.irlp.net
[7]   APRS local map: http://aprs.fi
[8]   UI-View: www.ui-view.net/
[9]   APRS Internet System: www.aprs-is.net
[10   APRS Satellite Tracking and Reporting System: www.aprs.org/astars.html
[11]   PCSat downloads: www.findu.com/cgi-bin/pcsat.cgi

A live map from the aprs.fi web site showing APRS activity in the previous 24 hour period.

THE SPACE RACE STARTED on 4 October 1957, when the former Soviet Union launched Sputnik 1, the first man-made object to leave Earth's atmosphere. The 84kg spherical satellite measured 58cm across and for three weeks its two transmitters, on 20MHz and 40MHz, sent data associated with the density of the upper atmosphere, radio propagation and the temperature of the spacecraft. Its launch shocked the Americans, who could scarcely believe they had been beaten into space by their cold-war rivals.

In an era of space being dominated by national governments and before the commercialisation of space, Radio amateurs had the distinction of creating the very first non-military, non-governmental satellite to go into orbit when on 19 December 1961, only four years after Sputnik 1, OSCAR-1 was launched. OSCAR-1, Orbiting Satellite Carrying Amateur Radio weighed 10kg and measured 30x25x12cm was the first in a very long line of successes for the amateur radio community. In those pioneering days, rides into space were available free or at low cost as new launch vehicles were being tested. It's not surprising that amateurs were keen to take advantage of satellites. They are, after all, simply repeater stations, but at a very great altitude. This gives them excellent coverage, allowing intercontinental contacts to take place on the VHF and UHF bands. But there are some specific issues associated with satellites, which mean that operating through them isn't quite as straightforward as operating through a terrestrial relay station. This chapter gives an introduction to those issues, explains how to get started with satellite operation and provides an overview of how the Amateur Satellite service is continuing the tradition started in 1961.

SPACE EDUCATION AND COMMUNICATION

Todays' space environment is every part as challenging as that experienced in the pioneering days of the 1960s and 1970s. Major obstacles remain, yet radio amateurs have adapted, and continue to adapt, to the changing nature of Space. Free rides to space are no longer a reality as the commercial sector is now a major user of launch services and prices for launching any payload into space significantly exceed the cost of building the satellite in the first place. It is within this environment that radio amateurs have excelled in promoting amateur radio as the "Greatest Technical Hobby" and using this to great effect in STEM (Science, Technology, Engineering and Mathematics) outreach. From random, and scheduled, contacts with astronauts/cosmonauts on board first the US Space Shuttle, then the Soviet Union MIR space station and now the International Space Station, to the reception of telemetry from educational CubeSATs and imagery from weather satellites, there are many different

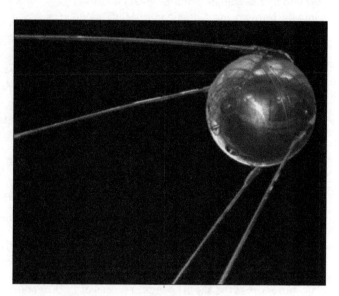

Sputnik-1, the world's first artificial satellite.

aspects of space communication that everyone from the general public to students and radio amateurs can take part in.

Education and STEM Outreach are key factors that radio amateurs use to promote radio, space and communications. They are also important elements in helping to secure launch opportunities.

REPEATERS AND SATELLITES - THE KEY DIFFERENCES.

Land based repeaters are typically designed to be operated on mains power with a specific purpose - be that analogue or digital voice, television or packet and with a fixed modulation type. Terrestrial repeaters typically have power output levels that limit the coverage area to perhaps 100 miles or so. Satellites, even those in low Earth orbit (LEO), have coverage areas in the range of several thousand miles. The power output levels are, however, typically in the sub-1W region to a maximum of perhaps just a few watts. This is due to the fact that the satellites are operated on batteries with solar cells providing a recharging mechanism. In many cases, satellites have failed because the batteries have shorted out, only to return to service many years later when the short has cleared - in these circumstances, the solar panels have provided the power to operate the satellite when in sunlight, hence the low power nature of satellite operations. This leads to one of the key design criteria of any satellite station being sufficient gain on the receiving side - a requirement usually fulfilled with appropriate antennas and preamplifiers mounted as close to the antennas as possible.

The receiver on the satellite can be very sensitive and it is generally recommended, especially for low Earth orbit satellites, that the power transmitted (by the users) is kept to a reasonably low level. For example, the command team for FUNcube-1/AO-73 [1] recommend that a maximum of 25W EIRP (5W into a 7dBi gain antenna) is used for normal contacts through the transponder. Many satellites, including FUNcube-1/AO-73, will work just as well with lower power levels, but higher levels result in the satellite being overloaded. This is the origin of one of the most common pieces of advice to all satellite operators - that being "it is better to have big ears than a big mouth".

Satellites also tend to be multi-function devices with some offering a range of operating modes that include SSB, CW, SSTV and packet whilst others just operate in one mode such as FM only. They also tend to have receivers and transmitters on different amateur bands to avoid desensing effects that are common when receivers and transmitters are physically close to each other.

Amateur satellites in anything other than a geostationary orbit move across the sky at speeds in excess of 17,000mph. There are a few consequences of this, namely requiring ground stations to have the ability to track the satellite and compensating the frequencies for Doppler Shift. Ideally, antenna systems should track the satellites but, as we will see later, full tracking in azimuth and elevation is far from essential.

Doppler Shift is the phenomenon that causes the receive frequency to keep changing as the relative velocity of the satellite changes with respect to your location on Earth. Satellites are designed and built to operate on fixed frequencies or passbands so it is important that ground stations compensate their up/down link frequencies for Doppler to ensure that the frequency at the satellite always remains constant.

Despite all these differences, there is significant help available from the Amateur Satellite community and many computer programs and multiband transceivers exist to assist the operator. Many operators fine tune their skills by performing satellite contacts by carrying out contacts on nothing more than a handheld/portable radio and a handheld antenna that they point to the satellite's approximate location in the sky.

SATELLITE DESIGNATION

Amateur satellites have come a long way since the simple devices launched in the 'sixties, and those currently in orbit include sophisticated communications and research satellites which would have cost millions of dollars if constructed on a commercial basis. The main organisation involved with the launch of amateur satellites is AMSAT [2], the Radio Amateur Satellite Corporation, with its headquarters in the USA. There are affiliated groups across the globe, including AMSAT-UK [3], AMSAT-DL and others.

Many of these AMSAT groups have been actively engaged in the design, building and launch operations with over 120

Organisation	Project Name	OSCAR Designation
AMSAT-NA	Phase IIB	AO-7 AMSAT-OSCAR - 7
King Abdulaziz City for Science and Technology	SaudiSat 1-C	SO-50 Saudi-OSCAR - 50
AMSAT-UK / AMSAT-NL	FUNcube-1	AO-73 AMSAT-OSCAR - 73
AMSAT-UK / AMSAT-NL	QB50 Precursor 1, FUNcube-3	EO-79 Europe-OSCAR - 79
AMSAT-FR	QB50 Precursor 2	EO-80 Europe-OSCAR - 80

Table 1: Some examples of satellites active at the time of writing.

launches to date. Each region around the world uses a designation for their satellites. AMSAT groups in USA, UK, Germany, Europe, Mexico, Israel, South Africa, and Japan (loosely known as AMSAT-International) are generically known as OSCAR (Orbiting Satellite Carrying Amateur Radio). These OSCARs will have their own name in their own countries and organisations (eg FUNcube-1), but once successfully commissioned and in orbit, will be given an OSCAR designation. Typically, the designation will be of the form xO-yy, where 'x' represents the organisation and 'yy' represents the sequence number. OSCAR numbers are managed by the AMSAT-NA Board of Directors [4] and examples of the current operational OSCARs are shown in **Table 1.**.

The OSCAR Number indicates just how many amateur radio satellites have been successfully launched *and* commissioned. It is lower than the number of launches as many projects failed to reach orbit due to launch failure or other failure modes.

Russia (and the former USSR) has in the past launched several amateur satellites, co-ordinated by the Radio Sport

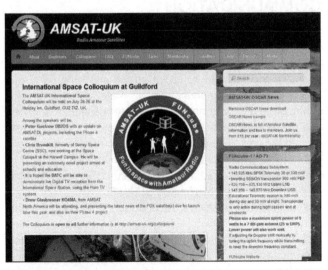

Much advice and information is available on the web site of AMSAT-UK.

Federation in that country. These are designated RS (Radio Sputnik), followed by a number.

Not all satellites that operate in the amateur bands are amateur radio satellites in the sense that they carry repeaters, or transponders. Some simply operate beacons in the amateur bands, allowing ground-based research and experimentation to take place. These are sometimes referred to as 'BeepSATs' because all they do is transmit telemetry and are most often built by universities and research institutes for single purpose functions. When these bodies collaborate with AMSAT organisations, it is often the case that the AMSAT team brings significant space communications skills and expertise that assist the project (eg in world-wide telemetry reception and forwarding, and transmitter/receiver design) and as a result, when the science mission is completed, the satellite can be switched into amateur radio mode and used by the world-wide amateur radio community as a way of saying "thank you" for the assistance with the project.

LOW EARTH ORBIT - LEO SATELLITES

LEO (Low Earth Orbit) satellites are perhaps the easiest to get started with. Signals are strong and you can access them with a simple station. They orbit the Earth at heights of somewhere between 400 and 1000km, meaning they will be accessible for up to 20 minutes on a given orbit as the footprint will extend for several thousand miles (see picture below). Usually they operate in the 2m and 70cm bands, and it is possible to work through some of them with a dual-band handheld transceiver and suitable dual-band whip antenna, or, better, a handheld Yagi. There is even tracking software available for use on smartphones and tablet computers, so

your whole satellite station is something you can carry round with you. In practice, a more advanced ground station would consist of a crossed or circularly-polarised Yagi with control of both elevation and azimuth, run directly from a suitable program on your PC, a full-duplex multiband transceiver with computer-controlled tuning, TNC and soundcard for data modes, and a masthead preamp to improve reception.

HIGH EARTH ORBIT - HEO SATELLITES

HEO (High Earth Orbit) in this context means a satellite in a very elliptical orbit so that it comes close to the Earth for part of it, but then swings way out into space, beyond 40,000km, creating a very large footprint. The picture below shows the typical footprint of the now non-operational HEO satellite AO-40. The intention is that the satellite spends most of its orbital period above the more heavily-populated parts of the Earth, allowing more time for contacts to take place. Pass time can range from 12 to 18 hours, simplifying the tracking and allowing more time for contacts to take place. The Russians pioneered this type of orbit which has an inclination of 63.4 degrees, is very stable and is termed a Molniya orbit. Radio amateurs have used it successfully for several long-life satellites but unfortunately the current fleet of HEO satellites are non-operational. As launch platforms have matured, AMSAT organisations around the world have found that launch providers are now only offering commercial rates which are prohibitively expensive to volunteer organisations such as AMSAT.

The latest HEO satellites, Eagle by AMSAT-NA has now been cancelled and the other satellite designated for HEO, Phase3E, built by AMSAT-DL is still awaits affordable launch opportunities.

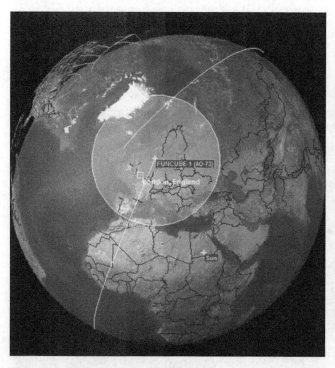

Footprint of FUNcube-1/AO-73 in LEO.

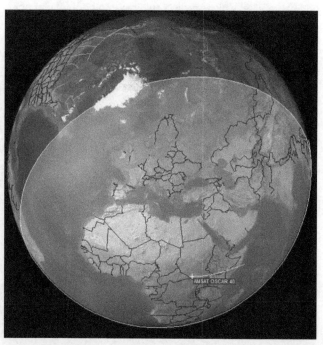

Typical footprint of HEO satellite AO-40 (the satellite is currently non-operational).

Mode	Uplink Band	Downlink Band
Mode A	2m	10m
Mode B	70cm	2m
Mode J	2m	70cm
Mode K	15m	10m
Mode L	23cm	70cm
Mode S	70cm	13cm
Mode T	15m	2cm

Table 2: Original satellite operating modes.

Letter	Band / Frequency	Notes
H	15m / 21MHz	Uplink only
V	2m / 145MHz	Used as uplink or downlink
U	70cm / 435MHz	Used as uplink or downlink
L	23cm / 1.2GHz	Uplink
S	13cm / 2.4GHz	Can act as uplinks and downlinks
S2	9cm / 3.4GHz	
C	5cm / 5GHz	Uplink
X	3cm / 10GHz	Downlink only
K	1.2cm / 24GHz	Downlink only
R	6mm / 47GHz	

Table 3: Current satellite operating modes.

SATELLITE OPERATING MODES

When you read about satellite operating, you will see reference to various 'operating modes'. Don't confuse these with modes as in SSB, RTTY, etc. Rather, they refer to the bands on which the satellite receives and retransmits signals. The original modes, which you will still see in older publications, are shown in **Table 2**.

More recently, a new type of designation has come into use, whereby two or more letters are used for each mode, the first to designate uplink and the second the downlink, eg Mode B is now called Mode U/V and Mode J is now Mode V/U. See **Table 3**.

TRACKING SATELLITES

Since radio communication via an amateur satellite is essentially line-of-sight, it follows that it can only take place when the satellite is above the user's horizon, and it is therefore necessary to determine the periods when this occurs. In addition, if beam antennas are in use it will be necessary to ascertain the beam headings to track the satellite across the sky. Many satellite stations use antennas adjustable in 'az-el', azimuth and elevation. All this information can be derived quite simply from orbital data, or Keplerian elements - 'Keps' (see 'Orbital data' below).

It is important to note that in order to enjoy satellites it is not necessary to have a complex station with full az-el antennas and computerised steering: contacts can be achieved and plenty of interest generated with a much simpler set-up.

ORBITAL DATA

The simplest way to understand satellite orbits is to consider a typical LEO satellite (see previous page). It will travel around its orbit completing a revolution approximately every 90 minutes. During this 90 minutes the Earth is rotating on its axis from west to east. Calculating the position of the satellite relative to your location on Earth - the 'ground station' - is a simple enough task for a computer. We need three things: the co-ordinates of your ground station, the physical parameters of the satellite's orbit, and an observation by radar that gives the precise position of the satellite at a specified time. This data - the Keplerian elements ('Keps') - is produced by the North American Aerospace Defense Command (NORAD) in the USA and are widely available over the internet from *CelesTrak* [5] and many other sites.. Popular paid-for tracking programs for the PC include *SatPC32* [6] and *NOVA for Windows* [7] (both illustrated here) whilst open source and/or free to use versions include *GPredict* [8] and *Orbitron* [9]. *MacDoppler* [10] is by far the most recommended program for Apple Mac whilst *GPredict* [8] is available on most Linux distributions.

How frequently should you update the elements set used by your tracking software? For most of the unmanned satellites, once a week will be more than sufficient but for other satellites, including the International Space Station which has to carry out regular orbital re-boosts, it is always recommended to use the most up to date element set that is available. However, with the prevalence of computers and fast internet access, it is recommended that if you are using computer Doppler correction, always use an up-to-date set and ensure your tracking computer clock is accurate to a fraction of a second, otherwise you will not be 'on frequency'. For all

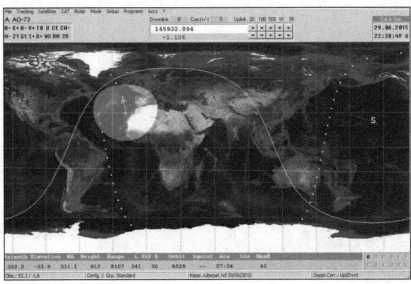

The *SatPC32* satellite tracking program in action.

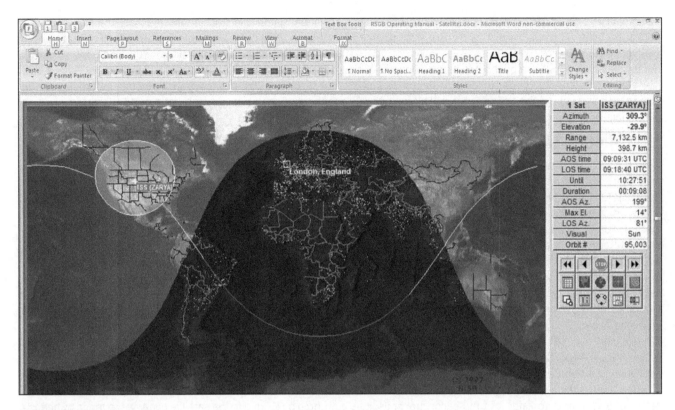

NOVA for Windows in action.

aspects of satellite working we use UTC so check that your shack computer and clock take this into account.

POLARISATION

Imagine a satellite in orbit without a sophisticated stabilisation system. That satellite is likely to roll and tumble according to external influences of solar and terrestrial origin, and so the orientation of the satellite's antennas, as seen from the ground, can (and do) change in direction. To add a further complication, radio signals passing through the ionosphere are subject to a distortion called 'Faraday rotation'. Theoretically the polarisation to cater for all orientations and to combat fading is circular. In the real world perfectly satisfactory results can be obtained with horizontal or vertical polarisation alone for most of the time, but fading will occasionally be troublesome. Improved results can be obtained by having both polarisations available and switching between them to select the strongest signal. This can be achieved by using crossed Yagi antennas with switched phasing lines between the horizontal and vertical elements. Some satellite antenna systems are themselves circularly polarised (on VHF and upwards) in which case ground stations should use the same sense of circular polarisation.

DOPPLER SHIFT

Doppler shift is a frequency and velocity-related effect which is very obvious in amateur satellite operation. The typical speed of a satellite is about 17,000mph. As the satellite approaches, its frequency starts high and drifts lower throughout the pass. As frequency increases, so does the amount of Doppler shift for a given velocity. Use of higher frequencies, such as 435MHz and 1270MHz, results in a

Doppler correction that can get extremely large. Remember that the shift of both up and down links has to be taken into account. Designers of transponders can, in the mixer stage, extract a negative component rather than a positive component (or turn it upside down) such that one Doppler shift is subtracted from another. As an example, Doppler shift on the 145MHz uplink (4 - 5kHz) is subtracted from that on the 435MHz downlink (about 12kHz) resulting in only 6 or 7kHz instead of the 18kHz which would result if the positive component were used. It is for this reason that the transponder is made inverting. As a result, frequencies at the top of the uplink band come out at the bottom of the downlink band and vice versa. Consequently the convention of transmitting lower sideband results, through the translation process being inverted, in upper sideband being received.

It was originally thought that SSB would not be possible on satellites due to the Doppler shift. However, with a little practice it's easy to pick up the skill to tune the radio during a QSO. The important practical point to keep in mind is that the published frequencies are always the nominal frequency at zero Doppler: the satellite will always be several kilohertz higher of the published frequency as it comes into range. It's also worth considering that the Doppler shift you are experiencing at your QTH may be quite different from that of your QSO partner, particularly if the satellite is overhead for one of you and near the horizon for the other.

A question that is frequently asked when operating "Which frequency should I compensate for Doppler?" Within the satellite community, this often raises considerable debate and in 1994, Paul Williamson, KB5MU, published a paper [11] which proposed that the best way was to compensate both the uplink and downlink for Doppler. However, as the equipment and computer capability to implement this did not exist at that time, a simpler version of the rule was promoted. This version of the rule "The One True Rule ", encouraged that the higher frequency in use be the one that is adjusted. With new-generation CAT-controlled radios, computers can take over the job and control the uplink and downlink frequencies automatically [12].

GETTING STARTED IN SATELLITES

Now that you have read through the basics, perhaps you are fired up to try satellite operating? It is well worth looking at the AMSAT-NA website [13] for the latest information on each of the satellites, and plenty of additional advice on getting started. You will need to know which satellites are operational, what mode they are using and, critically, when they will be in range of your station. You may want to download one of the tracking programs, but an easier way of getting started is to use the prediction and real-time tracking resources on the web, eg those on the AMSAT-NA [14] and 'Heavens Above' [15] websites, which will show when each satellite will be 'visible' at your location. KD5QGR's 'Live Oscar Status Page' [16] has daily postings showing which satellites have been heard or worked.

Before even thinking about transmitting through a satellite, select one and start to listen to the beacon transmissions and to amateur signals. This will allow you to get used to

tuning them in and tracking them across the sky. If you are using an omni-directional antenna (which will be sufficient to hear some of the LEO satellites), you won't even have to worry about tracking your antenna. Even if you use a Yagi most of the LEO satellites are low enough in the sky that an antenna fixed at an elevation of around 30 degrees will be sufficient, avoiding the need for elevation adjustment. If you have an unobstructed view of the sky in the appropriate direction, your current 2m and 70cm terrestrial beams will probably produce results when the satellite is low in the sky.

Because satellites are cross-band repeaters, the use of a separate transmitter and receiver allows full duplex operation, meaning that you can hear your transmitted signal coming back from the satellite as you speak, and so be alerted to any problems. There are no special considerations when operating through satellites, but a degree of courtesy is appropriate, especially when the satellite is busy. Listen for one of the satellite beacon signals or for other users before transmitting yourself, so that you know you are able to hear the satellite (meaning that your antenna is correctly pointed, etc).

For single-channel FM satellites (such as SO-50 or the ISS) probably the most important operating tip is to keep your receiver squelch fully open all the time. The satellite signal may not be strong enough to open the squelch, and you will want to be alerted to the satellite coming into range by hearing the quieting of the audio. Once you are confident that you

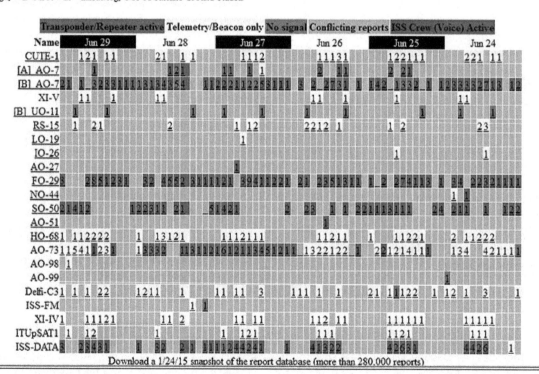

Live OSCAR satellite status page.

The Amateur Radio Operating Manual

	RX (MHz)	TX (MHz)
AOS	436.810	145.850
	436.805	145.850
TCA	436.800	145.850
	436.795	145.850
LOS	436.790	145.850

AOS = Acquisition of Signal
TCA = Time of Closest Approach
LOS = Loss of Signal

Table 4: Suggested settings for transceiver memories for SO-50 (FM single channel satellite, Mode V/U). Note the use of 'The One True Rule'.

can predict a satellite's appearance and receive signals at reasonable strength, you can think about making your first transmission.

Table 4 gives a suggested method of using the memories in your transceiver to track Doppler shift on an FM satellite. This is essential to maintain a clear received signal, though is not essential on the uplink, where the radio can be set on the nominal uplink frequency. This method works when using two separate hand-held radios where the transmitting radio can be pre-set.

If you are a beginner, try operating at less busy times such as weekdays or late evenings. Look at the satellite footprint and choose times when very large areas of population have dropped out of the footprint. Don't call CQ for long periods, just your callsign and locator will be fine. Keep contacts short and only make one or two contacts each pass, leaving the satellite for others. Be courteous to DXpeditions, special events, etc as they are probably on hand-held Yagis and using low power. Above all, keep your power down: 5W to a modest antenna is plenty. It is easily possible to work from Scotland to the east coast of the USA with 1W and a 5-element Yagi.

For SSB satellites (such as FUNcube-1/AO73) always listen to the transponder before transmitting to ensure that you are receiving well. Also check for other contacts because the transponder(s) may be switched off for some reason.

SSB satellites generally have inverting transponders, which means using LSB on the uplink to get a downlink on USB. It also means that your uplink signal at the lower end

CODE OF PRACTICE FOR SATELLITE OPERATION

Naturally the same ethics of amateur conduct and behaviour apply as they do to normal terrestrial communication on both the HF and VHF bands but, because each satellite is a DX 'band' with limited and power-sharing openings, certain additional points should be observed.

DO NOT turn on your carrier, whistle, send CW or otherwise until you can hear the satellite beacon. If you have a poor downlink receiver and a good uplink, as most European users seem to have, the chances are that someone else's DX contact will be ruined by your signal.

DO NOT run excessive power. Your received signal should not be louder than the beacon on SSB satellites. By running more than the recommended EIRP at any time you will ruin contacts for those who are 'playing the game', and give them grounds for the same irresponsible behaviour.

DO NOT call stations in your own area when the satellite is near the horizon. DX stations may be trying to make contacts and may only have a few seconds.

DO NOT call CQ incessantly on single-channel FM satellites.

DO pay maximum attention to your receiving system: when it is good enough you will hear returns from even 100mW uplink power, and hence work much more DX for less power. Attention to higher gain, and less noise on your downlink reception is cheaper and far more productive than anything else you can do.

DO use the outer limits of the pass band, thus avoiding the overcrowded centre, and encouraging others to spread out.

DO listen to AMSAT nets and / or check websites so that you know the operational state of the satellites, modes of operation, instructions from the control stations etc.

DO uphold the tradition of courtesy and consideration; crowded satellites can be frustrating.

DO try to have proper amateur contacts via amateur satellites, rather than merely exchanging a few numbers contest-style. Try spreading the word about AMSAT, new stations, schedules or other satellite interest information.

DO pay attention to special service channels and avoid transmitting on these. They may be required at that time to control the spacecraft for your better enjoyment.

DO NOT work stations obviously using more power than required for a reasonable signal. These stations are stopping the enjoyment of all other users of the satellite and they degrade the transponder efficiency. If they are louder in your receiver than the beacon (telemetry) they are in excess of design parameters for the transponder. This is a fact, not a myth, and can be easily proven by you, the listener.

DO persuade all stations to reduce power to the minimum for a satisfactory QSO.

DO Support your national AMSAT organisation. If your country doesn't have one, start one or join an AMSAT group in your region. Amateur satellites are designed, built and funded by radio amateurs. If you enjoy satellite operating, be prepared to give something back.

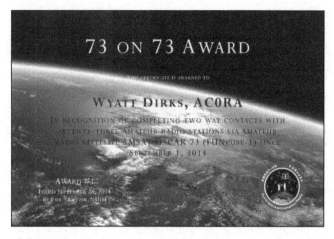

This award aims to promote activity on AO-73 by needing the claimant to work 73 unique stations on that satellite.

of the pass-band will be re-transmitted by the satellite at the upper end or, put another way, an increase in transmit frequency results in a decrease in receive frequency.

Find a clear spot on the downlink: towards the upper end of the frequency range is probably a good place to try as many operators tend to go for the middle of the passband. To get your transmitter and receiver synchronised, keep your transmit frequency fixed for the present, give your callsign and a short message like "MOxxx test test" and at the same time tune your receiver either side of the expected frequency. You should hear your own signal and be able to tune on to it quite quickly. This procedure fixes the up / down frequency relationship, and in modern multi-band transceivers this can be locked so that as you tune through the pass-band look-

ing for stations to call, your transmit frequency moves appropriately, although you should still expect to make slight adjustments. Your QSO partner may not be too adept at keeping on frequency. This all sounds hard to do when in print but a bit of practice and the technique is soon mastered.

A good tip whilst getting used to this method, is to work the satellite at lower elevations; the Doppler shift will be less, so less frequent tuning will be needed and the steps smaller. Try a few tests in a quiet part of the pass-band, transmit "MOxxx, test test", and the satellite name, and practice keeping your transmission on a fixed receive frequency without it wandering across the pass-band. The use of headphones is essential, otherwise there is the likelihood of creating serious feedback through the satellite.

APRS

Oscar-44, NO-44, is solely dedicated to APRS using 1200bps standard packet on 145.827MHz. If you have equipment for terrestrial APRS you can receive and operate through NO-44. Due to a limited power budget the satellite is not operational all the time, so check the AMSAT website's status page [13] for details and tips on correct operation. APRS can also be digipeated through the ISS. Ensure you operate according to the correct protocols otherwise you will block the channel for other users.

SATELLITE AWARDS

Several awards are available for operating through amateur satellites, ranging from the Satellite Communicators' Club award for making your very first satellite contact, to awards for working 100 countries or 1000 two way satellite contacts or even making 73 contacts on AO-73. At the time of writing, some 19 amateurs had gained the "73 on 73 Award" [17] including the first operator to have achieved this award using just CW (Hideo Kambayashi JH3XCU).

TELEMETRY

Ground control stations need to monitor the health of the satellite in respect of on-board temperatures, battery charge condition, solar array currents, and numerous other parameters including science experiments data. Transmitted to Earth, this data is called telemetry. The satellite beacon signal often doubles up as the telemetry signal, so that the transmission consists of the satellite identifier followed by the data. Various modulation schemes are used from the simplest Morse code beacons on Cubesats to 1200 baud BPSK from AO-73.

Telemetry study is receive-only and can become an interest in itself. It becomes especially exciting when we have a new satellite launch. Generally the telemetry

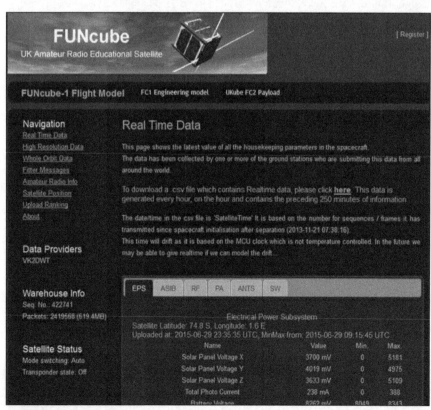

The FUNcube Data Warehouse.

beacon is switched on right at the start of the mission and it's a challenge to be amongst the first to capture the data. Often ground stations welcome the captured data files as it enables them to receive data when the satellite is out of range of their own ground station.

Websites are usually set up where radio amateurs can upload their received data. The AMSAT-UK/AMSAT-NL FUNcube-1/AO-73 CubeSAT became one of the first to host an online data warehouse [18] that not only allowed the submission of received telemetry but also allowed users to download data, including Whole Orbit Data (WOD) for offline analysis - see picture opposite. Satellite web pages are extremely useful locations to get details of the telemetry available, the data format and the decode equations.

Several Radio Amateurs around the world, especially JE9PEL [19] and DK3WN, also host their own websites giving information and telemetry decode utilities that can help operators understand the data being transmitted. Also visit the JE9PEL [19] and DK3WN [20] websites to download free software to decode your captured data. Satellite telemetry data is regularly posted on DK3WN's blog and Twitter feeds.

WEATHER SATELLITES

If your ground station has 2m FM capability and you can receive out of band, you should be able to receive signals from the NOAA series of weather satellites on 137 - 138MHz. By feeding the audio into a PC soundcard and using software free from the Internet you can receive real-time weather images as the satellite passes over Europe and the UK.

Receivers with wide IFs are used so that all of the picture data is captured, however, acceptable results can be achieved on communications receivers using appropriate software such as *Wxtolmg* [21], which is free, although registration is required for use of all its features.

The Group for Earth Observation [22] is an independent organisation for weather satellite and Earth observation enthusiasts and much information on this aspect of the hobby can be found on their website.

THE INTERNATIONAL SPACE STATION

The first manned space flight Amateur Radio contact was carried out by Owen Garriott, W5LFL, when he operated from the Space Shuttle STS-9 mission in 1983. Since that pioneering flight, the use of amateur radio on manned spaceflight has gone from strength to strength and expanded from other Shuttle missions to the MIR Space station, and now the International Space Station.

It has also been recognised as an important backup communications facility for NASA and the other Space Agencies and provides inspiration to students around the world to study STEM subjects by allowing them to talk to astronauts and cosmonauts as the orbit above them.

Amateur radio on the International Space Station (ARISS) [23] is a volunteer body which supports amateur radio contacts from the International Space Station. It is entrusted by

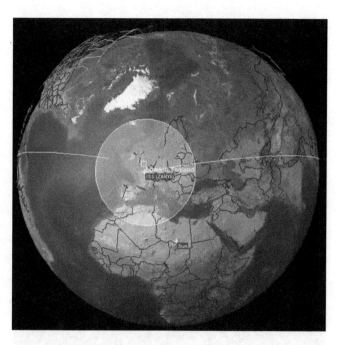

Footprint of the ISS over Europe.

the major space agencies with co-ordinating contacts between students and the astronauts/cosmonauts on board the space station. Normally these would be scheduled voice contacts with schools or other educational establishments and limited to the 10 minutes or so that the space station is in range of a single location on Earth as it passes overhead. A recent enhancement to the amateur radio equipment is

Mode V APRS (Worldwide APRS Digipeater):	
Simplex:	145.8250MHz FM 1200 BPS
Downlink:	145.8250MHz FM 1200 BPS
Mode V/V Crew Contact (Region 1):	
Uplink:	145.2000MHz FM
Downlink:	145.8000MHz FM
Mode V/V Crew Contact (Regions 2 & 3):	
Uplink:	144.4900MHz FM
Downlink:	145.8000MHz FM
Mode U/V (B) FM Voice Repeater (World-wide):	
Uplink:	437.8000MHz FM
Downlink:	145.8000MHz FM
Mode V/U (J) FM Voice Repeater (World-wide):	
Uplink:	145.8000MHz FM
Downlink:	437.8000MHz FM
Mode V Imaging:	
Downlink:	145.8000MHz SSTV
Mode V/V Packet (World-wide):	
Uplink:	145.9900MHz AFSK 1200 BPS
Downlink:	145.8000MHz AFSK 1200 BPS
USA Callsign:	NA1SS
European Callsign:	OR4ISS
Russian callsigns:	RSOISS and RZ3DZR
Mailbox callsign:	RSOISS-11
Digipeater alias:	ARISS

Table 5: ISS Frequencies and callsigns.

ISS SSTV picture received by Andrew Adams G1EGZ.

the introduction of the HAMVideo [24] system in the ISS Columbus module which will allow the transmission of video from the ISS as an ARISS contact is in progress.

Other amateurs are, of course, more than welcome to listen in to these communications on the world-wide voice downlink frequency of 145.800MHz. As many of the astronauts and cosmonauts hold amateur radio licences themselves, and amateur radio is an approved crew activity during rest periods, it is possible that they may use the radios for 'random' contacts with other amateurs on Earth. Information on how to set up a scheduled schools contact with the ISS is available on the ARISS websites[23]. It even has its own fan club [25], which provides a good deal of news about the ISS.

The frequencies and callsigns used by the ISS are given in **Table 5**. The frequency 143.625MHz FM is also worth monitoring when the ISS is in range of your station and Moscow. This was the command link frequency for the Russian Mir space station and it is still activated from time to time, usually in Russian. The Russian Orlan spacesuits are equipped with VHF FM transceivers, which create an interesting opportunity for anyone with a modest VHF receive setup. The frequencies are either 121.125, 121.700 or 130.167MHz. Your regular 2m antenna should give good results.

The ARISS station consists of several units, permanently installed into the ISS, including a VHF FM transceiver and the HAMVideo system in the Columbus Module and a multi-mode transceiver with SSTV capability in the Russian Zarya Module which is activated from time to time.

Important: if you intend to make any communications with the ISS, or via the ISS such as digipeating, it is essential to consult the information on the ARISS website or the ARISS news page on the AMSAT website to ensure you have the latest information on the operating modes to be activated.

REFERENCES

[1] AMSAT-UK/AMSAT-NL, FUNcube-1/AO-73 - An Educational 1U CubeSAT with a 20kHz Linear Transponder, http://funcube.org.uk

[2] AMSAT-NA, Radio Amateur Satellite Corporation, 10605 Concord St, #304 Kensington MD 20895-2526: www.amsat.org

[3] AMSAT-UK, The Secretary, 'Badgers', Letton Close, Blanford, Dorset DT11 7SS: www.amsat-uk.org

[4] OSCAR Number Policy, AMSAT-NA policy on OSCAR Numbering, www.amsat.org/?page_id=2478

[5] CelesTrack.com, CelesTrak - Keplerian elements from TS Kelso: www.celestrak.com

[6] *SatPC32* Satellite Tracking Program: www.dk1tb.de

[7] *NOVA for Windows*, Northern Lights Software: www.nlsa.com/nfw.html

[8] *GPredict* by Alexandru Csete OZ9AEC: http://gpredict.oz9aec.net/

[9] *Orbitron* - Satellite Tracking System by Sebastian Stoff: www.stoff.pl/

[10] *MacDoppler* - Ham Radio Satellite Tracking Software for the Mac: www.dogparksoftware.com/MacDoppler.html

[11] K Paul Williamson, 'The One True Rule for Doppler Tuning': www.amsat.org/amsat/features/one_true_rule.html

[12] '"What frequency is the DX on?", Bringing the One True Rule of Doppler Tuning into the 21st Century', Alan Biddle, WA4SCA: www.amsat.org/wordpress/wp-content/uploads/2015/02/FDT-WA4SCA.pdf

[13] AMSAT-NA. List of currently active amateur satellites: www.amsat.org/?page_id=177

[14] AMSAT-NA. AMSAT Online Satellite Pass Predictions: www.amsat.org/amsat-new/tools/predict/index.php

[15] Heavens Above - Online satellite prediction: www.heavens-above.com/

[16] David Carr, KD5QGR, Live OSCAR Satellite Status Page: http://oscar.dcarr.org/

[17] Paul Stoetzer N8HM, The '73 on 73' Award: http://amsat-uk.org/funcube/73-on-73-award/

[18] AMSAT-UK/AMSAT-NL, FUNcube Data Warehouse: http://warehouse.funcube.org.uk/

[19] Mineo Wakita, JE9PEL, WiSP Program and Satelitte telemetry page: www.ne.jp/asahi/hamradio/je9pel/

[20] Mike Rupprecht, DK3WN, Website of Mike Rupprecht, DK3WN: www.dk3wn.info/satellites.shtml

[21] *WXtoImg* - software to decode weather satellite images: www.wxtoimg.com/

[22] Group for Earth Observations, the Independent Organisation for Weather Satellite and Earth Observation Enthusiasts: www.geo-web.org.uk/

[23] ARISS - Amateur Radio on the International Space Station: www.ariss.org and www.ariss-eu.org

[24] HAMVideo - a DATV transmitter installed in the Columbus module of the ISS: www.ariss-eu.org/columbus.htm

[25] The ISS Fan Club: www.issfanclub.com/

*T*HE FOLLOWING IS BASED on the official ARRL DXCC List and shows every DXCC entity (340 at the time of writing) in the order of its usual prefix or prefixes, the entity's continent, ITU and CQ zone numbers and the ADIF entity number (as used in computer logging software).

The ITU (see Chapter 2) allocates one or more prefix block to each country. The prefixes used by a country for both commercial and amateur radio purposes are taken from those prefix blocks. Note that special prefixes are sometimes issued by licensing authorities from alternative prefix blocks that are not normally used by the Amateur Service (eg Spanish stations are sometimes granted permission to use the AN or AO prefix in place of the usual EA).

Also shown below are those DXCC entities that use unofficial prefixes not allocated by the ITU, ie 1A (SMOM) and S0 (Western Sahara). Not shown are unofficial prefixes used by some amateurs that are not recognised for DXCC purposes, eg 1B (used in the Turkish area of Northern Cyprus). Full information on prefixes can be found in the RSGB Prefix Guide.

A great circle map based on London and an ITU zone map can be found at the end of appendix, together with locator maps.

Prefix	Entity	Continent	ITU Zone	CQ Zone	Entity Code	Prefix	Entity	Continent	ITU Zone	CQ Zone	Entity Code
1A	Sov Mil Order of Malta (SMOM)	EU	28	15	246	8P	Barbados	NA	11	08	062
						8Q	Maldives	AS/AF	41	22	159
3A	Monaco	EU	27	14	260	8R	Guyana	SA	12	09	129
3B6, 7	Agalega & St Brandon Is	AF	53	39	004	9A	Croatia	EU	28	15	497
3B8	Mauritius	AF	53	39	165	9G	Ghana	AF	46	35	424
3B9	Rodrigues I	AF	53	39	207	9H	Malta	EU	28	15	257
3C	Equatorial Guinea	AF	47	36	049	9J	Zambia	AF	53	36	482
3C0	Annobon I	AF	52	36	195	9K	Kuwait	AS	39	21	348
3D2	Fiji	OC	56	32	176	9L	Sierra Leone	AF	46	35	458
3D2	Conway Reef	OC	56	32	489	9M, DX0	Spratly Is	AS	50	26	247
3D2	Rotuma I	OC	56	32	460	9M2	West Malaysia	AS	54	28	299
3DA	Swaziland	AF	57	38	468	9M6, 8	East Malaysia	OC	54	28	046
3V	Tunisia	AF	37	33	474	9N	Nepal	AS	42	22	369
3X	Guinea	AF	46	35	107	9Q	Dem Rep of Congo	AF	52	36	414
3Y	Bouvet I	AF	67	38	024	9U	Burundi	AF	52	36	404
3Y	Peter 1 I	AN	72	12	199	9V	Singapore	AS	54	28	381
4J, 4K	Azerbaijan	AS	29	21	018	9X	Rwanda	AF	52	36	454
4L	Georgia	AS	29	21	075	9Y-9Z	Trinidad & Tobago	SA	11	09	090
4O	Montenegro	EU	28	15	514	A2	Botswana	AF	57	38	402
4S	Sri Lanka	AS	41	22	315	A3	Tonga	OC	62	32	160
4U_ITU	ITU HQ	EU	28	14	117	A4	Oman	AS	39	21	370
4U_UN	United Nations HQ	NA	08	05	289	A5	Bhutan	AS	41	22	306
4W	Timor-Leste	OC	54	28	511	A6	United Arab Emirates	AS	39	21	391
4X, 4Z	Israel	AS	39	20	336	A7	Qatar	AS	39	21	376
5A	Libya	AF	38	34	436	A9	Bahrain	AS	39	21	304
5B	Cyprus	AS	39	20	215	AP	Pakistan	AS	41	21	372
5H	Tanzania	AF	53	37	470	B	China	AS	33, 42-44	23, 24	318
5N	Nigeria	AF	46	35	450						
5R	Madagascar	AF	53	39	438	BS7	Scarborough Reef	AS	50	27	506
5T	Mauritania	AF	46	35	444	BU-BX	Taiwan	AS	44	24	386
5U	Niger	AF	46	35	187	BV9P	Pratas I	AS	44	24	505
5V	Togo	AF	46	35	483	C2	Nauru	OC	65	31	157
5W	Samoa	OC	62	32	190	C3	Andorra	EU	27	14	203
5X	Uganda	AF	48	37	286	C5	Gambia	AF	46	35	422
5Z	Kenya	AF	48	37	430	C6	Bahamas	NA	11	08	060
6O, T5	Somalia	AF	48	37	232	C9	Mozambique	AF	53	37	181
6V-6W	Senegal	AF	46	35	456	CA-CE	Chile	SA	14, 16	12	112
6Y	Jamaica	NA	11	08	082	CE0	Easter I	SA	63	12	047
7O	Yemen	AS/AF	39	21	492	CE0	Juan Fernandez Is	SA	14	12	125
7P	Lesotho	AF	57	38	432	CE0	San Felix & San Ambrosio	SA	14	12	217
7Q	Malawi	AF	53	37	440	CM, CO	Cuba	NA	11	08	070
7X	Algeria	AF	37	33	400	CN	Morocco	AF	37	33	446

Prefix	Entity	Continent	ITU Zone	CQ Zone	Entity Code	Prefix	Entity	Continent	ITU Zone	CQ Zone	Entity Code
CP	Bolivia	SA	12, 14	10	104	HA, HG	Hungary	EU	28	15	239
CT	Portugal	EU	37	14	272	HB	Switzerland	EU	28	14	287
CT3	Madeira	AF	36	33	256	HB0	Liechtenstein	EU	28	14	251
CU	Azores	EU	36	14	149	HC	Ecuador	SA	12	10	120
CV-CX	Uruguay	SA	14	13	144	HC8	Galapagos Is	SA	12	10	071
CY0	Sable I	NA	09	05	211	HH	Haiti	NA	11	08	078
CY9	St Paul I	NA	09	05	252	HI	Dominican Republic	NA	11	08	072
D2-3	Angola	AF	52	36	401	HK	Colombia	SA	12	09	116
D4	Cape Verde Is	AF	46	35	409	HK0	Malpelo I	SA	12	09	161
D6	Comoros	AF	53	39	411	HK0	San Andres & Providencia	NA	11	07	216
DA-DR	Fed Rep of Germany	EU	28	14	230	HL, DS	Republic of Korea	AS	44	25	137
DU	Philippines	OC	50	27	375	HP	Panama	NA	11	07	088
E3	Eritrea	AF	48	37	051	HR	Honduras	NA	11	07	080
E4	Palestine	AS	39	20	510	HS, E2	Thailand	AS	49	26	387
E5	North Cook Is	OC	62	32	191	HV	Vatican City	EU	28	15	295
E5	South Cook Is	OC	62	32	234	HZ, 7Z	Saudi Arabia	AS	39	21	378
E6	Niue	OC	62	32	188	I	Italy	EU/AF	28	15, 33	248
E7	Bosnia-Herzegovina	EU	28	15	501	ISO, IMO	Sardinia	EU	28	15	225
EA	Spain	EU	37	14	281	J2	Djibouti	AF	48	37	382
EA6	Balearic Is	EU	37	14	021	J3	Grenada	NA	11	08	077
EA8	Canary Is	AF	36	33	029	J5	Guinea-Bissau	AF	46	35	109
EA9	Ceuta & Melilla	AF	37	33	032	J6	St Lucia	NA	11	08	097
EI-EJ	Ireland	EU	27	14	245	J7	Dominica	NA	11	08	095
EK	Armenia	AS	29	21	014	J8	St Vincent	NA	11	08	098
EL	Liberia	AF	46	35	434	JA	Japan	AS	45	25	339
EP	Iran	AS	40	21	330	JD1	Minami Torishima	OC	90	27	177
ER	Moldova	EU	29	16	179	JD1	Ogasawara	AS	45	27	192
ES	Estonia	EU	29	15	052	JT	Mongolia	AS	32, 33	23	363
ET	Ethiopia	AF	48	37	053	JW	Svalbard	EU	18	40	259
EU-EW	Belarus	EU	29	16	027	JX	Jan Mayen I	EU	18	40	118
EX	Kyrgyzstan	AS	30, 31	17	135	JY	Jordan	AS	39	20	342
EY	Tajikistan	AS	30	17	262	K, N, W, AA-AK	United States of America	NA	6, 7, 8	3, 4, 5	291
EZ	Turkmenistan	AS	30	17	280						
F	France	EU	27	14	227	KG4	Guantanamo Bay	NA	11	08	105
FG, TO	Guadeloupe	NA	11	08	079	KH0	Northern Mariana Is	OC	64	27	166
FH, TO	Mayotte	AF	53	39	169	KH1	Baker & Howland Is	OC	61	31	020
FJ, TO	St Barthelemy	NA	11	08	516	KH2	Guam	OC	64	27	103
FK, TX	New Caledonia	OC	56	32	162	KH3	Johnston I	OC	61	31	123
FK, TX	Chesterfield Is	OC	56	30	512	KH4	Midway I	OC	61	31	174
FM, TO	Martinique	NA	11	08	084	KH5	Palmyra & Jarvis Is	OC	61, 62	31	197
FO, TX	Austral Is	OC	63	32	508	KH5K	Kingman Reef	OC	61	31	134
FO, TX	Clipperton I	NA	10	07	036	KH6, 7	Hawaii	OC	61	31	110
FO, TX	French Polynesia	OC	63	32	175	KH7K	Kure I	OC	61	31	138
FO, TX	Marquesas Is	OC	63	31	509	KH8	American Samoa	OC	62	32	009
FP	St Pierre & Miquelon	NA	09	05	277	KH8	Swains I	OC	62	32	515
FR, TO	Reunion I	AF	53	39	453	KH9	Wake I	OC	65	31	297
FS, TO	St Martin	NA	11	08	213	KL	Alaska	NA	1, 2	1	006
FT_G	Glorioso Is	AF	53	39	099	KP1	Navassa I	NA	11	08	182
FT_J, E	Juan de Nova, Europa I	AF	53	39	124	KP2	US Virgin Is	NA	11	08	285
FT_T	Tromelin I	AF	53	39	276	KP3, 4	Puerto Rico	NA	11	08	202
FT_W	Crozet I	AF	68	39	041	KP5	Desecheo I	NA	11	08	043
FT_X	Kerguelen Is	AF	68	39	131	LA	Norway	EU	18	14	266
FT_Z	Amsterdam & St Paul Is	AF	68	39	010	LU	Argentina	SA	14, 16	13	100
FW	Wallis & Futuna	OC	62	32	298	LX	Luxembourg	EU	27	14	254
FY	French Guiana	SA	12	09	063	LY	Lithuania	EU	29	15	146
G, M	England	EU	27	14	223	LZ	Bulgaria	EU	28	20	212
GD, MD	Isle of Man	EU	27	14	114	OA	Peru	SA	12	10	136
GI, MI	Northern Ireland	EU	27	14	265	OD	Lebanon	AS	39	20	354
GJ, MJ	Jersey	EU	27	14	122	OE	Austria	EU	28	15	206
GM, MM	Scotland	EU	27	14	279	OH	Finland	EU	18	15	224
GU, MU	Guernsey	EU	27	14	106	OH0	Åland Is	EU	18	15	005
GW, MW	Wales	EU	27	14	294	OJ0	Market Reef	EU	18	15	167
H4	Solomon Is	OC	51	28	185	OK	Czech Republic	EU	28	15	503
H40	Temotu Province	OC	51	32	507	OM	Slovak Republic	EU	28	15	504

Prefix	Entity	Continent	ITU Zone	CQ Zone	Entity Code	Prefix	Entity	Continent	ITU Zone	CQ Zone	Entity Code
ON	Belgium	EU	27	14	209	V3	Belize	NA	11	07	066
OX	Greenland	NA	5, 75	40	237	V4	St Kitts & Nevis	NA	11	08	249
OY	Faroe Is	EU	18	14	222	V5	Namibia	AF	57	38	464
OZ	Denmark	EU	18	14	221	V6	Micronesia	OC	65	27	173
P2	Papua New Guinea	OC	51	28	163	V7	Marshall Is	OC	65	31	168
P4	Aruba	SA	11	09	091	V8	Brunei Darussalam	OC	54	28	345
P5	D P R Korea	AS	44	25	344	VE, VO, VY	Canada	NA	2-4, 9, 75	1-5	001
PA	Netherlands	EU	27	14	263	VK	Australia	OC	55, 58-59	29, 30	150
PJ2	Curacao	SA	11	09	517	VK0	Heard I	AF	68	39	111
PJ4	Bonaire	SA	11	09	520	VK0	Macquarie I	OC	60	30	153
PJ5, 6	Saba & St Eustatius	NA	11	08	519	VK9C	Cocos (Keeling) Is	OC	54	29	038
PJ7	St Maarten	NA	11	08	518	VK9L	Lord Howe I	OC	60	30	147
PY	Brazil	SA	12-13, 15	11	108	VK9M	Mellish Reef	OC	56	30	171
PY0F	Fernando de Noronha	SA	13	11	056	VK9N	Norfolk I	OC	60	32	189
PY0S	St Peter & St Paul Rocks	SA	13	11	253	VK9W	Willis I	OC	55	30	303
PY0T	Trindade & Martim Vaz Is	SA	15	11	273	VK9X	Christmas I	OC	54	29	035
PZ	Suriname	SA	12	09	140	VP2E	Anguilla	NA	11	08	012
R1_F	Franz Josef Land	EU	75	40	061	VP2M	Montserrat	NA	11	08	096
S0	Western Sahara	AF	46	33	302	VP2V	British Virgin Is	NA	11	08	065
S2	Bangladesh	AS	41	22	305	VP5	Turks & Caicos Is	NA	11	08	089
S5	Slovenia	EU	28	15	499	VP6	Pitcairn I	OC	63	32	172
S7	Seychelles	AF	53	39	379	VP6	Ducie I	OC	63	32	513
S9	Sao Tome & Principe	AF	47	36	219	VP8	Falkland Is	SA	16	13	141
SM, SA	Sweden	EU	18	14	284	VP8	South Georgia	SA	73	13	235
SP, SQ	Poland	EU	28	15	269	VP8, LU_Z	South Orkney Is	SA	73	13	238
ST	Sudan	AF	47, 48	34	466	VP8	South Sandwich Is	SA	73	13	240
SU	Egypt	AF	38	34	478	VP8, CE9, HF0	South Shetland Is	SA	73	13	241
SV	Greece	EU	28	20	236	VP8, KC4 etc*	Antarctica	AN	67, 69-74,	12- 13, 29-30, 32, 38-39	013
SV/A	Mount Athos	EU	28	20	180	VP9	Bermuda	NA	11	05	064
SV5	Dodecanese Is	EU	28	20	045	VQ9	Chagos Is	AF	41	39	033
SV9	Crete	EU	28	20	040	VR	Hong Kong	AS	44	24	321
T2	Tuvalu	OC	65	31	282	VU	India	AS	41	22	324
T30	Western Kiribati	OC	65	31	301	VU4	Andaman & Nicobar Is	AS	49	26	011
T31	Central Kiribati	OC	62	31	031	VU7	Lakshadweep Is	AS	41	22	142
T32	Eastern Kiribati	OC	61, 63	31	048	XE	Mexico	NA	10	06	050
T33	Banaba I	OC	65	31	490	XE4	Revillagigedo Is	NA	10	06	204
T6, YA	Afghanistan	AS	40	21	003	XT	Burkina Faso	AF	46	35	480
T7	San Marino	EU	28	15	278	XU	Cambodia	AS	49	26	312
T8	Palau	OC	64	27	022	XV, 3W	Vietnam	AS	49	26	293
TA	Turkey	AS/EU	39	20	390	XW	Laos	AS	49	26	143
TF	Iceland	EU	17	40	242	XX9	Macao	AS	44	24	152
TG	Guatemala	NA	12	07	076	XZ	Myanmar	AS	49	26	309
TI	Costa Rica	NA	11	07	308	YB	Indonesia	OC	51, 54	28	327
TI9	Cocos I	NA	12	07	037	YI	Iraq	AS	39	21	333
TJ	Cameroon	AF	47	36	406	YJ	Vanuatu	OC	56	32	158
TK	Corsica	EU	28	15	214	YK	Syria	AS	39	20	384
TL	Central African Rep	AF	47	36	408	YL	Latvia	EU	29	15	145
TN	Congo Republic	AF	52	36	412	YN	Nicaragua	NA	11	07	086
TR	Gabon	AF	52	36	420	YO	Romania	EU	28	20	275
TT	Chad	AF	47	36	410	YS	El Salvador	NA	11	07	074
TU	Côte d'Ivoire	AF	46	35	428	YT, YU	Serbia	EU	28	15	296
TY	Benin	AF	46	35	416	YV-YY	Venezuela	SA	12	09	148
TZ	Mali	AF	46	35	442	YV0	Aves I	NA	11	08	017
UA, RA	European Russia	EU	19-20, 29-30	16	054	Z2	Zimbabwe	AF	53	38	452
UA2F, RA2	Kaliningrad	EU	29	15	126	Z3	Macedonia	EU	28	15	502
UA9, 0	Asiatic Russia	AS	20-26, 29-35	16-19, 23	015	Z8	South Sudan	AF	48	34	521
UK	Uzbekistan	AS	30	17	292	ZA	Albania	EU	28	15	007
UN, UP	Kazakhstan	AS	29-31	17	130						
UR-UZ,	Ukraine	EU	29	16	288						
V2	Antigua & Barbuda	NA	11	08	094						

Prefix	Entity	Continent	ITU Zone	CQ Zone	Entity Code	Prefix	Entity	Continent	ITU Zone	CQ Zone	Entity Code
ZB2	Gibraltar	EU	37	14	233	ZL7	Chatham Is	OC	60	32	034
ZC4	UK Sov Base Areas on Cyprus	AS	39	20	283	ZL8	Kermadec Is	OC	60	32	133
						ZL9	Auckland & Campbell Is	OC	60	32	016
ZD7	St Helena	AF	66	36	250	ZP	Paraguay	SA	14	11	132
ZD8	Ascension I	AF	66	36	205	ZS	South Africa	AF	57	38	462
ZD9	Tristan da Cunha & Gough I	AF	66	38	274	ZS8	Prince Edward & Marion Is	AF	57	38	201
ZF	Cayman Is	NA	11	08	069						
ZK3	Tokelau Is	OC	62	31	270						
ZL	New Zealand	OC	60	32	170						

* Antarctica is considered to be an international territory. Prefixes used include those of countries with research bases on the territory.

Great Circle Map Centred on London

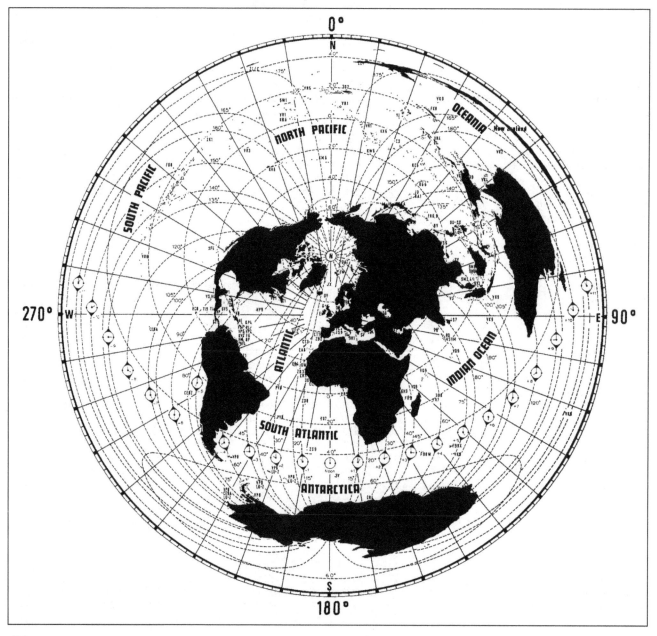

ITU Zone Map of the World

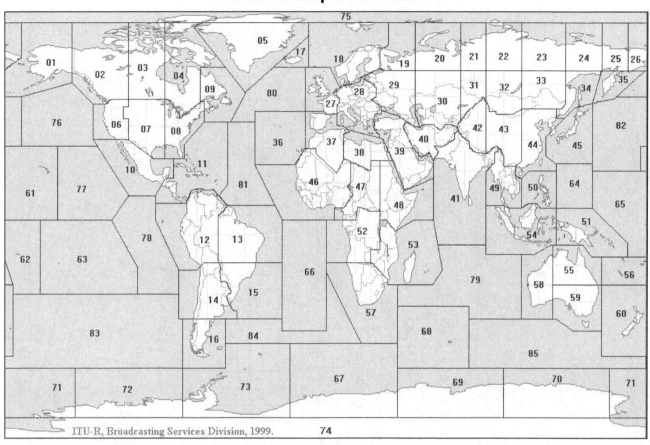

ITU-R, Broadcasting Services Division, 1999.

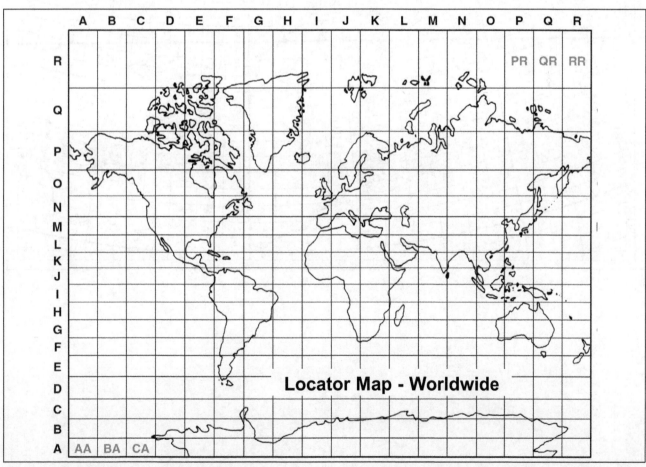

Locator Map - Worldwide

Locator Map - Europe and North Africa

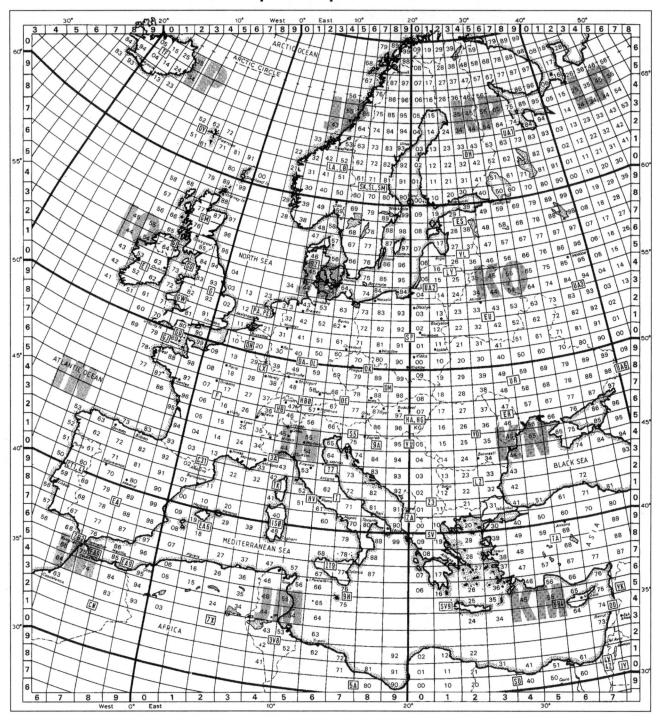

THOUSANDS OF OPERATORS across the world have contacts with only 100 or so words in a second language. It gives them great satisfaction, as well as many contacts which would otherwise have been impossible.

Phone Contacts

A basic contact consists of ten parts: (1) calling CQ, (2) acknowledge reply, (3) name, (4) QTH, (5) signal report, (6) equipment used, (7) weather, (8) QSL via bureau, (9) 'Thanks for contact', (10) 73. Nearly every contact comes over in that order and all ten parts usually come over in three of four transmissions, grouping two or three parts together in each one.

For familiarisation and pronunciation of any of these four languages, search around the band for someone calling CQ who is speaking clearly and slowly with a strong signal. Do not waste time with weak signals or trying to understand a ragchew!

After some listening practice, make out a memory page with your name, QTH, rig etc from the lists in the next few pages. There are eight types of weather to choose from and the numbers at the foot of the page will cover station reports and temperatures up to 30°C. The memory page is just a prompt so that you do not forget your words in the middle of a transmission and so that you are able to give the other operator the information required correctly.

When ready to start transmitting, you will find it easier to contact an English-speaking station. After the preliminaries are established, tell your contact that you wish to practice his language and change straight over, reading from the prepared memory page. Do not be put off if your contact continues in English - he may wish to practice as well!

When you advance to calling CQ it is advisable to tell the other station that you "only speak the language for the QSO". This should prevent questions coming across which cannot be understood; if they do, repeat the same statement and continue to the end of the contact.

While four languages are given here in **Tables 1-4**, you are strongly advised not to attempt more than one at a time - probably the second language which you learned at school - as it is very easy to get the words mixed up, particularly when you start to rely on memory.

CW Contacts

Chapter 7 gave an outline of making contacts in a foreign language. In many ways it is easier than using phone as you don't have to worry about pronunciation and a basic contact relies on abbreviations. Nevertheless it is courteous to use some phrases in your QSO partner's language and it can also be a very rewarding exercise.

As a start, it is popular to say 'Goodbye' in the appropriate language, and a 15-language list is given in **Table 5**.

For those who are a little bolder, a list of 24 phrases (**Table 6**), which may be combined in various ways, will cover the requirements of most simple contacts and enable a QSL card to be made out in the appropriate language. No doubt, over time, you could collect other useful ones, too. Of course, there is always the danger that the other amateur may assume that your knowledge of his language is greater than it really is: a combination of phrases 17 and 18 in the table will meet this situation without giving offence! The words in Roman type are for general use in almost all contacts. Those in Italic type are for occasional use or for use on QSL cards. It is desirable to write the month in words on QSL cards to avoid the confusion which may arise from different conventions when figures only are used. After each list there is information on accented letters for easy reference. It should, however, be noted that in French and Spanish working, the accents are often omitted and in German 'Ä' is sometimes sent as 'AE', 'Ö' as 'OE' and 'Ü' as 'UE'.

In English, the use of endearments between persons of the same sex would be regarded as unusual, but these are quite common in some languages - *lieber Hans*, *cher Marcel*, *amigo Juan* etc. To avoid complications, feminine forms have not been given and so care should be taken when working YLs!

Phrase 8 can be easily adapted; if the rig is an internationally known one, the type number can be inserted in place of '100 WATTS'. As to antennas, those known by the inventor's callsign present no difficulty and the expressions '3 EL', 'YAGI' and 'QUAD' are used in all languages.

It is suggested that German should be the first language to be attempted because it is already used extensively in CW operation and the procedure and abbreviations are well known. In addition to Germany and Austria, the language is used in a large part of Switzerland. All these countries are easy to contact on a number of bands.

French is not so easily abbreviated but it is used over the air quite extensively. The language is spoken in parts of Africa and it is the first language in Quebec Province (VE2). French-speaking Canadians particularly value contacts in their own language.

Spanish is used throughout South America (except Brazil) and it is for that reason that it is include here. It will be noticed that, in some cases, the English abbreviations are retained (or given as alternatives) when the equivalent wording in the foreign language is rather long. In contacts between, say, two Italian amateurs, one will often hear a number of English expressions.

It is important to remember that, in some countries, language is an explosive political matter. This usually occurs in a country where only a very small minority of the people speak a particular language. In these circumstances, it is wise to make sure that use of the language concerned will be welcome before using it over the air.

Table 1: FRENCH

Calling CQ, CQ, this is G . . . . . .
calling CQ on the . . . . . . metre band.
G . . . . . . standing by.

CQ, CQ, (SAY KOO) *appel général, appel général, ici G . . . . .*
qui lance appel bande . . . . . . mètres.
G . . . . . . pass a l'écoute.

F . . . . . ., G . . . . . . returning.
The name here is . . . . . .
and the QTH . . . . . .
I spell . . . . . .
Your report here is . . . . . . and . . . . . .
F . . . . . ., G . . . . . . over to you.

F . . . . . ., G . . . . . . qui revient
Le prénom ici est . . . . . .
et le QTH (KOO TAY ASSH) . . . . . .
je vous épele . . . . . .
Votre rapport ici est . . . . . . et . . . . . .
F . . . . . ., G . . . . . . à vous.

F . . . . . ., G . . . . . . returning,
the rig here is . . . . . .
with a . . . . . . antenna
and a . . . . . . microphone
the WX here is . . . . . .

1. sunny   5. fog
2. cloudy   6. warm
3. raining   7. cold
4. windy   8. snowing

and the temperature C
F . . . . . ., G . . . . . . back to you

F . . . . . ., G . . . . . . de retour
la condition de travail ici est . . . . . .
avec une antenne . . . . . .
et un micro . . . . . .
Le WX (DOUBLA VAY EKS) ici est . . . . . .

1. *ensoleillé*   5. *du brouillard*
2. *nuageux*   6. *chaud*
3. *il pleut*   7. *froid*
4. *du vent*   8. *il neige*

et la température . . . . . . dégrées Centigrad
F . . . . . ., G . . . . . . à vous

F . . . . . ., G . . . . . . returning for the final
I will send you my QSL card via the bureau,
Thank you for the very good QSO,
73, OM,
F . . . . . ., G . . . . . . closing, cheerio.

F . . . . . ., G . . . . . . qui revient pour le final
Je vous enverrai ma carte QSL (KOO ES EL) via le bureau.
Merci bien pour le très bon QSO (KOO ES AW)
Soixante-treize, cher OM
F . . . . . ., G . . . . . . qui termine. maintenant, au revoir.

ADDITIONAL PHRASES WHICH MAY BE REQUIRED

I only speak French for the QSO.
Please speak slowly.
Please give me my report again.
Please give me your name again.
Please give me your QTH again.

Je parle français seulement pour le QSO.
Parlez lentement, s'il vous plâit.
Donnez-moi mon rapport encore une fois, s'il vous plâit.
Donnez-moi votre prénom encore une fois, s'il vous plâit.
Donnez-moi votre QTH encore une fois, s'il vous plâit.

0	*zero*	*17*	*dix-sept*
1	*un, une*	*18*	*dix-huit*
2	*deux*	*19*	*dix-neuf*
3	*trois*	*20*	*vingt*
4	*quatre*	*21*	*vingt et un*
5	*cinq*	*22*	*vingt-deux*
6	*six*	*23*	*vingt-trois*
7	*sept*	*24*	*vingt-quatre*
8	*huit*	*25*	*vingt-cinque*
9	*neuf*	*26*	*vingt-six*
10	*dix*	*27*	*vingt-sept*
11	*onze*	*28*	*vingt-huit*
12	*douze*	*29*	*vingt-neuf*
13	*treize*	*30*	*trente*
14	*quatorze*	*40*	*quarante*
15	*quinze*	*80*	*quatre-vingts*
16	*seize*		

Table 2: GERMAN

CQ, CQ, CQ, ... metres	CQ, CQ, CQ (SEE KOO), ... meter Band
This is English station G	Hier ruft die englische Station G . . . . . .
calling CQ	mit einem allgemeinen Anruf
G . . . . . . going over to receive, stand by.	G . . . . . . geht auf empfang, bitte kommen.
D . . . . . ., G . . . . . . returning	D . . . . . ., G . . . . . . zurück
My name is	Mein Name ist . . . . . .
and my QTH is	und mein QTH (KOO TAY HAA) ist . . . . . .
I spell	Ich buchstabiere . . . . . .
Your report here is . . . . . . and	Ihr Rapport hier ist . . . . . . und . . . . . .
D . . . . . ., G . . . . . . back to you	D . . . . . ., G . . . . . . bitte kommen
D . . . . . ., G . . . . . . coming back	D . . . . . ., G . . . . . . zurück
My station is	Meine Station ist . . . . . .
with a . . . . . . antenna	mit eine . . . . . . antenne
and a . . . . . . microphone	und ein . . . . . . mikrophon
The weather here is	Das Wetter hier ist

1. sunny	5. foggy	1. sunnig	5. nebelig
2. cloudy	6. warm	2. bewoelkt	6. warm
3. raining	7. cold	3. es regnet	7. kalt
4. windy	8. snowing	4. windig	8. es schneit

and the temperature . . . . . . degrees C	und das Temperatur . . . . . . Grad
back to you D . . . . . ., G	zurück zu Ihnen D . . . . . ., G . . . . . ., bitte kommen
D . . . . . .,. G . . . . . . Thank you for the QSO	D . . . . . ., G . . . . . . Dankeschön für das QSO (KOO ES OH)
I will send you my QSL card via the bureau	Ich werde meine QSL-Karte via Bureau senden
Best wishes and good DX	Die besten Grüsse und gut DX
73 until we meet again	drei und siebzig, auf wiederhören
D . . . . . ., G . . . . . . cheerio	D . . . . . ., G . . . . . . Tschuess

ADDITIONAL PHRASES WHICH MAY BE REQUIRED

I only speak German for the QSO.	Ich spreche Deutsch nur für das QSO.
Please give me your callsign again.	Bitte, geben Sie mir Ihr Rufzeichen noch einmal.
Please give me your name again.	Bitte, geben Sie mir Ihr Name noch einmal.
Please give me your QTH again.	Bitte, geben Sie mir Ihr QTH (KOO TAY HAA) noch einmal.
I give you back the microphone.	Ich gebe Ihnen das Mikrophon wieder zurück.

0	null, zero	17	siebzehn
1	ein, eins	18	achtzehn
2	zwei, zwo	19	neunzehn
3	drei	20	zwanzig
4	vier	21	ein und zwanzig
5	fünf	22	zwei und zwanzig
6	sechs	23	drei und zwanzig
7	sieben	24	vier und zwanzig
8	acht	5	fünf und zwanzig
9	neun	26	sechs und zwanzig
10	zehn	27	sieben und zwanzig
11	elf	28	acht und zwanzig
12	zwolf	29	neun und zwanzig
13	dreizehn	30	dreissig
14	vierzehn	40	vierzig
15	fünfzehn	80	achtzig
16	sechszehn		

Table 3: ITALIAN

CQ . . . . . . metres, this is the English station	*Chiamata generale . . . . . . metri, questo è la stazione inglese*
G . . . . . . standing by	*G . . . . . . e vi ascolto, avanti*
I . . . . . . , G . . . . . . returning,	*I . . . . . . , G . . . . . . ritornando.*
many thanks for the call.	*tante grazie per la risposta.*
The name here is	*Il mio nome è . . . . . .*
and the QTH is	*Il mio QTH (KOO TEE ACCA) è . . . . . .*
Your report is . . . . . . and	*Il vostro controllo è . . . . . . e . . . . . .*
Mike back to you, I . . . . . . , G	*Vi ripasso il micro, I . . . . . . , G . . . . . . avanti, cambio*
I . . . . . . , G . . . . . . returning	*I . . . . . . , G . . . . . . ritornando*
The rig here is	*Il mio apparechio è . . . . . .*
with . . . . linear	*con amplificatore . . . . . .*
The microphone is	*Il micro è . . . . . .*
My antenna is	*La mia antenna è . . . . . .*
The WX here is	*Il tempo qui è*

1. sunny	5. foggy	*1. bellissimo*	*5. nebbioso*
2. cloudy	6. warm	*2. nuvoloso*	*6. caldo*
3. raining	7. cold	*3. piovoso*	*7. freddo*
4. windy	8. snowing	*4. fa vento*	*8. nevica*

The temperature is . . . . . . degrees	*La temperatura è . . . . . . gradi*
I . . . . . . , G . . . . . . over to you	*Vi ripasso il micro, I . . . . . . , G . . . . . . avanti, cambio*
I . . . . . . , G . . . . . . returning for the final	*I . . . . . . , G . . . . . . ritornando, per il finale.*
I will send my QSL card via the bureau.	*Vi mandero la mia cartolina QSL (KOO ESS ELLE)*
	via bureau (associazione).
Thank you for the excellent QSO, best wishes and good DX.	*Molti grazie per il QSO eccellente, tanti saluti e buon DX.*
The mike to you for the final. Bye-bye.	*Il micro a voi caro amico per il finale. Ciao (CHOW).*
I . . . . . . , G 73	*I . . . . . . , G . . . . . . , avanti, cambio, 73 (settanta tre)*

ADDITIONAL PHRASES WHICH MAY BE REQUIRED

I only speak Italian for the QSO.	*Parlo Italiano soltanto per il QSO.*
Please speak slowly.	*Prego, parlate lentamente.*
I did not get your callsign.	*Non ho capito il vostro nominativo.*
What is my report?	*Cos' è il mio controllo?*

0	zero	17	diciasette
1	uno	18	diciotto
2	due	19	diciannove
3	tre	20	venti
4	quattro	21	ventuno
5	cinque	22	ventidue
6	sei	23	ventitré
7	sette	24	ventiquattro
8	otto	25	venticinque
9	nove	26	ventsei
10	dieci	27	ventisette
11	undici	28	ventotto
12	dodici	29	ventinove
13	tredici	30	trenta
14	quattordici	40	quaranta
15	quindici	80	ottanta
16	sedici		

Table 4: SPANISH

Calling CQ CQ CQ, this is G . . . . . . calling CQ
on . . . . . . metres, G . . . . . . standing by.

EA . . . . . . , from G . . . . . .returning,
Thank you for returning my call.
My name is . . . . I spell . . . .
My QTH is . . . . . .,. I spell . . . .
Your report here is . . . . . . and . . . .
EA . . . . . . from G . . . . come in.

EA . . . . . . from G . . . .
Thank you for your message.
My station is . . . . . .
my antenna is dipole/multiband/beam.
My microphone is crystal/dynamic.
The weather here is
1. sunny   5. fog
2. cloudy   6. warm
8. raining   7. cold
4. windy   8. snowing
The temperature is . . . . . . degrees.
EA . . . . . . from G . . . . . . , come in

EA . . . . . . from G . . . . . . for the final.
I will send my QSL card via the bureau.
Thank you for the QSO, 73, Cheerio.

ADDITIONAL PHRASES WHICH MAY BE REQUIRED
I only speak Spanish for the QSO.
Please speak slowly.
Please repeat my report/your name/your QTH.
Can you QSY . . . kHz higher/lower.
I am sorry, I cannot copy, bad QRM.

Llamada general, G . . . . . . llamando,
CQ . . . . . . metros, y G . . . . escuchando.

EA . . . . . . , G . . . . . .retornando.
Gracias por haber contestado a mi llamada.
Mi nombre es . . . . . . , como
Mi QTH es . . . . . . , como
Su control es . . . . . . y . . . . . .
EA . . . . . . de G . . . . adelante

EA . . . . . . de G . . . .
Gracias por su mensaje.
Mis condiciones de trabajo . . . . . .
mi antena es dipolo/multibanda/directional.
Mi microfono es cristal/dinamico.
El tiempo aqui
1. hace sol   5. niebla
2. nublado   6. hace calor
3. lloviendo   7. hace frio
4. hace viento   8. nevando
La temperatura . . . . . . grados.
EA . . . . . . de G . . . . ., adelante

EA . . . . . . de G . . . . . . por el final.
Me enviaré la tarjeta de QSL via el bureau.
Gracias por el QSO, 73 (setenta y tres).
EA . . . . de G . . . . adios!

Hablo el español solamente por el QSO.
Por favor hable despacio.
Por favor repete mi control/su nombre/su QTH.
Puede Usted QSY . . . kHz alto/bajo.
Lo siento, no puedo copiar, mucho QRM.

0	cero	17	diez y siete
1	uno	18	diez y ocho
2	dos	19	diez nueve
3	tres	20	veinte
4	cuatro	21	veintiuno
5	cinco	22	veintidos
6	seis	23	veintitres
7	siete	24	veinticuatro
8	ocho	25	veinticinco
9	nueve	26	veintiseis
10	diez	27	veintisiete
11	once	28	veintiocho
12	doce	29	veintinueve
13	trece	30	treinta
14	catorce	31	treinta y uno
15	quince	40	cuarenta
16	diez y seis	80	ochenta

Table 5: 'Goodbye' in Morse in 15 languages

Danish:	FARVEL
Dutch:	TOT WERKENS
English:	GB (CHEERS)
Esperanto:	ḠIS
Finnish	HEI
French:	AU REVOIR
German:	AWDH
Italian:	CIAO
Norwegian:	HEI
Polish:	CZESC
Portuguese:	ATÉ BREVE
Russian:	DSW
Spanish:	ADIOS (HLV)
Swedish:	HEJ
Welsh:	POB HWYL

Ḡ = dah-dah-di-dah-dit É = di-di-dah-di-dit

English

1. GM / GA / GE / GN OM
2. TNX FR CALL (ES FIRST QSO)
3. Nice to meet u agn
4. We have met B4
5. UR RST ... QTH ... NAME ...
6. HW?
7. TNX ... FR (FB) REPORT
8. HR RIG [100 WATTS] ANT [DIPOLE]
9. WX (1) FINE (2) CLEAR (3) CLOUDY (4) RAINY (5) WINDY (6) FOGGY (7) WARM (8) COLD (9) SNOW TEMP ... C
10. TNX ... FR INFO ON UR RIG (ES WX)
11. Only partly OK
12. All OK except ur QTH
13. Some / much / too much QSB, QRM (etc)
14. Pse rpt my report / ur name / ur QTH
15. Pse QSY up / down ... kHz
16. Band vy noisy
17. Sri but I do not understand completely
18. I speak only a little English
19. QSL OK VIA BURO
20. I have recd ur crd
21. Have u recd my crd?
22. I am QRU nw
23. Best 73 es DX
24. TNX ... FR QSO NW QRU 73 DX ES GB

January February March April May June July August September October November December

Ä di-dah-di-dah
Ö dah-dah-dah-dit
Ü di-di-dah-dah

German

1. GM / GT / GA / GN LBR FRD
2. VLN DK ... FR DEN ANRUF (UND ERSTES QSO)
3. Es freut mich sehr Sie wiederzutreffen
4. Wir haben uns schon mal getroffen
5. IHR RST ... QTH ... NAME ...
6. WIE?
7. VLN DK FR DEN (NETTEN) RPRT
8. RIG (Gerät) HR IST [100 WATT] UND ANT IST [EIN DIPOL]
9. DAS WX IST (1) SCHÖN (2) KLAR (3) BEWÖLKT (4) REGNERISCH (5) WINDIG (6) NEBELIG (7) WARM (8) KALT (9) ES SCHNEIT TEMP ... C
10. DKE ... FR BRT ÜBER IHR RIG (Gerät) (UND WX)
11. Nur teilweise OK
12. Alles OK ausser Ihrem QTH
13. Etwas / vl / zu vl QSB, QRM (etc)
14. Bte wiederholen Sie meinen Rprt / Ihren Namen / Ihr QTH
15. Bte QSY / höher / tiefer ... kHz
16. Auf dem Bande ist vl Lärm
17. Leider habe ich nicht alles verstanden
18. Ich spreche nur wenig Deutsch
19. QSL OK VIA BÜRO
20. Ich habe Ihre Karte bekommen
21. Haben Sie meine Karte bekommen?
22. Ich bin nun QRU
23. Die besten Grüsse und DX
24. DKE SEHR ... FR QSO NUN QRU 73 GUTES DX UND AWDH (auf wiederhören)

Januar Februar März April Mai Juni Juli August September Oktober November Dezember

Ä di-dah-di-dah
Ö dah-dah-dah-dit
Ü di-di-dah-dah

Spanish

1. GM / GA / GE / GN OM
2. MUCHAS GRACIAS POR TU LLAMADA (Y POR ESTE PRIMER QSO)
3. Tengo un gran placer en enco trarle
4. Nos hemos encontrado ya antes
5. TU RST ... QTH ... NOMBRE ...
6. HW?
7. MUY TNX (muchas gracias) ... POR RPRT
8. MI TX TIENE [100 VATIOS] MI ANT ES [UN DIPOLO]
9. EL WX AQUÍ ES (1) MUY BUENO (2) CLARO (3) NUBLADO (4) LLUVOSO (5) VENTOSO (6) NEBULOSO (7) ACALORADO (8) FRIO (9) ESTA NEVANDO TEMP ... C
10. TNX FR INFO
11. OK sólo en parte
12. Completamente OK con excepción de u QTH
13. Poco / mucho / demasiado QSB, QRM (etc)
14. Pse repetirme mi RST/tu nombre/tu QTH
15. Pse QSY más alto/más bajo cerca ... kHz
16. La banda está muy turbulenta
17. Sri pero no he comprendido completamente
18. Hablo solamente un poco español
19. QSL OK VIA BURO
20. He recibido tu QSL tnx
21. Has recibido mi QSL?
22. Tengo ahora QRU
23. 73 y buenos DX
24. MUCHAS GRACIAS ... POR QSO QRU 73 DX Y ADIOS

Enero Febrero Marzo Abril Mayo Junio Julio Agosto Septiembre Octobre Noviembre Dicembre

Á di-dah-dah-di-dah
Ñ dah-dah-di-dah-dah
Ó dah-dah-dah-dit

French

1. BJR / - / BSR / BN MON VIEUX
2. MCI BCP POUR VOTRE APPEL (ET POUR PREMIER QSO)
3. Je suis enchanté de vous rencontrer de nouveau
4. Nous avons déjà fait QSO
5. VOTRE RST ... QTH ... NOM ...
6. HW? (Quel est mon contrôle?)
7. MCI BCP ... POUR RPRT (contrôle) (Bien aimable)
8. ICI RIG (appareil) [100 WATTS] ANT [DIPOLE]
9. WX (1) MERVEILLEUX (2) CLAIR (3) NUAGEUX (4) PLUVIEUX (5) IL Y A DU VENT (6) IL Y A BROUILLARD (7) CHAUD (8) FROID (9) IL NEIGE TEMP ... C
10. MCI BCP ... POUR L'INFO SUR VOTRE RIG (appareil) (ET WX)
11. OK seulement en partie
12. Complètement OK excepté votre QTH
13. Peu / bcp / trop de QSB, de QRM (etc)
14. Repetez mon rprt (contrôle) / votre nom / votre QTH svp
15. QSY plus haut / plus bas ... kHz svp
16. Il y a bcp de bruit sur la bande
17. Je regrette bcp mais je ne vous ai pas complètement compris
18. Je parle un peu le français
19. QSL OK PAR BUREAU
20. J'ai reçu votre carte mci bcp
21. Avez vous reçu ma carte?
22. Je suis maintenant QRU
23. Mes meilleurs amitiés et bonne chance pour le DX
24. MCI BCP ... POUR QSO ICI QRU 73 DX ET AU REVOIR

Janvier Février Mars Avril Mai Juin Juillet Août Septembre Octobre Novembre Décembre

Â di-dah-dah-di-dah
Ç dah-di-dah-di-dit
È and É di-di-dah-di-dit
Ê dah-di-di-dah-dit
Ô dah-dah-dah-dit
Û di-di-dah-dah

Table 6: Morse phrases in English, German, Spanish.and French.